THE ILLUSTRATED ENCYCLOPEDIA OF
SPACE
& SPACE EXPLORATION

W9-BTR-622

THE ILLUSTRATED ENCYCLOPEDIA OF SPACE & SPACE EXPLORATION

Discovering the Secrets of the Universe

General Editors:
Giles Sparrow, Judith John & Chris McNab

METRO BOOKS
New York

METRO BOOKS
New York

An Imprint of Sterling Publishing
387 Park Avenue South
New York, NY 10016

METRO BOOKS and the distinctive Metro Books logo are trademarks
of Sterling Publishing Co., Inc.

© 2014 by Amber Books Ltd.

All rights reserved. No part of this publication may be reproduced, stored in a retrieval system
or transmitted in any form or by any means (including electronic, mechanical, photocopying,
recording, or otherwise) without prior written permission from the publisher.

Editorial and design by
Amber Books Ltd
74–77 White Lion Street
London N1 9PF
www.amberbooks.co.uk

Project Editor: Michael Spilling
Design: Hawes Design and Mark Batley
Picture Research: Terry Forshaw
Additional Text: Chris McNab and Judith John

ISBN 978-1-4351-5490-2

For information about custom editions, special sales, and premium and corporate purchases,
please contact Sterling Special Sales at 800-805-5489 or specialsales@sterlingpublishing.com.

Manufactured in China

2 4 6 8 10 9 7 5 3 1

www.sterlingpublishing.com

Contents

INTRODUCTION

"**A**ll you really need to know for the moment is that the universe is a lot more complicated than you might think, even if you start from a position of thinking it's pretty damn complicated in the first place."

– Douglas Adams, *Mostly Harmless*

APOLLO 17
The sixth and final Apollo lunar landing, Apollo 17, was also the sixth time that humans had ever landed on the Moon. The mission launched on December 7, 1972, carrying a three-man crew. The successful mission included a three-night stay on the Moon's surface, a lunar rover and the collection of samples and deployment of experiments.

LIVING MOON?
Usually thought of as unchanging—even dead—the Moon is still able to surprise astronomers. Occurances of lunar transient phenomena (LTP) actually date back to as early as the 16th century, although little has been proven to date. However, landslides, gas emissions and glowing lights mean the Moon is certainly not as dormant as was once believed.

The enormity of space is truly hard to conceive from Earth. *The Illustrated Encyclopedia of Space & Space Exploration* aims to break this vastness down accessibly by providing the most important and interesting facts and stories alongside visually stimulating and appealing photographs, diagrams and artworks. Each topic also contains a table providing key facts about the theme discussed. While it is hard to cover the minutia of every topic, even in such a detailed book, here you will find information about our solar system and beyond, learning about the fascinating and constantly changing celestial bodies that dance—and sometimes crash—through the night skies. The history of space exploration is also provided, taking you from the earliest pioneers in space to the latest missions, with accessible and absorbing facts about their incredible new technology, discoveries, and what this could

mean for our understanding of the outer regions of the solar system here on Earth.

THE BEGINNING TO THE BIG BANG

Written by science consultants who are specialists in their field, *The Illustrated Encyclopedia of Space & Space Exploration* seeks to present often complicated topics of immense, hard-to-fathom sizes in clear and comprehensible language. Taking a 4.6 billion year journey beginning with the origins of the universe, through to the Big Bang and formation of our solar system, the future of the universe and the many still unexplored possibilities of space are also considered. With the atmospheres and geology of planets and major moons covered, asteroids, comets and meteors are explained in terms of their past significance and future threat. Moving on to study the night sky, the many

spectacular images will inspire and educate, as the star atlases and astronomical data provide a starting point to mapping the sky above you. Stars, star clusters, galaxies, galaxy clusters and even the matter and dark matter of the entire cosmos are made more reachable. The dominant principles of how the universe works are also studied in terms of our solar system, galaxy and beyond, giving a tantalizing glimpse at the future of the universe that none of us will be alive to witness.

SPACE TODAY

Not least among the many fascinating facts about space is how our knowledge of what is beyond our own tiny planet has leapt forward over the past half-decade with the dawn of space travel. New discoveries are made every day—as well as new classifications such as Pluto being classed as a dwarf planet in 2006.

These discoveries constantly change the shape of the galaxy and allow scientists to piece together answers to the many remaining questions about our very existence. We take a look at the space giants of the U.S. and Russia, as well as the work of the ESA and newly-emerging countries keen to explore space, such as China and India. The many fascinating missions that are underway to explore previously unknown parts of space are explained, as are new missions returning to previously studied planets and moons, which use the latest cutting edge technology to tell us much more than we were able to discover in the past.

With these technologies making possible some journeys that were impossible only twenty years ago, we can only guess at some of the mysteries still to be encountered in space exploration, as well as envy those men and women lucky enough to travel to the stars and beyond.

INTRODUCING THE SOLAR SYSTEM

The solar system consists of everything that comes within the Sun's region of influence—a volume of space extending out to approximately one light-year (six trillion miles/10 trillion km) from the Sun itself. The vast majority of the solar system's material lies much closer to the Sun, however—even Pluto orbits just a few thousand million miles away from the center. This inner region is the realm of the planets, eight of which follow more-or-less circular orbits around the Sun, with the ninth, Pluto—designated a dwarf planet since 2006—in a more elongated orbit. In fact Pluto's original designation as a planet was little more than an accident of history, as we shall see. The major planets divide neatly into two types: rocky or terrestrial planets orbiting close to the Sun (of which Earth is the largest), and giant gas planets such as Jupiter, orbiting further out. Many of the planets have their own natural satellites or moons, and the gas giants are also encircled by ring systems, of which Saturn's is the most spectacular. A belt of rocky asteroids divides the terrestrials from the giants between Mars and Jupiter, while beginning around Neptune's orbit is the Kuiper Belt, a region of small icy worlds of which Pluto is the largest known member. Some comets originate here, while others orbit further out, at the very limits of the Sun's gravitational reach, in the Oort Cloud.

A montage of images shows the planets and four of Jupiter's moons, with the surface of Earth's moon in the foreground.

OVERVIEW OF THE SOLAR SYSTEM

O nce, the solar system seemed a simple place, its members forming a neat hierarchy: a central star, nine planets in stately orbit, a dozen or so dead moons, the occasional comet, and a collection of asteroids. At the orbit of Pluto, the most distant dwarf planet, our system appeared to end. In the last 30 years, modern technology has helped to change this simple image. Moons can be larger than planets, and comets swarm by the trillion halfway to the nearest star. We live in a dynamic and complex neighborhood.

SOLAR SYSTEM PROFILE

LIFE-SCALE	4.6 BILLION YEARS
DIAMETER	3 LIGHT-YEARS
DIAMETER OF PLANETARY ZONE	7.4 BILLION MILES (11.9 BILLION KM)
KNOWN PLANETS	9 COMMONLY ACCEPTED
SATELLITES	AT LEAST 140
KNOWN LIFE-BEARING PLANETS	1
LARGEST PLANET	JUPITER (318 TIMES THE MASS OF THE EARTH)
SMALLEST (DWARF) PLANET	PLUTO (1/5 THE DIAMETER OF THE EARTH)
PLANET WITH FASTEST SPIN	JUPITER (9 HOURS 55.5 MINUTES)

SYSTEM TOUR

As we approach the solar system, the first thing that strikes us is that it is a single-star system. The galaxy is full of multiple star systems, which can lead to very eccentric planet orbits. The Sun's single state may result from its birth in a modest-size gas cloud, leaving it to develop a system of planets that all orbit in the same direction and in the same plane.

This is not to say that everything in the solar system is well organized. In the Oort Cloud, the outermost shell of the solar system, icy bodies orbit slowly in all directions, taking millions of years to do so. But as we move inward, the orbits become more regular. At the fringe of the planetary area lies the Kuiper Belt, home to numerous small ice worlds, including Pluto—reclassified in 2006 as a dwarf planet—and perhaps several other Kuiper Belt Objects of similar size.

Closer in lie the giant planets, with extended gaseous or liquid atmospheres. The largest, Jupiter, dominates the rest. No planet can exist without feeling the pull of Jupiter, which carries with it most of the solar system's momentum around the Sun.

Closest in are the rocky planets, no more than a tenth the diameter of Jupiter. At their outer fringes are the asteroids, small bodies that were prevented by Jupiter's gravity from clumping into a planet. One of the rocky planets, Earth, has the good fortune to be in an almost circular orbit at a distance from the Sun where water can exist as a liquid on its surface. This has led to a remarkable development—life.

ONE MORE—OR LESS?

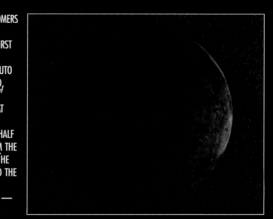

In 2005, astronomers announced the discovery of the first new Kuiper Belt Object to rival Pluto in size. This world, nicknamed "Santa" for its discovery at Christmas 2004, orbits two and a half times further from the Sun than Pluto. The discovery reignited the debate about the number of planets — some said the new object should be classed as a tenth planet, while others argued that both Pluto and Santa should be classed as dwarf planets. The latter group were successful. It is now known officially as Haumea.

JOURNEY TO THE CENTER

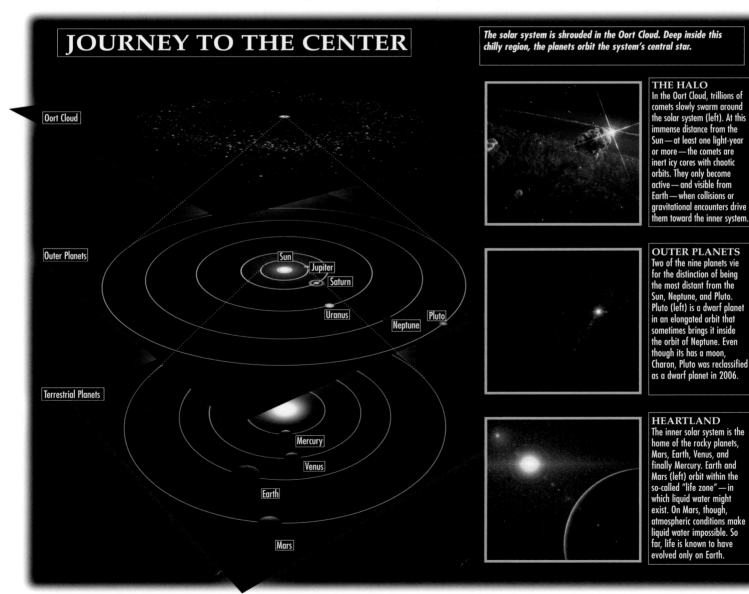

The solar system is shrouded in the Oort Cloud. Deep inside this chilly region, the planets orbit the system's central star.

Oort Cloud

Outer Planets

Terrestrial Planets

Sun
Jupiter
Saturn
Uranus
Neptune
Pluto

Mercury
Venus
Earth
Mars

THE HALO
In the Oort Cloud, trillions of comets slowly swarm around the solar system (left). At this immense distance from the Sun—at least one light-year or more—the comets are inert icy cores with chaotic orbits. They only become active—and visible from Earth—when collisions or gravitational encounters drive them toward the inner system.

OUTER PLANETS
Two of the nine planets vie for the distinction of being the most distant from the Sun, Neptune, and Pluto. Pluto (left) is a dwarf planet in an elongated orbit that sometimes brings it inside the orbit of Neptune. Even though its has a moon, Charon, Pluto was reclassified as a dwarf planet in 2006.

HEARTLAND
The inner solar system is the home of the rocky planets, Mars, Earth, Venus, and finally Mercury. Earth and Mars (left) orbit within the so-called "life zone"—in which liquid water might exist. On Mars, though, atmospheric conditions make liquid water impossible. So far, life is known to have evolved only on Earth.

SCALE OF THE SOLAR SYSTEM

The Sun is enormous, packing within its huge globe 99 percent of the total matter in our solar system. Yet measured on the scale of the entire solar system, the Sun is almost as insignificant as its planets. The dwarf planet Pluto, at its most distant, is 4.65 billion miles (7.5 billion km) from the Sun.

If its orbit were reduced to the size of a tennis court, the Sun would be smaller than a pinpoint. Yet beyond Pluto, the solar system continues—in the form of the Kuiper Belt, and the Oort cloud, a swarm of comets surrounding the Sun—one-third of the way to the nearest star.

SOME STEPS IN THE SCALE

OBJECT	DIAMETER	SIZE COMPARED WITH PREVIOUS OBJECT
JUPITER RING PARTICLE	0.00004 IN (0.001 MM)	N/A
SATURN RING PARTICLE	Up to 15 FT (4.5 M)	5,000,000 TIMES
TYPICAL ASTEROID	300 FT (90 M)	20 TIMES
LARGEST KNOWN CRATER (ON MARS)	1,550 MILES (2,500 KM)	5.2 TIMES
LARGEST KNOWN MOON (GANYMEDE)	3,270 MILES (5,250 KM)	2.1 TIMES
EARTH	12,800 MILES (20,600 KM)	3.9 TIMES
LARGEST KNOWN PLANET (JUPITER)	88,800 MILES (143,000 KM)	6.9 TIMES
SATURN'S RING SPAN	210,000 MILES (337,962 KM)	2.4 TIMES
SUN	865,000 MILES (1.4 MILLION KM)	4 TIMES
ORBIT OF INNER PLANET (MERCURY)	36 MILLION MILES (58 MILLION KM)	42 TIMES

SIZE MATTERS

The human brain evolved to deal with a small-scale environment. Whether hunting prey or avoiding predators, near was more important than far. The horizon was as distant a perspective as early Homo sapiens needed to care about, and even today it is difficult for humans to comprehend the truly large-scale. The Earth seems vast to us. But all the planets and even the Sun itself, a glowing ball of plasma some 865,000 miles (1.4 million km) in diameter, are insignificant specks in the immensity of the whole solar system.

To reduce such vastness to sizes that humans can grasp, imagine the entire solar system scaled down by a factor of 13 billion. That's the number needed to reduce the Sun to the size of a grapefruit. On such a scale, Earth becomes a pinhead about 38 ft (11.5 m) away, while the Moon, smaller than a grain of sand, swings around its parent planet at a distance of just 1.1 in (28 mm). Farther away, some 200 ft (61 m) from the grapefruit Sun, lies the giant planet Jupiter, which on this scale is about the size of a pea. Jupiter's largest moons could easily pass through the eye of a

needle—and the smallest are too tiny to be seen with the naked eye. Far beyond Jupiter, a barely discernible fleck of dust orbits more than a quarter of a mile from the grapefruit Sun. This is the outermost dwarf planet, Pluto, whose elliptical orbit carries it 50 times farther away from the Sun than the Earth is. To drive there at a steady 60 miles an hour (96 km/h) without stopping would take almost 9,000 years.

THE OUTER REACHES

Pluto marks the commonly accepted boundary of the realm of the planets—as far as we know. But the Sun's family actually extends much farther afield than that. Surrounding the Sun at a distance of perhaps 9 trillion miles (15 trillion km)—one-and-a-half light-years and one-third of the way to the nearest stars—is the Oort cloud. Named after the Dutch astrophysicist Jan Hendrik Oort, this structure is a vast, spherical swarm of icy debris, left over from the formation of the solar system more than 4.5 billion years ago. Oort cloud objects are so far from the Sun that the tether of gravity is feeble. From time to time, a passing star will nudge objects from their fragile orbits

and send them falling into the inner system, where their icy material boils off and they shoot across our sky as comets. If we took our grapefruit Sun and placed it in Salt Lake City, Utah, the Oort cloud would stretch from the Mexican border to Canada—a distance of about 1,400 miles (2,250 km).

Within the immense span of the solar system are objects that range from dust grains to planets. Between them, they have a remarkable range of sizes. Among the smallest orbiting objects are the flecks of dust that make up Jupiter's rings—each particle is only about 0.00004 in (0.001 mm) across. At the other extreme is the entire Oort cloud— in scientific parlance, 22 orders of magnitude larger. An order of magnitude simply means a factor of 10, and in scientific notation 22 orders would be written as 10^{22}— that is, one followed by 22 zeroes, or the mind-numbing figure of 10 billion trillion.

MIGHTY MODEL

PEORIA, ILLINOIS, BOASTS ONE OF THE WORLD'S LARGEST SOLAR SYSTEM MODELS. THE SUN, COMPLETE WITH SUNSPOTS, IS REPRESENTED BY A 36-FT (11-M) DISK AT THE CITY'S LAKEVIEW MUSEUM (ABOVE). THE EARTH IS A 4-IN (10-CM) GLOBE ¾ MILE AWAY. VISITORS WHO WANT TO TAKE A LOOK AT THE MARBLE-SIZE MODEL PLUTO MUST DRIVE 40 MILES (64 KM) TO THE TOWN OF KEWANEE. SOME DISTANT COMET MODELS ARE LOCATED OUT-OF-STATE—AND EVEN OUTSIDE OF THE U.S.

The middle of this scale corresponds to a length of about 100 miles (160 km), the diameter of a fairly large asteroid. So an asteroid is as big compared with a Jovian ring particle as the Oort cloud is compared with the asteroid. Our own planet Earth, roughly two orders of magnitude larger than the asteroid, is still a billion times smaller than the Oort cloud. Yet even the almost inconceivable vastness of the Oort cloud cannot compare with the expanse of the universe itself—which is 20 billion times bigger still.

THE SUN AND ITS OFFSPRING

When the Sun and its nine planets are shown together to the same scale, tiny Pluto is so small that it could easily be mistaken for a background star. And there is no room to show more than a section of the Sun's 865,000-mile (1.4 million km) disk.

Mercury
Earth
Venus
Mars
Jupiter
Saturn
Uranus
Neptune
Pluto

HARD EVIDENCE

PALE BLUE DOT
As Voyager 1 passed beyond Neptune and headed into the depths of space, it turned to face the Sun one last time to capture a grainy but inspiring image of a blue dot suspended in a sunbeam (the beam is actually an illusion caused by spacecraft reflections). The insignificant speck is Earth and all it contains. The image inspired the late Carl Sagan to write his last book, appropriately entitled *The Pale Red Dot*.

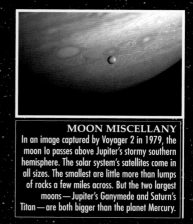

MOON MISCELLANY
In an image captured by Voyager 2 in 1979, the moon Io passes above Jupiter's stormy southern hemisphere. The solar system's satellites come in all sizes. The smallest are little more than lumps of rocks a few miles across. But the two largest moons—Jupiter's Ganymede and Saturn's Titan—are both bigger than the planet Mercury.

PLANETARY ORBITS

The movements of the planets in the sky are not easy to account for. Some follow fairly predictable paths; others roam without any obvious pattern and appear to change direction almost at random. Over the centuries, many of humanity's best brains tried to find an explanation. But until the 17th century and the genius of Johannes Kepler, they failed. Kepler was the first to realize that the planetary orbits are ellipses, not circles, and that the Earth moves around the Sun in just the same way as the other planets do.

ORBITS OF THE PLANETS

PLANET	CLOSEST TO SUN (MILLIONS OF MILES/KM)	FARTHEST FROM SUN (MILLIONS OF MILES/KM)	ORBITAL VELOCITY (MILES/KM PER SECOND)	TIME TAKEN FOR ONE ORBIT
MERCURY	28.5/45.9	43.3/69.7	29.80/47.96	87.97 DAYS
VENUS	66.7/107.3	67.7/109.0	21.77/35.04	224.70 DAYS
EARTH	91.3/146.9	94.4/151.9	18.50/29.77	365.26 DAYS
MARS	129.0/207.6	155.0/249.4	15.00/24.14	686.98 DAYS
JUPITER	460.4/740.9	506.9/815.8	8.11/13.05	11.86 YEARS
SATURN	837.0/1,347.0	936.0/1,506.3	6.00/9.66	29.46 YEARS
URANUS	1,699.0/2,734.3	1,867.0/3,004.6	4.23/6.81	84.07 YEARS
NEPTUNE	2,769.0/4,456.3	2,819.0/4,536.7	3.37/5.42	164.82 YEARS
PLUTO	2,939.0/4,729.9	4,583.0/7,375.6	2.90/4.67	248.60 YEARS

CIRCLING THE SUN

When Polish astronomer Nicolas Copernicus died in 1543, he left an explosive legacy to his fellow scholars. In a book that he had quietly prepared for publication after his death, he declared that the Earth was not at the center of the universe, as most scholars and the Church still firmly believed. Instead, the Earth orbited the Sun—just like all the other planets.

But Copernicus was unable to explain just how the planets revolved around the Sun. He believed that they moved in perfect circles or, sometimes, in circles within circles. But observations of the night sky did not match his theory. The main problem was Mars, which seemed to wander back and forth almost as it pleased. Why did Mars move in this way? It was another half century before the German astronomer Johannes Kepler (1551–1630) provided the answer.

Kepler broadly agreed with Copernicus' theory, but saw the need for fine-tuning, and went to work with Danish astronomer Tycho Brahe (1546–1601). Over the course of several decades, Brahe and his team had logged a huge number of very accurate measurements of Mars' position in the sky. Given Brahe's data—obtained without telescopes—Kepler soon realized that Mars could not orbit the Sun in a perfect circle. By trial and error, he calculated that its course could only be explained if it moved in an ellipse, a type of elongated circle. All points on a circle are the same distance from the center, but an ellipse has two "centers," or foci. And from any point on an ellipse, the sum of the distances to each of the foci remains constant.

KEPLER'S LAWS

If one planet orbited in an ellipse, why not all the others? On that assumption, backed up by careful observation, Kepler proposed three laws of planetary motion. First, planetary orbits are ellipses, with the Sun at one of the foci. Second, a line drawn from the Sun to a moving planet sweeps through equal areas in equal times.

Third, the square of the time each planet takes to orbit the Sun is proportional to the cube of its mean distance from the Sun. The second and third laws mean that a planet moves fastest when it is closest to the Sun, and slowest when it is most distant. Kepler had discovered that the governing force was gravity. After his death, another great scientist—Isaac Newton—would explain gravity. But Kepler's laws still hold true, and combined with Newton's laws, they explain the movements of any object in space—planet, satellite or spacecraft.

JOHANNES KEPLER

JOHANNES (OR JOHANN) KEPLER BECAME ASSISTANT TO DANISH ASTRONOMER TYCHO BRAHE IN 1600 AND COMPLETED BRAHE'S TABLES OF PLANETARY MOTION. THIS DATA AND KEPLER'S OWN GENIUS LED TO HIS LAWS OF PLANETARY MOTION, WHICH HAVE GIVEN HIM A PLACE AMONG THE GREAT SCIENTISTS OF HIS AGE. HE PUBLISHED A DESCRIPTION OF A SUPERNOVA — NOW KNOWN AS KEPLER'S STAR — THAT HE HAD OBSERVED IN 1604 IN THE CONSTELLATION OPHIUCHUS. HE LATER BUILT ONE OF THE FIRST TELESCOPES AND IN 1611 PUBLISHED A BOOK ON OPTICS.

Dominating the sky, a rogue planet the size of Jupiter looms above a flooded, stormy Earth. Its gravity would produce tides at least 100 times higher than those raised by the Moon. It would also buckle the Earth's crust and drag our planet into a new orbit.

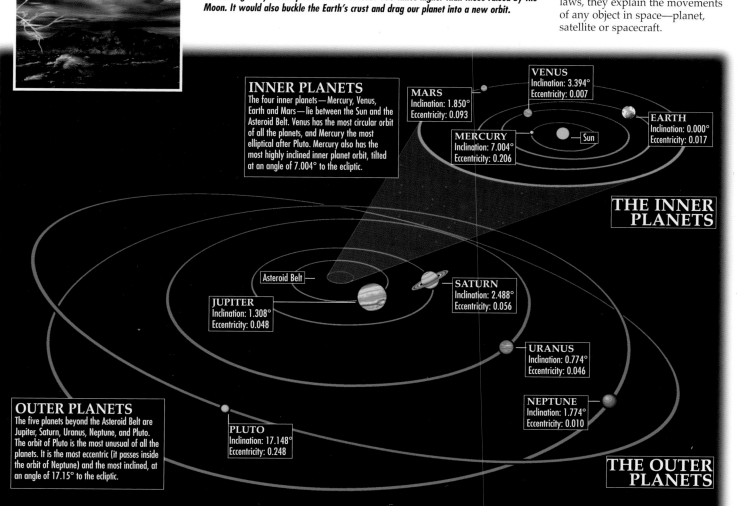

INNER PLANETS
The four inner planets—Mercury, Venus, Earth and Mars—lie between the Sun and the Asteroid Belt. Venus has the most circular orbit of all the planets, and Mercury the most elliptical after Pluto. Mercury also has the most highly inclined inner planet orbit, tilted at an angle of 7.004° to the ecliptic.

MARS
Inclination: 1.850°
Eccentricity: 0.093

VENUS
Inclination: 3.394°
Eccentricity: 0.007

EARTH
Inclination: 0.000°
Eccentricity: 0.017

MERCURY
Inclination: 7.004°
Eccentricity: 0.206

Sun

THE INNER PLANETS

Asteroid Belt

JUPITER
Inclination: 1.308°
Eccentricity: 0.048

SATURN
Inclination: 2.488°
Eccentricity: 0.056

URANUS
Inclination: 0.774°
Eccentricity: 0.046

NEPTUNE
Inclination: 1.774°
Eccentricity: 0.010

OUTER PLANETS
The five planets beyond the Asteroid Belt are Jupiter, Saturn, Uranus, Neptune, and Pluto. The orbit of Pluto is the most unusual of all the planets. It is the most eccentric (it passes inside the orbit of Neptune) and the most inclined, at an angle of 17.15° to the ecliptic.

PLUTO
Inclination: 17.148°
Eccentricity: 0.248

THE OUTER PLANETS

BIRTH OF THE INNER PLANETS

The planets formed 4.6 billion years ago from a vast disk of gas and dust that surrounded the newly forming Sun. The material in the disk began to cool and condense, initially forming grain-sized bodies and then coalescing into the planets as we know them today. Only rocky and metallic materials could survive the imense heat close to the Sun, and the inner planets—Mercury, Venus, Earth and Mars—still have compositions that reflect this. These planets probably took 100 million years to grow—and another 700 million to mature into the planets that continue to fascinate us.

PLANET-BUILDING TIMES

Event	Duration
COLLAPSE OF GAS GLOBULE TO FORM SOLAR NEBULA	1–2 MILLION YEARS
CONDENSATION FORMS FIRST GRAINS	2,000 YEARS
GROWTH OF ASTEROID-LIKE PLANETESIMALS	A FEW THOUSAND YEARS
APPEARANCE OF MOON-SIZE PROTOPLANETS	10,000 TO 100,000 YEARS
INNER FOUR PLANETS REACH HALF THEIR EVENTUAL MASS; ACCRETION SLOWS	10 MILLION YEARS
INNER PLANETS REACH MODERN MASS; CRUSTS SOLIDIFY	100 MILLION YEARS
BOMBARDMENT MODIFIES PLANETS' CRUSTS	100 TO 800 MILLION YEARS
EVOLUTION OF PLANETS TO PRESENT DAY	3.8 BILLION YEARS

SIGNS OF CREATION

SOME METEORITES, KNOWN AS CHONDRITES, HAVE INTERIORS THAT CONSIST OF COLLECTIONS OF DIFFERENT MINERALS LUMPED TOGETHER (RIGHT). THE INDIVIDUAL PARTICLES WITHIN THEM ARE THOUGHT TO BE LARGELY UNCHANGED SINCE THE EARLY DAYS OF THE SOLAR SYSTEM, AND SHOW THE SORT OF PEBBLE-SIZE BODIES THAT ACCRETED TO FORM LARGER BODIES. THE ELEMENTS IN THEM SEEM TO BE IN THE SAME PROPORTIONS AS ASTRONOMERS BELIEVE EXISTED IN THE SOLAR NEBULA AT THE BIRTH OF THE SOLAR SYSTEM.

HOT START

Some 4.6 billion years ago, the Earth and all the other planets existed as little more than a thin scattering of gas and grains of dust. The raw material from which the planets sprang probably took the form of a vast disk known to astronomers as the solar nebula.

Like the newly forming Sun, or protosun, that it surrounded, the solar nebula was born when a much larger cloud of gas and dust particles contracted under gravity. Close to the protosun in the center of the solar nebula, temperatures may have been greater than 3,000°F

(1,650°C). Eventually, with material in the disk spiraling in to the protosun, the disk grew sparser and its heat was able to escape into space. Then the disk began to cool and its material started to condense, with single atoms grouping together one at a time until they had grown into tiny grains less than a ten-millionth of a inch across.

This process, condensation, was the first step in the planet-building process. Far from the protosun, cooler conditions allowed water, ammonia and methane to condense into their ice form. But closer in, only rocky and metallic materials could condense.

As the condensed particles orbited the protosun, all swirling in the same direction, some of them began to stick to their neighbors. Astronomers are uncertain what caused the grains to stick together, but it might have been electrostatic forces. Because of this "agglomeration," individual grains grew steadily larger as they merged with adjacent particles.

BOMBARDMENT BEGINS

Within perhaps 2,000 years, the innermost regions of the solar nebula were swarming with countless pebble-size particles. After a few more thousand years, these pebbles had grown to the dimensions of asteroids, with the biggest being miles in diameter. Known as planetesimals, these fragments were by now so large that they grew not only by chance collisions with others, but because they could actually attract their neighbors by virtue of their gravity—a process known as accretion. It was at this point that the planet-building process stepped up another gear.

After about 10 million years, the innermost regions of the disk were populated by four dominant protoplanets that would later become Mercury, Venus, Earth and Mars, plus maybe one or two others. But by now these objects had

mopped up much of the available debris, so their growth rate diminished. It took perhaps another 100 million years for these protoplanets to double in mass to their modern values.

Violent times lay ahead. For some 800 million years—a period known to astronomers as the heavy bombardment phase—the primitive planets continued to sweep up smaller pieces of debris as they orbited around the Sun. Only after this period ended, about 3.8 billion years ago, did the inner planets as we know them truly emerge.

MOON CRASH

THE MOON IS THOUGHT TO HAVE BEEN CREATED SHORTLY AFTER THE EARTH STARTED TO SOLIDIFY. ASTRONOMERS SUSPECT THAT A LARGE PROTOPLANET—PERHAPS UP TO THREE TIMES AS MASSIVE AS MARS—COLLIDED OBLIQUELY WITH THE EARTH, AND THE IMPACT TOTALLY VAPORIZED THE PROTOPLANET, ALONG WITH A SUBSTANTIAL PART OF THE EARTH'S CRUST. THE DEBRIS WENT INTO ORBIT AROUND THE EARTH, WHERE MUCH OF IT LATER FORMED THE MOON.

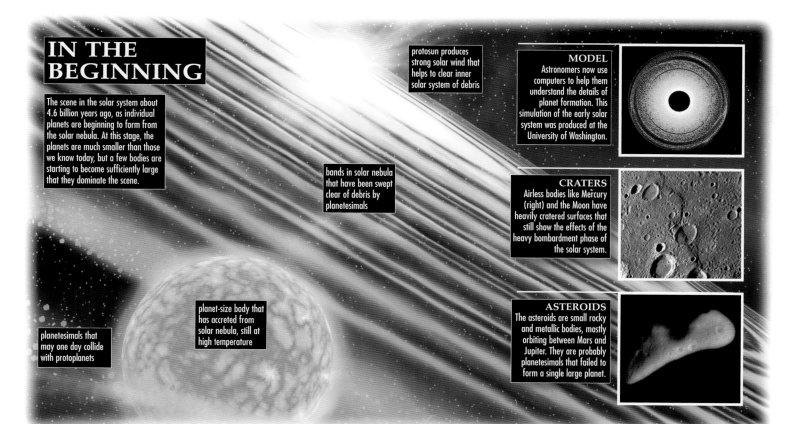

IN THE BEGINNING

The scene in the solar system about 4.6 billion years ago, as individual planets are beginning to form from the solar nebula. At this stage, the planets are much smaller than those we know today, but a few bodies are starting to become sufficiently large that they dominate the scene.

planetesimals that may one day collide with protoplanets

planet-size body that has accreted from solar nebula, still at high temperature

bands in solar nebula that have been swept clear of debris by planetesimals

protosun produces strong solar wind that helps to clear inner solar system of debris

MODEL
Astronomers now use computers to help them understand the details of planet formation. This simulation of the early solar system was produced at the University of Washington.

CRATERS
Airless bodies like Mercury (right) and the Moon have heavily cratered surfaces that still show the effects of the heavy bombardment phase of the solar system.

ASTEROIDS
The asteroids are small rocky and metallic bodies, mostly orbiting between Mars and Jupiter. They are probably planetesimals that failed to form a single large planet.

BIRTH OF THE GAS GIANTS

All planets form by accretion—the lumping together of material in a vast spinning disk of dust and gas. But our solar system has planets of two very different kinds. Near the Sun, the four inner planets are small and rocky. Farther out, where conditions were cooler, planets grew from accumulations of snowflakes. In time, they became large enough to attract hydrogen and helium. But the four giant planets—Jupiter, Saturn, Uranus and Neptune—have differences that are not so easy to explain.

OTHER STARS WITH GIANTS

STAR NAME	LOCATION	PLANET MASS (JUPITER=1)
51 Pegasi	Pegasus	0.4
Upsilon Andromedae	Andromeda	0.7
55 Cancri	Cancer	0.8
Rho Coronae Borealis	Corona Borealis	1.1
16 Cygni B	Cygnus	1.6
Iota Horologii	Horologium	2.2
47 Ursae Majoris	Ursa Major	2.3
Tau Bootis	Bootes	3.6
14 Herculis	Hercules	4.7
70 Virginis	Virgo	7.4

FROM PROTOPLANET TO GIANT

GAS GIANTS
This far from the Sun, protoplanets begin forming around cores of ice. Soon, they are so large that their gravity traps light, fast-moving atoms of hydrogen and helium. They grow until they sweep a clear space along their orbit.

JUPITER
At more than twice the mass of all the other planets, and 1,300 times as large as the Earth, Jupiter is a vast ball of hydrogen and helium around a small core of rock and ice.

At the center of the protoplanetary disk, the Sun is forming. At this stage in the process, it is only a protostar, very much larger than its final size and still collapsing under gravity. It shines dimly, not by nuclear fusion but by the heat released during gravitational contraction.

INNER TERRESTRIALS
Close to the protosun, ice cannot form. But rocky and metallic fragments begin to coalesce to form the inner, terrestrial planets.

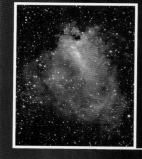

HYDROGEN
A cloud of hydrogen gas in the Swan Nebula gives some indication of what our solar system may have looked like before it formed. Hydrogen is by far the most common material in the universe.

70 VIRGINIS
This star has a planet more than seven times the mass of Jupiter. Astronomers suspect that this and other planets found around other stars—all of them very large—are gas giants of the Jovian type.

BIG BABIES

The solar system contains two distinct classes of planet. Huddled close to the Sun are small, dense planets made of rock and metal such as Earth and Mars. But farther out, the planets are much more massive, composed primarily of hydrogen and helium. These outer giants are so large that they contain about 99 percent of the combined mass of all the planets, satellites and asteroids we know of. How they grew so large, and how the solar system developed these characteristics, is a natural consequence of the way the system was born.

About 4.6 billion years ago, a cloud composed mainly of hydrogen and helium, with water

and other ices and particles of carbon dust, began to collapse under its own gravity. As it contracted, the cloud rotated steadily faster. Its material spread into a disk, with the Sun slowly taking shape at its center. At this stage the Sun was not a true star: It had not yet grown massive enough to ignite thermonuclear reactions in its core. It shone only dimly by gravitational contraction—the heat generated when a body shrinks under its own weight. In the disk, gas and dust particles were colliding to form progressively larger objects: grains, boulders, asteroids and then little protoplanets. Although the Sun was relatively cool, the inner system was still too warm for ice

to form. Only rock and metal could contribute to the planet-building process this far in. When these materials were all used up, the innermost protoplanets then stopped growing.

Much farther out in the disk, the planetary nursery was still in full production: The giants were forming. The relatively cool environment meant that outer protoplanets could grow by the accumulation not only of rocky material but also of the plentiful ice—orbiting snowflakes squeezed by gravity into ever-larger snowballs. With so much material on hand, these distant protoplanets grew more massive—several times larger than Earth. By the time the protoplanets that were to become Jupiter and Saturn had grown to 15 to 20 Earth-masses of material, their gravity was strong enough to haul in the light gases hydrogen and helium.

After one–10 million years, raw material in the disk became scarce. Far beyond Jupiter and Saturn, in the vicinity of Uranus and

ANOMALIES

URANUS AND NEPTUNE ARE FAR LARGER THAN THEORY SAYS THEY OUGHT TO BE. IN THEIR FAR-FLUNG ORBITS, THERE WOULD HAVE BEEN TOO LITTLE MATERIAL FOR THESE PLANETS TO HAVE GROWN TO THEIR PRESENT SIZES. RECENT WORK BY EDWARD THOMMES (ABOVE) AND MARTIN DUNCAN OF QUEENS UNIVERSITY, TORONTO, CANADA, SUGGESTS THAT URANUS AND NEPTUNE ACTUALLY FORMED MUCH CLOSER TO THE SUN, NEAR JUPITER. THERE THEY WOULD HAVE BEEN ABLE TO GROW UNTIL JUPITER'S GRAVITY EJECTED THEM AND THEY SETTLED INTO THEIR CURRENT, DISTANT ORBITS.

Neptune, the combination of the rapidly thinning material and the longer orbital timescales meant that these planets could not accumulate as much mass as Jupiter or Saturn had. As a result, they remained as largely water ice, without the extensive hydrogen and helium atmospheres of the closer giants.

It was also about this time that the Sun first grew hot enough to become a true star. Very soon, its increasing heat blew any remaining gaseous material in the planetary disk into interstellar space, and the planets effectively stopped growing altogether. The result was the solar system we see today.

In this hypothetical image, this backlit ring system of a far-off giant planet makes an impressive sight from its outermost moon, which has a polar orbit.

ORIGINS OF ATMOSPHERES

Only some of the planets in the solar system have a recognizable atmosphere—a film of gases that clings to the surface of the planet. Of the rocky planets, Venus, Earth and Mars have substantial atmospheres—mostly carbon dioxide, oxygen, water and nitrogen gas.

An atmosphere can make all the difference in a planet's history and atmosphere erosions can be deadly. On Earth, it has crucially helped protect and provide for life, while on Venus, it has covered the surface with an acidic overcoat. But where did such different atmospheres come from?

ATMOSPHERIC BREAKDOWN

	PERCENTAGE OF TOTAL ATMOSPHERE			PRESSURE CREATED BY EACH GAS (FULL PRESSURE OF THE EARTH'S ATMOSPHERE = 100%)		
	VENUS	EARTH	MARS	VENUS	EARTH	MARS
CARBON DIOXIDE	96%	0.035%	95%	8,640%	0.035%	0.62%
NITROGEN	3.5%	77%	2.7%	320%	78%	0.018%
OXYGEN	–	21%	–	–	21%	–
WATER VAPOR	0.01%	1%	0.006%	0.9%	1%	$3.9 \times 10{-5}$ %
ARGON	0.007%	0.93%	1.6%	0.63%	0.94%	0.01%

TRAPPED GAS

An atmosphere first coalesces around a planet as the planet is forming. Some 4.6 billion years ago, the solar system formed out of a giant spinning pancake of dust and gas particles. Asteroid-size lumps of rocky material called planetesimals picked up thin shrouds of gas—hydrogen and helium. But in the inner solar system, this first atmosphere dissipated easily, because the planetesimals' gravity was too weak to keep a grip on the gas.

Planet-building continued. Planetesimals grew by colliding and clumping together—and the force of impact heated the rock to release gas. This secondary gas formed atmospheres around the inner planets.

But how do rocks make gas? They are a bit like mushrooms: They do not drip when you squeeze them, but they give off lots of steam when fried. Even solid rock—rock without holes or pores—can contain molecules such as water or carbon dioxide, chemically bound up in its mineral structure. When rock is heated—by impacts or by volcanic activity—its chemical bonds are broken, and it releases molecules as vapor.

The secondary gases were heavier than hydrogen and helium, so they were attracted more strongly to the surface. But by the time the solar system came of age, not every planet had held on to an atmosphere. At a given temperature, there is a minimum mass for a planet with an atmosphere and the Moon and Mercury are below it. Gases can escape the relatively weak gravity of these small worlds. Unlike Venus, Earth and Mars, neither the Moon nor Mercury is large enough to hold on to gases.

LOST ATMOSPHERES

At double the mass of Mercury, but only a tenth that of the Earth, Mars may have an intermediate history. Although its eroded surface suggests the planet once flowed with water and had a thick atmosphere, today its atmosphere is thin and its surface is dry.

Not all the gas in the atmospheres of the rocky planets has come from within. The dirty balls of water ice and dry ice called comets have also made contributions. Unlike planetesimals, which formed near the hot center of the solar nebula, comets coalesced near the edge of the nebula, at temperatures low enough to allow ice. Comets may have been tipped off their wide orbits by the gravity of large chunks of passing debris and flown down toward the center of the forming solar system to collide with planetesimals. On impact, they would have vaporized, releasing gas that originated at the edge of the solar system into a planetary atmosphere. Some scientists think that the Earth's oceans could not have been filled without help from ancient comets.

An alien visitor to our solar system would quickly realize that the atmosphere of the third planet cannot be explained by volcanic outgassing and comet impact alone. On our world—uniquely—the atmosphere is modeled and managed by the engine of life.

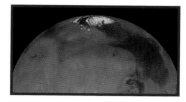

MARS
Surface features suggest that Mars once had a dense atmosphere and liquid water. Now, though, the atmosphere is only 1/100 as abundant as the Earth's. Weak gravity may have let Mars' gases slip away.

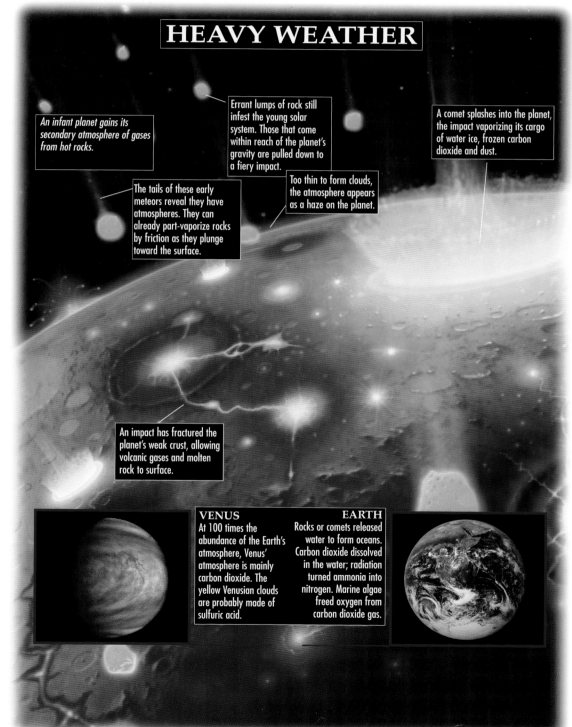

HEAVY WEATHER

An infant planet gains its secondary atmosphere of gases from hot rocks.

Errant lumps of rock still infest the young solar system. Those that come within reach of the planet's gravity are pulled down to a fiery impact.

A comet splashes into the planet, the impact vaporizing its cargo of water ice, frozen carbon dioxide and dust.

The tails of these early meteors reveal they have atmospheres. They can already part-vaporize rocks by friction as they plunge toward the surface.

Too thin to form clouds, the atmosphere appears as a haze on the planet.

An impact has fractured the planet's weak crust, allowing volcanic gases and molten rock to surface.

VENUS
At 100 times the abundance of the Earth's atmosphere, Venus' atmosphere is mainly carbon dioxide. The yellow Venusian clouds are probably made of sulfuric acid.

EARTH
Rocks or comets released water to form oceans. Carbon dioxide dissolved in the water; radiation turned ammonia into nitrogen. Marine algae freed oxygen from carbon dioxide gas.

IMPACTS IN THE SOLAR SYSTEM

Nothing alters a landscape more dramatically than an impact from space. On some worlds, the resulting craters are filled in by erosion or geological processes. But the surfaces of most moons and planets are sterile, and still bear the scars of billions of years of bombardment. Impacts are far less common today than they were in the young solar system. But the vast reservoirs of comets and asteroids still supply plenty of ammunition, and impacts will continue to pound the solar system for billions of years.

BIG HITS

Name	Location	Diameter
Caloris	Mercury	830 miles (1,340 km)
Mead	Venus	180 miles (290 km)
Aitken	Moon	1,560 miles (2,510 km)
Vredefort	Earth	190 miles (310 km)
Hellas Planitia	Mars	1,550 miles (2,500 km)
Valhalla	Callisto	370 miles (600 km)
Herschel	Mimas	80 miles (130 km)
Odysseus	Tethys	250 miles (400 km)
Mazomba	Triton	17 miles (28 km)

STRIKE OUT

At the beginning of the solar system, 4.6 billion years ago, there was little going on except impacts. The planets grew out of the mass of dust that swirled around the young Sun. These particles were welded together by collisions. The impact rate tailed off as more debris was locked away, but on asteroids, moons and planets, there are still crater scars everywhere.

All impacts are basically explosions. As one body hits another, its velocity is converted into energy. But there are big differences between the craters on various bodies. Impacts on the Moon show a central bowl surrounded by debris or ejecta. In larger craters, the rock is not strong enough to hold a bowl shape, and the crater slumps into a central peak. The craters on Mercury formed in the same way. But because bodies orbit faster the closer they are to the Sun, these impacts occurred at a higher velocity. Still, the impact ejecta on the Moon sprayed over a wider area—the stronger gravity of Mercury brought it back to the ground before it could travel far.

COMPARING SCARS

On Mars there is another difference. Some of the larger craters sit on splatters that look like the white of a fried egg. These were created as the force of the impact melted subsurface ice. Farther out in the solar system, ice plays an even larger part in shaping impact craters. The moons of Jupiter are mainly ice, and strange craters called palimpsests occur, most dramatically on the moon Ganymede. These are probably ghost craters—impact scars that formed early in the moon's history and have been all but erased by the ice melted through later collisions.

Smaller bodies have not escaped impacts either. The size of the largest crater on an asteroid is a good index of its strength—some withstand a strike that blasts a hole nearly as large as their diameter without breaking.

Crater counts in a region of a planet or moon are good indicators of the area's age. For example, craters are less common on the Moon's young lava seas than they are on the old highlands. And Venus' low crater score indicates that the planet's surface is only about 500 million years old. The plentiful craters gathered on older surfaces are a sobering reminder of what is to come. Impacts may be less frequent than they were, but the numerous asteroids that comtinue to roam the solar system promise that one day, the Earth will be back in the crosshairs.

DEATH BY IMPACT

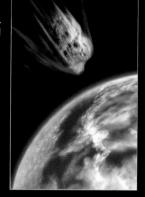

ASTEROID OR COMET IMPACTS HAVE BEEN BLAMED FOR SEVERAL MASS EXTINCTIONS IN THE HISTORY OF LIFE ON EARTH — MOST FAMOUSLY FOR THE DEATH OF THE DINOSAURS, 65 MILLION YEARS AGO. THE IMPACT OCCURRED IN WHAT IS NOW MEXICO, AND LEFT A CRATER OVER 100 MILES (160 KM) ACROSS. BESIDES REGIONAL ANNIHILATION, A COLLISION OF THIS SIZE COULD PUT ENOUGH DUST INTO THE ATMOSPHERE TO BLOCK OUT THE SUN, LEADING TO A GLOBAL FOOD CRISIS.

JUPITER STRIKE
The July 1994 collision of Shoemaker-Levy 9 and Jupiter (right) provided a graphic insight to the fall-out of a large impact. The strike left Jupiter's gaseous atmosphere with huge impact scars: some larger than the Earth.

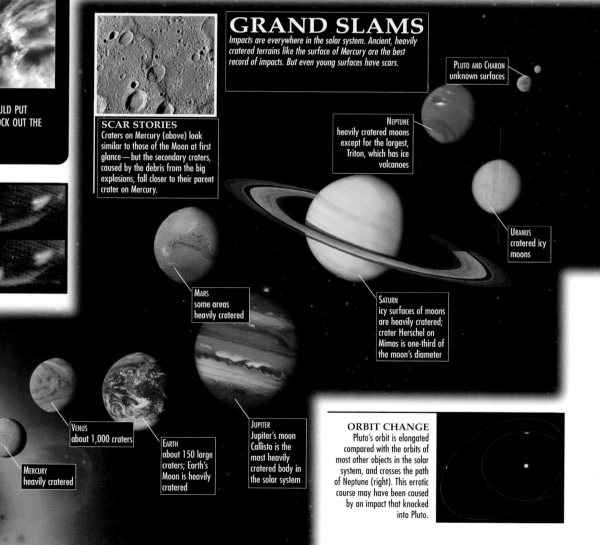

GRAND SLAMS
Impacts are everywhere in the solar system. Ancient, heavily cratered terrains like the surface of Mercury are the best record of impacts. But even young surfaces have scars.

SCAR STORIES
Craters on Mercury (above) look similar to those of the Moon at first glance—but the secondary craters, caused by the debris from the big explosions, fall closer to their parent crater on Mercury.

PLUTO AND CHARON
unknown surfaces

NEPTUNE
heavily cratered moons except for the largest, Triton, which has ice volcanoes

URANUS
cratered icy moons

SATURN
icy surfaces of moons are heavily cratered; crater Herschel on Mimas is one-third of the moon's diameter

MARS
some areas heavily cratered

JUPITER
Jupiter's moon Callisto is the most heavily cratered body in the solar system

VENUS
about 1,000 craters

EARTH
about 150 large craters; Earth's Moon is heavily cratered

MERCURY
heavily cratered

MOON BUILDER
A giant impact may have been responsible for forming our own Moon (above). After the Earth formed, it may have been struck by a rogue protoplanet. The collision blasted debris into Earth orbit, which coalesced to form the Moon.

ORBIT CHANGE
Pluto's orbit is elongated compared with the orbits of most other objects in the solar system, and crosses the path of Neptune (right). This erratic course may have been caused by an impact that knocked into Pluto.

PLANETARY RINGS

The first set of planetary rings was spotted around Saturn in 1610, but it took almost four more centuries for observers to put the rings of Uranus, Jupiter and Neptune in place. For giant planets, it seems that rings are the rule rather than the exception. Each is a thin pancake of particles—perhaps the remains of moons that failed to form, or those that have shattered. None of the inner planets have ring systems—at least, not yet. Human activity in space could eventually provide Earth with the strangest rings of all.

PLANETARY RINGS SPECS

Planet	Year of Ring Discovery	Outermost Diameter miles/km	Thickness miles/km	Particle Size in/mm
Saturn	1610	300,000/480,000	0.006–0.06/0.01–0.1	0.5–200/13–6000
Uranus	1977	32,000/52,000	0.006–0.06/0.01–0.1	4–400/100–10,000
Jupiter	1979	143,000/23,000	20/32	0.00004/0.01
Neptune	1984	39,000/63,000	20/32	0.5–50/13–1,250

CIRCLE STORY

Saturn, Jupiter, Uranus and Neptune: Every giant planet in our solar system is surrounded by rings. In photographs, these structures appear solid, but in fact each one consists of millions of particles doing their own thing. Although they all circle in the same thin plane, each one follows its own individual orbit.

No two ring systems are the same. Saturn's are the boldest—broad bands of icy fragments that reflect light. The rings of Uranus are much narrower and jet black. Jupiter's rings are also dark, but their particles are finer. And the rings of Neptune—again, dark and narrow—have an unusual brightening along certain stretches that gives the appearance of arcs rather than whole rings.

There are several plausible models of ring formation, but the definitive version has yet to be agreed. All of these ideas involve the Roche limit—the minimum distance from a planet at which a satellite can remain stable. Inside this limit, tidal forces from the nearby planet induce enough stresses to tear the body apart.

Most of the rings in the solar system orbit well inside their respective Roche limits—which suggests that they are the debris of something that strayed too close. But what? Some scientists argue that the rings came from the planet's own moons, others that they are the shattered remains of comets or asteroids that came from afar. In either case, the composition of the destroyed body would determine the makeup of the rings—and that might explain some of the differences that exist between the ring systems.

EARLY STARTERS

Another school of thought dates the rings back to the time when the planets themselves formed. Some scientists believe that the planets condensed out of a vast doughnut of gas and dust that surrounded the young Sun. As these particles collided, they stuck together and eventually grew into planets. The giant planets were surrounded by excess material, some of which coalesced to form their moons. But this was not the fate of material inside the Roche limits. Instead, it gradually collapsed into a plane that encircled the planets and then spread out to form the rings as we see them today.

But there are aspects of ring formation that do not fit into any current model. Astronomers think that ring systems persist for less than a few hundred million years. So the fact that we see rings today is not consistent with their creation alongside the planets 4.6 billion years ago. But the breakup of a moon or comet suggested by the alternative model asks for too much of a coincidence—it implies that all of the catastrophes that formed ring systems happened in the recent past. Also, the solar system does not carry as much debris as it did billions of years ago when the existing rings were formed. This means that impacts capable of forming ring systems grow less likely as time goes on—and unless we are lucky enough to see one in the making soon, we may never know for sure how the giant planets originally got their rings.

FILLING IN THE GAPS

IN 1675, FRENCH ASTRONOMER GIOVANNI CASSINI (1625–1712) BECAME THE FIRST PERSON TO OBSERVE STRUCTURE WITHIN SATURN'S RINGS. CASSINI (RIGHT) OBSERVED A DARK BAND IN THE RINGS, AND TODAY THIS AREA IS KNOWN AS THE CASSINI DIVISION. THE DIVISION WAS FIRST THOUGHT TO BE A GAP BETWEEN TWO MAIN RINGS, BUT VOYAGER PHOTOS REVEALED SEVERAL FAINT AND NARROW RINGS IN THE REGION.

RINGS TRUE

SATURN'S RINGS WERE DISCOVERED IN THE 1600s, BUT IT TOOK TWO MORE CENTURIES AND THE GENIUS OF SCOTTISH PHYSICIST JAMES CLERK MAXWELL (1831–79) TO FINALLY UNRAVEL THEIR TRUE NATURE. MAXWELL (RIGHT) DEMONSTRATED THAT THE RINGS MUST BE COMPOSED OF COUNTLESS INDIVIDUAL PARTICLES, EACH IN AN INDEPENDENT ORBIT AROUND THE PLANET — NOT SOLID SHEETS OF MATTER. MAXWELL PROVED THAT SOLID OR FLUID RINGS WOULD BE PHYSICALLY UNSTABLE.

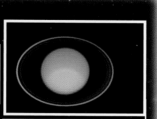

In the far future, a ring arches above the Earth—one consequence of the Space Age. Made of metallic debris, the ring reflects light well and is visible even by day.

GROWING RINGS

A cloud of fragments—from the early solar system or a shattered moon—surrounds the planet

Although every giant planet in our solar system has rings, their origins are unclear. Scientists know how rings form, but little about how they disperse.

Collisions between particles reduce their size and push them toward a common plane, which lies perpendicular to the spin axis

Collisions push the innermost particle farther in and the outer farther away. This spreads the ring radially so a true ring system takes shape

JUPITER'S HALO
Particles in Jupiter's rings are charged, so they are affected by the planet's magnetic field. For very small particles, this magnetism overpowers gravity. This Galileo image (above) shows how particles are pulled out of the main ring (yellow) into a halo (blue).

SHARP EDGES
From the Earth, the structure of ring systems is best revealed by the planet's movement in front of a star. Uranus' rings were discovered in this way in 1977. Uranus' ring boundaries are very crisp (above)—evidence that their edges are "supervised" by nearby moons.

WATER IN THE SOLAR SYSTEM

Of all the molecules in the solar system, the one that holds the greatest interest for the human race is water. Not only do we depend on it for our survival, but it is easily broken down into its components—hydrogen and oxygen—which together make a very useful fuel. Although water made up only about one percent of the gas cloud from which the solar system formed, it is common throughout the solar system in the form of ice—though Earth remains the only planet with large amounts of surface water.

DISCOVERING ICE

1957 Gerard Kuiper detects ice on Europa and Ganymede

1971 Mariner 9 confirms water ice at poles of Mars

1979 Passing Jupiter, Voyagers 1 and 2 reveal first detailed views of Callisto, Ganymede, Europa and Io

1980 Voyager 1 provides first images of Saturn's icy moons

1981 Bypassing Saturn, Voyager 2 gives more details of Tethys, Phoebe and Iapetus: All contain large amounts of water ice

1986 Passing Uranus, Voyager 2 finds ice on five moons

1988 Charon, one of Pluto's moons, shown to be icy

1991 Radar images of Mercury suggest polar ice

1995 Galileo spacecraft provides close-ups of ice-covered Europa

1996 Clementine mission finds polar crater on Moon, where water may exist

1998 Lunar Prospector finds further evidence for the existence of ice at lunar poles

WATER WORLDS

Water is everywhere in the solar system. It has been found from Pluto's tiny moon Charon to the Sun's neighbor Mercury—and on the seven other planets and their moons that fill the billions of miles of space in between. Water only makes up one percent of the solar system's mass, but most of this bulk is contained in the Sun—so a much greater proportion of the planets and their moons is water.

Much of this water exists as ice, which occurs anywhere that temperatures are cool enough: either far away from the Sun in the outer solar system, or shielded from the fierce heat on the planets closest to the Sun.

Most of the water has always been there. The raw ingredients of water—hydrogen and oxygen—were abundant in the solar nebula that condensed into our Sun and planets. The inner zone of the nebula was too hot for water to freeze into ice, but farther away from the infant Sun, water ice was stable. The Jovian planets may have formed around icy nuclei whose gravity attracted more and more material. The cores of Jupiter and Saturn attracted nebular gases,

so their composition is similar to that of the Sun. Farther out, both Uranus and Neptune consist of little else but water and carbon ices. In the outermost zone of the nebula, temperatures at the birth of the solar system were lower still. Here, water ice mixed with dust to form the comets in the Kuiper Belt.

HIDDEN OCEANS?

One of the most watery worlds in the solar system is Jupiter's satellite Europa. This moon is covered with a crust of water ice 100 miles (160 km) thick, and some of the surface fissures are

impossible to explain unless the ice floats on a liquid layer. Scientists now believe that there is an ocean on Europa, kept liquid by the heat of tidal stresses from Jupiter's gravitational pull.

Vast stores of water ice were expected, and found, in the environs of all the planets in the outer solar system. Closer to the Sun, water is scarcer—but the mystery is why the inner solar system contains any water at all. The standard model for the appearance of water on the Earth's surface is outgassing. Soon after the planet formed, volcanoes pumped out water vapor that had

been trapped deep within the planet though fractures in the surface. This model explains how water arrived in the first place, but it does not explain why it has stuck around: In its early days, the Earth was hot enough to boil any water off into space. Now, some scientists believe that bombardment from the distant comet and asteroid belts was at least as important as volcanoes as a source of the water on Earth, Venus and Mercury. These impactors released their icy load into atmospheres and surfaces—and delivered a little of the water in the outer solar system to the inner worlds.

WATER ON THE SUN

THE TEMPERATURE OF THE SUN'S SURFACE IS AROUND 10,000°F (5,530°C) —MUCH TOO HOT FOR WATER TO EXIST. BUT SUNSPOTS (RIGHT) ARE MUCH COOLER, AT 5,300°F (2,900°C), AND THE INTENSE MAGNETIC ACTIVITY THAT GENERATES THEM ALSO SUPPRESSES THE FLUX OF HOT MATERIAL FROM THE STAR'S INTERIOR. OXYGEN AND HYDROGEN ARE ABLE TO COMBINE, AND SMALL AMOUNTS OF SOLAR WATER APPEAR AS SUPERHOT STEAM.

FINDING WATER

ASTRONOMERS DETECT SPACE WATER BY ANALYZING THE SPECTRUM OF LIGHT FROM DISTANT OBJECTS. DARK LINES IN THE SPECTRUM REVEAL THE ABSENCE OF CERTAIN WAVELENGTHS. DIFFERENT MOLECULES ABSORB DIFFERENT WAVELENGTHS, SO THE SPECTRUM IS, IN EFFECT, A BAR CODE THAT LISTS THE ELEMENTS AND COMPOUNDS AT THE LIGHT'S ORIGIN — INCLUDING WATER. EARTH-BASED TELESCOPES— THE MCMATH-PIERCE TELESCOPE AT KITT PEAK, ARIZONA (ABOVE) CAN NOW "SEE" WATER AS FAR AWAY AS THE DWARF PLANET PLUTO.

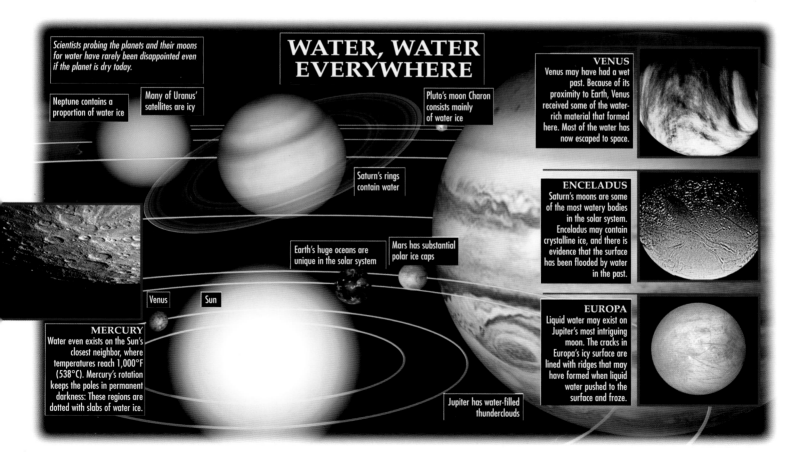

WATER, WATER EVERYWHERE

Scientists probing the planets and their moons for water have rarely been disappointed even if the planet is dry today.

Neptune contains a proportion of water ice

Many of Uranus' satellites are icy

Pluto's moon Charon consists mainly of water ice

Saturn's rings contain water

Earth's huge oceans are unique in the solar system

Mars has substantial polar ice caps

Venus

Sun

MERCURY
Water even exists on the Sun's closest neighbor, where temperatures reach 1,000°F (538°C). Mercury's rotation keeps the poles in permanent darkness: These regions are dotted with slabs of water ice.

Jupiter has water-filled thunderclouds

VENUS
Venus may have had a wet past. Because of its proximity to Earth, Venus received some of the water-rich material that formed here. Most of the water has now escaped to space.

ENCELADUS
Saturn's moons are some of the most watery bodies in the solar system. Enceladus may contain crystalline ice, and there is evidence that the surface has been flooded by water in the past.

EUROPA
Liquid water may exist on Jupiter's most intriguing moon. The cracks in Europa's icy surface are lined with ridges that may have formed when liquid water pushed to the surface and froze.

THE FUTURE OF THE SOLAR SYSTEM

Six and a half billion years from now, the Sun will swell up into a red giant, engulfing the orbit of Mercury and melting the surfaces of Venus and the Earth. Approximately two billion years later, the Sun will shrink and cool into a dim white dwarf. Computer simulations suggest that much of the rest of the solar system will survive these cataclysms. Shifted into new orbits, the fiercely altered planets will still revolve around the dying Sun. And on a few favored moons, there is even a chance that new life could once again spring forth somewhere in our solar system.

FUTURE ORBITS

THE SUN WILL HAVE LOST HALF ITS MASS BY THE TIME IT EXITS THE RED GIANT PHASE TO BECOME A WHITE DWARF. THE ORBITS OF THE SURVIVING PLANETS WILL SHIFT ACCORDINGLY, HEADING FARTHER OUT INTO SPACE.

SOLAR SYSTEM TODAY MILES/KM	SOLAR SYSTEM CIRCA 8000000000 A.D. MILES/KM
MERCURY: 35,983,000/57,909,000	MERCURY: destroyed
VENUS: 67,232,000/108,196,000	VENUS: 124,379,000/200,163,000
EARTH: 92,957,000/149,596,000	EARTH: 171,970,000/276,751,000
MARS: 141,635,000/227,933,000	MARS: 262,025,000/421,677,000
JUPITER: 483,633,000/778,310,000	JUPITER: 894,721,000/1,439,875,000
SATURN: 886,661,000/1,426,904,000	SATURN: 1,640,323,000/2,639,772,000
URANUS: 1,783,954,000/2,870,917,000	URANUS: 3,300,315,000/5,311,197,000
NEPTUNE: 2,794,356,000/4,496,957,000	NEPTUNE: 5,169,559,000/8,319,371,000
PLUTO: 3,674,500,000/5,913,373,000	PLUTO: 6,797,825,000/10,939,740,000

END OF AN ERA

The Sun and the solar system were born together around 4.6 billion years ago, forming from a huge contracting cloud of interstellar dust and gas. As the cloud contracted and became denser, the temperature at its core increased until it became hot enough to start a self-sustaining nuclear reaction. The Sun burst into life, and for four and a half billion years it has been fusing together hydrogen atoms to generate heat and light. There is enough hydrogen left for this process to continue for billions of years to come—but not forever. In six and a half billion years the Sun's hydrogen will be exhausted, and this 11-billion-year nuclear reaction will cease.

The only element left in the Sun's core will be helium, which reacts at a higher temperature than hydrogen. Without the pressure generated by nuclear reactions, the core will shrink under the force of its own gravity. But as it becomes denser, it will heat up until the nuclear reaction temperature of helium is reached. The sudden ignition of helium atoms will cause the Sun to grow bigger and brighter than ever before—200 times its present size and 5,000 times more luminous.

The solar wind, a stream of charged subatomic particles emitted by the Sun, will increase in strength as the star expands. And in a series of pulsations every 10,000 years or so, the outer layers of the Sun will be hurled out into space, creating a series of shells of gas known as a planetary nebula. Some astronomers believe that the Sun will lose almost half its mass through a combination of increased solar wind and planetary nebula generation.

So what effects will the Sun's expansion have on the planets of the solar system? Mercury has no chance of survival and will be swallowed up by the expanding star. The diminished mass of the Sun also means that its gravitational pull will decrease. As a result, the orbits of Venus and Earth will expand outward until both planets are almost double their present-day distances from the Sun. This should save both planets from being engulfed, although the Sun's increased luminosity could still be sufficient to boil away both planets' atmospheres, and reduce Earth to red-hot liquid rock. Venus is probably doomed to fall into the Sun's scorching atmosphere, and some astronomers believe that Earth may suffer the same fiery fate. After two billion years, the Sun will run out of helium. During that time, the outer solar system may have a happy future. Warm, comfortable environments on some of the moons of Jupiter and Saturn could see life emerge. If so, the organisms of Europa or Titan will have to evolve in a hurry. On Earth, it took 4.5 billion years for life to develop from bacteria to the high-tech civilization we live in today. Any Titanians will have less than half that time to acquire the skills of deep space travel—and possible escape—before the Sun finally dims to a white dwarf and their environments freeze around them.

MISNAMED NEBULAE

THE PLANETARY NEBULA THAT WILL MARK THE END OF THE SUN HAS NOTHING WHATSOEVER TO DO WITH PLANETS. SUCH NEBULAE OWE THEIR NAME TO ENGLISH ASTRONOMER SIR WILLIAM HERSCHEL (1738–1822). WHEN HE VIEWED THESE OBJECTS THROUGH HIS TELESCOPE, HERSCHEL NOTED THAT MANY NEBULAE APPEARED AS DEFINITE DISKS, LIKE PLANETS. SO HE CALLED THEM "PLANETARY" NEBULAE, AND THE NAME STUCK. THE "TURTLE IN SPACE" — NGC 6210 (ABOVE, WITH DETAIL OF CENTER INSET) — IS A GOOD EXAMPLE.

THE SOLAR SYSTEM'S LATE LATE SHOW

MARS
With its climate warmed by the enlarged Sun, the Martian environment will improve. Liquid water will flow once more across the planet's surface, making Mars more hospitable to life—for a brief summer. Soon, rising temperatures will spell doom for life.

THE SUN
By 7000000000 A.D., the Sun will have expanded out as far as the current orbit of the Earth, engulfing Mercury in the process. The loss of about half of the star's mass through the ejection of its outer layers will also have diminished it gravitational pull. As a result, the remaining planets will have drifted further out into space.

THE EARTH
The atmosphere will have boiled away into space. A home to life no longer, the planetary surface will be a wasteland of molten rock at temperatures of up to 2,400°F (1,300°C).

VENUS
Scorched hot enough to melt rock, Venus may be susceptible to tidal effects that could cause it to spiral into the Sun.

JUPITER
Increased solar output will thaw the giant planet's icy moons. For a short time at least, they may become new worlds with oceans and atmospheres.

SATURN
Saturn's moon Titan, now at a temperature of −290°F (−550°C), will be warm enough for organic chemicals to react. The moon is the late solar system's best bet for a chance at life being formed.

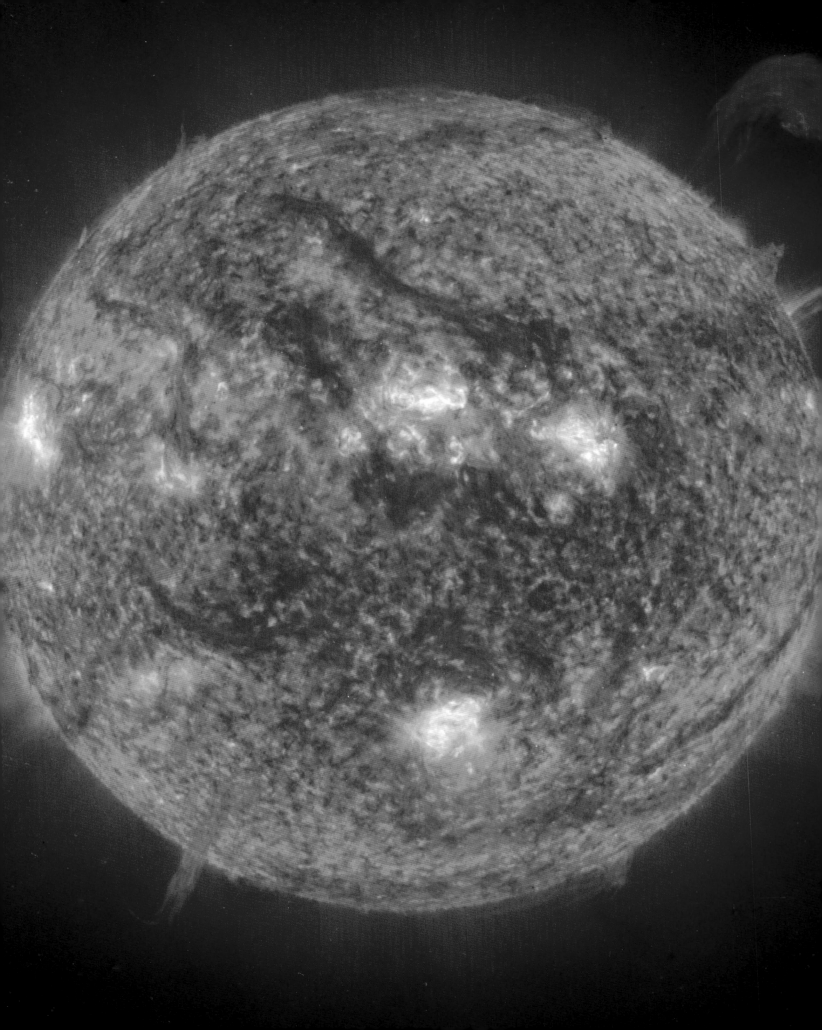

THE SUN

Our local star is the dominant force in the solar system. The Sun's vast mass holds everything in its gravitational grasp, and the streams of material blown out in its solar wind create "space weather" that affects the planets as far out as Jupiter and beyond. As stars go, the Sun is a fairly average middle-aged example. It creates energy by nuclear fusion in its core, but the amount of energy emitted is small compared to that of more massive stars. Fortunately this means that the Sun will have a long lifespan—it has existed for five billion years, and will not undergo any major changes until it runs out of fuel in at least another five billion. In its present life stage, the Sun produces energy at a steady rate, although it is constantly changing on a small scale. Sunspots (cooler regions on the surface) and solar flares (vast outbursts of gas and particles into space) are both signs of the solar cycle, in which the Sun breaks down its magnetic field and regenerates it roughly every eleven years.

The feature at the top right of this image of the Sun is a prominence, a huge cloud of relatively cool dense plasma erupting from the Sun's hot, thin corona. In this image taken by the Extreme ultraviolet Imaging Telescope (EIT), the hottest areas appear almost white, while the darker red areas indicate cooler temperatures.

THE SUN

The warmth that you feel on your skin on a sunny day originated in one of the most extreme environments in the entire universe—the nuclear cauldron that lies at the heart of a star. The star in question is the Sun, the body that supplies heat and light to the small planet we call Earth. The way the Sun generates energy in its fiery furnace, and the means by which that energy moves outward from the core to radiate as sunshine on the surface, are the keys to the evolution of life on this planet.

SOLAR STATISTICS

Average distance from Earth	92.957 million miles (149.595 million km)
Diameter	864,950 miles (1.392 million km)
Age	4.5 billion years
Mass	1.99 million, trillion, trillion tons (1.7 million, trillion, trillion tonnes)
Average density	1.4 times the density of water
Surface temperature	10,900°F (6,040°C)
Core temperature	27 million°F (15 million°C)
Composition	At least 90% hydrogen, the rest mostly helium with traces of other elements

THE SHINING

The Sun is made of gas, mainly hydrogen. But because this body of gas is so massive, the Sun's own gravity creates enormous heat (27 million°F/15 million°C) and pressure (500 billion pounds per square inch/3.5 billion megapascals) at the core. Under these conditions, the hydrogen atoms cannot exist in their usual form; they become stripped of their orbiting electrons, leaving just the naked nuclei, called protons.

The heat and pressure agitates these protons to a point where they continually collide with each other. This causes some pairs of hydrogen atoms to fuse together, creating a single atom of a new element—helium. Each time this happens, a minute amount of matter is converted into energy. For each ounce of matter annihilated, enough energy is produced to power a 100W light bulb for about 750,000 years. And in the Sun, some 5 million tons of matter is annihilated every second.

The energy released in these nuclear reactions heats up the core of the Sun still further, and produces high levels of radiation. Photons—tiny "packets" of this radiation—slowly make their way outward from the core through a superdense region called the radiative zone. After that, the photons reach the convective zone where the Sun is less dense and where giant pockets of super-hot gas bubble to the surface.

Eventually, the energy-carrying photons reach the surface and radiate out into space. Much of the energy takes the form of visible light, but there are also infrared light, x-rays and harmful ultraviolet rays. The light comes from a region known as the photosphere which, effectively, is all we see of the Sun.

The photosphere appears grainy and is constantly moving. The grains seem to come and go, each one lasting some 25 minutes. These 600- to 1,000-mile-wide (1,000- to 1,600-km-wide) "granules" are actually the surface bubbling as energy is carried up from below. The surface of the Sun also shows a larger pattern, called supergranulation. Supergranules are each about 20,000 miles (32,000 km) across, and are related to the massive convection bubbles in the convective zone situated below the Sun's photosphere.

OTHER FEATURES

Above the photosphere is the chromosphere, which can be seen as a pink ring around the Sun during an eclipse. Above this is the corona, from which a hot, thin stream of particles—the solar wind—blows outward into space. Other visible features of the Sun include darker regions called sunspots and bright flares.

The internal workings of the Sun may be complex, but they are nevertheless crucial to our existence. Without them, we would have no light, no energy, and, of course, no life on Earth.

IT'S WHITE

ALTHOUGH THE SUN APPEARS YELLOW WHEN SEEN FROM EARTH, IT IS ACTUALLY WHITE. WE SEE THE SUNLIGHT AFTER IT HAS BEEN FILTERED THROUGH THE EARTH'S ATMOSPHERE. AIR SCATTERS THE BLUE COMPONENT, MAKING THE SKY APPEAR BLUE AND THE SUNLIGHT YELLOW.

GETTING TOGETHER

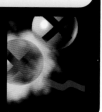

SCIENTISTS HAVE CALCULATED THAT THE AVERAGE TIME ANY ONE PROTON IN THE SUN'S CORE WILL SPEND WAITING TO COLLIDE WITH ANOTHER PROTON IS GREATER THAN THE AGE OF THE UNIVERSE! EVEN SO, THERE ARE SO MANY PROTONS IN THE CORE OF THE SUN THAT THERE ARE COUNTLESS COLLISIONS EVERY SPLIT SECOND.

INSIDE THE SUN

The Sun is a star over 250,000 times nearer to Earth than the next closest star. The way it generates light and heat is a bit like millions of hydrogen bombs all going off together.

1 IN THE CORE

Pairs of hydrogen atoms combine to form helium atoms in the process of nuclear fusion, where matter is destroyed and energy given off. The energy generated is measured by Einstein's famous equation $E=mc^2$ (energy = mass x the speed of light x the speed of light). The numbers are huge, as is the amount of energy generated!

2 RADIATIVE ZONE

The matter near the center of the Sun is so densely packed that energy-carrying photons produced during the nuclear reactions have trouble finding their way through. They bounce from particle to particle in a so-called "random walk pattern" through the radiative zone. Their path is so slow that it can take over a million years for a photon to find its way out.

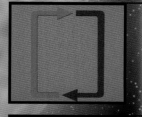

3 CONVECTION ZONE

Energy is carried from the radiative zone outward through the convective zone. Here, the hot gases boil up in giant convection cells like soup boiling in a pot—except that these "pots" are up to 20,000 miles (32,000 km) across. The gases radiate the energy to the surface, then cool and sink again, ready to pick up more energy.

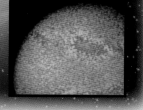

4 PHOTOSPHERE

Here, smaller convection cells—up to 600 miles (1,000 km) across—bubble up to the surface with more energy, giving the surface of the Sun a grainy appearance. The sunshine we see on Earth comes from the photosphere, which is the only part of the Sun we can see directly. The corona and flares are only visible during an eclipse.

ROTATION OF THE SUN

Like the planets, the Sun spins around its axis. But because the Sun is a ball of plasma, not solid like the Earth, its rotation period varies with latitude and depth. The area near the equator moves the fastest, completing a revolution in about 25 days—compared with a revolution taking 35 days at the poles. This latitude variation is detected 30 percent of the way into the Sun, and then there is a change: The core of the Sun seems to rotate more like a rigid body. The Sun's rotation is also linked to the magnetic knots we see as sunspots.

ROTATION PERIODS

Object	Orbital period	Rotation period
Sun	N/A	25–35 Earth days
Mercury	0.24 Earth years	58.65 Earth days
Venus	0.62 Earth years	243.01 Earth days
Earth	1.00 Earth years	1.00 Earth days
Mars	1.88 Earth years	1.03 Earth days
Jupiter	11.86 Earth years	0.41 Earth days
Saturn	29.46 Earth years	0.43 Earth days
Uranus	84.01 Earth years	0.75 Earth days
Neptune	164.79 Earth years	0.80 Earth days
Pluto	248.54 Earth years	6.39 Earth days

TWISTER SUN

The first recorded observations of the Sun's rotation were made about 400 years ago. Among the handful of Europeans at the forefront of this new science was Italian astronomer Galileo Galilei (1564–1642). With his newly invented telescope, he observed dark spots superimposed on the solar disk and suggested that they were physically associated with the Sun itself—they were not, as was previously believed, dark clouds or planets situated between us and the Sun. It was a simple step to measure the time it took for these spots—now called sunspots—to move across the solar disk. Galileo found that the Sun's "day" was a little under one month long.

But there were problems. As more astronomers carried out the same experiment, it became clear that the Sun's rotation rate was difficult to calculate exactly. Sometimes the spots appeared to move quickly across the Sun, and at other times they moved quite slowly. It was not until the mid-19th century that English astronomer Richard Carrington (1826–75) found the answer to the puzzle. In 1863, he observed that the solar equator was spinning once every 27 days as seen from Earth, but that at a latitude roughly halfway to the poles, the period was closer to 30 days. The Sun's rotation rate does indeed vary with latitude, and shows a smooth variation in spin period from 25 days at the equator to 35 days or even more at the poles. This rotation at different speeds is known as differential rotation. It is also seen in the gas planets of our solar system and in spiral galaxies.

THE SUN'S HUM

More recently, with the advent of helioseismology, astronomers have been able to see how the Sun rotates internally. Just as the study of earthquakes, or seismology, reveals properties about our planet's interior, so the study of vibrations on the Sun—helioseismology—offers clues to the interior of the solar furnace. The Sun is a violent place, and so it is also very noisy. The sound waves that carry this noise move through the Sun and change direction when they encounter regions of different density. This process is similar to the bending of light rays when they cross the boundary between water and air, an effect that makes swimming pools appear shallower than they really are. When the sound waves reach the Sun's surface, they cause it to pulsate. By observing these pulsations, astronomers can make accurate deductions about the interior movements of the Sun.

The results suggest that the convective zone—the outer layer of the Sun—has the same rotation pattern as the surface. Near the boundary region between the convective zone and the deeper radiative zone, the Sun starts to show a difference in rotation rate with depth. The equatorial rotation speed decreases while the polar rotation rate increases. The rates equalize around 40 percent of the way into the Sun. From here on in, the Sun rotates as a rigid body. The exact period is uncertain, but it appears to spin roughly once every 25 days.

What happens at even greater depths, though, is a mystery. Because the deepest sound waves suffer the most modifications in their journey to the surface, the information that they carry about the deep interior is easily drowned out. To study the Sun's core requires much more sensitive equipment than that currently available, and is a puzzle that future generations of astronomers will have to face.

MURDER MYSTERY

RICHARD CARRINGTON, THE WEALTHY AMATEUR ASTRONOMER WHO DISCOVERED THE SUN'S DIFFERENTIAL ROTATION, WAS INVOLVED IN ONE OF THE SHADIEST EPISODES IN THE HISTORY OF ASTRONOMY. IN 1875, TWO WEEKS AFTER HIS UNFAITHFUL WIFE WAS FOUND SUFFOCATED IN HER BED, CARRINGTON HIMSELF WAS FOUND DEAD IN HIS OBSERVATORY HOUSE IN SUSSEX, ENGLAND WITH EMPTY SEDATIVE BOTTLES NEARBY.

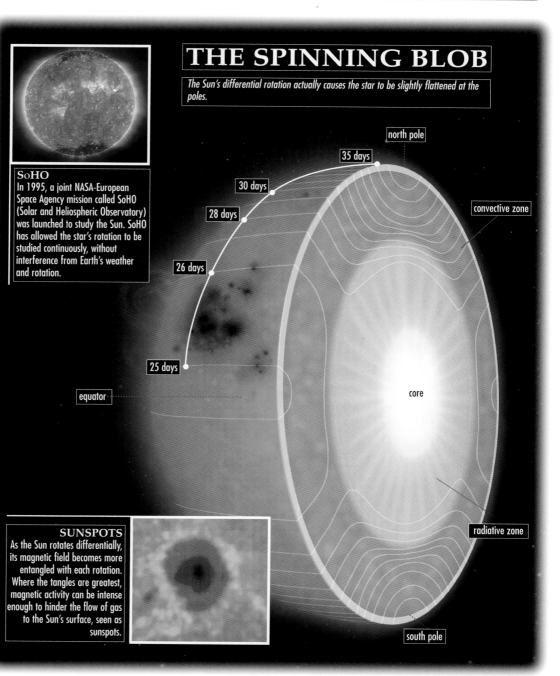

THE SPINNING BLOB

The Sun's differential rotation actually causes the star to be slightly flattened at the poles.

SoHO
In 1995, a joint NASA-European Space Agency mission called SoHO (Solar and Heliospheric Observatory) was launched to study the Sun. SoHO has allowed the star's rotation to be studied continuously, without interference from Earth's weather and rotation.

north pole

35 days

30 days

28 days

26 days

25 days

convective zone

core

radiative zone

equator

south pole

SUNSPOTS
As the Sun rotates differentially, its magnetic field becomes more entangled with each rotation. Where the tangles are greatest, magnetic activity can be intense enough to hinder the flow of gas to the Sun's surface, seen as sunspots.

SOLAR ECLIPSES

A total eclipse occurs when the Moon passes between the Earth and the Sun, blotting out the Sun's disk entirely and turning day into night. Throughout history, few natural phenomena have filled the human race with such awe. Even for professional astronomers, the sudden and dramatic darkening of the Sun, accompanied by a spectacular range of optical effects, is an experience never to be forgotten. But eclipses are not just entertaining—they also enable us to examine features of the Sun that are invisible at other times.

TOTALLY ECLIPSED...

Date	Duration (minutes)	Max. Umbra Width (miles/km)	Where visible
2006, March 29	4:06	114/183	Africa, Turkey, Azerbaijan, Kazakhstan, Russia
2008, August 1	2:27	147/237	Greenland, Russia, China
2009, July 22	6:38	160/257	India, China, Pacific Ocean
2010, July 11	5:20	160/257	S. Pacific Ocean, southern tip of S. America
2012, November 13	4:02	111/179	Australia, Pacific Ocean
2015, March 20	2:46	287/461	N. Atlantic Ocean, Norwegian Sea
2016, March 9	4:09	96/154	Indonesia, N. Pacific Ocean
2017, August 21	2:40	71/114	United States of America
2019, July 2	4:32	124/200	S. Pacific Ocean, Chile, Argentina
2020, December 14	2:09	56/90	Chile, Argentina
2021, December 4	1:54	260/418	Antarctica, S. africa, S. atlantic
2023, April 20	1:16	30/48	S.E. Asia, Australasia
2024, April 8	4:28	122/196	N. & C. America
2026, August 12	2:18	369/594	N. America, W. Africa, Europe

DARKNESS IN THE DAYTIME

As the Moon orbits the Earth every month or so, it reaches a point at which it is in roughly the same direction as the Sun when seen from Earth. From this you might imagine that a total eclipse of the Sun would be a monthly event—but as we know, it is actually quite rare.

Partial eclipses, where just part of the Sun is obscured by the Moon, are infrequent enough. In most years there are between two and four, although in 1935 there were five. Total eclipses are rarer still: There are seldom more than about 70 per century.

The infrequency of eclipses is largely explained by the angle of the Moon's orbit around the Earth, and by the size of the Moon relative to the Sun. The Moon's orbit is at about 5° relative to the orbit of the Earth around the Sun. This means that the Moon does not pass over the face of the Sun every time it orbits the Earth. The Moon is also relatively small, which means that its shadow often misses the Earth altogether.

When the Moon does cast its shadow on the Earth, its path crosses the Earth in a general west-to-east direction. Those fortunate enough to be lining the route are in for a spectacular show.

It takes several hours for the eclipse to unfold—a sequence of events that astronomers call contacts. Each point along the path sees exactly the same thing, but at a later time of day the farther east you go. For this reason some dedicated eclipse watchers take to aircraft, in an effort to chase the eclipse around the globe.

ANATOMY OF AN ECLIPSE

The first stage of an eclipse, called first contact, occurs when the Moon appears to touch the edge of the Sun. The eclipse is now in its partial phase. Second contact, or totality, starts at the instant the Moon is completely in front of the Sun and usually lasts no more than a few minutes. Third contact is when the Sun is just about to be revealed again. From then on the eclipse reverts to being partial until, at fourth contact, the Moon clears the Sun's disk completely. Because the Sun is so bright, there is no noticeable reduction in daylight until some 80 percent of it is covered. But toward second contact, an eerie darkness begins to descend with increasing rapidity.

In ancient times, people reported that the ground became filled with "writhing snakes." We now know that these mysterious serpents are, in fact, moving bands of shadow—the result of the Sun's narrowing crescent being focused by turbulence in the air.

NIGHT AND DAY

Despite the darkness, the path of an eclipse is narrow enough for light to remain visible on the horizon. Stars appear overhead and the air temperature becomes several degrees cooler.

As the bright disk of the Sun becomes obscured, the dimmer reddish prominences and outer layer, or chromosphere, become visible. Beyond them is the Sun's corona, which appears as a halo of bright, white light around the black disk of the Moon and is a truly awe-inspiring sight. For those lucky enough to watch, it is an unforgettable experience.

BAD LUCK

In India it is considered unlucky for pregnant women to watch an eclipse, and a child born during an eclipse is a bad omen. In some places it is also believed that to stop the Sun from being "consumed by the celestial beast," people should plunge their heads into water.

PROFILE OF AN ECLIPSE

When the Sun, Moon and Earth align, the Moon casts a cone-shaped shadow on the Earth. The inner, darker part of the shadow is the umbra; the outer shadow the penumbra. On Earth, the eclipse is total within the umbra and partial in the penumbra, which covers a much larger area.

direction of lunar orbit

penumbra

Moon

Sun

umbra

SHINING ON
When the brilliant disk of the Sun is obscured, there is a good chance of seeing the normally invisible red tongues of hydrogen known as prominences. Usually these are tiny, but if the Sun is in a very active phase they can be spectacular.

SOLAR JEWELS
Just before and after totality, a small part of the Sun's surface may peek out from behind the Moon. This glint of light is known as the Diamond Ring. Sometimes, an entire string of such gems—known as Baily's Beads—can appear.

INVISIBLE SUN
The Sun's outer corona becomes visible during an eclipse, but its appearance varies according to the amount of solar activity. If this is high, streamers emerge in all directions, otherwise they are often confined to the solar equator.

SKY SPECTACLE
Although totality lasts only minutes, the entire show, including partial phases, can last up to 5 hours. Astronomers and other enthusiasts travel around the world in pursuit of solar eclipses and some tour firms make eclipses a specialty.

The size of the umbra varies from eclipse to eclipse. It depends on how far the Moon is away from the Earth, how far the Earth is away from the Sun and on which latitude of the Earth the shadow falls. Its maximum possible size is about 400 miles (650 km) across.

CASTAWAY

Stranded in Jamaica in 1504, the explorer Christopher Columbus intimidated the natives into giving him food by telling them that he would make the sky dark. A scheduled eclipse followed and the terrified natives complied.

SUNSPOTS

The Sun is a far from perfect star. Its surface is blemished by sunspots—gigantic blotches, often larger in diameter than the Earth, where the temperature is 3,500°F (2,000°C) cooler than the surrounding area. Sunspots usually occur in groups, up to 100 at a time, which can last from half a day to several weeks when the Sun's magnetic field is affected by its uneven rotation. But despite the vast range of their size and duration, and their dark appearance, all occur in active zones where the Sun's seething magnetic activity penetrates the outermost layer of hot gas, its photosphere. Through these sunspot windows we can see the soul of the Sun.

SUNSPOT FACTS

PENUMBRA TEMPERATURE	9,400°F (5,200°C)
UMBRA TEMPERATURE	6,400°F (3,500°C)
TYPICAL SUNSPOT DIAMETER	8,000 MILES (13,000 KM), OR THE EARTH'S DIAMETER
MINIMUM DIAMETER OF SUNSPOT VISIBLE TO THE NAKED EYE	27,152 MILES (43,696 KM), OR SEVEN TIMES THE EARTH'S DIAMETER
TYPICAL SUNSPOT LIFETIME	A FEW DAYS
SHORTEST-EVER SUNSPOT LIFETIME	LESS THAN AN HOUR
LONGEST-EVER SUNSPOT GROUP LIFETIME	200 DAYS
EARLIEST RECORDED SUNSPOT SIGHTING	800 B.C., IN CHINA

IMPERFECT STAR

When Chinese astronomers saw dark spots on the Sun's disk one sunset 2,800 years ago, they had no real explanation. The great Italian astronomer Galileo Galilei (1564–1642) claimed that he first saw the strange markings in 1610. He wisely protected his eyesight by projecting the image of the Sun from his new telescope onto a card, and was the first to realize that the marks were on the "spotty and impure" solar globe itself. But it took a 20th-century science called spectroscopy to show that sunspots are a by-product of the Sun's magnetism. Spectroscopy is the tool that reveals what stars are made of. Each element in the Sun's atmosphere absorbs light of certain wavelengths. So if sunlight is split into its spectrum of component colors, the missing wavelengths leave dark lines—showing which elements are in the Sun.

WILDLY ATTRACTED

Often, light can give more information. In 1908, the American astronomer George Hale (1868–1938) noticed that the "signature" lines in the spectrum split in the presence of sunspots. Where there should have been one spectral line, he saw several. This phenomenon was known to occur in the presence of a strong magnetic field. Hale concluded that sunspots are vast regions of magnetic turmoil where the Sun's own magnetic field can be up to a thousand times stronger than its average level.

Part of the disruption comes from the Sun's own rotation. It spins just as the Earth does, completing a full turn in a month. But the Sun is not solid; its equator turns faster than its poles. This so-called differential rotation plays havoc with the solar magnetic field.

Magnetic field lines spanning the Sun resemble sections of an orange. The Sun pulls these vertical lines around with it as it spins. Since the Sun spins fastest at its equator, the lines begin to stretch and eventually become so twisted that they poke out of the Sun's outer layers, its photosphere, and form huge loops.

Sunspots occur at the bases of these magnetic loops—just where theory would predict them. Astronomers believe that the loops inhibit charged particles of hot gas and so prevent them from carrying heat to the surface. Cut off from this circulation, areas at the base of loops grow much cooler—and darker—than the rest of the photosphere. We see these shaded areas as sunspots.

Theory also predicts that magnetic fields will tend to tangle most around the equator. Again, this is exactly what observations show: Sunspots do indeed appear to migrate from high to low latitudes on a timescale of about 11 years. The only question that remains is why, exactly, the process should take 11 years.

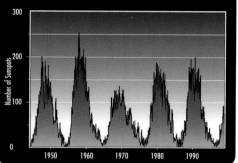

SUNSPOT LIFE CYCLE

JUST LIKE MANY SPECIES OF ANIMALS, SUNSPOTS HAVE REGULAR CYCLES OF BIRTH AND MIGRATION. FOR SUNSPOTS, SPRING ARRIVES ABOUT ONCE A DECADE. AT THE BEGINNING OF A NEW CYCLE, MANY APPEAR AT LATITUDES OF AROUND 40°. EACH SPOT NORMALLY LASTS A FEW DAYS AND THEN DIES. AS THE CYCLE PROGRESSES, MORE AND MORE SPOTS ARE BORN AT LOWER AND LOWER LATITUDES — THOUGH THEY NEVER ACTUALLY FORM ON THE EQUATOR ITSELF. FOR OVER A CENTURY, SCIENTISTS HAVE KNOWN THAT THE CYCLE PEAKS EVERY 11 YEARS, BUT THEY ARE STILL NOT SURE WHY IT HAPPENS.

WHAT'S IN A SUNSPOT?

SOLAR GRANULES
Although they look like small bubbles, granules are in fact enormous clouds of hot gas rising from below. Unlike sunspots—whose intense magnetic fields block any circulation—these areas are heated continually.

UMBRA
The darkest and coolest part of a sunspot is the umbra, with a temperature of about 6,400°F (3,500°C)—3,500 degrees cooler than the rest of the Sun. Sometimes it contains brighter regions called umbral dots measuring 200 miles (320 km) across.

PENUMBRA
The brighter area around the umbra is the penumbra, with a temperature around 9,400°F (5,200°C). In a large sunspot the penumbra occupies up to 70 percent of the spot's area, but small sunspots often have no penumbra at all. The filaments in the penumbra are large packets of gas which eventually form umbral dots.

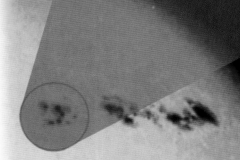

Sunspots usually appear in groups (shown circle). Some contain up to 100 different members. Each sunspot group may last for months.

SOLAR FLARES

The surface of the Sun is in a state of perpetual turmoil, creating loops of magnetic field lines that arch high into the Sun's atmosphere, the corona. Sometimes, for reasons that astronomers still cannot fully explain, one of these loops becomes unstable, causing the field lines to snap together around a seething cauldron of energized plasma. The result is a solar flare, which is a gigantic outpouring of electromagnetic radiation across a broad range of wavelengths that takes less than 30 minutes to reach the Earth.

SOLAR FLARE STATISTICS

First Recorded Sighting	England, 1859
Average Energy Release	1032 ergs*
Maximum Energy Release	1037 ergs
Average Local Temperature	20–40 million°F (11–22 million°C)
Maximum Local Temperature	200 million°F (110 million°C)
Average Duration	15 minutes
Frequency	30–40 per day when the Sun is most active
Frequency of Major Flares	three–five per year

*1032 ergs = 26 million times the energy released in the bombing of Hiroshima

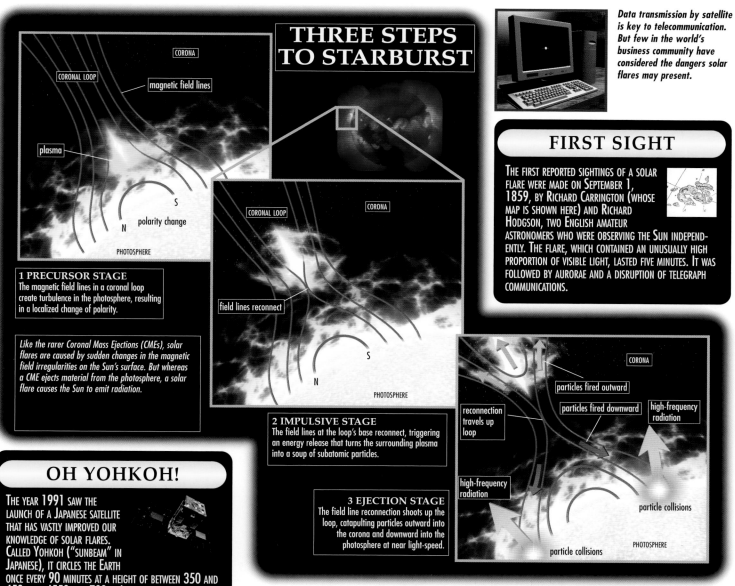

THREE STEPS TO STARBURST

CORONA

CORONAL LOOP

magnetic field lines

plasma

S

N

polarity change

PHOTOSPHERE

1 PRECURSOR STAGE
The magnetic field lines in a coronal loop create turbulence in the photosphere, resulting in a localized change of polarity.

Like the rarer Coronal Mass Ejections (CMEs), solar flares are caused by sudden changes in the magnetic field irregularities on the Sun's surface. But whereas a CME ejects material from the photosphere, a solar flare causes the Sun to emit radiation.

CORONAL LOOP

CORONA

field lines reconnect

S

N

PHOTOSPHERE

2 IMPULSIVE STAGE
The field lines at the loop's base reconnect, triggering an energy release that turns the surrounding plasma into a soup of subatomic particles.

3 EJECTION STAGE
The field line reconnection shoots up the loop, catapulting particles outward into the corona and downward into the photosphere at near light-speed.

CORONA

particles fired outward

reconnection travels up loop

particles fired downward

high-frequency radiation

high-frequency radiation

particle collisions

particle collisions

PHOTOSPHERE

Data transmission by satellite is key to telecommunication. But few in the world's business community have considered the dangers solar flares may present.

FIRST SIGHT

THE FIRST REPORTED SIGHTINGS OF A SOLAR FLARE WERE MADE ON SEPTEMBER 1, 1859, BY RICHARD CARRINGTON (WHOSE MAP IS SHOWN HERE) AND RICHARD HODGSON, TWO ENGLISH AMATEUR ASTRONOMERS WHO WERE OBSERVING THE SUN INDEPENDENTLY. THE FLARE, WHICH CONTAINED AN UNUSUALLY HIGH PROPORTION OF VISIBLE LIGHT, LASTED FIVE MINUTES. IT WAS FOLLOWED BY AURORAE AND A DISRUPTION OF TELEGRAPH COMMUNICATIONS.

OH YOHKOH!

THE YEAR 1991 SAW THE LAUNCH OF A JAPANESE SATELLITE THAT HAS VASTLY IMPROVED OUR KNOWLEDGE OF SOLAR FLARES. CALLED YOHKOH ("SUNBEAM" IN JAPANESE), IT CIRCLES THE EARTH ONCE EVERY 90 MINUTES AT A HEIGHT OF BETWEEN 350 AND 450 MILES (550 AND 700 KM) AND CARRIES FOUR INSTRUMENTS FOR STUDYING THE SUN AT X-RAY AND GAMMA-RAY FREQUENCIES. DATA FROM YOHKOH SHOWS THE SUN'S ACTIVITY IN A STRANGE AND BEAUTIFUL NEW LIGHT, RESULTING IN SPECTACULAR IMAGES.

FLASH IN THE PAN

Like many of the other spectacular events that take place within the Sun, solar flares are caused by irregularities in the Sun's magnetic field that disrupt the visible surface, or photosphere. Flares are linked with prominences, where the localized pull of the magnetic field counteracts the Sun's gravity and causes the photosphere to bulge. But in a flare, the effect is more sudden—and more violent: A big flare can liberate more energy than a billion thermonuclear explosions in just a few minutes, raising the temperature of the corona by tens of millions of degrees.

Despite their dramatic effects, solar flares remained a mystery until well into the 20th century because very little of their energy takes the form of visible light. The development of radio astronomy in the 1950s revealed that most flares radiate a combination of low-frequency radio waves and ultra-high-frequency X- and gamma- rays. But since most of the high-frequency waves are absorbed by the Earth's atmosphere, it took the latest generation of solar observation satellites to reveal solar flares in all their glory. In fact, at X-ray frequencies and above, a flare can briefly outshine the entire Sun.

Solar flares also create gusts in the solar wind—the stream of charged particles that is constantly pouring forth from the Sun.

Traveling at up to 70 percent of the speed of light, some of these particles collide with the Earth's magnetic field to produce colorful auroral displays in the atmosphere and disrupt radio communications.

Astronomers have only a partial understanding of what triggers solar flares, but they seem to originate in the type of solar prominences known as coronal loops. These arise when distorted lines of the Sun's magnetic field reach out high into the corona, drawing material with them and stirring up the photosphere below. But sometimes, the turbulence creates localized changes in the polarity of the field that in a split second cause the field lines to reconnect with each other. As this reconnection occurs, there is an enormous release of pent-up energy—rather like an elastic band that is stretched until it snaps.

PARTICLE ACCELERATOR

As the field lines reconnect, the plasma around them is turned into maelstrom of highly energized particles—mostly electrons and protons. Some of these particles are fired straight out into the corona, later to become gusts in the solar wind; others are fired downward into the photosphere, where they collide with other particles to trigger a massive burst of high-frequency X- and gamma-ray radiation that takes only minutes to reach the Earth.

The entire event is over in a matter of minutes. Within half an hour, the field lines in the coronal loop have reformed, leaving the never-ending cycle of turmoil on the Sun's surface to start afresh.

THE SOLAR CYCLE

As the Sun beats down on a long, hot summer day, it is all too easy to believe—as our ancestors did—that our parent star is an inexhaustible and never-changing source of energy. But in fact, like most stars, the Sun goes through a series of regular changes in structure and output that astronomers refer to collectively as the solar cycle. Though we rarely notice them on Earth, these changes can have dramatic consequences for our planet. They also reveal much about the internal workings of the Sun's nuclear furnace.

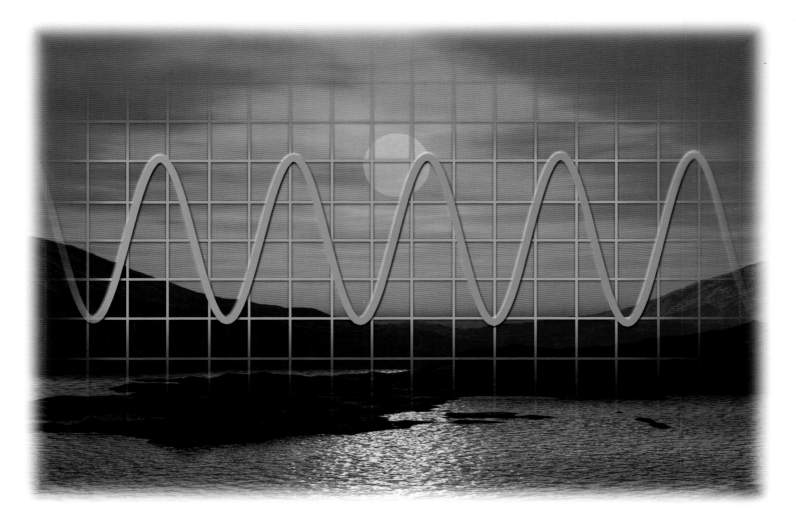

11-YEAR ITCH

The Sun is a more volatile place than most of us realize. The surface changes from day to day, as sunspots come and go and prominences send loops of hot gas arching into the Sun's atmosphere (corona). Then there are solar flares—gusts in the solar wind of charged gas particles that are ejected into space along the lines of the Sun's magnetic field. And, more rarely, there are coronal mass ejections, when the Sun suddenly and explosively rids itself of billions of tons of matter.

When the appearance of these solar phenomena is logged over time, a pattern emerges. The Sun undergoes periods of intense activity and relative calm that alternate every 11 years or so in a pattern called the solar cycle.

The cycle is most obvious in the changes to sunspots—areas that appear darker because they are thousands of degrees cooler than the surrounding surface (even though they are still around 6,400°F/3,500°C). At the start of the 11-year cycle, the Sun's disc is relatively clear: There are just a few sunspots gathered at roughly 40° north and south of the solar equator. Most of these appear in pairs, one of which (the preceding spot) moves ahead of the other and is slightly closer to the equator. Individual sunspots left over from the old cycle may linger, while new ones appear and fade in anything from half a day to a few weeks. But as the cycle continues, the average number of sunspots gradually increases: They last longer, and groups of them appear closer to the equator.

MAXIMUMS AND MINIMUMS

Sunspots reach a peak at the so-called solar maximum, around four years after the start of a cycle, at which point they are concentrated around 15° north and south of the equator. Over the next seven years, their numbers decline and they draw closer to the equator. By the end of the cycle, at the solar minimum, just a few sunspots remain around the equator, while a new generation of spots begins to form at higher latitudes.

The fluctuations in sunspots reflect changes that take place in the Sun's magnetic field over the length of the cycle. The Sun reverses polarity every 11 years, so the full magnetic cycle lasts 22 years. Other aspects of the Sun's behavior also change. Although sunspots signify cooler areas of the surface, the Sun's energy output actually increases slightly during a solar maximum. This variation amounts to only tenths of a percent in the visible part of the spectrum, but there is a tenfold increase in ultraviolet radiation and a one hundredfold increase in X-ray radiation. The Sun is also generally far more active at its solar maximum: Prominences and solar flares both increase in size and become more frequent.

The effect of these changes on the Earth is the subject of "heated" debate. In the past, surges in the Sun's output and in the solar wind have been smoothed out by the protective shroud of our atmosphere. Magnetic storms—disruptions to the Earth's magnetic field that occur during high levels of solar activity—have occasionally taken their toll on power lines and electronic equipment. But there is little evidence that the solar cycle affects global temperatures, the ozone layer, or any of the other "hot potatoes" that climatologists are currently concerned about.

Things could be different though, as we venture farther into space and place increasing reliance on communications satellites. With more and more spacecraft exposed to the full fury of the Sun, we may have to follow the solar cycle more closely in the future.

TURNING BACK THE CLOCK

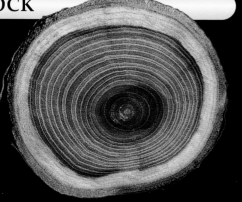

GEOLOGICAL EVIDENCE FOR THE REGULARITY OF THE SOLAR CYCLE EXTENDS MUCH FARTHER BACK IN TIME THAN ASTRONOMICAL RECORDS. ONE CLUE COMES FROM MEASURING THE LEVELS OF RADIOACTIVE CARBON-14 IN THE GROWTH RINGS OF VERY ANCIENT TREES, SUCH AS THOSE FOUND IN PARTS OF AUSTRALIA (RIGHT). TRACES OF CARBON-14 IN VEGETATION ARE NORMALLY THE RESULT OF COLLISIONS BETWEEN HIGH-ENERGY COSMIC RAYS AND NITROGEN ATOMS IN THE EARTH'S ATMOSPHERE. WHEN THE SUN'S MAGNETIC FIELD IS AT ITS STRONGEST, THE EARTH IS BETTER PROTECTED FROM COSMIC RAYS AND LESS CARBON-14 IS PRODUCED. THE EFFECTS OF THIS CAN BE MEASURED AND USED TO TRACE SOLAR CYCLES A FEW THOUSAND YEARS BACK. OVER LONGER PERIODS, TRACES OF CARBON-14 IN THE FOSSIL RECORD OF SOIL SEDIMENTS LAID DOWN IN RIVER BEDS ALSO REVEAL AN 11-YEAR PATTERN THAT GEOLOGISTS THINK MAY BE LINKED TO THE SOLAR CYCLE.

COMPONENTS OF THE SOLAR CYCLE

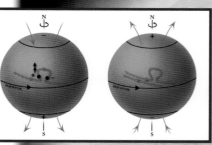

MAGNETIC FIELD
Parts of the Sun rotate at different rates. In time, this causes the magnetic field lines to kink and burst through to the surface, where they form sunspots. Over a single solar cycle, it also causes the Sun's magnetic field to reverse polarity (above). So a full cycle of magnetic events lasts for two cycles, or about 22 years.

SUNSPOTS
These cooler areas of the surface reveal the effect of the loops of magnetic field lines at different parts of the cycle. The view at left is typical of the Sun's appearance near its solar maximum: The spots are concentrated at latitudes 15° north and south, in groups that run roughly parallel to the equator.

CORONA
The corona, or outer atmosphere, also changes during the solar cycle. The eclipse of July 11, 1991 (right), which occurred at near solar maximum, showed the corona extended for millions of miles in all directions. At solar minimum, it is more flattened along the equator, with prominent streamers that resemble wings.

SOLAR WIND

Heat and light are not the only things that reach our planet from the Sun. There is also the solar wind—a fluctuating gale of subatomic particles. These fragments of electrically charged matter are hurled into space at colossal speeds by the magnetism of the Sun.

For the most part, we are shielded from these winds and their effects by the Earth's own magnetic field. But the solar wind still has the power to knock out communications satellites, and in polar regions it draws out shimmering bows of color: the aurorae.

STRENGTH OF THE WIND

FREQUENCY OF WINDS	27-DAY CYCLE, MATCHING THE SUN'S ROTATION
SOLAR WIND SEASON	11-YEAR CYCLE, MATCHING SUNSPOT AND OTHER SOLAR ACTIVITY
VELOCITY OF LOW-SPEED FLOW THROUGH CORONAL HOLES	900,000 MILES PER HOUR (1,500,000 KM/H)
VELOCITY OF HIGH-SPEED FLOW THROUGH CORONAL HOLES	1,900,000 MILES PER HOUR (3,100,000 KM/H)
SUN'S MASS LOST THROUGH SOLAR WIND, PER SECOND	1,000,000 TONS (910,000 TONNES)
TIME TAKEN FOR SUN TO LOSE 1% OF ITS MASS	1 BILLION YEARS
DENSITY OF SOLAR WIND AT THE EARTH'S ORBIT	140,000 PARTICLES PER CUBIC FT (0.03 CUBIC M)
WIND SPEED AT THE SUN	150,000 MILES PER HOUR (250,000 KM/H)
WIND SPEED AT THE EARTH	500,000 MILES PER HOUR (800,000 KM/H)
DISTANCE REACHED BY SOLAR WIND	MORE THAN TWICE PLUTO'S DISTANCE FROM THE SUN

OUR BLUSTERY STAR

Like sunlight, the solar wind comes from the Sun and blows over all the planets in the solar system. But unlike sunlight, solar wind is invisible, composed of charged particles, and varies with the Sun's 11-year activity cycle.

The wind is an extension of the corona—the region of hot, ionized gas that surrounds the Sun. At a temperature of over a million degrees, coronal matter is moving fast enough to escape the Sun's gravity at the incredible rate of about a million tons a second. Just why the corona becomes so hot—the temperature of the Sun's surface is only about 10,900°F (6,000°C)—is still a mystery. But Sun-observing satellites have identified the magnetic paths by which some of the wind makes its escape into interplanetary space.

There are two types of magnetic fields in the Sun's outer atmosphere, both fluctuating with general solar activity. One type is a "closed" field. Its lines of force emerge from the surface, loop up into the corona, and then return to the surface. Like bars on a cage, closed fields restrain the coronal gas. But the lines of force in the second kind of field are open. They stretch right through the corona and out into space. The solar wind is then able to pass through these magnetic gateways.

The solar wind is similar to Earthly winds in one respect: Both are prone to gusts created by atmospheric changes. Coronal gas ejections usually coincide with eruptions of solar flares, sunspots and solar filaments.

BLOWING THROUGH SPACE

The hot gas of the solar wind continues to expand into space. Since the backward pull of the Sun's gravity decreases with distance, the solar wind actually travels faster the farther it goes. By the time it reaches Earth, the wind is traveling at half a million miles per hour (800,000km/h).

By that stage, the coronal gas is very thin—only a few hundred protons and electrons to every cubic inch (16.4 cubic cm) of space. Yet it is still powerful enough to produce some dramatic effects.

From most angles, the Earth's magnetic field protects us from the onslaught of the wind's charged particles. But at the North and South poles, the lines of magnetic force curve down toward the planetary surface. Just as the wind escaped the sun through open magnetic fields, so it now slides into the Earth's upper atmosphere. As the solar wind's ions strike molecules of air far above the ground, the energy they discharge creates the spectacular light shows of the aurorae.

The solar wind whistles past the outer planets at nearly a million miles an hour. Spreading itself ever thinner, the wind will continue accelerating until far beyond the orbit of Pluto. At one hundred times the distance from Earth to the Sun—more than double the distance to Pluto—the solar wind at last merges with the almost imperceptibly thin gas of the interstellar medium. This point—the heliopause—marks the final frontier of the solar system.

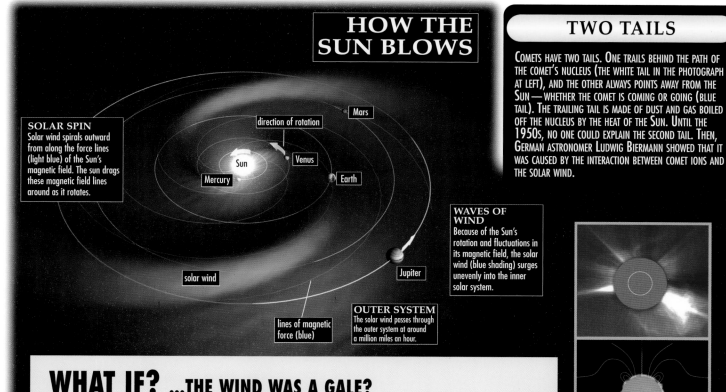

HOW THE SUN BLOWS

SOLAR SPIN
Solar wind spirals outward from along the force lines (light blue) of the Sun's magnetic field. The sun drags these magnetic field lines around as it rotates.

direction of rotation

Mars

Sun

Venus

Mercury

Earth

Jupiter

solar wind

lines of magnetic force (blue)

OUTER SYSTEM
The solar wind passes through the outer system at around a million miles an hour.

WAVES OF WIND
Because of the Sun's rotation and fluctuations in its magnetic field, the solar wind (blue shading) surges unevenly into the inner solar system.

TWO TAILS

COMETS HAVE TWO TAILS. ONE TRAILS BEHIND THE PATH OF THE COMET'S NUCLEUS (THE WHITE TAIL IN THE PHOTOGRAPH AT LEFT), AND THE OTHER ALWAYS POINTS AWAY FROM THE SUN — WHETHER THE COMET IS COMING OR GOING (BLUE TAIL). THE TRAILING TAIL IS MADE OF DUST AND GAS BOILED OFF THE NUCLEUS BY THE HEAT OF THE SUN. UNTIL THE 1950S, NO ONE COULD EXPLAIN THE SECOND TAIL. THEN, GERMAN ASTRONOMER LUDWIG BIERMANN SHOWED THAT IT WAS CAUSED BY THE INTERACTION BETWEEN COMET IONS AND THE SOLAR WIND.

ESCAPE ROUTE
Solar wind escapes from the regions of the Sun that appear darkest in the coronagraph image at top. These regions correspond to points where the Sun's magnetic fields do not loop back to the surface (bottom image).

WHAT IF? ...THE WIND WAS A GALE?

When scientists proved the existence of the solar wind in the 1950s, it was only seen as the benign cause of aurorae. But as electronic devices spread and grow more sensitive, it is more likely we will be affected by the Sun's "weather."

The Sun's weather seems to have a cycle of about 11 years. During the solar maximum around 1990, magnetic storms caused power failures in Canada and Sweden, and disrupted satellites. The maximum around the year 2000 was milder, and satellite operators were better prepared. However, it is still a wide precaution for astronauts to avoid spacewalks during major bursts of solar activity.

The expected 2000–1 peak produced intense auroral activity. But this time, the Sun surprised us. The magnetic storm of March 2003 was among the most spectacular in living memory.

By comparison, the 2013 solar maximum was unusually quiet, with fewer sunspots and displays of the aurora than astronomers had expected.

THE HELIOSPHERE

The Sun is cocooned at the center of a magnetic plasma bubble of its own making, known as the heliosphere. Extending far beyond the planets, the heliosphere is made up of the solar wind and the Sun's magnetic field. It fills the solar system with a thin dusting of material and touches all the planets and moons. Only when spacecraft reach the heliopause—the edge of the heliosphere and the boundary between the solar system and interstellar space—will we know exactly how enormous the heliosphere is.

SOLAR WIND STATISTICS

COMPOSITION	GASEOUS PLASMA OF SUBATOMIC PARTICLES
ORIGIN	SUN'S ATMOSPHERE (THE CORONA)
SPEED	SLOW SOLAR WIND FROM SUN'S EQUATORIAL REGION: 900,000 MPH (1.5 MIL KM/H)
	FAST SOLAR WIND NEAR POLES: 1,728,000 MPH (2,780,946 KM/H)
DENSITY	.5 PARTICLES PER CUBIC CM (0.06 CUBIC IN) WHEN THE SUN IS QUIET
TEMPERATURE	ABOUT 180,000°F (100,000°C)
TERMINATION SHOCK	AROUND 10 BILLION MILES (16 BILLION KM) FROM THE SUN
HELIOPAUSE	AROUND 13.5 BILLION MILES (22 BILLION KM) FROM THE SUN

THE EDGE OF THE HELIOSPHERE

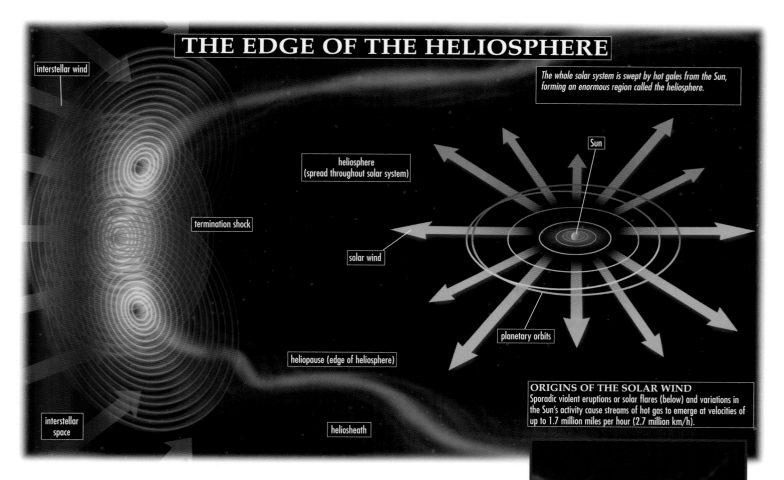

The whole solar system is swept by hot gales from the Sun, forming an enormous region called the heliosphere.

interstellar wind

heliosphere (spread throughout solar system)

termination shock

solar wind

Sun

planetary orbits

heliopause (edge of heliosphere)

interstellar space

heliosheath

ORIGINS OF THE SOLAR WIND
Sporadic violent eruptions or solar flares (below) and variations in the Sun's activity cause streams of hot gas to emerge at velocities of up to 1.7 million miles per hour (2.7 million km/h).

WINDS OF TIME

Until a probe ventured into interplanetary space, we had no proof that the heliosphere existed. A few scientists thought the Sun sent out particles and not just light and heat, but most believed its gravity was too great for anything to escape from it. So when Mariner 2 detected a blanket of particles (the solar wind) streaming from the Sun and filling space in all directions, understanding of the solar system deepened. The solar wind is a plasma, a super-hot, electrically charged gas, that erupts from the Sun in high-velocity gusts, depending on activity at the Sun's surface.

No one knows exactly how far the wind blows, but estimates have suggested over 100 astronomical units (AU), or 100 times the distance from the Earth to the Sun. This means the heliosphere goes far beyond the remotest planet, Pluto, which is at a mere 40 AU.

The heliosphere also marks out the extent of the Sun's magnetic field. Near the surface of the Sun, the magnetic field is so strong that plasma blasts erupt from the boiling surface only to be dragged back. But there are gaps in the magnetic field through which the wind escapes. When it does so, the electrical charges of the plasma particles carry the Sun's magnetic field with them. The magnetic field

can then extend as far as the wind itself. It is weaker the farther it goes, but at 60 AU the heliospheric current sheet—the boundary that separates the northern and southern halves of the Sun's magnetic field—is still detectable by spacecraft.

THINNING OUT

Data from the Voyager and Pioneer probes indicates that there are other changes occurring in the farthest reaches of the heliosphere. Freed from the immense solar gravity, the solar

wind races even faster, and the speed variations between streams are reduced as the gas combines with faster or slower moving particles. The solar wind also thins, becoming as thin as the best vacuum on Earth. The two Voyagers may tell us where the wind becomes as thin as the interstellar matter, marking the end of the heliosphere.

THEORIES PROVED

COMET TAILS ALWAYS POINT AWAY FROM THE SUN. U.S. SCIENTIST EUGENE PARKER LINKED THIS FACT TO THE IDEAS OF SIDNEY CHAPMAN, WHO SHOWED THAT GAS FROM THE SUN'S CORONA SHOULD EXTEND BEYOND EARTH. PARKER RELATED THE EXTENDED CORONA TO THE SOLAR PARTICLES THOUGHT TO CAUSE AURORAE AND COMET TAILS, CALLING THIS PHENOMENON THE SOLAR WIND. FOUR YEARS LATER, IN 1962, MARINER 2 (ABOVE) CONFIRMED THE SOLAR WIND EXISTED.

RADIO WAVES

IN 1992, THE TWO VOYAGER PROBES RELAYED A STRANGE BURST OF RADIO WAVES TO THE GOLDSTONE TRACKING STATION IN CALIFORNIA. ABOUT 400 DAYS PREVIOUSLY, THE SUN HAD EXPERIENCED VIOLENT OUTBURSTS. SCIENTISTS REALIZED THAT THE RADIO WAVES WERE CAUSED BY BLASTS OF SOLAR WIND SMASHING INTO THE HELIOPAUSE. THEY ESTIMATED THAT THE HELIOPAUSE WAS AROUND 145 AU OR 13.5 BILLION MILES (21.5 BILLION KM) AWAY.

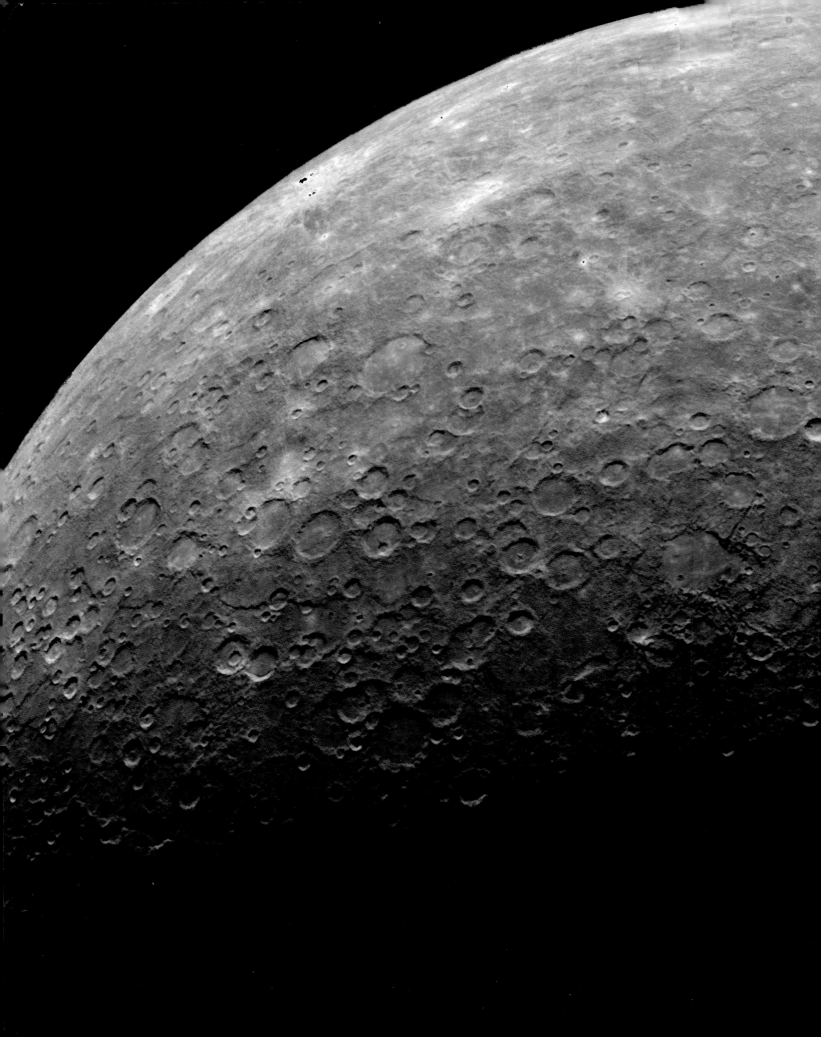

MERCURY

Mercury is the smallest planet in the solar system and also the closest planet to the Sun, completing an orbit once in every 88 days. Mercury is named after the winged Roman messenger of the gods due to its rapid movement in Earth's skies, where it is only ever briefly seen before sunrise or after sunset. Because it is always appears so close to the Sun, Earth-based telescope images of the planet are frustratingly blurry. The details of Mercury's surface remained a mystery until the arrival of the Space Age. In 1974, NASA's Mariner 10 space probe made a series of fly-bys in which it photographed half of Mercury's surface, revealing an airless world with a strong initial resemblance to our Moon. The NASA MESSENGER spacecraft—launched in 2004—currently orbits Mercury. Mercury has had a very different history from our satellite, however, as revealed by the great geological faults that crisscross its surface. One side of the planet is also dominated by a huge impact scar called the Caloris Basin.

Mariner 10's first image of Mercury, acquired on March 24, 1974, when the spacecraft was 3,340,000 miles (5,380,000 km) from the planet's surface. Temperatures on the sunward side of Mercury (top) can reach 800°F (420°C), while in the perpetual shadow of its craters the temperature can be as low as −300°F (−180°C).

MERCURY

arren Mercury, the first planet out from the Sun, is a small, rocky world that is scarred by impact craters and scorched by solar radiation almost seven times fiercer than that on Earth. With no substantial atmosphere to counteract the Sun's rays, the surface can reach a searing 800°F (420°C) during the day and plunge to –290°F (–140°C) at night. But the near-vacuum on the surface of Mercury has also helped to preserve the planet's contours, and the imprints left there by countless meteoroid scars have provided valuable information about the early days of the solar system.

MERCURY FACTS

Mercury		Earth
3,031 miles (4,878 km)	Diameter	7,973 miles (12,831 km)
0°	Axis Tilt	23°27'
87.97 Earth days	Length of Year	365 days
58.64 Earth days	Rotation Period	23.93 hr
36 million miles (58 million km)	Average Distance from Sun	93.5 million miles (150 million km)
+806°F to –292°F (+430°C to –145°C)	Surface Temperature	average 59°F (15°C)
0.38 g	Surface Gravity	1g
Potassium, sodium, Oxygen, Argon, Helium	Atmosphere	Nitrogen (78%), oxygen (21%), argon (1%)
Negligible	Atmospheric Pressure	1,000 millibars
Large iron core, mantle of silicate minerals	Probable Composition	Mainly iron, nickel and silicates

SUNBURN AND SCARS

At first sight, Mercury has more in common with the Moon than with any major planets. Both share jagged, impact-scarred landscapes, thanks to the absence of wind and water that softened the contours of the Earth and Mars. Mercury is also close to the Moon in size, a little under 1½ times larger. This is significantly smaller than both Jupiter's moon Ganymede and Saturn's moon Titan.

Yet Mercury is much denser than the Moon, and apart from the Earth itself, it is the densest body in the solar system. Scientists believe this is explained by a massive body of iron at the planet's core. In fact, the Earth may only be denser than Mercury because of its superior mass, which increases the strength of its gravitational field and pulls it together more tightly. It is possible that Mercury's iron core accounts for most of the planet's interior.

Pressures and temperatures at Mercury's core are likely to be so high that at least some of the iron remains permanently liquid. Further evidence for this comes from Mercury's magnetic field, which is much stronger than those of Venus and Mars, but only about one percent as strong as Earth's. Scientists believe that the magnetic fields of all the rocky inner planets are generated by ripples in the molten metal at their cores.

MYSTERIES OF THE PLAINS

Mercury's surface is not totally peppered with craters: There are also smoother plains, like the seas of the Moon. No one is sure how these plains were formed. One theory is that after cataclysmic impacts like the one that created the mighty Caloris Basin, lava from the planet's molten interior gushed out over the surface. Other plains may consist of matter sprayed out after meteoroid impacts.

With no erosion by wind and water and no tectonic plates to shift and crumple, Mercury has never experienced the natural forces that constantly reshape the Earth. As a result, the pattern of impacts provides important clues to the evolution of the solar system. When Mercury's plains were formed, they provided a fresh surface for impacts. But the largest craters on Mercury are found only in the older, more rugged regions that pre-date the plains, which

suggests that massive impacts by interplanetary debris were a regular occurrence during the early days of the solar system, but that by the time Mercury's plains were formed, they had petered out.

Mercury's most unusual features are the huge ridges or scarps that snake across the surface—sometimes for over 100 miles—and rise to nearly 10,000 ft (3,000 m) above the surrounding landscape. These wrinkles are a sign that Mercury once shrank by over 3,000 ft (900 m)—0.1 percent of the planet's surface area—as the core cooled.

Because it is so close to the Sun, Mercury is difficult and dangerous to observe. Little was known about Mercury until the Mariner 10 probe visited in the mid-1970s, but the planet's slow rotation allowed Mariner 10 to map only 40 percent of the surface. Recently, the MESSENGER probe completed its full map of Mercury, with further data still being analyzed.

SUN DANCE

A "DAY" ON MERCURY IS UNLIKE ANY OTHER IN THE SOLAR SYSTEM: IT LASTS TWO YEARS, AND THE SUN REGULARLY APPEARS TO MOVE BACKWARD IN THE SKY. THE REASON IS MERCURY'S UNIQUE COMBINATION OF SLOW ROTATION ABOUT ITS AXIS AND RAPID PERIOD OF ORBIT AROUND THE SUN. TOGETHER, THESE EXTEND THE MERCURIAN "SOLAR DAY"— FROM NOON TO NOON — TO 176 EARTH DAYS, OR TWO MERCURIAN YEARS. FROM CERTAIN SPOTS ON THE PLANET ONE WOULD SEE THE SUN RISE, THEN DIP BACK BELOW THE HORIZON BEFORE RISING FOR GOOD. SIMILARLY, OTHER POINTS ON MERCURY WOULD WITNESS A "DOUBLE SUNSET."

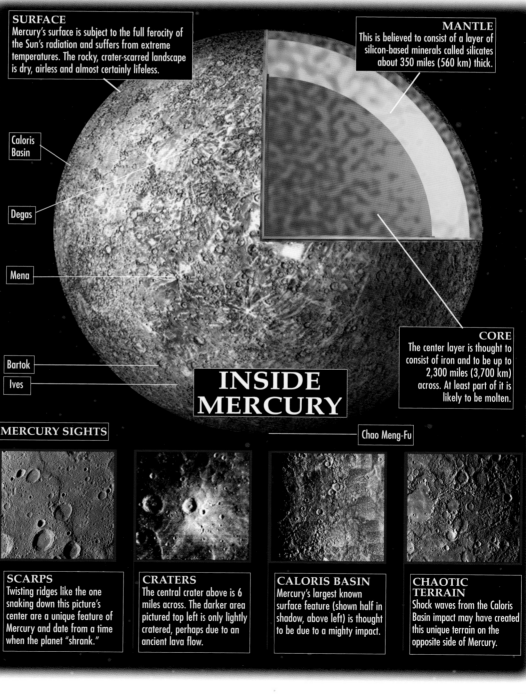

SURFACE
Mercury's surface is subject to the full ferocity of the Sun's radiation and suffers from extreme temperatures. The rocky, crater-scarred landscape is dry, airless and almost certainly lifeless.

Caloris Basin

Degas

Mena

Bartok

Ives

MANTLE
This is believed to consist of a layer of silicon-based minerals called silicates about 350 miles (560 km) thick.

CORE
The center layer is thought to consist of iron and to be up to 2,300 miles (3,700 km) across. At least part of it is likely to be molten.

INSIDE MERCURY

MERCURY SIGHTS

Chao Meng-Fu

SCARPS
Twisting ridges like the one snaking down this picture's center are a unique feature of Mercury and date from a time when the planet "shrank."

CRATERS
The central crater above is 6 miles across. The darker area pictured top left is only lightly cratered, perhaps due to an ancient lava flow.

CALORIS BASIN
Mercury's largest known surface feature (shown half in shadow, above left) is thought to be due to a mighty impact.

CHAOTIC TERRAIN
Shock waves from the Caloris Basin impact may have created this unique terrain on the opposite side of Mercury.

SURFACE OF MERCURY

Little changes on the surface of Mercury: Some of its craters are over 4 billion years old. Yet comparisons with the Moon—Mercury's cosmic lookalike—show that the planet has been resurfaced more than once. Our first good look at Mercury came in 1974, when the Mariner 10 probe imaged 45 percent of its surface. This data provided evidence of large scale impacts and volcanism. We are getting to know the rest of Mercury through radar. And one day, the innermost planet could attract a crewed mission.

MERCURY'S MAIN FEATURES

Maximum surface temperature	.806°F (430°C)
Minimum surface temperature	−292°F (−145°C)
Length of year	.87.97 Earth days
Age of intercrater plains	.4.2–5.0 billion years
Age of lowland plains	.3.8 billion years
Diameter of largest impact basin	.830 miles (1,300 km)
Size of largest impactor	.100 miles (160 km)
Length of largest scarp	.300 miles (480 km)
Height of largest scarp	.1 mile (1.6 km)

LUNAR LOOKS

At first glance, the surface of Mercury looks very similar to that of the Moon. Meteors and asteroids have left a lasting impression on both bodies: Neither one possesses the weather or the geological activity that erode impact craters on the Earth. Many of Mercury's scars date back more than 4 billion years, when rocks left over from planetary formation—known as planetesimals—often crashed into the newly formed planets and left their marks.

These ancient collisions threw up mountains on Mercury that are slowly being pulled down. A steady rain of meteorites and dust grains wears the peaks away, while they are assaulted by a 1,170°F (630°C) variation in temperature as the planet's surface spins in and out of the Sun. At the same time, gravity pulls the dust stirred up by continued meteorite strikes into lowlands and craters.

But Mercury's extra gravity—over twice as strong as the Moon's—makes for different crater shapes. Impacts on Mercury and the Moon both eject blankets of molten rock. The ejecta does not travel as far on Mercury—gravity slams it down closer to the crater rim. This causes more damage to the new crater than occurs on the Moon. Scientists can work out the age of Mercury's craters from the rate of their decay.

The most interesting craters on Mercury are the missing craters. Although the planet must have taken a battering much like the Moon's, Mercury bears far fewer impact scars, and is especially short of craters measuring less than 30 miles (50 km) across.

BLOTTED OUT

Many of Mercury's missing craters are buried beneath its rolling plains. Intercrater plains are mixed into the planet's highlands. When this terrain formed 4 billion years ago it blotted out many craters: Small impact sites were covered more fully due to their shallow depths.

Lowland plains stretch across the floors of huge impact basins. These plains carry fewer craters than the intercrater ones, so they probably formed more recently.

The plains solve the missing crater mystery, but where did these landscapes come from? Some scientists believe that they were formed by collisions. A large impact

THE SIGHTS OF MERCURY

A mosaic of the planet (main picture) was constructed out of 3,500 photographs taken by Mariner 10 in 1974–5.

CALORIS BASIN
A huge meteor gouged out this giant basin about 3.85 billion years ago. Within it lie a patchwork of cratered plains that probably formed by the rock melting on impact.

RUPES RIDGE
This type of lobate scarp is unique to Mercury. The Rupes ridge extends over 300 miles (480 km) long, and over 1 mile (1.6 km) high. It was thrust above Mercury's surface by a 1- or 2-mile (0.6- or 3-km) decrease in its diameter as it solidified and cooled.

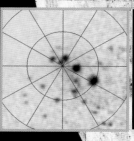

POLAR ICE?
The black spots in this radar image of Mercury's south pole may be ice. Mercury's surface may reach 800°F (425°C), but it has no axial tilt—year after year, it is always dark and cold at the poles.

VOLCANO VS. IMPACT
Volcanic flows reflect light differently than rock melted by impact. This image shows iron-rich volcanic flows—if this image is analyzed in UV light, it reflects light in the orange part of the spectrum.

CHANGE OF FACE

THE SUN'S GLARE MEANS THAT ALMOST NO SURFACE DETAIL ON MERCURY CAN BE SEEN FROM EARTH. BUT THAT DID NOT STOP ITALIAN ASTRONOMER GIOVANNI SCHIAPARELLI (RIGHT) FROM TRYING. BETWEEN 1881 AND 1889, HE MADE SKETCHES THAT SUGGESTED THAT MERCURY ALWAYS KEEPS THE SAME FACE TOWARD THE SUN. THIS WAS DISPROVED IN 1962, WHEN MICROWAVE STUDIES SHOWED THAT THE "DARK SIDE" OF MERCURY WAS HOT, AND SO MUST SOMETIMES SPIN INTO THE SUN.

can melt huge volumes of rock. Giant sheets of impact melt may have oozed across Mercury to solidify in the form of the lowland plains. Other astronomers suggest that the plains came from within: They could be the result of enormous volcanic eruptions. But so far, no volcanic features have been found on Mercury—so the plains question remains unanswered.

That we know even this much is largely due to images from Mariner 10: The spacecraft delivered our first good look at Mercury in 1974. Now, reanalysis of Mariner data may at last prove the origin of the planet's plains. Minerals in Mercury's surface reflect light at different wavelengths. In some areas the signature of iron has been found—a sure sign of a volcanic flow—while

other plains can now be defined as the result of impact melt.

Mariner has taught us a great deal, but it only scanned 45 percent of Mercury's surface. In 1991, radar images of the unseen areas made an amazing discovery. They picked up two bright spots at Mercury's north and south pole. These spots appear similar to the south polar ice cap on Mars. No one expected to find ice on the closest planet to the Sun. But Mercury's orbit means that some polar craters may never see the light—and the minus 290°F (145°C) low on the planet's night side keeps the ice permanently frozen. It seems we still have a few secrets left to map out on the surface of Mercury.

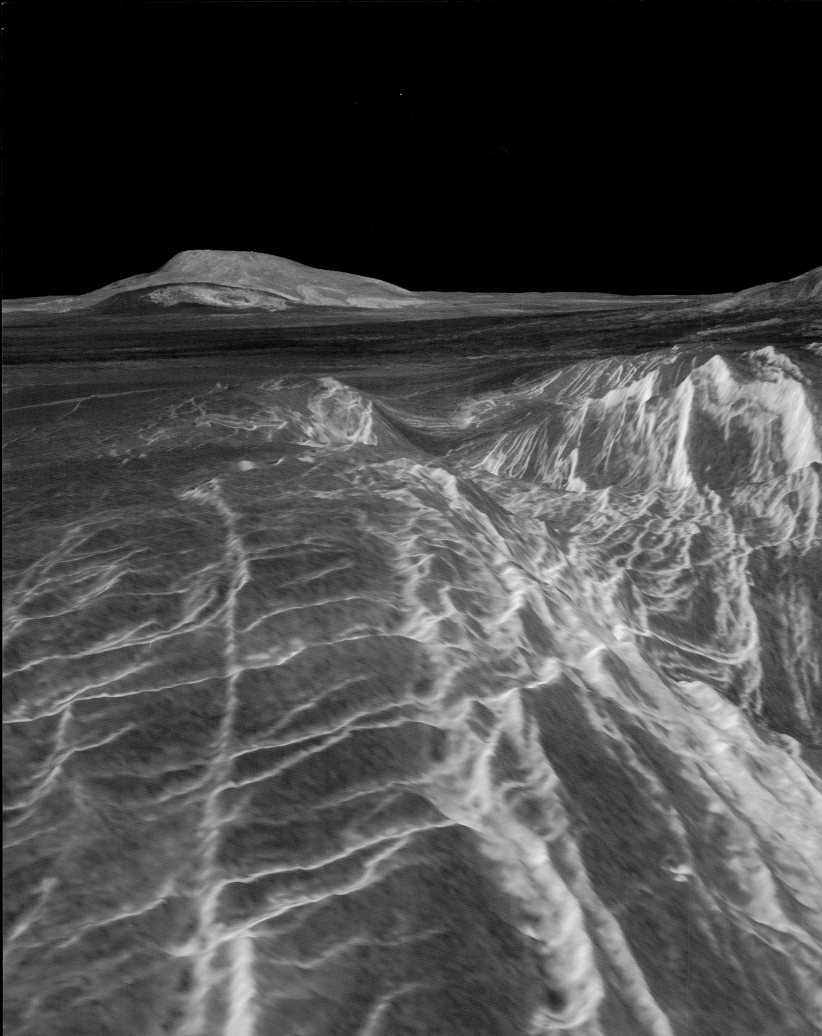

VENUS

Venus has been described as Earth's "deadly twin." With its orbit a little closer to the Sun than to Earth, and its diameter and mass slightly smaller, astronomers long suspected that the brightest planet in Earth's skies would be a hospitable place, perhaps even a home to alien life. The arrival of the first space probes in the 1960s shattered this illusion, revealing instead a world permanently veiled in brilliant yellow-white clouds of sulfur dioxide, and with a surface temperature far hotter than even Mercury. Robot landers broke down during descent or after just a few minutes on the ground, but revealed that the atmosphere was dominated by carbon dioxide, with sulfuric acid raining from its clouds. Now that orbiting probes have used radar to look through the clouds and map the surface, we know that Venus is a very different world from the Earth—one that is periodically racked by huge volcanic eruptions that apparently resurface the entire planet every few hundred million years.

This three-dimensional, computer-generated view of the surface of Venus shows two of the spectacular volcanoes on Venus. Gula Mons, the volcano on the right horizon, reaches 1.8 miles (3 km) high, while Sif Mons, the volcano on the left horizon, has a diameter of 186 miles (300 km) and a height of 1.2 miles (2 km).

VENUS

Venus, the second planet from the Sun, is similar to the Earth in size and mass. But there the resemblance ends. Both planets formed at about the same time from similar materials, and once had similar atmospheres. Now, Venus is dry and lifeless with not a trace of water on its surface, but the Earth teems with life and over two-thirds of it is covered in oceans. Searing temperatures, crushing pressures and a suffocating atmosphere have made Venus a very different world from our own.

VENUS PROFILE

VENUS		EARTH
7,523 miles (12,108 km)	Diameter	7,973 miles (12,831 km)
177°	Axis tilt	23° 27'
225 Earth days	Length of year	365 days
243 Earth days	Length of day	24 hr
67.2 million miles (108.1 million km)	Distance from Sun	93.5 million miles (150.4 million km)
855°F (457°C)	Surface temperature	59°F (15°C)
0.9 g	Surface gravity	1 g
Carbon Dioxide (96.5%), Nitrogen (3.5%)	Atmosphere	Nitrogen (78%), Oxygen (21%), Argon (1%)
90,000 millibars	Atmospheric pressure	1,000 millibars
Silicon, Aluminum, Iron, Nickel	Composition	Silicon (60%), Aluminum (15%)

A BARREN WASTELAND

Our knowledge of the cloud-shrouded surface of Venus comes from radar images produced by Earth-based radio telescopes and orbiting spacecraft. These images have revealed a landscape of massive volcanoes, surrounded by extensive lava plains crossed by lava flow channels thousands of miles long. The few impact craters are large, because only the most massive meteorites have been able to penetrate the atmosphere. Volcanic activity may still be occurring here and there, and the curious blisterlike features called coronae are believed to be bulges caused by heat within the planet melting and blistering the crust.

Venus' huge number of volcanoes seems puzzling at first, given its resemblance to the Earth. From measurements of the gravitational field of Venus, scientists conclude that the planet has an iron core, about the same size as the Earth's, overlaid by a rocky mantle, again just like that of the Earth. Both planets should produce about the same amount of internal heat, largely from the decay of radioactive elements. So

why, then, is the surface of Venus dominated by volcanoes while the Earth's is not?

The explanation may lie in a crucial difference revealed by radar mapping from the Magellan spacecraft. Where the Earth's crust is fractured into constantly moving "plates," with earthquakes and volcanoes occurring along their margins, the crust of Venus seems to be intact. Instead of internal heat being lost through volcanoes at plate margins, as it is on Earth, it is thought to escape through the numerous "hot spot" volcanoes that cover the surface of Venus.

Scientists think that the original atmospheres of both Venus and the Earth were created from gases released by volcanoes when both planets were very young and volcanic activity was much more intense. But the closeness of Venus to the Sun meant that the "greenhouse effect," in which heat is trapped within the atmosphere, resulted in the temperature rising so high that all the remaining surface water evaporated.

With all the water now in the atmosphere, the intense ultraviolet radiation from the Sun split the water molecules into hydrogen and oxygen. The

hydrogen escaped into space and the oxygen combined with other chemicals in the atmosphere. So eventually, Venus lost virtually all its water.

In contrast, the Earth cooled down, oceans formed, and life began to develop. The Earth became a living planet while Venus remained barren.

TRANSIT

In 1769, observers watching Venus pass in front of the Sun saw that it appeared elongated as it crossed the edge of the Sun's disk. It was later realized that this could only have happened if Venus had an atmosphere.

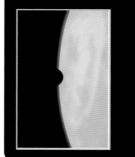
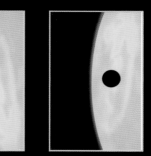

HOT PROBE

The temperatures and pressures on Venus are so extreme that the first three probes that were sent into the atmosphere were destroyed on the way down. Venera 7 was the first to land safely, in December 1970, but its signals were lost after 23 minutes.

Aphrodite Terra

Atalanta Planitia

North Pole

Tethys Regio

Beta Regio

Ishtar Terra

Lakshmi Planum

Cleopatra Patera

Maxwell Montes

Gula Mons

Eistla Regio

SURFACE FEATURES

RIFT VALLEYS
The large rift valley in the west of the Eistla Regio area is an indication of past movements in the crust. It was formed when two parts of the crust moved apart and the ground between them sank.

RADAR MAP
Although the surface of Venus is shrouded with clouds, its features can be mapped with radar. This map was based on data gathered by the Magellan radar-mapping spacecraft that went into orbit around Venus in 1990.

MOUNTAIN HIGH
Gula Mons, an extinct volcano in the western Eistla Regio area, rises about 9,800 ft (3,000 m) above the surrounding plains.

THE SURFACE OF VENUS

Beneath Venus' mask of sulfuric acid cloud lies a planetary surface like none other in the solar system. Due to high temperatures and rampant volcanism, the Venusian landscape is a boiling brew of volcanoes, craters, rifts, ridges and chasms.

Untouched by the erosive forces that smooth out the Earth's landscapes, these geological contortions appear in raw and rugged detail. U.S. and Soviet probes have sent back images of these extraordinary surface features, but there are mysteries still unsolved.

VENUS FACTS

FEATURE	NAME	LOCATION	SIZE
LARGEST CRATER	Mead	12° N, 57° E	175 MILES (280 KM) IN DIAMETER
HIGHEST MOUNTAINS	Maxwell Montes	65° N, 3° E	7.5 MILES (12 KM) HIGH
HIGHEST VOLCANO	Maat Mons	1° N, 194° E	5 MILES (8 KM) HIGH
LARGEST CORONA	Artemis	35° S, 135° E	1,625 MILES (2,615 KM) IN DIAMETER
LONGEST CANALE	Baltis Vallis	49–51° N, 165–8° E	ABOUT 4,300 MILES (6,920 KM) LONG
LARGEST PLAINS AREA	Guinevere Planitia	Northern hemisphere	ABOUT 4,700 MILES (7565 KM) ACROSS
DEEPEST VALLEY	Dali Chasma	18° S, 167° E	ABOUT 4.4 MILES (7 KM) DEEP

VENUS UNVEILED

Until the space age, the surface of Venus—our nearest planetary neighbor—remained hidden. Now, planetary probes—the U.S. Magellan mission and the ESA's Venus Express—have used powerful radars to pierce the planet's dense, obscuring clouds. Russian spacecraft have even briefly landed on the surface of Venus. Between them, these probes have given us a global picture of Venus' tortured landscapes.

The radar images show a world where volcanoes run rampant. More than 80 percent of the landscape was formed by volcanic activity, itself the result of heat rising from the planet's interior. Most of the surface consists of volcanic plains called planitiae with other volcanic features scattered across them. The largest are huge shield volcanoes (volcanoes with gently sloping sides) surrounded by lava flows hundreds of miles long. Formations such as the spidery arachnoids and coronae (Latin for crown), created by upwelling molten rock, have warped the crust. So-called

"pancake domes" have formed where a sticky type of lava oozed onto the surface, like toothpaste from a tube. And enigmatic snake-like channels called canali meander for hundreds of miles—streambeds cut by extremely hot, fluid lava.

The first detailed pictures of the surface of Venus were taken during the 1970s by four Soviet Venera landers. After a perilous descent to the hostile surface, with its extreme temperatures and pressures, they survived just long enough to transmit images back to Earth. The surface had a slab-like appearance, covered in dark rock and surrounded by soil which, at some landing sites, contained gravel-sized rock fragments. In the short time before the Venusian environment destroyed them, two of the landers were able to analyze the surface rocks. The results suggested a similarity with basaltic rocks that can be found beneath the Earth's oceans.

Later, in the early 1990s, orbital radar on the U.S. probe Magellan returned images of the surface that showed a maze of fractures, faults and rifts. Crisscrossing the planitiae is a fine network of ridges

known as wrinkle ridges. Mountain belts in the northern hemisphere mark where powerful compression forces have buckled the crust. Elsewhere, stretching forces have torn the surface apart, producing rift valleys.

Approximately 1,000 craters have been counted on Venus, far more than on Earth (where crater impact sites are soon eroded) but many fewer than on the Moon, Mercury or Mars. Since craters accumulate over time, the more

craters there are, the older the surface must be. The same simple rule can also be applied to a specific area of a planet. An area with more craters is probably an older surface than one with fewer craters. But impact craters appear to be randomly distributed all over Venus, which makes it difficult to tell the age of different parts of the surface. Overall, the number of craters implies an age of up to 500 million years—so Venus has a surface younger than the Earth.

TRUE COLOR

THE FIRST COLOR IMAGE FROM THE VENUSIAN SURFACE WAS MADE BY VENERA 13 IN 1982. IF WE COULD STAND ON VENUS, WE WOULD SEE A LANDSCAPE BATHED IN AN EERIE ORANGE GLOW, THE ONLY LIGHT THAT FILTERS THROUGH THE THICK CLOUDS. THE PHOTO TO THE FAR RIGHT IS ADJUSTED TO SHOW THE SAME AREA IN NORMAL SUNLIGHT.

A FIRE-TORMENTED LANDSCAPE

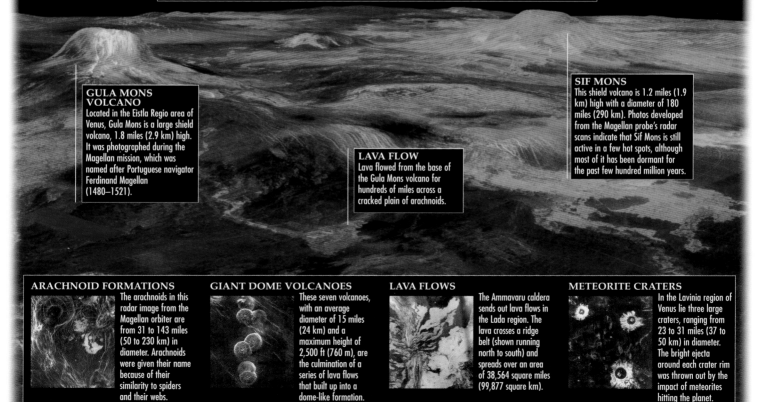

GULA MONS VOLCANO
Located in the Eistla Regio area of Venus, Gula Mons is a large shield volcano, 1.8 miles (2.9 km) high. It was photographed during the Magellan mission, which was named after Portuguese navigator Ferdinand Magellan (1480–1521).

LAVA FLOW
Lava flowed from the base of the Gula Mons volcano for hundreds of miles across a cracked plain of arachnoids.

SIF MONS
This shield volcano is 1.2 miles (1.9 km) high with a diameter of 180 miles (290 km). Photos developed from the Magellan probe's radar scans indicate that Sif Mons is still active in a few hot spots, although most of it has been dormant for the past few hundred million years.

ARACHNOID FORMATIONS
The arachnoids in this radar image from the Magellan orbiter are from 31 to 143 miles (50 to 230 km) in diameter. Arachnoids were given their name because of their similarity to spiders and their webs.

GIANT DOME VOLCANOES
These seven volcanoes, with an average diameter of 15 miles (24 km) and a maximum height of 2,500 ft (760 m), are the culmination of a series of lava flows that built up into a dome-like formation.

LAVA FLOWS
The Ammavaru caldera sends out lava flows in the Lada region. The lava crosses a ridge belt (shown running north to south) and spreads over an area of 38,564 square miles (99,877 square km).

METEORITE CRATERS
In the Lavinia region of Venus lie three large craters, ranging from 23 to 31 miles (37 to 50 km) in diameter. The bright ejecta around each crater rim was thrown out by the impact of meteorites hitting the planet.

GEOLOGY OF VENUS

For good reason, Venus has sometimes been called the "volcano planet." Unlike the Earth, where eruptions are mainly a byproduct of plate movements, volcanoes seem to be the principal geologic driving force on Venus. The ceaseless motion of subterranean lava cracks Venus' surface and scars it with volcanic domes. But volcanism in its past was more violent still. Outpourings of lava may have resurfaced the entire planet 500 million years ago, and Venus could be headed for another volcanic makeover today.

GEOLOGICAL FACTS

CORE COMPOSITION . . . . PROBABLY IRON AND NICKEL

CRUST COMPOSITION . . . VOLCANIC ROCKS

AVERAGE SURFACE AGE . . MORE THAN 500 MILLION YEARS

ACTIVE VOLCANOES . . . . PROBABLY, ALTHOUGH NO ERUPTIONS HAVE ACTUALLY BEEN OBSERVED

SEISMIC ACTIVITY . . . . . UNKNOWN

PLANET TECTONICS . . . . . NO EVIDENCE SO FAR — VENUS IS PROBABLY A 1-PLATE PLANET

SURFACE WEATHERING . . . BY CHEMICAL WEATHERING, VOLCANIC ACTIVITY, MINOR WIND EROSION AND ROCK FRACTURE BY HIGH TEMPERATURES

HOT ROCKS

Around half a billion years ago, Venus turned itself inside out. Molten rock from the interior bubbled to the surface—and covered the entire planet to a depth of up to 6 miles (10 km). At the same time, rock at the bottom of Venus' crust plunged downward to cool the hot depths and slow the resurfacing process. When it was over, Venus was left with a new skin, unblemished by the ridges and impact craters that mark old age.

Of all the theories that describe Venus' current face, catastrophic resurfacing on a planetary scale is the most dramatic. Other models hold that the planet's surface was recycled into its hot interior over a more prolonged period, which only stopped as the crust stiffened.

Both of these scenarios are consistent with the widely held view of Venus as a "one-plate planet." Before space probes took a closer look, scientists thought that Venus—so Earth-like in terms of mass and size—might have familiar geology, too.

PLANETARY MAKEOVER

lava flows spread into a new surface

volcanoes form over upwellings

hot, plastic crust

magma upwelling

VIOLENT VOLCANOES?
Despite their very active past, none of Venus' volcanoes have been seen in mid-eruption. But there is evidence that some, like the 1.2-mile (1.9-km) high Sif Mons (above) may still be active in a few spots.

Venus produces new crust over convective upwellings in the mantle. As Venus is a one-plate planet, the crust slowly gets thicker as new layers are added.

BRIEF GLIMPSE
The Soviet Venera probes of the 1970s were quickly destroyed by Venus' searing heat. But they survived long enough to beam back images of the surface. The color of these flat rocks (left) suggests that they contain iron.

CRATER CLUES

THE PATTERN OF IMPACT CRATERS ON VENUS (RIGHT) SUPPORTS THE THEORY THAT VOLCANOES GAVE THE PLANET A WHOLE NEW SURFACE SOME 500 MILLION YEARS AGO. THE DISTRIBUTION OF CRATERS APPEARS TO BE RANDOM — IF SOME REGIONS OF THE SURFACE WERE OLDER THAN OTHERS, CONCENTRATIONS OF CRATERS WOULD BE EXPECTED TO GATHER IN THESE AREAS. THE FACT THAT CRATERS ARE EVENLY SPREAD SUGGESTS THAT EVERY PART OF VENUS' SURFACE IS AS OLD AS THE NEXT. THE CRATERS ALSO TELL US THAT THE RESURFACING EPISODE WAS BRIEF COMPARED TO THE IMPACT RATE: ONLY BY COVERING THE ENTIRE PLANET QUICKLY COULD VOLCANOES MAINTAIN THE RANDOMNESS OF THE IMPACT RECORD.

The main geologic process on the Earth is called plate tectonics. Miles-thick "plates" of lightweight rock float slowly across the denser rock below. Mountains and volcanoes form where the plates collide, while new crust wells up where they pull apart.

But Venus' geology does not bear any family resemblance to Earth's. High temperatures keep the planet's crust plastic, or pliable, and its surface features seem to have been created by periods of contraction and extension. Volcanoes rule—and on Venus, they are not restricted to the surrounds of plate margins.

VOLCANIC VENUS

Radar images taken through Venus' dense clouds by NASA's Magellan spacecraft show that over 80 percent of the planet's land forms have volcanic origins—from vast plains to giant shield volcanoes that cover areas of up to 25,000 square miles (65,000 square km). Magellan data suggested that some volcanoes are still active, although the probe was not able to capture any actual eruptions of lava.

The planet within is even more mysterious. Scientists assume that the early Venus separated into layers, as Earth did, with iron and nickel sinking to form the core, while lighter minerals settled in the mantle and crust.

But once again, Venus may have grown apart from its planetary twin. Local variations in Venus' field of gravity were mapped out from the changes of speed that they cause in orbiting spacecraft. Variations in the Earth's field of gravity are paired to currents in the mantle. But on Venus, field anomalies are coupled to areas of altered crust density. This difference suggests that Venus lacks an asthenosphere, the partially molten layer that separates convection patterns in the mantle from plate motions on Earth. Venus may not qualify for this layer because it is too dry. Water lowers the melting point of rocks on Earth to make an asthenosphere possible. But Venus' water probably escaped into space.

The lack of water may give Venus rocks extra structural strength. Some geophysicists think that Venus' dry crust can support larger loads for longer, including steeper mountains than on Earth.

For now, this and every other theory of Venus' geology is open to debate. While we cannot explain it, we do know that the resurfacing of Venus obliterated important clues to the planet's past. In this way, at least, Venus is like the Earth: Whether it is remodeled by volcanoes, plate tectonics or weather, neither planet's surface stays the same for long.

ATMOSPHERE OF VENUS

After the Sun and the Moon, Venus is the brightest object in our sky. The 17th-century Dutch astronomer Christiaan Huygens thought this brightness could be explained by an atmosphere surrounding Venus. He was right. Since then, Venus has been observed by the Mariner, Pioneer, Venus and Venera probes of the 1960s and 1970s and by Magellan in the 1990s. They have revealed Venus' atmosphere to be unbreathable and hot enough to melt lead, with a surface pressure 90 times greater than the Earth's.

ATMOSPHERIC FACTS

VENUS		EARTH
96%	CARBON DIOXIDE	0.03%
3%	NITROGEN	77%
0.4%	OXYGEN	21%
0.0007%	ARGON	0.93%
180PPM*	SULFUR DIOXIDE	0.0002PPM*
0.001%	WATER	71%
No	MAGNETIC FIELD	YES
100%	CLOUD COVER	50%
RETROGRADE	ROTATION	NORMAL

* PARTS PER MILLION

LAYERS OF HEAT

Like all our solar system's planets, Venus shines with light reflected from the Sun. Venus bounces 75 percent of the sunlight that strikes it back into space, while the Earth reflects only 33 percent. This is because a thick layer of clouds circling high above Venus wraps the planet in an all-over reflective cloak. These clouds also kept Venus' surface screened from astronomers' gaze for centuries—until radar was used to penetrate the barrier.

If we could descend with the ease of a radar beam from the top of Venus' atmosphere, 250 miles (400 km) above the planet's surface, we would pass through five layers: the photochemical zone, the cloud deck, the evaporation zone, the thermochemical zone and the mineral buffering zone. Our first encounter would be with the photochemical zone. Composed chiefly of sulfur dioxide (SO_2) and water vapor, this layer is bombarded by the Sun's ultraviolet rays. This causes a photochemical reaction between the SO_2 and water vapor. The result—sulfuric acid—sinks to form the cloud deck.

Venus' clouds are yellow—the color of the sulfuric acid that created them. They are also thin and wispy, like a fine mist on Earth. Yet at the altitude of the cloud deck, we still can't see through the clouds to the surface. Towering 14 miles (22 km) high from 44 miles (71 km) above the surface, what the clouds lack in density they make up for in depth. These clouds that reflect back most of the Sun's light, making Venus a beacon visible from the Earth's surface even in daylight.

FAST CLOUD, SLOW PLANET

The clouds circle Venus in just four days, reaching speeds of over 200 mph (300 km/h), while Venus itself takes 243 Earth days to rotate on its axis. This phenomenon—in which the clouds orbit much faster than the planet rotates—is called superrotation. Scientists think it may be caused by solar energy or photochemistry in the upper atmosphere, but they have no clear and convincing explanation for the clouds' behavior. They do know that superrotation is limited to the cloud deck. On the surface, winds barely exist, circulating about as much as water at the bottom of the Earth's oceans.

Like clouds on Earth, Venusian clouds also make rain. But on Venus, these clouds drizzle sulfuric acid instead of water. This acid rain is captured by the evaporation zone as it falls to the surface. The extreme heat (200°F/93°C) in this zone causes the acid rain to decompose. The rain molecules split into sulfur dioxide and water vapor; some evaporate and rise back up to the clouds, starting the process all over again.

Below this boiling rain lies the thermochemical zone. At this level, the air is so hot (approaching 600°F/315°C) that it causes further chemical reactions among the gases. Carbon dioxide (CO_2)— the major gas here—creates a runaway greenhouse effect. The sunlight that gets past the clouds heats the planet's surface. This energy is then re-emitted as infrared radiation, which rises to the thermochemical zone where it is absorbed by the CO_2. Because the heat is unable to escape into space, temperatures on Venus' surface maintains a hellish 900°F (480°C).

Finally, we reach that searing surface. We are in the atmospheric region called the mineral buffering zone, made up of minerals—sulfur is the most abundant—that seep out of surface rocks. As the sulfur molecules become airborne, they interact with the CO_2 above. This strong alliance between the hot sulfur and the CO_2 drives the runaway greenhouse effect that produces Venus' extreme surface temperatures. This effect is also responsible for Venus' lack of liquid water—the surface heat would have boiled away any Venusian lakes or seas long ago.

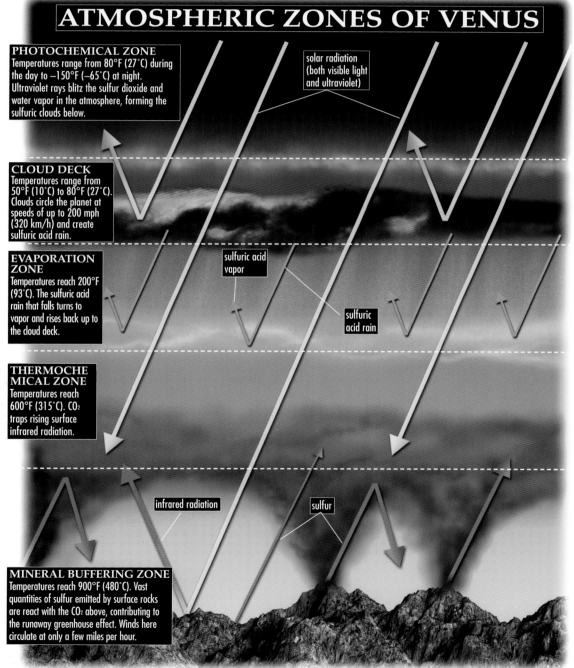

ATMOSPHERIC ZONES OF VENUS

PHOTOCHEMICAL ZONE
Temperatures range from 80°F (27°C) during the day to −150°F (−65°C) at night. Ultraviolet rays blitz the sulfur dioxide and water vapor in the atmosphere, forming the sulfuric clouds below.

solar radiation (both visible light and ultraviolet)

CLOUD DECK
Temperatures range from 50°F (10°C) to 80°F (27°C). Clouds circle the planet at speeds of up to 200 mph (320 km/h) and create sulfuric acid rain.

sulfuric acid vapor

sulfuric acid rain

EVAPORATION ZONE
Temperatures reach 200°F (93°C). The sulfuric acid rain that falls turns to vapor and rises back up to the cloud deck.

THERMOCHE MICAL ZONE
Temperatures reach 600°F (315°C). CO_2 traps rising surface infrared radiation.

infrared radiation

sulfur

MINERAL BUFFERING ZONE
Temperatures reach 900°F (480°C). Vast quantities of sulfur emitted by surface rocks are react with the CO_2 above, contributing to the runaway greenhouse effect. Winds here circulate at only a few miles per hour.

EARTH

Earth has been called the solar system's "Goldilocks planet." At just the right distance from the Sun, and with just the right mass and gravity for liquid water to exist in large amounts, it is also the only rocky planet large enough to retain a molten interior, and this drives the plate tectonics that steadily redraw its surface. These two influences have shaped the planet we know more than any others, and laid the way for another great force—the evolution of life itself. The first living organisms seem to have arisen almost as soon as the Earth became habitable, and through billions of years the action of single-celled organisms (and more recently multicellular plants and animals) have transformed Earth's atmosphere, seas, and landscape. Earth is our key to understanding the other rocky planets and moons of the solar system—despite the gaps in our knowledge, it is still the planet we understand best, and all serious models for the histories of other planets seek to take the processes seen on Earth and apply them elsewhere.

This stunning image of sunlight striking a cloud-covered Earth was taken with a simple 35-mm camera by the crew of the Space Shuttle Discovery. The view of Earth from space is a common photographic image today, but just over 50 years ago no human being had ever witnessed this incredible and iconic sight.

EARTH

The blue-green Earth is the only place in the solar system known to have large quantities of water in liquid form. Water was almost certainly a prerequisite for Earth's unique characteristic among the solar system and even the universe: its living things. Life on Earth is responsible for its unusual atmosphere, rich in the highly reactive gas oxygen. Earth is the birthplace and current sole residence of a race of intelligent bipeds. Recently, spacecraft built by these humans have allowed them to see their planet from space—and recognize its place in the solar system and beyond.

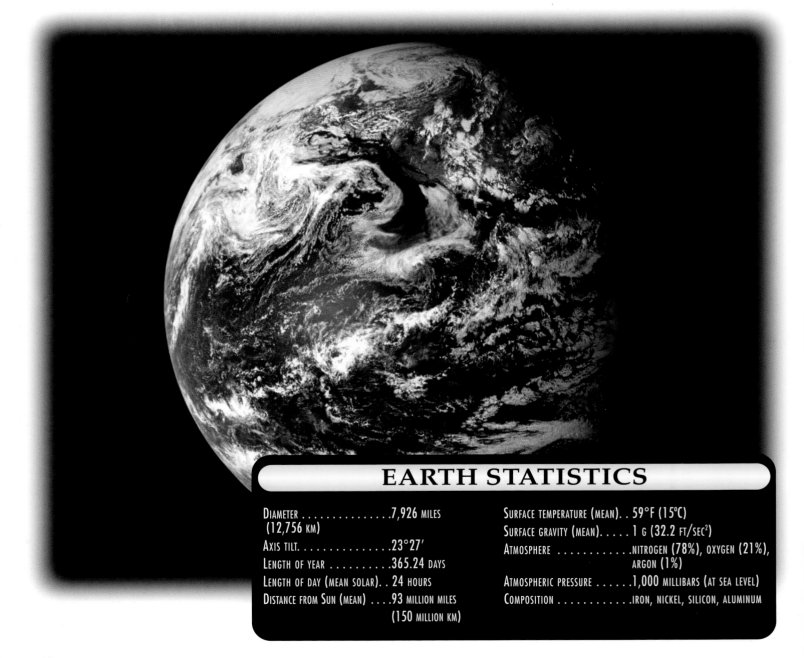

EARTH STATISTICS

DIAMETER . . . . .7,926 MILES (12,756 KM)	SURFACE TEMPERATURE (MEAN). . 59°F (15°C)
	SURFACE GRAVITY (MEAN). . . . . 1 G (32.2 FT/SEC²)
AXIS TILT. . . . . .23°27'	ATMOSPHERE . . . . .NITROGEN (78%), OXYGEN (21%), ARGON (1%)
LENGTH OF YEAR . . . . .365.24 DAYS	
LENGTH OF DAY (MEAN SOLAR). . 24 HOURS	ATMOSPHERIC PRESSURE . . . . . .1,000 MILLIBARS (AT SEA LEVEL)
DISTANCE FROM SUN (MEAN) . . . .93 MILLION MILES (150 MILLION KM)	COMPOSITION . . . . .IRON, NICKEL, SILICON, ALUMINUM

LIVING WORLD

Of the four rocky worlds that make up the inner solar system, Earth is probably the only one that is still geologically active—4.5 billion years after its formation. Vast, continent-sized plates of crustal rock float on top of molten magma, continually replenished by new material that pushes upward along mid-ocean ridges from the planet's interior. These plates push powerfully against each other, forcing up new mountain ranges and constantly rebuilding the planet's surface.

Earth's living geology is one reason why the planet bears so few of the craters that mark the faces of the other inner planets and the Earth's own Moon. Back in the early years of the solar system, Earth must have received its fair share of the asteroid bombardments that scar its neighbors to this day. But crustal movement has long since healed the damage and replaced any impact craters with new landscapes.

In any case, on Earth both meteoric craters and new-made mountains are under attack by erosion as soon as they form. The planet's surface is dominated by a vast blanket of liquid water, which is several miles deep on average. The Earth's water is a powerful scouring force, especially coupled with the winds that are a constant feature of its atmosphere. The atmosphere itself is far less dense than that of neighboring planet Venus. But coupled with the

Earth's pronounced axial tilt and its speedy, 24-hour daily rotation, it is more than enough to give the planet powerful weather systems that are visible as swirling cloud patterns from far off in space.

It is the composition of Earth's atmosphere, rather than its density, that distinguishes it from Mars and Venus. Earth's air is 21 percent oxygen, a reactive gas discernible only in minute quantities elsewhere in the solar system. There are also traces of other gases—notably methane—that should not be able to coexist for long with oxygen. And carbon dioxide, the major component of the atmospheres of Mars and Venus, exists only as a few hundred parts per million—just enough to provide a modest greenhouse effect. Oxygen provides energy for the Earth's extraordinary array of life—and is in turn renewed by the plants that depend on it.

The unusual atmosphere is a clear indication of the Earth's most remarkable feature: life. The first microorganisms appeared more than 3.5 billion years ago, and ever since then, they have been at work on the Earth's atmosphere—and a lot of other things, too. Living organisms are almost certainly

responsible for the high oxygen content of the air, which without constant replenishment would soon be locked up in chemical oxides, just as on Mars and Venus. Over time, life has diversified into millions of genetically diverse species, some of which can exist in even the most inhospitable terrestrial environments.

One of Earth's life-forms has even found ways of sending itself or its artifacts outside the atmosphere: A few have escaped Earth's gravity altogether. But it is too early to say whether Earth life will prove an entirely local phenomenon, or whether it will spread throughout the solar system and even across interstellar space to other stars. With other planets or celestial bodies potentially able to sustain life, perhaps one day evolution will result in life on Mars.

GOLDILOCKS AND GAIA

THE SIMPLEST EXPLANATION FOR THE EARTH'S COMFORTABLE TEMPERATURE AND ATMOSPHERE IS THE "GOLDILOCKS THEORY". VENUS, A LITTLE CLOSER TO THE SUN, WAS TOO HOT TO ALLOW THE APPROPRIATE CHEMISTRY. MARS, AN EXTRA 50 MILLION MILES (80 KM) OUT, WAS TOO COLD. BUT EARTH, LIKE THE PORRIDGE GOLDILOCKS ATE AND THE BED IN WHICH SHE SLEPT IN THE FAIRY TALE (ABOVE), WAS JUST RIGHT. MOST SCIENTISTS NOW THINK THAT THE INFLUENCE OF LIFE ON ITS OWN ENVIRONMENT WAS ALSO VERY IMPORTANT. THE EXTREME VERSION OF THIS VIEW IS THE GAIA THEORY, IN WHICH THE EARTH IS CONSIDERED TO BE A SELF-REGULATING SUPERORGANISM.

TWIN PLANET

THE EARTH'S OVERSIZED SATELLITE IS A SOLAR SYSTEM ODDITY. WHEREAS MOST PLANETARY MOONS ARE A TINY FRACTION OF THEIR PRIMARY'S DIMENSIONS, THE MOON IS MORE THAN A QUARTER OF THE EARTH'S DIAMETER — THOUGH LESS THAN 2 PERCENT OF ITS MASS. SEEN FROM DEEP SPACE, THE EARTH-MOON SYSTEM APPEARS ALMOST AS A DOUBLE PLANET — AS IS STRIKINGLY APPARENT IN THIS PICTURE TAKEN BY THE GALILEO SPACECRAFT IN 1992, 4 MILLION MILES (6.5 KM) OUTBOUND ON ITS WAY TO JUPITER.

COLD POLES
Because the Earth's axial tilt restricts the sunlight falling on the poles, both are covered with ice. Antarctica's ice sheet (right) is up to 3 miles (5 km) deep. The poles are also cold because snow and ice reflects most of the little sunlight that they receive.

INSIDE OUT
Magma from the Hawaiian volcano of Kilauea flows into the sea in an explosion of sparks (above). Such outbursts of lava—which can reach temperatures of up to 3,500°F (1,920°C)—can transform landscapes very quickly.

IN THE WIND
Water evaporates off seas and forms clouds, which, pushed by wind, travel inland and distribute water to the surface. Water vapor also transports vast quantities of energy around the Earth's atmosphere.

CRUMPLED CRUST
The Earth's mountain chains (the Alaska Range is shown above), are driven upward by collisions between adjacent crustal plates. Around the Pacific rim, some 10 plates rub together. The area is so volcanically active that it is called the ring of fire.

In this satellite image of the east coast of Oman, the sea is dominant. If humans had arrived from space as colonists, "Ocean" would be a far better name for the planet than Earth.

EARTH'S INTERIOR

The Earth beneath our feet may seem steady enough, but anyone who has witnessed an erupting volcano or experienced an earthquake will know that our planet's restless interior harbors violent and destructive forces. Beneath the thin shell that we call the crust, the Earth is a seething mass of molten rock. And recent discoveries have led scientists to now believe that around the Earth's core there may be ever-shifting continents and oceans like those that exist on the surface.

THE EARTH, LAYER BY LAYER

LAYER	DEPTH (MILES/KM)	PROPORTION OF EARTH'S MASS
OCEANIC CRUST	0–6/0–10	0.099%
CONTINENTAL CRUST	0–30/0–50	0.374%
UPPER MANTLE	6–410/10–660	15.3%
LOWER MANTLE	410–1,790/660–2,880	49.2%
"D" LAYER	1,670–1,790/2,690–2,880	3.0%
OUTER CORE	1,790–3,190/2,880–5,130	30.8%
INNER CORE	3,190–3,950/5,130–6,360	1.7%

GOING DEEP

Most people think of the Earth as a solid ball of rock, as if what lies below the soil continued all the way to the center. In fact, our planet is more like a soft-boiled egg. The outside is a thin, hard shell of rock called the crust. Immediately below it, no more than 30 miles (50 km) down, is the mantle, where the rock is hot and soft. Far beneath the mantle, some 1,860 miles (2,990 km) down, is a core of metal. In the outer part of this core the metal is molten, since it is heated by natural radioactivity to temperatures approaching those of the Sun's surface. The enormous pressure at the very center of the Earth keeps the inner core solid.

Much of what lies deep within the Earth remains a mystery, for the simple reason that it is impossible to see it. Mining and drilling barely penetrate even a quarter of the way through the crust, and we may never be able to cope with the enormous pressures and temperatures in the regions beyond even if they did.

Instead, we have to rely on indirect evidence. Much of the interplanetary debris in our part of the solar system was formed from the same material as the Earth.

When this debris falls to Earth in the form of meteorites, it yields important clues about the interior of the planet. Geoscientists also delve deep into the ocean to analyze the molten rock that is forced up from the mantle at mid-ocean ridges. Mantle minerals such as olivine often come to the surface in this way.

SHOCK TACTICS

Ironically, most of our knowledge about the Earth's interior has come from studying the seismic shock waves that accompany earthquakes. Seismic waves travel at different speeds through different rocks—for example, they travel much faster through the cold, hard rocks of the continental crust than they do through the softer, warmer rocks of the oceanic crust. So by measuring the speed of these shock waves, scientists can build up directional patterns of the rock formations below.

The most extraordinary discoveries of recent years have come from probing even farther down, to the mysterious zone of transition between the mantle and the core known as the "D" layer—short for "D double prime." As the solid minerals of the mantle give way to the molten iron and nickel of the outer core, there is an astonishing leap in density—one even greater than the difference between air and rock.

There are even more surprises at the bottom of the "D" layer, on the very boundary between mantle and core. Just as there are continents and ocean basins on the surface of the Earth, so there appear to be "anticontinents" on the core-mantle boundary that continue to shift and change in just the same way.

SOUNDINGS

THE 25-TON (23-TONNE) "VIBROSEIS" TRUCK (RIGHT) PRODUCES CONTROLLED SHOCK WAVES THAT TRAVEL DEEP INTO THE EARTH. SCIENTISTS MEASURE THE FREQUENCY AND DIRECTION OF THOSE WAVES THAT RETURN TO THE SURFACE TO BUILD UP A PICTURE OF WHAT THE WAVES ENCOUNTERED DURING THEIR SUBTERRANEAN JOURNEY.

THE FLOOD

THE ENGLISH CLERIC THOMAS BURNET (1635–1715) ARGUED THAT THE EARTH CONSISTED OF WATER CONTAINED BY A SMOOTH SHELL, AND THAT THE BIBLICAL FLOOD (RIGHT) OCCURRED WHEN GOD CAUSED THIS SHELL TO CRACK. BURNET ALSO THOUGHT THAT MOUNTAINS WERE THE FRAGMENTS OF THIS SHELL. NOW IT SEEMS THAT HE WAS NOT SO FAR WRONG — EVEN THOUGH THE "FLOODING" IS BY MOLTEN ROCK, NOT WATER.

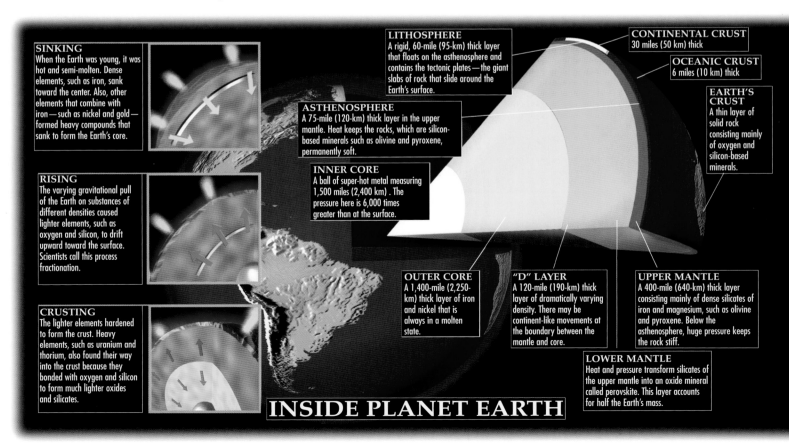

SINKING
When the Earth was young, it was hot and semi-molten. Dense elements, such as iron, sank toward the center. Also, other elements that combine with iron—such as nickel and gold—formed heavy compounds that sank to form the Earth's core.

RISING
The varying gravitational pull of the Earth on substances of different densities caused lighter elements, such as oxygen and silicon, to drift upward toward the surface. Scientists call this process fractionation.

CRUSTING
The lighter elements hardened to form the crust. Heavy elements, such as uranium and thorium, also found their way into the crust because they bonded with oxygen and silicon to form much lighter oxides and silicates.

LITHOSPHERE
A rigid, 60-mile (95-km) thick layer that floats on the asthenosphere and contains the tectonic plates—the giant slabs of rock that slide around the Earth's surface.

ASTHENOSPHERE
A 75-mile (120-km) thick layer in the upper mantle. Heat keeps the rocks, which are silicon-based minerals such as olivine and pyroxene, permanently soft.

INNER CORE
A ball of super-hot metal measuring 1,500 miles (2,400 km) . The pressure here is 6,000 times greater than at the surface.

CONTINENTAL CRUST
30 miles (50 km) thick

OCEANIC CRUST
6 miles (10 km) thick

EARTH'S CRUST
A thin layer of solid rock consisting mainly of oxygen and silicon-based minerals.

OUTER CORE
A 1,400-mile (2,250-km) thick layer of iron and nickel that is always in a molten state.

"D" LAYER
A 120-mile (190-km) thick layer of dramatically varying density. There may be continent-like movements at the boundary between the mantle and core.

UPPER MANTLE
A 400-mile (640-km) thick layer consisting mainly of dense silicates of iron and magnesium, such as olivine and pyroxene. Below the asthenosphere, huge pressure keeps the rock stiff.

LOWER MANTLE
Heat and pressure transform silicates of the upper mantle into an oxide mineral called perovskite. This layer accounts for half the Earth's mass.

INSIDE PLANET EARTH

EARTH'S IMPACT CRATERS

Every 200,000 years or so, a massive meteorite, comet or asteroid weighing at least several hundred tons slams into Earth's surface and gouges out a huge impact crater. Scientists have identified about 150 of these "extraterrestrial impressions," ranging in size from a few hundred yards to more than a hundred miles (160 km) in diameter. Many older impact craters, dating back to dinosaur times and beyond, will never be found. They have been erased from the landscape, etched away by the continuous erosion and geological activity that continues to occur on Earth.

TOP TEN IMPACT CRATERS

LOCATION	DIAMETER	AGE
VREDEFORT, ORANGE FREE STATE, SOUTH AFRICA	187 MILES (301 KM)	2 BILLION YEARS
SUDBURY, ONTARIO, CANADA	156 MILES (251 KM)	1.85 BILLION YEARS
CHICXULUB, YUCATAN PENINSULA, MEXICO	125 MILES (201 KM)	65 MILLION YEARS
MANICOUAGAN, QUEBEC, CANADA	62 MILES (100 KM)	212 MILLION YEARS
POPIGAI, EASTERN SIBERIA, RUSSIA	62 MILES (100 KM)	35 MILLION YEARS
ACRAMAN, SOUTH AUSTRALIA, AUSTRALIA	56 MILES (90 KM)	570 MILLION YEARS
PUCHEZH-KATUNKI, WESTERN RUSSIA	50 MILES (80 KM)	220 MILLION YEARS
KARA, NORTHERN RUSSIA	40 MILES (64 KM)	73 MILLION YEARS
BEAVERHEAD, MONTANA, UNITED STATES	37 MILES (60 KM)	600 MILLION YEARS

SCARS FROM SPACE

Until the 1960s, most geologists believed that the craters dotted across the Earth were ancient volcanoes. Then analysis of lunar rock samples collected by Apollo astronauts proved that most of the Moon's craters had been gouged out by impacts of massive debris from space. Since our atmosphere provides no defense against objects larger than about 500 ft (152 m) across, geologists were forced to conclude that the Earth must have suffered an equally severe pounding in the planets' past.

The bombardment was most intense between about 4.6 and 3.8 billion years ago, when the solar system was forming and countless rocky lumps, some the size of planets, were orbiting in a disk of swirling dust and rubble around the Sun. Since then, the storm has subsided to a "drizzle," but the threat is still there. While hundreds of tons of harmless meteorite dust fall to the Earth's surface each day, estimates suggest that a meteorite half a mile wide hits the Earth every 200,000 years on average, and an object 6 miles (10 km) in diameter collides every 50–100 million years. The last major impact event on Earth was in 1908, in sparsely populated Siberia, Russia. Luckily, there was no loss of life that time.

So where are the other impact craters? Unlike the inert Moon, the Earth is very efficient at healing impact scars. Erosion wipes out the smaller depressions within a few hundred thousand years, and even craters spanning hundreds of miles are eventually obliterated by recycling of the Earth's crust. No impact craters older than two billion years have ever been found on its surface.

Most surviving craters are either "young"—dated at a few million years old—or are located in the geologically stable continental shields of Canada, Australia and Russia.

CRATER CREATION

While it may take millions of years to wipe away an impact crater, it only takes seconds to create one. A 60-mile (100-km) wide depression is formed in about 100 seconds. It all starts when the projectile—an asteroid or comet—hits the Earth's surface at a speed of hundreds of miles per second. At such a high velocity, crater formation is driven by shockwaves generated at the point of impact. The crater is circular even if the projectile hits the surface at an oblique angle, because the shockwaves automatically excavate a round hole and fling out a "curtain" of fragmented rock called ejecta that is dispersed over the surrounding terrain. The crater ends up about 20 times the diameter of the projectile.

Fragments of the projectile survive only in small craters. Bodies big enough to produce a hole more than half a mile wide are vaporized or melted by impact pressures up to 9 million times the atmospheric pressure and temperatures that may reach 8,000°F (4,430°C). But these forces inflict telltale shock damage on the rocks. Markers include deformed minerals and rock shock patterns that indicate the craters were created by forces from above. These signs can be read long after the crater landmarks have gone. In Canada, the pattern of shock effects has helped geologists map the vanished rim of Manicouagan, a 62-mile (100-km) wide crater created 212 million years ago. Clearly, the Earth's impact craters have made their mark.

DOUBLE WHAMMY
The Clearwater Lakes in Quebec, Canada, conceal a rare phenomenon—twin impact craters, thought to have been formed together by two separate but related impacts landing adjacently.

CRATER LAKE
An infrared satellite image of Elgygytgyn Lake in Siberia, Russia, shows what was once a fiery hole made by a giant meteorite. Many impact craters then fill with water, which speeds up the erosion process.

Puchezh-Katunki, western Russia

Kara, northern Russia

Beaverhead, Montana, U.S.

Manicouagan, Quebec, Canada

Sudbury, Ontario, Canada

Popigai, eastern Siberia, Russia

The sheer size of most of the Earth's impact craters makes it hard to see them clearly from the ground.

EARTH ATTACKED

Chicxulub, Yucatan Peninsula, Mexico

Vredefort, Orange Free State, South Africa

Acraman, South Australia, Australia

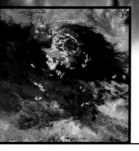

SANDBLAST
Located in the Namib Desert in southern Africa, the Roter Kamm crater — the bright circle at the upper center of this space radar image — is hard to see from the ground because its floor is covered by shifting sand dunes.

STANDING PROUD
The Wolfe Creek crater in Australia is one of only a few impact craters on Earth that is well-preserved and prominently visible from the ground. The arid local environment slows down the weathering of rocks.

EARTH'S TIDES

Gravity, the force that binds the universe, is also the key to the Earth's rising and falling tides. The combined gravitational effects of the Sun and Moon constantly pull the world's oceans in different directions and create tidal effects. But there are many other factors that complicate this basic process. Friction, the Earth's spin, the tilt of its axis and the waning power of the Moon's attraction on the far side of the Earth all conspire to make our planet's oceans a complex battleground of forces.

U.S. TIDAL VARIATIONS

	CITY	MAXIMUM TIDAL VARIATION
1	SEATTLE, WASHINGTON	14.9 FT/4.5 M
2	CRESCENT CITY, CALIFORNIA	10.2 FT/3.1 M
3	SAN DIEGO, CALIFORNIA	8.9 FT/2.7 M
4	GALVESTON, TEXAS	2.4 FT/0.7 M
5	MOBILE, ALABAMA	2.3 FT/0.7 M
6	CHARLESTON, SOUTH CAROLINA	8.0 FT/2.4 M
7	WASHINGTON, D.C.	4.1 FT/1.2 M
8	NEW YORK, NEW YORK	7.0 FT/2.1 M
9	BOSTON, MASSACHUSETTS	14.7 FT/4.5 M
10	PORTLAND, MAINE	13.5 FT/4.1 M

MAKING WAVES

The water of the oceans is bound to our planet by the force of the Earth's gravity. But the Earth is not alone in space, and both the Moon and the Sun throw their own gravitational pulls into the equation. The combined effect is to tug the oceans this way and that around the globe.

The Moon's gravity stretches the Earth into an oval. The effect is so tiny that the land masses of the planet are distorted by little more than 8 in (20 cm). But because of the fluidity of water, the effect on the oceans is more noticeable. At the point on the Earth directly beneath the Moon, the ocean is tugged into a bulge of high water. At the same time, a second tidal bulge forms on the opposite side of the planet. This is partly a result of the centrifugal force created by the Moon and Earth's combined rotation around their common center of mass, a theoretical point called the barycenter.

Because the Earth spins on its axis once every 24 hours, the two bulges sweep around the planet in waves, creating two high tides per day at every point on the globe. But the twice-daily cycle is complicated by the fact that the Earth is tilted, which puts the Moon alternately to the north and south of the Equator. This creates slight differences between the two tides each day and adds a daily set of local variations to the twice-daily rhythm.

THE PLOT THICKENS

A further complication is added by the Sun, whose gravitational pull on the Earth also affects the tides. The tidal force of the Sun and Moon together is almost a third more than that of the Moon alone, with the Sun imposing a solar rhythm on the lunar rhythm. At the new and full moons, when the two bodies are in line, they combine to create extra-high spring tides. When the Moon is in its first and last quarters, the Sun is at right angles to it, and their gravitational pulls work against each other to create extra-low neap tides.

If the Earth were completely smooth, this would probably be the end of the story. But in reality, the tidal forces are weakened by friction between the ocean and the seabed to the point where the twice-daily tidal waves get slightly left behind the orbiting Moon. The waves are also continually disrupted by areas of land as they sweep around the Earth, creating yet more local variations.

At the same time, the Earth's continuous spinning on its axis causes the tidal waves to oscillate around the world's ocean basins like water in a bath. This means that high tides do not necessarily occur when the Moon is overhead, but when the oscillations accumulate to their greatest height. Each ocean basin is a different shape and so has its own unique pattern of oscillations. In the South Atlantic, for example, the tides oscillate from south to north and take around 12 hours to sweep from the tip of South Africa to the Equator. In contrast, in the North Atlantic seas, they sweep in a counterclockwise direction.

Until recently, the sheer complexity of tidal forces acting on the Earth meant that the only way to predict tides was by years of patient study. Now, developments mean computer programs do the job—for which oceanographers are extremely grateful.

PREDICTING TIDES

AS LATE AS THE 1960s, TIDE MACHINES WERE USED TO PREDICT LOCAL TIDAL PATTERNS. THE FIRST ONE (RIGHT) WAS CREATED BY WILLIAM THOMSON (LATER LORD KELVIN, OF TEMPERATURE SCALE FAME) IN 1873. AN EARLY FORM OF COMPUTER, IT USED COGS AND PULLEYS TO CALCULATE THE VARIOUS TIDAL FACTORS.

ATTRACTIVE NEIGHBORS

TIDAL POWER
In theory, the power of the tides can be harnessed to provide electricity. The world's first tidal power station, on the mouth of the Rance river in northern France (left), accumulates water at high tide and uses it to drive turbines. Sadly, it has not proved as efficient as was hoped.

The Moon's gravity has a marked effect on the Earth. The much larger Sun also exerts a big pull on the oceans. When the two bodies line up in space, tidal forces increase by almost a third.

BARYCENTER
The Earth and Moon's combined center of mass.

1 ALONE IN SPACE
Without the gravitational pull of the Sun and the Moon, the forces acting on the world's oceans would be confined to the Earth's own spin.

2 MOON AND SWING
Water heaps up directly under the Moon. On the opposite side of the Earth, the centrifugal force of the Earth and Moon's motion creates a second bulge.

3 JOINT FORCES
When the Sun and Moon are in line at new and full moon, their combined gravitational pull increases the tidal bulges to create spring tides.

IMPERIAL LESSONS

WHEN THE ROMAN EMPEROR JULIUS CAESAR SET OUT TO INVADE BRITAIN IN 55 B.C., HIS KNOWLEDGE OF TIDES WAS CONFINED TO THE LAND-LOCKED MEDITERRANEAN WHERE TIDAL EFFECTS ARE MINIMAL. ON HIS ARRIVAL IN BRITAIN, CAESAR LANDED HIS SHIPS ON A SLOPING BEACH AT LOW TIDE — AND NEARLY LOST THEM ALL WHEN THE TIDE CAME IN!

THE AURORAE

The "northern lights" of the aurora borealis are among nature's most beautiful sights. With shimmering curtains of colors, dazzling white streamers and bright green rays flashing with red, the aurorae regularly stage spectacular displays in the polar skies.

For centuries, the cause of this apparently supernatural light show remained a mystery. Only recently have we come to realize that they are created by high-energy particles that stream from the Sun and collide with the Earth's atmosphere.

THE AURORAE IN HISTORY

37 A.D.	A display seen from Rome tricks the Emperor Tiberius into sending soldiers to put out what is said to be a "fire" in the port of Ostia.
93–839 A.D.	Displays seen in Scotland are variously described as "armies fighting in the heavens" and "pools of blood in the firmament."
March 16, 1716	An aurora over London, England, is noted by the astronomer Sir Edmund Halley.
September 2, 1859	Displays reported in Hawaii and the tropics are linked to the activity of solar flares.
February 4, 1872	Displays are visible in India, Egypt and the Caribbean.
September 25, 1909	Displays are visible in Singapore (latitude 1°25′ north).
May 15, 1921	Displays are visible in Samoa (latitude 14° south).
January 25, 1938	A blood-red display is seen from England, Spain and Portugal.
March 30, 2000	Spectacular display visible as far south as Texas and Florida.

LIGHT SHOW

The aurorae (pronounced "or-ror-ree") are not occasional freaks of nature: They are a permanent feature of the Earth's upper atmosphere. Auroral displays vary in intensity, sometimes fading to almost nothing. But they are always there.

There are aurorae in both hemispheres of the Earth—the aurora borealis around the North Pole and the aurora australis around the South Pole. On satellite pictures, they show up as oval bands that encircle the Earth's magnetic poles like giant halos. The size and shape of these halos change continuously, but never disappear completely. The aurorae are gigantic and stretch high into the atmosphere. The lowest fringes hang about 50 miles (80 km) above the ground; the upper rays extend more than 600 miles (960 km) into space—three times farther than the Space Shuttle's orbit.

An auroral display resembles a giant television. In a TV, streams of electrically charged particles (electrons) from the tube are guided by a magnetic field onto the lines of the screen, causing the lines to glow. In an auroral display, charged particles from the Sun strike the atoms and molecules of the Earth's atmosphere, causing them to glow in a similar way. This stream of particles is called the solar wind: It radiates continuously from the Sun's corona at over 300 miles (480 km) per second.

Fortunately for us, most of the Earth is shielded from this hurricane of charged particles by its magnetic field, which surrounds the planet like a cocoon. But there are two holes in the magnetic field, one above each magnetic pole. It is through these holes, called the polar clefts, that the solar wind pours, giving rise to the glorious colors and shapes of the aurorae.

MIXING COLORS

Aurorae appear in so many colors because each gas in the atmosphere glows a different hue when struck by solar particles. The color also varies according to both the electrical state and concentration of the gas.

For example, oxygen, when struck at low altitudes (about 60 miles/100 km up), glows a brilliant green—the most common of auroral colors; at higher altitudes (around 200 miles/320 km), it results in the vivid red aurorae that are seen during major disturbances. Nitrogen atoms, by contrast, glow blue when electrically charged (ionized) and red when neutral. Nitrogen can also emit purple light, which happens when the atoms are struck by the ultraviolet radiation contained in sunlight.

Although aurorae are ever-present, they are also ever-changing. Satellites such as the IMP-8 (Interplanetary Monitoring Platform) have monitored the solar wind. From their observations we know that aurorae are at their most spectacular when the solar wind blows fiercely enough to create magnetic storms—disturbances in Earth's magnetic field. We also know that mirror-image aurorae flare simultaneously around the North and South poles. Yet it may still be some time before we fully understand the complex relationship between aurorae, the Sun and the Earth's magnetic field. For now, as they have done for centuries, the "northern lights" remain a beguiling mystery.

That's show business: If the Earth's magnetic field begins to reverse and the solar wind penetrates more of the atmosphere, the aurorae could become a regular sight in the night sky of some unlikely places.

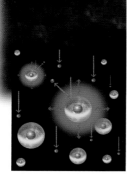

LIGHT NAMES

THE AURORAE HAVE BEEN GIVEN VARIOUS NAMES ACROSS THE WORLD. IN SCOTLAND YOU WOULD HEAR THEM REFERRED TO AS THE "MERRY DANCERS" OR THE "HEAVENLY DANCERS." THE NAME "AURORA" ITSELF COMES FROM THE LATIN WORD MEANING "DAWN." ITS FIRST KNOWN USE WAS IN A BOOK WRITTEN IN 1649 BY THE FRENCH ASTRONOMER PIERRE GASSENDI.

MAKING TRACKS
Aurorae follow the angle of the Earth's magnetic field lines. This angle varies depending on longitude.

THE AURORA

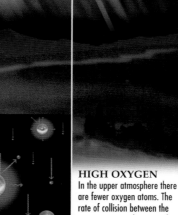

LOW OXYGEN
When solar particles strike oxygen atoms, the atoms glow green or red. In the lower atmosphere, there is mostly a green glow because the concentration of atoms is high.

HIGH OXYGEN
In the upper atmosphere there are fewer oxygen atoms. The rate of collision between the oxygen atoms is less, so red auroral displays predominate.

BLUE NITRO
Particle collisions with nitrogen are responsible for blue, purple and red displays, depending on whether the nitrogen atoms are charged (ionized) or not.

EARTH'S MOON

The Earth's giant satellite is a constant feature in our skies, changing its appearance as its orientation to the Sun shifts throughout each lunar orbit, but always keeping the same face turned toward us—trapped this way in aeons past by the same tidal forces that raise and lower the Earth's own seas. Earth is the only terrestrial planet with such a large satellite, and its origin was a mystery until relatively recently. Rocks returned from the Apollo lunar landings showed that it has a mixture of Earth-like and alien rocks, and it now seems that the Moon was born in a "big splash" collision between the still-molten Earth and a small rogue planet early in its history. Due to its lack of an atmosphere and geological activity, the Moon acts as an astronomical time capsule—it preserves details of meteor impacts that occurred billions of years ago, and has been used to piece together a history of the inner solar system. Indeed, some astronomers think that the Moon's influence has helped stabilize Earth's rotation and protect it from some meteor impacts, perhaps even helping to foster the development of life.

An arresting image of the Moon setting behind the Earth, taken from the Space Shuttle Discovery. The hugely ambitious and successful Apollo program of the late 1960s and 1970s allowed scientists a remarkable insight into the nature and history of our only natural satellite.

THE MOON

The Moon is the most familiar sight in the night sky. This is because it is the Earth's closest companion and travels with the Earth in space around the Sun. The Moon orbits the Earth at a distance of just 238,850 miles (384,392 km); yet, despite being so near, it is very different from our own planet—a gray desert, dotted with craters from ancient asteroid collisions. So far the Moon is the only body in space on which humans have landed. The recent discovery of water there has stimulated plans for an eventual return.

MOON FACTS & FIGURES

Diameter 2,160 miles (3,480 km)

Axis tilt 6° 41' relative to its orbit

Time to orbit Earth 27.3 Earth days

Length of day 27.3 Earth days

Distance from Earth 238,850 miles (384,392 km)

Surface temperature 253°F/123°C (day) to −387°F/−197°C (night)

Surface gravity 0.17 of the Earth's

Mass 0.012 of the Earth's

Volume 0.02 of the Earth's

Density 3.34 times that of water

MOONSCAPE

Since the Moon is so close, we can see its most prominent features with the naked eye. Most obvious are the dark areas that form the familiar "Man-in-the-Moon" pattern. In reality these are lowlands, formed by giant meteorites that smashed into the Moon long ago, which were then filled by dark lava. They are called maria, a Latin word meaning "seas" (singular: mare); although there has never been any water in them, that is what they looked like to early observers. Many of the maria are given fanciful names, such as Mare Tranquillitatis (Sea of Tranquillity) where Apollo 11 astronauts landed in 1969. The bright areas on the Moon are highlands.

The rugged, colorless appearance of the Moon is in stark contrast to the surface of the Earth. There is no air on the Moon, so there are no clouds to spoil our view. A look through a pair of binoculars reveals that the Moon is pitted with craters, the largest of which can engulf a fair-sized city. These, too, were formed long ago by meteorite impacts. Some of the craters are surrounded by bright streaks, called rays, which consist of crushed rock thrown out by the crater-forming impacts. Lunar craters are named after famous people, mostly astronomers. The most notable example is Tycho, in the Moon's southern hemisphere, where the formation is particularly noticeable around the time of a full Moon.

BIRTH OF THE MOON

Astronomers believe that the Moon was born about 4.6 billion years ago when the youthful Earth was hit by another body, larger than the present Moon. The colliding body shattered completely under the force of the impact, which also melted part of the Earth's outer layers. The debris from the collision then went into orbit around the Earth, where it collected together to form the Moon. The lack of air and liquid water means that there is no erosion, with the result that the Moon's surface features have remained virtually unchanged for millions of years.

Whenever we look at the Moon, we always see the same side. This is because the Moon turns on its axis in exactly the same time (27.3 days) that it takes to orbit Earth—a phenomenon known as "synchronous rotation." Until space probes orbited the Moon, no one knew what the far side looked like. The first probe to photograph the Moon's far side was Russia's Luna 3 in October 1959; since then, it has been fully mapped. The main difference is that the far side is mostly covered with bright, crater-marked highlands, and has fewer large, dark mare areas.

WHAT IF?
...WE ESTABLISHED A MOON BASE?

The discovery of water ice at the Moon's poles has stimulated plans to set up bases using pressurized cylinders, like those used in present-day space stations. The cylinders will be covered with lunar soil to protect them from cosmic rays and meteorites.

At first, scientists will use the bases to explore the mountains, craters and valleys of the Moon to find out more about its history. Observatories will be established to obtain a clearer view of the sky than is possible from Earth, where our atmosphere gets in the way. It will also be desirable to set up radio telescopes, to study the cosmos free of interference from radio transmissions on the Earth.

Energy to power the lunar bases will come from sunlight. Solar power will also be used to convert the water ice at the poles into hydrogen and oxygen for fuel; oxygen for breathing will be extracted from the deposits currently "locked away" as oxides in the Moon's rocks. The same rocks could be used to extend the bases. Plants for food will be grown in Moon soil, with added water and fertilizer; farm animals and fish will be kept in pressurized domes.

Eventually, we will mine the Moon for the valuable minerals that it contains. Instead of rockets, magnetic ramps called mass drivers may be used to propel containers of Moon rocks into space. The rocks will then be ferried to Earth or processed in space factories. One day it may also be possible for tourists to take vacations on the Moon, living in lunar hotels and visiting sites such as Tranquillity Base, where the first Apollo astronauts landed in 1969. Analysis of the rocks brought back by the Apollo astronauts show that they contain useful metals, such as aluminum, iron, titanium and magnesium.

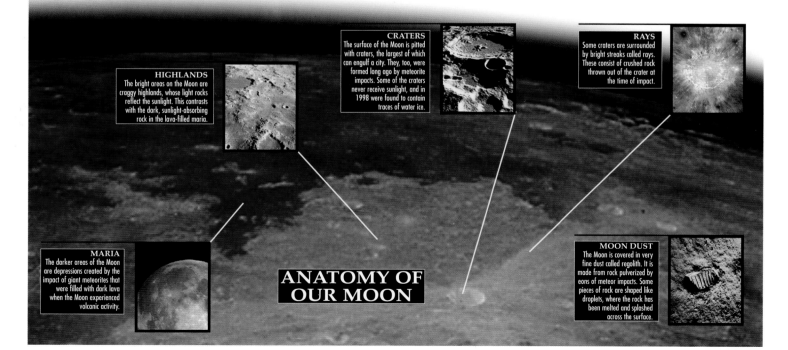

CRATERS
The surface of the Moon is pitted with craters, the largest of which can engulf a city. They, too, were formed long ago by meteorite impacts. Some of the craters never receive sunlight, and in 1998 were found to contain traces of water ice.

RAYS
Some craters are surrounded by bright streaks called rays. These consist of crushed rock thrown out of the crater at the time of impact.

HIGHLANDS
The bright areas on the Moon are craggy highlands, whose light rocks reflect the sunlight. This contrasts with the dark, sunlight-absorbing rock in the lava-filled maria.

MARIA
The darker areas of the Moon are depressions created by the impact of giant meteorites that were filled with dark lava when the Moon experienced volcanic activity.

ANATOMY OF OUR MOON

MOON DUST
The Moon is covered in very fine dust called regolith. It is made from rock pulverized by eons of meteor impacts. Some pieces of rock are shaped like droplets, where the rock has been melted and splashed across the surface.

PHASES OF THE MOON

At one time, the phases of the Moon controlled peoples' lives. The full Moon made it possible to travel at night, the new Moon was thought to bring good luck, and coastal communities knew that the tides depended on the position of the Moon. Today, few of us know what phase the Moon will be in tonight, and many people are unsure what causes its apparent changes in shape. Yet the truth is that the lunar cycle affects not only astronomers, but each and every one of us living on the Earth.

LUNAR CYCLE STATISTICS

Period of rotation around the Earth (sidereal month)	27.3 days
Interval between new moons (synodic month)	29.5 days
Number of new moons in a year	13
Best months for observing different phases	
Crescent new moon	April (end)
First quarter	March
Full moon	December
Last quarter	September
Crescent old moon	July (end)

MOONLIGHT SERENADE

The Moon's orbit around Earth is counterclockwise, like most of the orbits in our solar system. In the course of each orbit—or lunar cycle—its appearance changes from a thin crescent, through half phase to full, then back to a thin crescent again. These changes are entirely due to the angle at which the Sun's light strikes it: The Moon has no light of its own.

When the Moon is growing in size, up to full Moon, it is said to be waxing; after full, it is waning. The cycle begins at new Moon. Strictly speaking this takes place when the Moon is almost in line with the Sun, which means that it is in the daytime sky and can't normally be seen. But most people consider the Moon's first appearance as a thin crescent to be the new Moon, which occurs a day or two after the true new Moon.

The new Moon is a crescent because it is almost completely backlit. It can be seen in the western sky just after sunset, and sets soon after the Sun itself. The earliest sighting is some 14 hours after the true new Moon, but many people regard even a three- or four-day-old Moon as new. By the time the Moon is seven days old (that is, seven days after new) it has grown to a half Moon. Astronomers call this the first quarter, because the Moon is now one quarter of the way around its orbit.

WANING MOON

The half Moon can be seen more or less due south at sunset, and follows the sun down to the west just a few hours later. After another seven days, the Moon has grown to full. Now it rises at around sunset, but is more or less directly opposite the Sun in the sky—roughly due east. The phases just before and after full Moon are called gibbous, a word which comes from the Latin gibbosus meaning "hunchbacked."

About a week after full, the Moon is at half phase again but with the opposite side to the first quarter illuminated. It rises roughly an hour later each night, so you will probably only see this phase early in the morning. A few days after last quarter, the Moon is back to a crescent again—this time in the pre-dawn sky, rising an hour or two before the Sun in the east. Then, for a few days, the Moon "disappears" as it passes directly between the Earth and the Sun, signaling the start of a new cycle.

IN THE CRADLE

QUITE OFTEN WHEN THE MOON IS A CRESCENT THE WHOLE OF ITS DISK IS FAINTLY VISIBLE — SOMETIMES CALLED "THE OLD MOON IN THE NEW MOON'S ARMS." THE REASON FOR THIS PHENOMENON WOULD BE OBVIOUS IF YOU WERE STANDING ON THE MOON — ABOVE YOU WOULD BE THE NEARLY FULL EARTH WITH ITS BRILLIANT WHITE CLOUDS, CASTING LIGHT ON THE LANDSCAPE MANY TIMES BRIGHTER THAN THE FULL MOON DOES IN OUR SKY.

TRUE STORY

MANY PEOPLE OBSERVE THAT THE MOON APPEARS TO BE BIGGER WHEN IT IS RISING THAN WHEN IT IS HIGH UP IN THE SKY. BUT, IF ANYTHING, THE MOON IS SLIGHTLY SMALLER WHEN IT IS RISING: ITS APPARENT SIZE IS AN ILLUSION. THE REASON FOR THIS IS THAT YOUR EYE COMPARES THE RISING MOON WITH DISTANT OBJECTS ON THE LANDSCAPE — NOT, AS SOME BOOKS SUGGEST, THE LENSING EFFECT OF THE AIR NEAR THE HORIZON "MAGNIFYING" THE IMAGE.

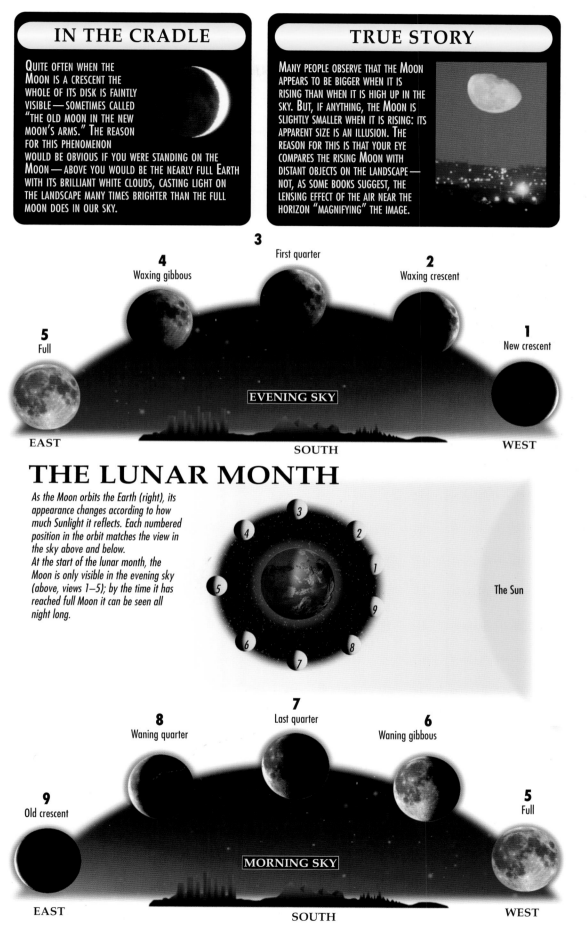

THE LUNAR MONTH

As the Moon orbits the Earth (right), its appearance changes according to how much Sunlight it reflects. Each numbered position in the orbit matches the view in the sky above and below.
At the start of the lunar month, the Moon is only visible in the evening sky (above, views 1–5); by the time it has reached full Moon it can be seen all night long.

3 First quarter
4 Waxing gibbous
2 Waxing crescent
5 Full
1 New crescent

EVENING SKY
EAST SOUTH WEST

The Sun

8 Waning quarter
7 Last quarter
6 Waning gibbous
9 Old crescent
5 Full

MORNING SKY
EAST SOUTH WEST

FORMATION OF THE MOON

The Moon is an oddity—a satellite so large that the Earth-Moon system is almost a double planet. For generations, rival theories strove to explain its origin. But evidence brought back by the Apollo landings may have settled the argument. Most scientists now believe that 4.5 billion years ago, the molten, new-made Earth was struck a glancing blow by another planet. The impact destroyed the wanderer and hurled huge chunks of the Earth into space. From this ancient collision, our nearest neighbor was born.

THEORIES THAT FAILED

BEFORE THE APOLLO MISSIONS OF 1969–72, THERE WERE THREE COMPETING THEORIES ON THE MOON'S FORMATION. DATA FROM THE MOON LANDINGS NOW SUPPORT A FOURTH THEORY — THAT THE MOON WAS FORMED IN A GIGANTIC COSMIC COLLISION.

CO-ACCRETION HYPOTHESIS

STATED THAT THE EARTH AND MOON FORMED INDEPENDENTLY, AS A DOUBLE PLANET, FROM THE ORIGINAL NEBULA (CLOUD OF GAS AND DUST) THAT CREATED THE SOLAR SYSTEM.

PROBLEM IF THE EARTH AND MOON HAD EVOLVED FROM THE SAME EMBRYONIC ENVIRONMENT, THE GEOLOGICAL COMPOSITION OF THE BODIES WOULD BE MORE SIMILAR.

FISSION HYPOTHESIS

PROPOSED THAT THE MOON "SPUN OFF" ITS PARENT PLANET WHEN THE EARTH WAS NEWLY FORMED AND ROTATING MORE RAPIDLY ON ITS AXIS.

PROBLEM IF THE EARTH AND MOON FORMED OUT OF THE SAME FULLY FORMED PLANET, THE OUTER LAYERS, AT LEAST, WOULD BE MORE ALIKE. THE MOON SHOULD ALSO ORBIT IN THE PLANE OF THE EARTH'S EQUATOR, WHICH IT DOES NOT.

CAPTURE HYPOTHESIS

SUGGESTED THAT THE MOON WAS ORIGINALLY A SEPARATE ASTRONOMICAL OBJECT THAT WAS DRAWN IN BY THE EARTH'S GRAVITY.

PROBLEM THE MOON IS PROBABLY TOO MASSIVE EVER TO HAVE BEEN CAPTURED IN THIS WAY. NOR DOES THE THEORY ACCOUNT FOR THE GEOLOGICAL SIMILARITIES BETWEEN THE TWO BODIES.

IMPACT
A wandering planet, traveling at several miles per second, plunges into the young Earth, still hot from its recent formation. Within four hours, the core of the impacting planet merges with the Earth's mantle and the outermost layers of both planets are blasted into space.

DEBRIS
Under the influence of the Earth's gravity and centrifugal force (the force that pulls an orbiting body away from the center of its orbit), debris from the collision swirls into a gigantic disk. Much of the material in the disk falls back to Earth, but the rest begins to coalesce into steadily larger objects.

MOONBIRTH
Within a few years, the largest bodies in the disk have swept up most of the free debris and gathered together to form a single large satellite. The Earth–Moon system is now complete, but still young and hot. In time, the two bodies will cool and drift apart to form the system that exists today.

The Moon is the fifth-largest natural satellite in the solar system. Only Pluto's moon Charon—which is nearly half Pluto's diameter—is bigger in relation to its parent planet.

COSMIC COLLISION

Astronomers may never know for sure how the Moon was formed, but most today favor the so-called "giant impact" theory. The early solar system was a chaotic place—a whirling disk of spinning debris that slowly clumped together to form the planets. The giant impact theory proposes that in the midst of this maelstrom, the infant Earth was hit by another planet-sized body. The catastrophic collision sent a vast cloud of debris swirling around what remained of the Earth, and this debris later coalesced to form the Moon.

The beauty of the giant impact theory is that it explains both the differences and the similarities between the two bodies. The composition of the Moon and Earth are similar, but by no means identical. Some differences can be explained by gravity—the Earth's core has more iron than the Moon's, for instance, because the Earth's greater mass would naturally have attracted the heaviest material. But some lunar rock is quite unlike any on Earth—perhaps because it came from the debris of a shattered impacting planet.

The theory evolved in the early 1970s, when data from the Apollo missions began to cast doubt over earlier ideas on how the Moon was formed. Two astronomers, William Hartmann and Donald Davis, from the Planetary Sciences Institute in Tucson, Arizona, had been estimating the sizes of mini-planets, or planetesimals, that might have formed near to the Earth in the early days of the solar system.

IMPACT SIMULATIONS

Davis and Hartmann's research showed that several objects, each much larger than the present-day Moon, could have coalesced near enough to Earth to pose an impact threat, and that such an impact would create the right quantity of debris to form a satellite just like the Moon.

At first, astronomers could only guess at the size of impacting body needed to release such a vast amount of material. But now, with the help of computer simulations of impacts, they can follow the progress of between 1,000 and 3,000 interacting fragments that vary in size from a few dozen miles to a few hundred miles across. The simulations appear to confirm that a giant impact at a certain angle could have led to the formation of the Earth-Moon system within just a few years. And in July 1997, a team of scientists from the University of Colorado presented the latest estimate for impacting body's mass. They showed that around 60–85 percent of the debris in an orbiting disk simply falls to the surface of the parent planet. This implied that for the remainder to coalesce into a satellite the size of the present-day Moon, the Earth must have been hit by an object 2½–3 times the size of Mars.

Even so, the giant impact theory is not conclusively proved. To date, all of the computer simulations that lead from giant impact to the formation of a Moon-sized satellite leave the Earth rotating about twice as fast as geological evidence suggests that it should have been at the time. Our nearest neighbor is not about to give up its secrets so easily—if it ever does so.

REFORMED?

MIRANDA, ONE OF THE SATELLITES OF URANUS, WAS ONCE THOUGHT TO HAVE A HISTORY AS VIOLENT AS THE MOON'S. MIRANDA'S TERRAIN INCLUDES THREE RELATIVELY YOUNG AND HEAVILY RIDGED AREAS, WHILE THE REST OF THE LANDSCAPE IS OLDER AND CRATERED, IMPLYING THAT IT REFORMED AFTER BEING SHATTERED IN A GIANT IMPACT. BUT NOWADAYS MOST ASTRONOMERS THINK THAT THE GIANT RIDGES ARE DUE TO TIDAL VOLCANIC ACTIVITY OF THE TYPE THAT ALSO FLEXES JUPITER'S MOON IO.

MOTHER MOON

THE IROQUOIS BELIEVE, THE MOON WAS FORMED BY HAHGWEHDIYU, THE "GOOD CREATOR" (RIGHT). HE SHAPED THE SKY WITH THE PALM OF HIS HANDS, AND THEN USED HIS DEAD MOTHER'S BODY AS RAW MATERIAL TO MAKE THE SUN, THE MOON AND THE STARS.

WATER ON THE MOON

On March 5, 1998, NASA excitedly declared that its uncrewed Lunar Prospector probe had detected water on the Moon—tons of it, in fact—in the guise of ice deposits at the lunar poles. If NASA's estimates are correct, the Moon could well be our stepping stone to the stars. A plentiful water supply in the solar system is essential for human space colonization—not only to provide us with water to drink, but with oxygen to breathe and fuel for our rockets in the form of liquid hydrogen and oxygen.

THE LUNAR PROSPECTOR

MANUFACTURER LOCKHEED MARTIN MISSILES AND SPACE, SUNNYVALE, CALIFORNIA

PROJECT COST $63 MILLION (INCLUDES $34M DEVELOPMENT)

PROBE DIMENSIONS HEIGHT 4.25 FT (1.3 M); DIAMETER 4.5 FT (1.4 M)

WEIGHT 650 LB (295 KG) (FULLY FUELED)

LAUNCHED JANUARY 6, 1998, 9:28:44 PM EST FROM PAD 46, KENNEDY SPACE CENTER, CAPE CANAVERAL, FLORIDA

LAUNCH VEHICLE LOCKHEED MARTIN ATHENA II, 3-STAGE SOLID-FUEL ROCKET

CELLS CHARGING 15-AMP-PER-HOUR NICKEL-HYDROGEN BATTERIES

FLIGHT TIME TO LUNAR ORBIT 105 HOURS

POLAR ORBITS
- JANUARY 11–DECEMBER 19, 1998; HEIGHT 63 MILES (101 KM); PERIOD 118 MINUTES; ORBITAL VELOCITY 3,668 MPH (5,903 KM/H)
- DECEMBER 19, 1998–JANUARY 28, 1999; HEIGHT 25 MILES (40 KM)
- JANUARY 28; HEIGHT 15 MILES (24 KM)

ONBOARD EQUIPMENT
- NEUTRON/GAMMA RAY SPECTROMETERS TO ANALYZE LUNAR SURFACE COMPOSITION
- MAGNETOMETER AND ELECTRON REFLECTOMETER TO ANALYZE AND MAP THE MOON'S MAGNETIC FIELD
- ALPHA PARTICLE SPECTROMETER TO IDENTIFY ALPHA PARTICLES IN RADON GAS PRODUCTS EMITTED FROM CRATERS
- DOPPLER GRAVITY EXPERIMENT TO ASSESS FIELD STRENGTH AND VARIATION BY S-BAND RADIATION SIGNALS

HIDDEN DEPTHS

After the Apollo 17 mission in 1972, NASA did not return to the Moon for more than 25 years. The next obvious step was to establish a moonbase, but one of the biggest problems was water— or the lack of it. Water is vital for living in space, not only for drinking, but as a source of oxygen. The cost of transporting large amounts from Earth is prohibitive, not least because the weight puts too much of a demand on the launcher. Unfortunately, the lunar rock samples brought back by the Apollo astronauts were bone dry, implying that the Moon was waterless—around the landing sites, at least.

The rock samples were all from near the lunar equator, where temperatures reach 250°F (121°C). Some people thought that there might be a better chance of finding water at the lunar poles. Their hopes were raised in November 1996 when NASA revealed that the probe Clementine, which had been testing radar instrumentation for the Pentagon during a mission in 1994, had picked up the radar signature of hydrogen at the Moon's south pole—an indicator of the presence of ice.

In January 1998, NASA launched the uncrewed Lunar Prospector with a mission profile that included searching for further evidence of water. Less than two months after the probe went into into lunar orbit, NASA proudly announced that one of the instruments on board—a neutron spectrometer—had confirmed that hydrogen was present in rocks at both lunar poles and that this hydrogen was bound up in frozen water. "Our expectation is that we have areas at both poles with layers of near-pure water ice," says Alan Binder of the Lunar Research Center in Gilroy, California.

Some NASA scientists have estimated that there is up to 6 billion tons (5.4 billion tonnes) of ice, buried beneath 18 in (46 cm) of dry lunar soil and concentrated in a 650-square-mile (1,685-square km) region at each lunar pole. Just one billion tons of water is enough to fill around 300,000 Olympic-sized swimming pools. It is also thought to be enough to support a community of at least 2,000 people living on the Moon for over a hundred years.

As a final attempt to prove the presence of water on the Moon beyond argument, the Lunar Prospector team planned a spectacular finale to the mission, sending the probe hurtling to its doom in a suspected ice-filled crater. Telescopes on Earth hoped to detect the ice and water flung up by the impact, but they saw nothing—perhaps because the probe was simply unlucky. So the case for water on the Moon is perhaps not yet quite closed.

LOCKED IN THE SHADOWS

Where did the Moon's water come from? Most scientists believe that it arrived there as ice, brought by countless meteorite and comet impacts over billions of years. Over time, most of this water evaporated in the intense heat of the lunar days and was lost to outer space through the atmosphere. Yet some of the deep craters that are found at the lunar poles lie in perpetual shadow, where temperatures may never rise above –280°F (–138°C). This creates "cold traps" in which some of the water could have remained frozen for billions of years. The water NASA found could have been deposited by direct impact, or by individual water molecules that migrated over the lunar surface and froze when they reached the polar craters.

The discovery of water has been particularly inspiring for planetary scientists. Probing the layers of polar ice on the Moon could yield fresh insights into what comets are made of and how often they have hit both the Moon and Earth. It could also help to reveal whether rate of impact changes over time— and whether it is likely to increase.

OH, MY DARLING

THE FIRST HINT OF LUNAR WATER CAME FROM THE CLEMENTINE PROBE, A JOINT PROJECT BETWEEN NASA AND THE STRATEGIC DEFENSE INITIATIVE (WHO PROPOSED THE STAR WARS SATELLITE NETWORK). LAUNCHED ON JANUARY 25, 1994, CLEMENTINE TESTED SENSORS AND SPACECRAFT COMPONENTS UNDER LONG EXPOSURE TO SPACE. IT CIRCLED THE MOON 348 TIMES, MAPPING THE SURFACE AND BOUNCING RADAR BEAMS OFF THE DEEPEST CRATERS. THE DATA FROM THE SOUTH POLE INDICATED THE EXISTENCE OF REFLECTIVE WATER ICE.

PROBING THE MOON'S POLAR DEPTHS

POLAR PUZZLE
NASA's probes detected twice as much water ice at the north pole as at the south pole. This was surprising, given that the permanently shadowed area near the north pole is considerably smaller than its south polar equivalent. Perpetually shadowed areas inside deep craters, known as "cold traps," were considered to be the most likely places to harbor water ice.

RADAR CLUE
Radar mapping beams bounced off the lunar surface by the probe Clementine first alerted NASA scientists to the presence of water.

NORTH POLE
Water ice detected in area covering between 3,600 and 18,000 square miles (9,300 and 46,600 square km).

SOUTH POLE
Water ice detected in area covering between 1,800 and 7,200 square miles (4,660 and 18,650 square km).

COLD TRAP
With no internal heat source and hardly any atmosphere to conserve radiant heat, temperatures on parts of the Moon's surface that receive no direct sunlight an hover below –280°F (–138°C). Areas of perpetual shadow within deep polar craters known as "cold traps" are most likely to contain water ice.

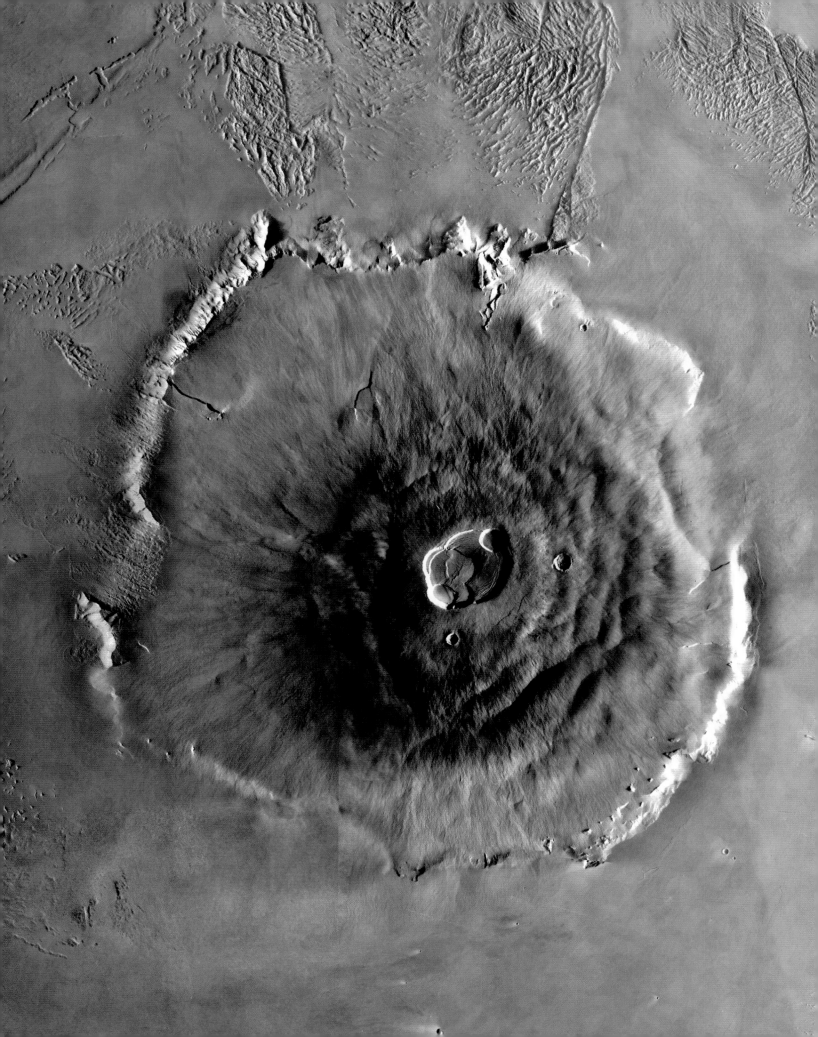

MARS

The famous "Red Planet," Mars is one of the most conspicuous objects in Earth's skies, and has fascinated people since ancient times. Like Venus, it was thought that it might be a hospitable environment for advanced life, and the discovery of polar caps and changing dark patches on the surface—as well as the infamous "canals"—encouraged the idea. When the first space probes flew past, there was huge disappointment at what they revealed—a dry, moonlike, cratered world. It was not until the first orbiters surveyed Mars in detail that its reputation as a fascinating planet was restored. Although they found no signs of life or water, the photographs revealed giant volcanoes, a canyon dwarfing any on Earth, and channels that looked suspiciously like dried-up rivers. Later probes have discovered even more: huge quantities of ice beneath the surface, complex weather systems, and conclusive evidence that Mars had oceans for a long period of its early history. Even the question of past and present life on Mars, once dismissed out of hand, is now taken seriously once more, and remains a key mission objective for Mars probes.

A color mosaic image of Olympus Mons, the largest volcano in the solar system and one of the most striking features of the Martian landscape. Olympus Mons is about 370 miles (600 km) in diameter and the summit is 15 miles (24 km) above the plains that surround the volcano.

MARS

Mars is the fourth planet from the Sun and one of Earth's nearest neighbors. It is also the only other planet in the solar system where humans may one day live. Mars is smaller and colder than Earth, but is otherwise remarkably similar: It has days and seasons, a thin atmosphere and, probably, significant reserves of water buried as ice beneath the surface. There is even a chance that Mars once played host to simple life-forms, and that the fossilized remains of long-extinct creatures are still buried there.

MARS AND EARTH

MARS		EARTH
4,228 MILES (6,804 KM)	DIAMETER	7,973 MILES (12,831 KM)
25° 11'	AXIS TILT	23° 27'
687 EARTH DAYS	LENGTH OF YEAR	365 DAYS
24 HOURS 37 MINUTES	LENGTH OF DAY	24 HOURS
141.6 MILLION MILES (227.9 MILLION KM)	DISTANCE FROM SUN	93.5 MILLION MILES (150 MILLION KM)
−9°F (−13°C)	SURFACE TEMPERATURE	59°F (15°C)
0.379 G	SURFACE GRAVITY	1 G
CARBON DIOXIDE (90%)	ATMOSPHERE	NITROGEN (78%), OXYGEN (21%), ARGON (1%)
10 MILLIBARS	ATMOSPHERIC PRESSURE	1,000 MILLIBARS
SILICON, IRON, OXYGEN	COMPOSITION	SILICON (60%), ALUMINUM (15%)

A COLD, ROCKY DESERT

Of all the planets in the solar system, Mars is the most like ours. Its axis is tilted like the Earth's, which gives it seasons. Mars has a relatively warm summer, when temperatures in the southern hemisphere can reach up to 68°F (20°C), but a long, cold winter that sees them plunge to −284°F (−140°C).

Over 4 billion years ago, Mars was covered with massive volcanoes—just like the Earth—and had surface water, which occasionally gathered in flash floods, carving water channels into the surface. There may even have been standing oceans over long periods of time. Like the Earth, too, Mars has a cloudy atmosphere; although the Martian "air" is much thinner, and the wispy clouds are made of carbon dioxide rather than water vapor.

So, despite its many similarities to Earth, Mars is a far from hospitable place. If you landed there without a spacesuit, not only would you suffocate but, due to the much lower atmospheric pressure, your blood would boil within minutes.

DUST STORMS

Apart from the lack of oxygen and the low atmospheric pressure, you would also have to withstand the continuous winds that blow across the Martian surface at speeds of over 125 miles per hour (200 km/h), whipping up giant clouds of fine orange-brown dust in their wake. It is this dust that has earned Mars the nickname "The Red Planet," although "Rusty Planet" might be more suitable, since the color is explained by the high proportion of iron in the planet's rocks—on average, this measures almost twice as much as on Earth. Mars is also very dry and cold. Even on a warm summer's day the ground rarely gets above freezing point, and on winter mornings the rocks

are often coated with a fine layer of carbon dioxide "frost."

Mars' two moons, Phobos and Deimos, race around the planet in about eight hours and 30 hours respectively. They are thought to be asteroids that strayed too close to the planet in the distant past and were captured by its gravity. If Phobos, the closer of the two, maintains its present orbit, it is likely to crash into Mars in about 100,000 years' time. Some evidence even suggests Mars has suffered similar collisions in the past.

NATURAL FEATURES

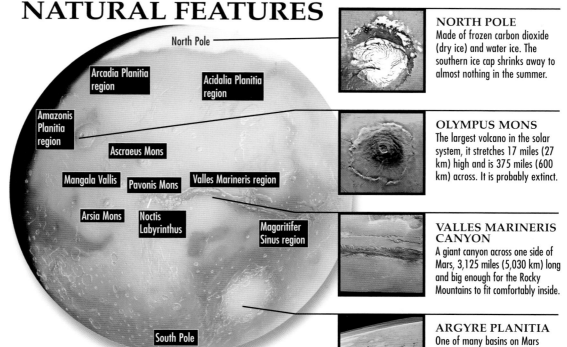

North Pole

Arcadia Planitia region

Acidalia Planitia region

Amazonis Planitia region

Ascraeus Mons

Mangala Vallis

Pavonis Mons

Valles Marineris region

Arsia Mons

Noctis Labyrinthus

Magaritifer Sinus region

South Pole

When the first truly detailed maps of Mars were made in the 1970s, scientists added descriptive Latin words such as Planitia ("plain") or Mons ("mountain") to the original place names.

NORTH POLE
Made of frozen carbon dioxide (dry ice) and water ice. The southern ice cap shrinks away to almost nothing in the summer.

OLYMPUS MONS
The largest volcano in the solar system, it stretches 17 miles (27 km) high and is 375 miles (600 km) across. It is probably extinct.

VALLES MARINERIS CANYON
A giant canyon across one side of Mars, 3,125 miles (5,030 km) long and big enough for the Rocky Mountains to fit comfortably inside.

ARGYRE PLANITIA
One of many basins on Mars created long ago by asteroid impacts. The crater Galle is about 125 miles (200 km) across.

CANAL MYTH

THE BIGGEST MYTH ABOUT MARS—THAT A RACE OF MARTIANS ONCE BUILT CANALS TO CARRY WATER FROM THE POLES TO THE EQUATOR—IS BASED ON A TRANSLATION ERROR. IN 1877, THE ITALIAN ASTRONOMER GIOVANNI SCHIAPARELLI SAW WHAT HE THOUGHT WERE "CANALI," MEANING "CHANNELS," THROUGH HIS TELESCOPE. IN ENGLISH THIS WAS TRANSLATED AS "CANALS" SO PEOPLE ASSUMED THEY MUST BE ARTIFICIAL WATERWAYS. IN FACT, THEY WERE AN OPTICAL ILLUSION.

LIVE FROM MARS
On July 4, 1997, the uncrewed U.S. probe Pathfinder became the first spacecraft to land on Mars since Viking in 1976. After a short delay due to technical glitches, Pathfinder released the Sojourner remote-controlled Mars rover, and the world held its breath as the probe's first pictures were broadcast back to Earth.

THE SURFACE OF MARS

Rust staining in the soil, imparted by iron oxide, is the simple reason why Mars' surface is so distinctly red. But its color is just one of the planet's unique surface features. In recent years, the Martian surface has been revealed as a rich and varied landscape, shaped by great natural forces such as meteorite impacts, floods, volcanoes, earthquakes and glaciers. Mars' surface is continuing to evolve, due to seasonal freezing and thawing and powerful winds that transport vast clouds of dust across its face.

TOP TEN SURFACE FEATURES

NAME OF FEATURE	TYPE OF FEATURE	LOCATION	SIZE MILES/KM
VALLES MARINERIS	TECTONIC CANYON SYSTEM	70°W, 10°S	2,500 MILES (4,023 KM) LONG, 373 MILES (600 KM) AT ITS WIDEST AND 5 MILES (8 KM) DEEP
THARSIS RIDGE	BASALT PLATEAU	100°W, 5°N	6 MILES (10 KM) HIGH BY 2,485 MILES (4,000 KM) WIDE
OLYMPUS MONS	EXTINCT SHIELD VOLCANO	135°W, 20°N	17 MILES (27 KM) HIGH BY 373 MILES (600 KM) WIDE (LARGEST VOLCANO KNOWN)
SYRTIS MAJOR PLANITIA	DARK, ELEVATED FLAT PLAIN	290°E, 10°N	785 MILES (1,265 KM) IN DIAMETER
NORTH POLE ICE CAP	FROZEN H_2O AND CO_2	EXTENDS TO 65°N IN WINTER	MAXIMUM THICKNESS OF 3 MILES (5 KM); 1,000 MILES (1,600 KM) WIDE IN WINTER, 375 MILES (600 KM) WIDE IN SUMMER
SOUTH POLE	COMPOSED MAINLY OF CO_2	EXTENDS TO 45°S IN WINTER	1,200 MILES (1,930 KM) WIDE IN WINTER, 250 MILES (400 KM) WIDE IN SUMMER
ARGYRE PLANITIA	IMPACT BASIN	42°W, 50°S	870 MILES (1,400 KM) IN DIAMETER
ACIDALIA PLANITIA	IMPACT BASIN	30°E, 50°N	1,625 MILES (2,615 KM) IN DIAMETER
HELLAS BASIN	IMPACT BASIN	294°E, 40°S	1,000 BY 1,250 MILES (1,600 BY 2010 KM) (MARS' LARGEST IMPACT CRATER)
ELYSIUM PLANITIA	IMPACT BASIN	210°E, 20°N	1,554 MILES (2,500 KM) IN DIAMETER

ROCKS OF AGES

We know a great deal about the Martian surface, thanks first to 19th-century astronomers, who identified and named many of its features, and more recently to uncrewed Mars probes that have provided us with stunning closeups of the entire planet.

Much of the surface of Mars is a barren stony desert that looks and behaves much like deserts on Earth. But Mars has a range of distinctive features. Most of them, such as mountains, canyons, extinct volcanoes and craters, were created early in the planet's life. Mars' rivers, and probably its seas, have since shaped and modified many of these landmarks. Some of Mars' most unusual features—like the "Main Pyramid," "City Square" and "The Face"—have even led to claims that they might be ruins left by an ancient civilization, although most scientists now believe they are natural features.

But the planet's reddish soil can be found everywhere on Mars—the result of billions of years of rock erosion by wind and water and pulverization by meteorites. This soil, blown around by the wind, covers virtually the entire planet and can be a few inches or many feet deep. It collects to forms drifts, which can be seen from high above the planet's surface as distinctive tapered streaks of soil, often deposited on the leeward sides of Mars' craters.

Most of what is known about the composition of Martian soil comes from experiments performed by the Viking landers. They detected iron-rich clays, calcium carbonate, iron oxides and magnesium sulfate, as well as silicon dioxide, which makes up 50 percent of Mars' soil. The strange oxidizing agent in the soil, which releases oxygen when wetted, is thought to be a type of peroxide.

The Martian surface can be split into two regions. The highlands, in the southern hemisphere, contain Mars' oldest surface rocks. Many craters and basins (craters more than about 50 miles/80 km wide) are found here. The lowlands, in the northern hemisphere, are less cratered. This is the flattest, smoothest region known in the solar system. Some scientists believe it was shaped by ancient ocean water, as it resembles the heavily sedimented floors of Earth's oceans. Mars' largest volcanoes also exist in the lowlands in an area known as Tharsis Ridge.

Next to Tharsis Ridge, in the equatorial region, lies the Valles Marineris, a canyon stretching almost the distance from New York to California. But unlike the Earth's Grand Canyon, which was cut by the Colorado River, the Valles Marineris canyon is thought to be an ancient tectonic feature, caused by movement in Mars' surface mantle. Other features found here are channels, probably cut by frequent flooding more than a billion years ago, and large sand dunes.

More impressive sand dunes surround each of the poles. A big dune field entirely circles the northern pole, showing just how important the strong Martian wind is in the carving and shaping of this unique landscape.

CLOSE CALL

The Viking Landers had to touch down on even ground for their experiments to succeed. Viking 1 landed on an area that looked like a smooth, sparsely cratered plain — from orbit. But it had come within 30 ft (9 m) of catastrophe in the shape of a 7-ft (2-m) wide rock, later named Big Joe (above). Viking 2 landed near several channels up to wide and four in (10 cm) deep. But both made it, despite these unseen obstructions.

ROMANTIC

Mars was first seen by Galileo in 1610, but it was not until 1867 that astronomer Richard Proctor systematically named Mars' features after scientists who had studied the planet. Ten years later, Italian astronomer Giovanni Schiaparelli (pictured) refashioned Mars romantically, creating evocative new names such as Mare Sirenum (Sea of Sirens) and Elysium Planitia (Delightful Plains), based on classical literature and the Bible. Arabia, Eden, Tharsis and Elysium — refashioned Mars as a romantic place.

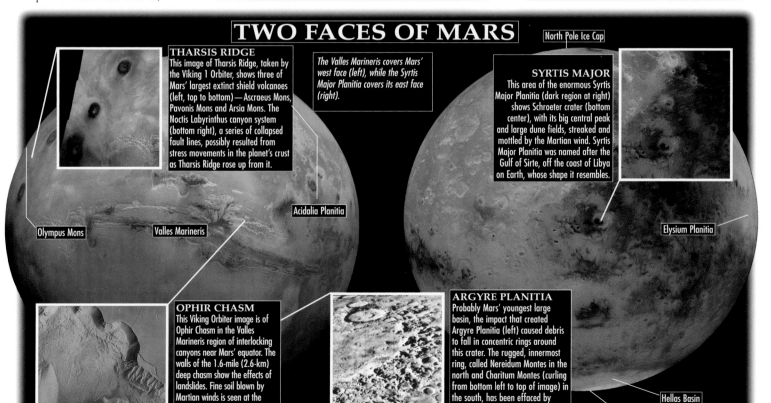

TWO FACES OF MARS

THARSIS RIDGE
This image of Tharsis Ridge, taken by the Viking 1 Orbiter, shows three of Mars' largest extinct shield volcanoes (left, top to bottom)—Ascraeus Mons, Pavonis Mons and Arsia Mons. The Noctis Labyrinthus canyon system (bottom right), a series of collapsed fault lines, possibly resulted from stress movements in the planet's crust as Tharsis Ridge rose up from it.

The Valles Marineris covers Mars' west face (left), while the Syrtis Major Planitia covers its east face (right).

North Pole Ice Cap

SYRTIS MAJOR
This area of the enormous Syrtis Major Planitia (dark region at right) shows Schroeter crater (bottom center), with its big central peak and large dune fields, streaked and mottled by the Martian wind. Syrtis Major Planitia was named after the Gulf of Sirte, off the coast of Libya on Earth, whose shape it resembles.

Acidalia Planitia

Olympus Mons

Valles Marineris

Elysium Planitia

OPHIR CHASM
This Viking Orbiter image is of Ophir Chasm in the Valles Marineris region of interlocking canyons near Mars' equator. The walls of the 1.6-mile (2.6-km) deep chasm show the effects of landslides. Fine soil blown by Martian winds is seen at the bottom left of the image.

ARGYRE PLANITIA
Probably Mars' youngest large basin, the impact that created Argyre Planitia (left) caused debris to fall in concentric rings around this crater. The rugged, innermost ring, called Nereidum Montes in the north and Charitum Montes (curling from bottom left to top of image) in the south, has been effaced by more recent craters, such as Galle crater (top left).

Hellas Basin

South Pole

GEOLOGY OF MARS

Mars is one of the smaller planets in the solar system, but its geology is on a grand scale. With a surface sculpted by almost every major geological process known, it has vast chasms, broad lava plains, ancient impact basins, and the largest volcano in the entire solar system—Olympus Mons. But all these landmarks have evolved over distinct epochs, with different geological processes dominating at different times. To date these geological periods precisely will probably require a future series of crewed trips to the Red Planet.

MARS' GEOLOGICAL TERMS

CATENA	CHAIN OF CRATERS	PLANITIA	PLAIN
CHASMA	CANYON	PATERA	SHALLOW CRATER WITH SCALLOPED EDGES
DORSUM	RIDGE		
FOSSA (PL. FOSSAE)	LONG, NARROW VALLEY	THOLUS	SMALL, DOME-LIKE MOUNTAIN OR HILL
LABYRINTHUS	INTERSECTING VALLEY COMPLEX		
MENSA (PL. MENSAE)	FLAT-TOPPED ELEVATION	VALLIS (PL. VALLES)	VALLEY
MONS (PL. MONTES)	MOUNTAIN	VASTITAS	WIDESPREAD LOWLANDS

ROCKS TO RICHES

About 4.5 billion years ago, at the same time as the Earth was taking shape, another rocky planet began to form slightly farther out from the Sun. It steadily coalesced from the primordial solar nebula—a place brimming with small bodies hurtling around and often crashing together. Mars eventually emerged as a planet from this molten turmoil of objects after about 10 million years.

The new planet gradually cooled from its traumatic, fiery birth, separating into a core, a molten mantle and a solid crust. Over the next billion years, new material was added regularly: Asteroids were still numerous in the solar system and continued to strike the young planet. During this period, the massive impact craters scarred Mars for life, covering the planet with deep pits and ejecta—rocky debris created by the explosive impacts. These craters are now best preserved in the ancient southern highlands of Mars.

By the time the solar system had settled down, impacts by asteroids had become rarer—and the impact rate has continued to decline. But then its cooling crust was leading Mars to an entirely new geological era. Volcanoes burst through fractures in the surface, and molten lava poured over the planet. The northern hemisphere, where the crust was thinner, took the brunt of the upheaval. The mountainous Tharsis ridge—the site of Mars' largest volcanoes—was formed.

BELCHING GAS AND VAPOR

At this volcanic time, Mars began to form a denser atmosphere than it has now. This was because volcanoes eject more than just lava—they belch forth gases and water vapor into the air. The thicker atmosphere allowed liquid water to remain on Mars' surface in the form of rivers, lakes and even oceans. But the planet grew colder. When temperatures fell below the freezing point of water, ground ice and possibly glaciers began to form, cutting swaths through the terrain. Landslides tumbled down mountainsides. Eventually the cold may have caused the water to freeze into the soil. Some of the carbon dioxide may have dissolved in the water, or become trapped in the surface rocks as carbon compounds. Much of Mars' atmosphere was also lost, blown away by massive impacts and stripped by the solar wind.

Next came another era of volcanism, covering much of the northern hemisphere with vast lava plains. The Tharsis ridge rose even higher. The Valles Marineris canyon yawned apart, dwarfing the Earth's Grand Canyon. New faults released torrents of water, carving channels and other features. Finally, the Tharsis region gave birth to the enormous volcanoes of Ascraeus Mons, Arsia Mons, Pavonis Mons and Olympus Mons.

Whether Mars still has active volcanoes is open to debate. Geologists have recently discovered volcanic cones at the north pole with no marks from cratering, suggesting that they formed in the very recent past. However, wind is the main force that sculpts Mars' features. Giant sand storms regularly scour the surface, often growing so large that they engulf the entire planet. Mars may not have the tectonic plates and abundant life that constantly reshapes the Earth's surface, but it has enjoyed no shortage of geological activity—and the planet is still changing.

GEOLOGICAL SCULPTURE ON MARS

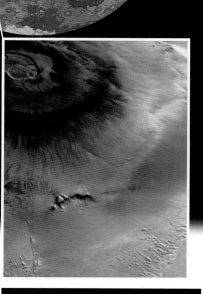

These geological maps of the eastern hemisphere (far left) and western hemisphere (below) of Mars show the types of materials in the Martian landscape. The materials that make up the surface features of each area are color-coded. Reddish areas indicate features formed by volcanic materials, greenish and bluish areas indicate features believed to have been formed by water, and brownish areas indicate features formed by impacts.

VALLES MARINERIS CANYON
Formed by faulting in the crust, the Valles Marineris (above) runs for 2,800 miles (4,500 km), from the Noctis Labyrinthus fracture zone (far left of image) to where three parallel canyons merge into a chasm 370 miles (600 km) wide and 5 miles (8 km) deep (center of image), ending in the dark-colored region of Margaritifer Sinus (far right of image).

UTOPIA PLANITIA
A close-up of the inside of one of the many craters in the Utopia Planitia (above) shows the uneven and cracked surface of the crater's floor, which is filled with a material believed to be sediment.

OLYMPUS MONS
Taken on an angle, this image of Olympus Mons (above) gives a sense of the volcano's enormous height. At 15 miles (24 km) high, it is the largest volcano in the solar system. The dark area seen on the top of the volcano and running down its side is the remains of lava flows.

HELLAS BASIN
With a diameter of 1,120 miles (1,800 km), Hellas (right) is the largest basin on Mars. Formed by the ancient impact of a huge asteroid, comet or meteor, the plain inside the basin is the site of many Martian dust storms.

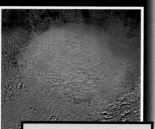

A geologist on Mars uses a drill while an astronaut looks on. The geological equipment used for the Moon landings will have been adapted to meet the special requirements of Mars' soil.

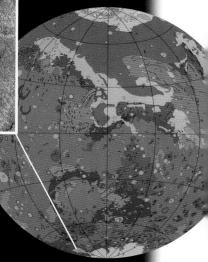

VALLES MARINERIS

Valles Marineris formed millions of years ago, when immense geological forces split the crust of Mars with a huge fissure at the planet's equator. Measuring four times as deep as the Grand Canyon and roughly as long as the U.S. is wide, Valles Marineris is one of Mars' most impressive surface features. The canyon's initial scar was broadened over time by colossal landslides and further erosion caused by the water that flowed over the surface of ancient Mars. Some channels in the fissure even contain dark layers of sediments that could be the remains of an ancient sea bed.

VALLES MARINERIS FACTS

LONGITUDE (OF CENTRAL POINT)	70°
LATITUDE (OF CENTRAL POINT)	11.6°
LENGTH	AROUND 2,500 MILES (4,020 KM)
GREATEST DEPTH	MORE THAN 4 MILES (6 KM)
MAXIMUM WIDTH	370 MILES (600 KM)
AGE	SEVERAL BILLION YEARS
DISCOVERER	NASA SCIENTISTS, USING DATA FROM THE MARINER 9 SPACECRAFT
YEAR DISCOVERED	1971

GRANDER CANYON

THE HUGE SCAR OF VALLES MARINERIS DOMINATES ALMOST A QUARTER OF THE WAY AROUND THE MARTIAN EQUATOR. ITS WESTERN PART WAS MAINLY SHAPED MAINLY BY TECTONIC FORCES, WHILE WATER EROSION PLAYED A BIGGER ROLE TO THE EAST.

LAVA MOUND
Valles Marineris is a blue stripe in this topographical map. The elevated Tharsis Bulge appears red. Its mass created part of the canyon complex by faulting the crust.

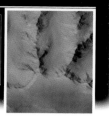

WATERY PAST
Multiple rock layers are visible in the slopes that descend from the center of this small plateau in Valles Marineris. Some of these rocks stacked up from sediments laid down underwater.

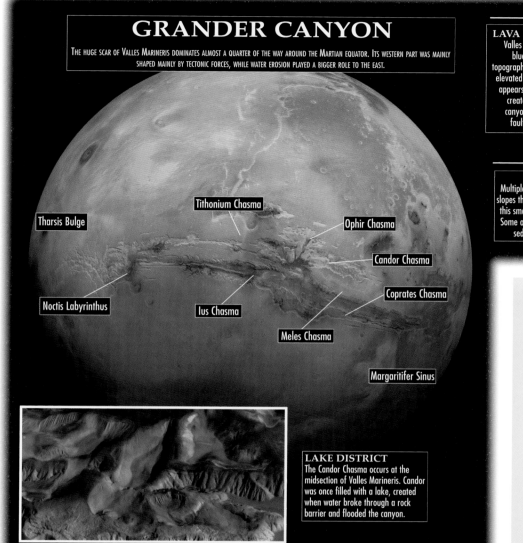

Tharsis Bulge

Tithonium Chasma

Ophir Chasma

Candor Chasma

Noctis Labyrinthus

Ius Chasma

Meles Chasma

Coprates Chasma

Margaritifer Sinus

LAKE DISTRICT
The Candor Chasma occurs at the midsection of Valles Marineris. Candor was once filled with a lake, created when water broke through a rock barrier and flooded the canyon.

WHAT IF?
...YOU FLEW THROUGH VALLES MARINERIS?

It may seem far-fetched, but aircraft are a logical next step for exploring Mars. Although Mars's atmosphere is far thinner than Earth's, it is still substantial enough to support an aircraft, provided one can be made light enough and with a large enough wingspan to support the weight. NASA considered the idea in the 1990s, intending to launch an aerial explorer toward Mars around 2006. However, budget cuts and changed priorities meant the project was shelved and is now a longer-term option. So, by the time humans reach Mars, our aircraft may have been circling the planet for some time.

RED VALLEYS

The Grand Canyon is the most spectacular chasm on Earth, but the sheer scale of Valles Marineris on Mars makes Arizona's greatest landmark look like a scratch. Valles Marineris stretches 2,500 miles (4,020 km) in length, just south of the Martian equator. In places it dips more than four miles beneath the planet's surface and gapes to 370 miles (600 km) wide. By comparison, the Grand Canyon is a paltry 220 miles (350 km) long and less than a mile deep—perhaps equivalent to one of Valles Marineris' smaller tributaries in size.

Valles Marineris' complex network of canyons and valleys is the result of several different forces. Unlike the Grand Canyon, which was eroded by the Colorado River, Valles Marineris was initially opened up as the crust faulted under tremendous pressures. The canyon walls are long and straight, often with linear ridges along their base—all the defining features of fault scarps. To find the strain that buckled Mars' crust, just look to the western end of Valles Marineris—a maze of fractures that start near the summit of a huge uplift called the Tharsis bulge. This region probably domed upward as lava welled up from below, and Tharsis' immense mass was the pressure that cracked open the surrounding crust.

The new canyons were widened by dust storms and enormous landslides. As parts of Valles Marineris were eroded, thick layers of sedimentary rock built up elsewhere. This was an especially exciting find. These sediments most likely settled out under water, so lakes must have filled some of the canyons in the past.

DAM BURSTERS

The Candor and Ophir Chasmas are two of the canyons that may have been water-filled. Some geologists think that these lakes were once dammed by a high ridge that divided Candor from the main canyon. When the rock barrier failed, the waters flooded the canyons.

This would explain the number of teardrop-shape islands in the northern and eastern channels of Valles Marineris, where rapidly flowing water eroded obstacles to give them a streamlined appearance. The floodgates also opened in other places. Seepage of groundwater was probably responsible for excavating the branched side valleys off Ius Chasma, the immense canyon that takes the network of channels eastward. Although the great lakes are long gone, fine mists of ice crystals still cling to the recesses of Valles Marineris—and prove that small quantities of water still exist on Mars today.

In Valles Marineris, scientists have dramatic evidence of Mars' past geological lives. The canyons were made by plate tectonics and water erosion—the same forces that have sunk the largest chasms on our own planet. But while wind, rain and shifting plates will bring Africa's Great Rift Valley and the Grand Canyon tumbling down in a few million years, the comparatively slow processes of erosion on Mars will allow Valles Marineris to stand and be studied for much longer.

MARTIAN ATMOSPHERE

Before the era of space probes, many astronomers believed that the Martian atmosphere was a relatively dense blanket that might even be able to support life. But from the 1960s onward, orbiting spacecraft and landers beamed back the disappointing news: The air on Mars was thin, desperately cold and composed mainly of life-choking carbon dioxide. However, it may not always have been so. The same spacecraft have also found evidence that the Martian air and atmosphere might once have been as thick as the air that supports life on Earth.

AIRS ON EARTH AND MARS

MARS' ATMOSPHERE

	ABUNDANCE (IN BARS)	PERCENTAGE
CARBON DIOXIDE	0.0062	95
NITROGEN	0.00018	2.7
ARGON	0.00010	1.6
OXYGEN	0.000002	0.13
WATER	0.00000039	0.03

PRESSURE: LESS THAN 10 MILLIBARS AT THE SURFACE

EARTH'S ATMOSPHERE

	ABUNDANCE (IN BARS)	PERCENTAGE
NITROGEN	0.78	77
OXYGEN	0.21	21
HYDROGEN	0.01	1
ARGON	0.94	0.93
CARBON DIOXIDE	0.000355	0.035

PRESSURE: AROUND 1,000 MILLIBARS AT SEA LEVEL

ABSENT AIR

Mars' atmosphere is laden with red dust, and its pink skies are some of the most scenic in the solar system. But any space tourist would certainly need a pressure suit to survive. At the surface, Mars has an atmospheric pressure of no more than 10 millibars. On Earth, you would have to travel to 120,000 ft (36,600 m), four times the height of Mount Everest, to reach such thin air.

What gas there is on Mars is mainly carbon dioxide, a greenhouse gas. But there is not nearly enough of it to warm up the chilly planet. Mars' atmosphere contributes only about 12°F (6.5°C) to the average temperature of –65°F (–18°C). On Earth, carbon dioxide makes up less than one percent of the air, but raises temperatures by around 63°F (35°C).

Scientists once thought that Mars' atmosphere was mainly made up of nitrogen, like the air on Earth. But the Viking landers uncovered the more inhospitable truth in 1976, when they found that only three out of every hundred atmosphere molecules were nitrogen. Atoms come in various isotopes—each with a different weight. Martian air contains a higher proportion of heavy nitrogen atoms than Earth's air: Many of the light isotopes have simply escaped.

If the young Mars did have a thicker atmosphere, the puzzle of its water-based features would be solved. The very thin, very cold Martian air means that water cannot exist as a liquid now—it appears as ice or vapor. Only flowing water in a thicker, warmer atmosphere could have shaped the channels recorded by the Mars orbiters.

GAS ESCAPE

So where is all the missing air? Some of it may have simply drifted away. The Red Planet has low gravity—only one-third of that on Earth—that is too weak to hang on to many air particles. Other parts were removed more violently when Mars was bombarded by meteors and much of the atmosphere was literally blasted into space. But other planets also came into the line of fire—and still managed to cultivate healthy second atmospheres.

One theory suggests that some of the Martian air was carried away by the solar wind. On Earth, the air is shielded by our planet's magnetic field. On Mars, the magnetic field is too weak to offer much protection.

Atoms in the upper atmosphere are ionized—given an electrical charge—by sunlight. The solar wind sweeps these charged particles out into space. Lighter atoms are the easiest to pluck away, and the heavyweight molecules that make up the majority of the air remain.

The liquid water that excavated rivers and channels on the young planet may also have destroyed much of the atmosphere. Carbon dioxide probably dissolved in the water, to be deposited later as carbonate minerals. The discovery of carbon in Martian meteorites supports this idea. The same process takes place on the Earth, with one essential difference—Earth has volcanoes. Carbon dioxide is absorbed into the Earth's surface in just the same way as it is on Mars, and is eventually blasted back into the atmosphere by lava flows.

But the lock-up of carbon dioxide in minerals is permanent on Mars: There are no plate tectonics to free the trapped carbon. There is evidence that Mars has had violent volcanic epochs in the past, but the planet's surface is still now. Mars' missing atmosphere is irretrievable—the Red Planet will remain cold, dry and inhospitable.

MARTIAN SKIES

CLOUDY SKY
These stratus clouds are about 10 miles (16 km) above Mars' surface. They consist of water ice condensed on dust particles suspended in the atmosphere. Clouds on Mars have been seen to cover vast regions.

MORNING MISTS
Mist forms over early-morning Mars. Martian water is constantly changing between gas and solid. Particles of ice condense on the surface at night, only to turn into vapor under the first rays of the Sun. The vapor recondenses in the cold atmosphere to form a haze of ice particles.

The Sun's movements create atmospheric havoc on Mars causing mists and often violent global dust storms.

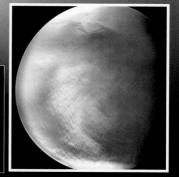

DUST RAGE
Planetwide dust storms are stirred by winds of more than 60 mph (96 km/h). The sand that covers Mars is very fine, and is easily whipped up to heights of 30 miles (48 km). The dust may shroud Mars for months before it settles to the surface.

SOIL SECRETS

THE ATMOSPHERE ABOVE THE YOUNG MARS MAY HAVE BEEN AS THICK AS EARTH'S AIR IS NOW. THE PROOF IS LOCKED AWAY IN THE RED SOIL THAT BLANKETS THE MARTIAN SURFACE (SHOWN HERE SAMPLED BY VIKING). LIQUID WATER RAN OVER MARS MILLIONS OF YEARS AGO. IN THE PROCESS, IT DISSOLVED MUCH OF THE CARBON DIOXIDE ATMOSPHERE AND TRAPPED IT WITHIN THE ROCKS AND SOIL.

WATER ON MARS

The Italian astronomer Giovanni Schiaparelli (1835–1910) started a myth when he said he'd seen canali (channels) on Mars. These were later found to be an optical illusion as well as a scientific impossibility—spectroscopic analysis of light from Mars showed a dry place with so little atmosphere that water would have boiled away instantly. Yet Mars wasn't always a desert. Space probes have discovered the remains of dried-up riverbeds, channels carved by water, flood plains and shallow seas, so what happened in the distant past to freeze-dry the entire planet?

EVIDENCE FOR WATER

1. **The Poles:** . . . . The south pole is almost entirely frozen CO_2 but the north pole is mainly water ice.

2. **Cirrus Clouds:** . . . . These clouds are formed by water ice crystals around 10 miles (16 km) up.

3. **Frost:** . . . . Frost appears on crater floors in the morning on Mars.

4. **Eroded Craters:** . . Older craters have been smoothed out by water flow.

5. **Chaotic Terrain:** . . Subsidence and scattered boulders indicate massive flood channels.

6. **Dry Rivers:** . . . . . . Formed by tributaries, these dry river channels end in deltas.

7. **Salts:** . . . . Soils examined by the Viking probe were as much as 20% water-deposited salts.

8. **Shallow Sea:** . . . . . The northern hemisphere is marked by the possible remains of an ancient ocean.

9. **Rounded Stones:** . These were seen by the Pathfinder probe in the Ares Vallis flood plain.

10. **Mars Meteorites:** . Apart from suspected "microfossils," Martian meteorites also show signs of water.

FROZEN IN TIME

Planetary scientists were slow to discover Mars' secret history. The first probes to fly past the Red Planet returned only a handful of images, which showed Moon-like cratered plains. And when Mariner 9 orbited Mars in 1971, it took many months for the spacecraft to begin mapping the planet—almost all of Mars' features were obscured by a global dust storm. But when the storm eventually cleared, Mariner 9's pictures proved to be worth the wait. They showed enormous volcanoes, far bigger than any found on Earth. They also showed a multitude of features that suggested liquid water had once scoured the planet's surface. These included vast canyons, eroded craters, chaotic terrain of broken rock caused by sudden flooding, and long, riverlike channels fed by tributaries that run downhill.

Although some researchers tried to dismiss this evidence, suggesting other processes such as lava flows that might have caused erosion, successive spacecraft have only strengthened the evidence for a once-watery Mars. Orbiter spacecraft such as the Vikings, Mars Global Surveyor, and Mars Express have provided ever-clearer images of water-formed features, while Mars rovers—in particular Spirit and Curiosity, which landed in 2012—have discovered minerals in the Martian soil that could only have formed if the surface was submerged for sustained periods of time. Astronomers still argue over the extent of the water, though—some imagine short-lived temporary lakes on the surface, but others suggest Mars was once a blue planet, with a great ocean, the Oceanus Borealis.

Another question is when and how the water disappeared. One suggestion is that radiation from the Sun was able to break up water molecules in the atmosphere, and because of the weak gravity, light hydrogen atoms were then carried away by the solar wind. Another idea is that the water remains in underground reservoirs. In 2002, the Mars Odyssey probe detected the signature from massive amounts of water ice just below the surface around both the north and south poles.

On Earth, the geological process of plate tectonics recycles carbonates from rocks into the air, as continental plate movements redistribute the molten mantle.

Mars lacked the energy for this process. If carbon and oxygen from the air got chemically locked into the Martian rocks, they stayed there—shrinking the atmosphere further. In a reverse greenhouse effect, the thinner the atmosphere got, the colder it became. Perhaps two billion years ago, much of the remaining atmosphere became frozen carbon dioxide—or dry ice—and the last of the water retreated below the surface, finding refuge at the planet's poles.

DELATA GROOVES

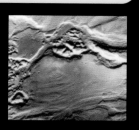

THE MARINER 9 SPACECRAFT BROUGHT BACK THE FIRST PICTURES OF MANGALA VALLIS—A 370-MILE (595-KM), WATER-CARVED OUTFLOW CHANNEL RUNNING ACROSS MARS' SOUTHERN HEMISPHERE. THE CHANNEL IS PROBABLY THE PRODUCT OF MASSIVE FLOODING BY WATER THAT BROKE THROUGH FROM BENEATH THE PLANET'S SURFACE CRUST. JUST LIKE A RIVER ON EARTH, IT BEGINS WITH A NETWORK OF TRIBUTARIES, WHICH THEN MEET IN A NARROW MAIN CHANNEL. THIS RUNS DOWNHILL, EVENTUALLY THICKENING OUT AT THE MOUTH (SEE ABOVE) LIKE A TERRESTRIAL RIVER DELTA. STRUCK BY ITS SIMILARITY IN SIZE AND SHAPE TO THE GREATEST RIVER ON EARTH, SCIENTISTS DECIDED TO NAME ITS DOWNSTREAM PLAIN AMAZONIS PLANITIA.

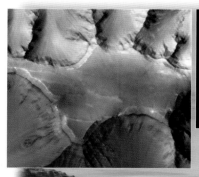

LAYERED ROCK
This image from the Mars Global Surveyor spacecraft shows layered rock in the Coprates Catena area, which lies at the center of the massive Valles Marineris canyon. Layered rock on Earth, such as that found in Arizona's Grand Canyon, is often the result of sediment deposited by ancient lakes.

ISLANDS
The water that carved channels to the north and east of the vast Valles Marineris canyon had huge erosive power. One consequence was the formation of streamlined islands where the water encountered obstacles. This image shows islands formed as the water was diverted by large craters in its path.

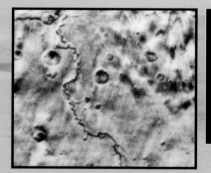

TRIBUTARIES
This Viking image of the Nirgil Vallis canyon shows tributaries off the main channel. They were probably formed by springs located on cliffs overlooking the canyon. As the water weakened the cliffs, they eventually collapsed. Each collapse forged a new tributary, which grew longer as the spring maintained it.

JUPITER

The king of the planets, giant Jupiter orbits the Sun far beyond Mars and the asteroid belt. Yet despite its great distance, it shines brilliantly in Earth's skies, and is frequently the brightest planet apart from Venus. Jupiter's brightness is largely due to its size—its diameter is nearly twelve times that of Earth. Unlike the inner planets, however, this giant world is composed almost entirely of gas—largely the same light hydrogen gas that makes up the Sun itself, but with an upper layer of more complex chemical compounds that have brought about chaotic and colorful weather systems such as the famous "Great Red Spot," a storm large enough to swallow Earth whole. Deeper inside the planet, the hydrogen gas is compressed to liquid form, while at the center there may be an Earth-sized planet, crushed under the weight of the huge atmospheric envelope. Like all the outer planets, Jupiter has a large family of satellites, dominated by Io, Europa, Ganymede, and Callisto, each of which is about the size of our own Moon or slightly larger. These four giant satellites, discovered by Italian astronomer Galileo in the 1600s and often called the Galilean moons, are complex worlds in their own right.

The first true-color photograph of Jupiter taken with the Wide Field Planetary Camera on the Hubble Space Telescope. Cloud formations in the atmosphere of Jupiter, containing small crystals of frozen ammonia and compounds of carbon, sulfur, and phosphorus, create the colorful belts and whorls. The temperatures of Jupiter's clouds are extremely cold, about −280°F (−173°C).

JUPITER

The fifth planet from the Sun, the mighty Jupiter is by far the largest in the solar system. Over 1,300 Earths could fit inside it, and it is more than twice as massive as all the other planets put together. Jupiter has a complex weather system, which generates the bands of clouds that swirl across its surface and also includes the planet's best-known feature, the Great Red Spot—itself up to three times the size of Earth. Like its neighbors in the outer solar system, Jupiter has rings. It also has at least 63 moons, which have been likened to a miniature solar system.

JUPITER PROFILE

JUPITER		EARTH
88,846 miles (142,983 km)	DIAMETER	7,973 miles (12,831 km)
3° 10'	AXIS TILT	23° 27'
4,329 days (11.86 Earth years)	LENGTH OF YEAR	365 days
9 hours 55 minutes 29 seconds	LENGTH OF DAY	24 hours
483.7 million miles (778.4 million km)	DISTANCE FROM SUN	93.5 million miles (150 million km)
−186°F (−85°C)	SURFACE TEMPERATURE	59°F (15°C)
2.53 G	SURFACE GRAVITY	1 G
HYDROGEN (90%), HELIUM (10%), METHANE (0.07%)	ATMOSPHERE	NITROGEN (79%), OXYGEN (21%)
700 millibars	ATMOSPHERIC PRESSURE	1,000 millibars
HYDROGEN (90%), HELIUM (10%), METHANE (0.07%)	COMPOSITION	SILICON (60%), ALUMINUM (15%)

GIANT PLANET

Like the other gas giants of the solar system—Saturn, Uranus and Neptune—Jupiter has no solid surface. The planet has a rocky core, but most of it consists of gases that become more and more dense toward the center until they eventually turn to liquid. The striking patterns observed by space probes and telescopes are not surface features but clouds. Their bands, swirls and eddies are the outward signs of the immensely powerful weather engine that drives Jupiter's atmosphere.

The clouds have arranged themselves into 19 clearly defined bands in shades of red, amber and brown. The winds in adjacent bands blow in opposite directions at speeds of 250 mph (400 km/h) or more. The cloud bands are probably the outer surfaces of thick layers of atmospheric material that rotate around the planet and extend deep into its interior. The bands themselves are remarkably stable. Although the cloud patterns within them are constantly changing, there are

features in Jupiter's cloudscapes that have been there for many years, or even centuries. The best-known of them is the aptly named Great Red Spot, a vast anticyclonic storm up to three times the size of the Earth and has existed for at least 300 years.

Jupiter's atmosphere is about 5,000 miles (8,050 km) thick and consists mostly of hydrogen. There is also some helium and small quantities of methane and ammonia, plus traces of other compounds. Beneath these gases

is an ocean of hot liquid hydrogen. Even at more than 3,150°F (1,732°C), the hydrogen does not boil away: It is kept under a pressure that measures some 90,000 times that of the atmosphere on Earth.

Jupiter's liquid hydrogen layer is over 30,000 miles (48,280 km) thick. Far beneath it, under what scientists believe may be a layer of water and ammonia, is a rocky core measuring around 4,200 miles (6,760 km) across.

Deep within the planet, the pressure reaches 45 million Earth atmospheres and temperatures rise to more than 20,000°F (11,000°C). Under these extreme conditions, the liquid hydrogen takes on some of the characteristics of a metal: Electric currents flow through it and generate Jupiter's magnetic field, which, after the Sun's, is the strongest in the solar system.

KINGS OF GODS

JUPITER IS NAMED FOR THE KING OF THE ROMAN GODS, WHO IS USUALLY DEPICTED HURLING A THUNDERBOLT. HE WAS ALSO KNOWN AS JOVE AND, TO THE ANCIENT GREEKS, AS ZEUS. THE PLANET'S MOONS ARE NAMED FOR OTHER CHARACTERS IN THE GREEK MYTHS OF ZEUS, MOST OF THEM HIS LOVERS.

BETHLEHEM'S STAR?

THE STAR OF BETHLEHEM MAY HAVE BEEN THE CONJUNCTION (COMING TOGETHER) IN THE SKY OF JUPITER AND ONE OR MORE OF THE OTHER BRIGHT PLANETS. SEVERAL CONJUNCTIONS OCCURRED AROUND THE TIME THE "STAR" IS SAID TO HAVE APPEARED.

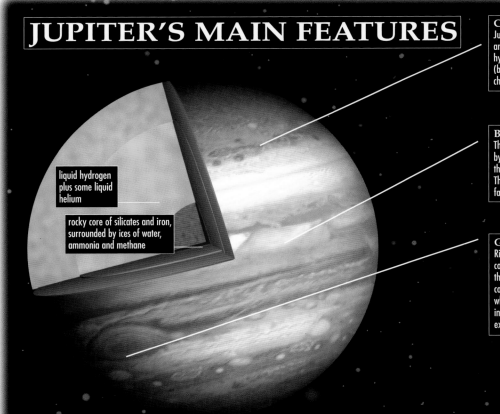

JUPITER'S MAIN FEATURES

CLOUD LAYERS
Jupiter has three layers of clouds, made of ammonia ice crystals (top), ammonium hydrosulfide (middle) and ice and water (bottom). The different colors are due to chemical reactions in the atmosphere.

BANDS
The moving bands of clouds are driven by convection currents that result from the heat generated within the planet. These currents create alternate rising and falling regions in the atmosphere.

GREAT RED SPOT
Rising currents of gas spiral counterclockwise into the spot and then sink again. The spot gets its color from phosphine. This chemical, which is drawn up from lower down in the atmosphere, turns red when exposed to sunlight.

liquid hydrogen plus some liquid helium

rocky core of silicates and iron, surrounded by ices of water, ammonia and methane

JUPITER'S ATMOSPHERE

Jupiter is the largest planet in the solar system—bigger than all the others put together—and its weather is on a scale to match. Turbulent winds, fierce lightning and raging storms keep the atmosphere constantly churning. Three multicolored cloud layers wrap the entire globe in ever-changing, swirling patterns, rotating in bands that move either with or against the planet's spin. The Voyager and Galileo probes have sent back vivid pictures and valuable data that reveal the complexity of Jupiter's atmosphere.

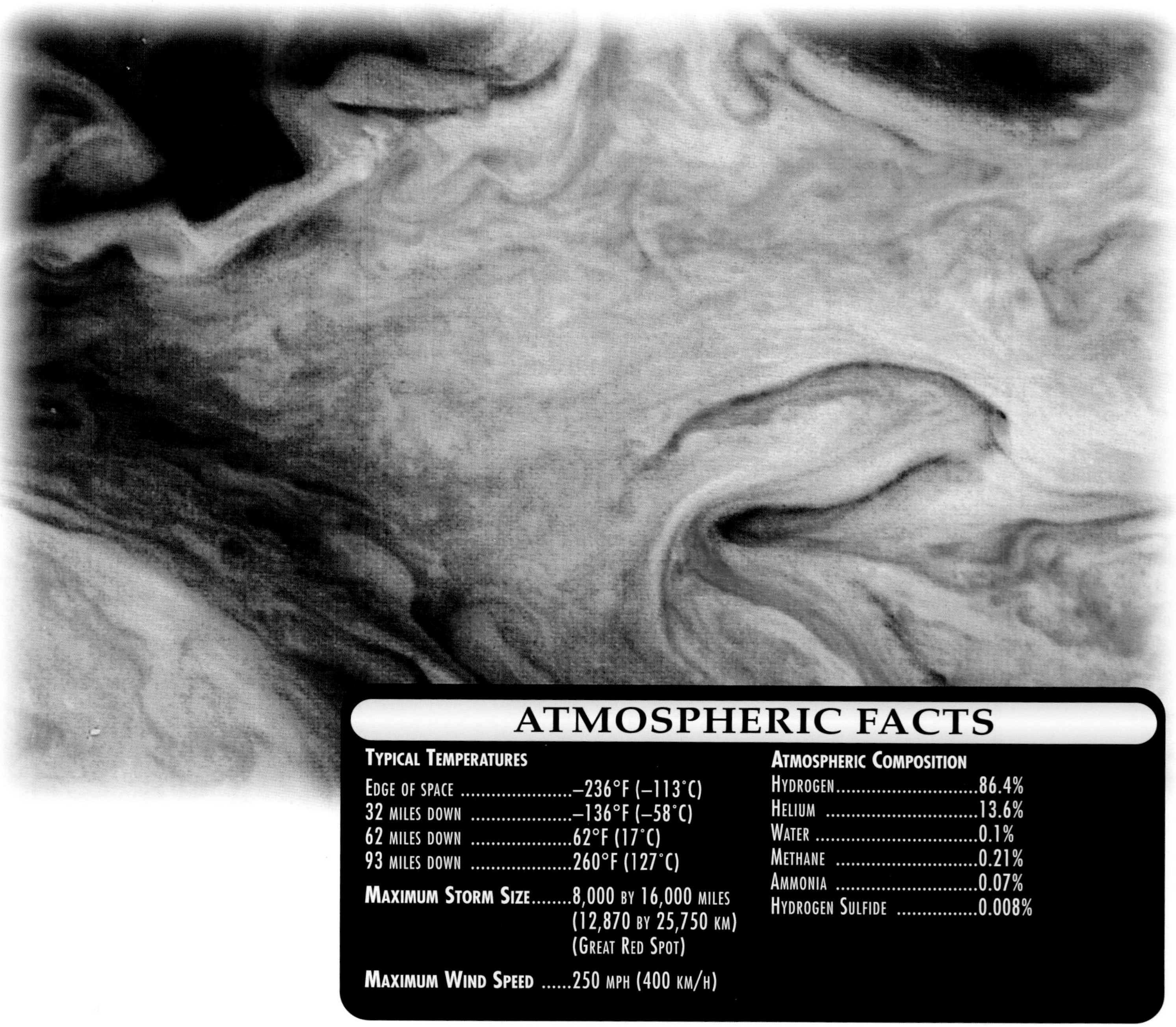

ATMOSPHERIC FACTS

TYPICAL TEMPERATURES

EDGE OF SPACE	−236°F (−113°C)
32 MILES DOWN	−136°F (−58°C)
62 MILES DOWN	62°F (17°C)
93 MILES DOWN	260°F (127°C)

MAXIMUM STORM SIZE........8,000 BY 16,000 MILES
(12,870 BY 25,750 KM)
(GREAT RED SPOT)

MAXIMUM WIND SPEED ......250 MPH (400 KM/H)

ATMOSPHERIC COMPOSITION

HYDROGEN	86.4%
HELIUM	13.6%
WATER	0.1%
METHANE	0.21%
AMMONIA	0.07%
HYDROGEN SULFIDE	0.008%

LIQUID SKY

Like all the gas giants, Jupiter is a spinning sphere of liquid. There is no "surface" at the planet's center—the atmosphere simply gets thicker the deeper it goes, until the pressure is so great that it causes gases to turn into liquid, becoming unlike anything we would call an atmosphere.

Jupiter's atmosphere is made up mainly of hydrogen with lesser amounts of helium, making it very similar to the Sun: If it were a lot bigger, nuclear reactions could start in Jupiter's center and cause it to burn like a star. It is the smaller amounts of heavier elements that cause cloud layers to form high in the atmosphere.

The winds are much stronger on Jupiter than on Earth. Without geographical features to get in the way, the winds whip around the huge globe in distinct weather bands. These bands stay in the same latitudes and have done so for at least 90 years—as long as astronomers have been using modern telescopes.

STORMY WEATHER

Jupiter is famous for the storms that move relentlessly within the different bands. But the most famous storm of all, the Great Red Spot, is big enough to hold up to three whole Earths and has been twirling around Jupiter for at least 150 years—and shows no signs of disappearing. Just as on Earth, Jupiter's violent weather is powered by heat. As gas warms, it expands and rises, creating eddies and swirls. Warm plumes rising from Jupiter's boiling interior cause storms. In turn, these storms create turbulence that powers the banded jet streams in their endless rotation.

The space age may have revealed many new aspects of Jupiter's atmosphere, but there is still much more to learn.

WHAT IF?
...WE COULD WATCH THE GALILEO PROBE DESCEND?

December 7, 1995: Galileo has just woken from cruising mode. It soon begins a kamikaze dive into Jupiter's atmosphere, falling at a top speed of 106,000 mph (170,590 km/h), causing the plasma in its path to heat to a temperature of 28,000°F (15,537°C).

Parachutes deploy after 170 seconds and the probe begins a more leisurely descent. Swirling layers of cloud and ammonia icemean the temperature dips to a frigid –238°F (–114°C), but it will increase as the probe continues its descent. As it drops deeper, the winds become fiercer, and the probe is buffeted mercilessly.

Sinking deeper still, the probe is now getting very hot. Eventually, having traveled 400 miles (645 km) through the atmosphere, it ceases to transmit. A few miles farther down, the probe starts to melt. But far above, the waiting orbiter has received its signals—the first ever sent from inside a gas giant and prepares to beam them back to the Earth.

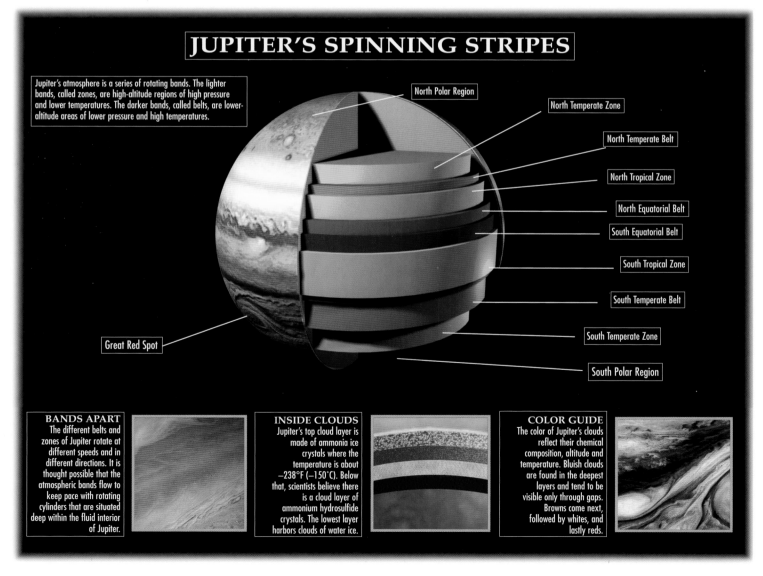

JUPITER'S SPINNING STRIPES

Jupiter's atmosphere is a series of rotating bands. The lighter bands, called zones, are high-altitude regions of high pressure and lower temperatures. The darker bands, called belts, are lower-altitude areas of lower pressure and high temperatures.

North Polar Region

North Temperate Zone

North Temperate Belt

North Tropical Zone

North Equatorial Belt

South Equatorial Belt

South Tropical Zone

South Temperate Belt

South Temperate Zone

South Polar Region

Great Red Spot

BANDS APART
The different belts and zones of Jupiter rotate at different speeds and in different directions. It is thought possible that the atmospheric bands flow to keep pace with rotating cylinders that are situated deep within the fluid interior of Jupiter.

INSIDE CLOUDS
Jupiter's top cloud layer is made of ammonia ice crystals where the temperature is about –238°F (–150°C). Below that, scientists believe there is a cloud layer of ammonium hydrosulfide crystals. The lowest layer harbors clouds of water ice.

COLOR GUIDE
The color of Jupiter's clouds reflect their chemical composition, altitude and temperature. Bluish clouds are found in the deepest layers and tend to be visible only through gaps. Browns come next, followed by whites, and lastly reds.

105

JUPITER'S MOON SYSTEM

A grand total of 67 moons are known to orbit the giant planet Jupiter. The four largest moons were discovered by Galileo in the 17th century, but nearly 300 years passed before the fifth was found. Amalthea—and Jupiter's other small moons—proved to be nothing like the larger Galilean satellites. The lumpy, irregularly shaped objects are more like asteroids than moons and they may well be captured asteriods. Their tiny size and great distance from Earth make them hard to study: Only visits by the Voyager 1 and Galileo spacecraft have revealed any of their features.

MINOR MOON ROUNDUP

Name	Diameter	Mean Distance from Center of Jupiter	Orbital Inclination	Discovery Date
Metis	37 x 21 miles (60 x 34 km)	79,510 miles (127,960 km)	0°*	1979
Adrastea	16 x 12 x 9 miles (26 x 19 x 14 km)	80,140 miles	0°*	1979
Amalthea	155 x 80 miles (249 x 129 km)	112,650 miles	0.4°	1892
Thebe	72 x 52 miles (116 x 84 km)	137,880 miles	0.8°*	1979
Leda	68 miles (109 km)	6,893,000 miles	27°	1974
Himalia	106 miles (171 km)*	7,133,000 miles	28°	1904
Lysithea	15 miles (24 km) *	7,282,000 miles	29°	1938
Elara	50 miles (80 km)*	7,293,000 miles	28°	1905
Ananke	12 miles (19 km)*	13,200,000 miles	147°	1951
Carme	19 miles (31 km)*	14,000,000 miles	163°	1938
Pasiphae	22 miles (35 km)*	14,600,000 miles	148°	1908
Sinope	17 miles (27 km)*	14,700,000 miles	153°	1914

*UNCERTAIN

JUPITER'S DISORDERLY MOONS

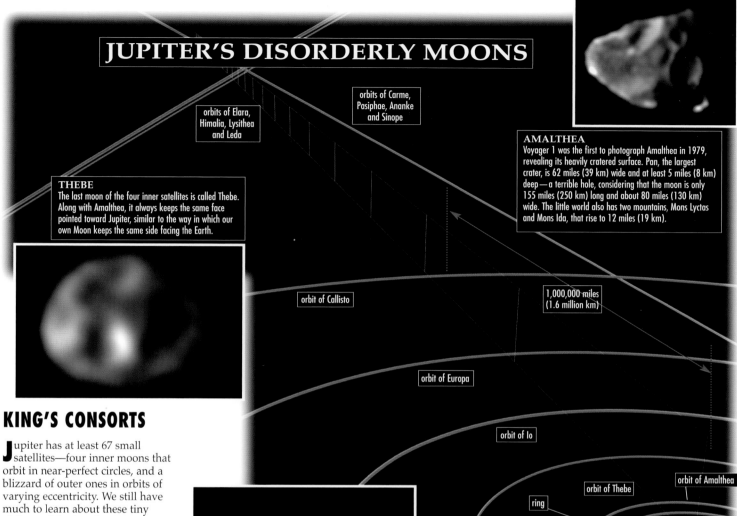

orbits of Elara, Himalia, Lysithea and Leda

orbits of Carme, Pasiphae, Ananke and Sinope

AMALTHEA
Voyager 1 was the first to photograph Amalthea in 1979, revealing its heavily cratered surface. Pan, the largest crater, is 62 miles (39 km) wide and at least 5 miles (8 km) deep—a terrible hole, considering that the moon is only 155 miles (250 km) long and about 80 miles (130 km) wide. The little world also has two mountains, Mons Lyctas and Mons Ida, that rise to 12 miles (19 km).

THEBE
The last moon of the four inner satellites is called Thebe. Along with Amalthea, it always keeps the same face pointed toward Jupiter, similar to the way in which our own Moon keeps the same side facing the Earth.

orbit of Callisto

1,000,000 miles (1.6 million km)

orbit of Europa

orbit of Io

orbit of Thebe

orbit of Amalthea

ring

orbits of Adrastea and Metis

Jupiter

METIS & ADRASTEA
Closest to Jupiter are Metis (right) and tiny Adrastea (above). These moons orbit within the gas giant's faint rings, and astronomers believe they could have been responsible for the formation of the main ring belt. Images taken by Galileo's namesake space probe suggest that Jupiter's rings are composed of the dust blasted into space by meteorites as they crashed into the little moons.

KING'S CONSORTS

Jupiter has at least 67 small satellites—four inner moons that orbit in near-perfect circles, and a blizzard of outer ones in orbits of varying eccentricity. We still have much to learn about these tiny siblings of the four large moons discovered by the astronomer Galileo. But by observing their orbits, analyzing their color and gleaning data from the few images we have, scientists are piecing together an ever-better understanding of them.

The largest and most photographed of the small satellites is Amalthea. The most surprising discovery has been the moon's color—Amalthea is the reddest object in the solar system. Astronomers believe the color comes from a layer of sulfur ejected from Io's violent volcanoes. The extremely active Io hurls vast quantities of material into space, and its volcanic substances fall in a stream toward Jupiter. Caught in its path, Amalthea is splattered red. But even odder than its red coating are the mysterious green patches that appear on the major slopes. At present, these are unexplained.

Thebe, Metis and Adrastea, the remaining inner moons, were caught on camera by Voyager 1 during its 1979 flyby of Jupiter, but were not photographed properly

until the Galileo probe arrived in the 1990s.

Around the same time, improvements to Earth-based telescopes led to a boom in the numbers of irregular outer satellites known to orbit all of the outer planets. We know even less about Jupiter's outer moons, orbiting beyond Callisto, than we do about the inner moons. One group, clustered at about 7 million miles (11.2 million km) from Jupiter, circle in the normal direction—that is, the same way the planet spins. An outer group of moons lying at

about 14 million miles (22 million km) have wild, elliptical orbits and retrograde rotation—in other words, they orbit backward. This backward motion adds weight to the theory that Jupiter's small outer moons are captured asteroids. An asteroid could have come from any direction, and would have had a 50% chance of ending up in a backward orbit. Moons that formed along with their parent planet, on the other hand, orbit in the same direction as the planet rotates. It could be that a large asteroid hurtled toward Jupiter and broke

into four pieces before being thrown backward into orbit.

Scientists also think the outer moons are former asteroids because they appear to be rich in carbon, or carbonaceous. A group of carbonaceous asteroids known as the Trojans travel in the same orbit as Jupiter, but always ahead of, or behind, the planet by 60° of the orbit. So the moons could well be escaped Trojans. However, we may have to wait many years before another robot visitor to the Jupiter system can help us shed more light on the problem of the moons' origins. NASA's New Horizons probe flew past Jupiter and its moons in February 2007 on its way to explore the dwarf planet Pluto, but it might yet be some time in the future before another robotic visitor arrives on the scene specifically to take the pictures of the other outer worlds.

SATURN

S aturn was the outermost planet known before the invention of the telescope, and is famous for its spectacular system of rings, discovered by Galileo in the early 1600s but not properly described until they were observed by Dutch astronomer Christiaan Huygens in 1656. The rings are now known to consist of billions of icy fragments, each in an independent orbit around the planet. They may be fragments of a comet broken up by Saturn's enormous gravity, or by a collision with one of the planet's huge family of moons. Saturn itself is a smaller version of Jupiter, similar in composition, though with a layer of haze in its upper atmosphere that masks the activity of its active weather systems. The satellite system contains a variety of very different icy satellites, dominated by Titan, a moon larger than the planet Mercury and dwarf planet Pluto, with a complex atmospheric system driven by the chemical compound methane.

This image of Saturn's south pole and the southern side of the planet's rings was produced by Hubble's Wide Field Planetary Camera using 30 different color filters. Filtering and combining different wavelengths of light allows researchers to better interpret data to unveil the secrets of Saturn.

SATURN

aturn is an enormous globe of whirling gas—it is made almost entirely of hydrogen and helium—that sits at the center of a complex system of rings and at least 62 moons. The planet and its companions are almost a solar system in miniature. Saturn's rings, which are composed of billions of separate particles and are usually visible in even a small telescope, long ago earned the planet the title "jewel of the solar system." But it was not until the Voyager probes reached the planet in the 1970s that astronomers (and everyone else who marveled at the glorious images) were able to take a closer look at the ringed planet and begin to unlock its mysteries.

SATURN PROFILE

SATURN		EARTH
74,898 MILES (120,537 KM)	DIAMETER	7,973 MILES (12,831 KM)
26° 42'	AXIS TILT	23° 27'
10,760 DAYS (29.46 EARTH YEARS)	LENGTH OF YEAR	365 DAYS
10 HOURS 39.4 MINUTES	LENGTH OF DAY	24 HOURS
888 MILLION MILES (14.3 MILLION KM)	DISTANCE FROM SUN	93.5 MILLION MILES (150 MILLION KM)
−292°F (−144°C)	SURFACE TEMPERATURE	59°F (15°C)
0.93 G	SURFACE GRAVITY	1 G
HYDROGEN (97%) HELIUM (3%) METHANE (0.05%)	ATMOSPHERE	NITROGEN (80%), OXYGEN (19%)
1,400 MILLIBARS	ATMOSPHERIC PRESSURE	1,000 MILLIBARS
HYDROGEN (97%) HELIUM (3%) METHANE (0.05%)	COMPOSITION	SILICON (60%), ALUMINUM (15%)

LORD OF THE RINGS

Ever since Galileo pointed his crude telescope at the giant planet back in 1610, Saturn's extraordinary rings have been recognized as a marvel of the solar system. But the planet itself, although less spectacular, is almost as extraordinary. Second only to Jupiter in scale, it is 750 times the size of the Earth.

From space, we can observe only the cloud tops of the giant planet, and even these are often obscured by a yellow haze. The entire atmosphere is divided into distinct bands, similar to Jupiter but not so clearly marked. These cloud bands whirl round the planet in jet streams blowing at up to 1,100 miles (1,770 km) an hour—10 times the speed of an earthly hurricane. Saturn's clouds are a bitterly cold –218°F (–103°C). Those we can see are no more than a frosting of ammonia ice on a huge mass of hydrogen and helium below.

There is nowhere on Saturn that could be described as a planetary surface. If we could send an indestructible space probe down through the clouds, it would record a steady increase in temperature and pressure. Thousands of miles down, the craft's barometer would register atmospheric pressure levels a million times higher than those on Earth. The temperature would rise to match, and would soon reach thousands of degrees.

In such extreme conditions, the hydrogen that makes up much of Saturn's atmosphere behaves very strangely. No longer a gas, it turns into something resembling a liquid metal, capable of conducting electricity. But there is no distinct threshold where atmospheric gas ends and an ocean of liquid hydrogen begins. It is likely that beneath the liquid hydrogen is probably a small core of rock, itself in a liquid state.

RINGS AND MOONS

Everything beneath Saturn's cloud tops is hidden from sight. Most of what we know about its interior has been deduced from what we can see of the cloud tops and what we have learned about how the planet behaves.

There is nothing hidden about the rings. Yet these present puzzles of their own. They are composed of billions of little fragments, mainly of ice, ranging from sand-grain size to lumps as big as a house. All of them orbit independently, engaged in an almost fantastically complex dance that is brought to some kind of order by the gravitational pull of Saturn's moons.

These, too, hold unsolved mysteries. Why is Iapetus half-blackened, and how did little Mimas acquire a crater a third the size of the entire moon? The Cassini spacecraft, which arrived at Saturn in 2004, is helping to solve some of these mysteries through a series of flybys of the Saturnian moons, currently expected to last until 2017.

FLOATER

SATURN IS THE ONLY PLANET IN THE SOLAR SYSTEM LESS DENSE THAN WATER. IF YOU COULD FIND A TUB BIG ENOUGH TO DUNK IT IN, THE GIANT WOULD FLOAT ON THE TOP LIKE AN APPLE IN A WATER BARREL. IN FACT, AT ONLY 69% THAT OF FRESH WATER, SATURN'S AVERAGE DENSITY IS MUCH THE SAME AS MANY APPLES. BY COMPARISON, THE EARTH IS ALMOST EIGHT TIMES AS DENSE AS ITS MUCH BIGGER NEIGHBOR.

SQUASHED

SATURN IS THE MOST FLATTENED PLANET IN THE SOLAR SYSTEM. ITS DIAMETER AT THE EQUATOR IS 74,898 MILES (120,540 KM), BUT ONLY 67,560 MILES (108,730 KM) MEASURED POLE TO POLE. THE EQUATORIAL BULGE IS CAUSED BY THE CENTRIFUGAL FORCE OF THE PLANET'S RAPID ROTATION: SATURN MAKES A COMPLETE REVOLUTION IN JUST 10.5 HOURS. EVEN OUR SLOWER-TURNING EARTH HAS A SLIGHT BULGE AT THE EQUATOR, AND EARTH IS A RIGID, ROCKY WORLD, NOT A GIANT BALL OF GAS.

SATURN'S MOONS

PORTRAIT OF A GIANT

IAPETUS
In a contrast as startling as soot on snow, half of the 900-mile-diameter (1,450-km-diameter) moon is dark and half bright. The dark hemisphere always leads in Iapetus' orbit around Saturn. The "soot" is probably a thin layer of space debris.

TETHYS
A ball of near-pure ice, Tethys has a 1,200-mile (1,930-km) chasm running over its cratered surface. It may be the result of water freezing inside the moon and cracking its crust.

DIONE
At almost the same distance from Saturn as the Moon is from Earth, Dione orbits well within the ring system. Its icy surface shows distinct cratering, as well as odd wispy features that may be a sign of new ice pushing its way out of an active interior.

Tethys' shadow

ENCELADUS
The brightest moon in the solar system, Enceladus reflects almost 100% of the sunlight that reaches it. Since it absorbs so little, its surface is the coldest part of Saturn's system, with a temperature of –392°F (–200°C). Tides driven by Saturn's gravity may stir the moon's interior.

SATURN'S ATMOSPHERE

Saturn's atmosphere is in some ways a low-contrast version of Jupiter's. The two gas giants show marked banding and oval-shape storms, but the colors on Saturn are much more muted. Both planets' atmospheres have a high hydrogen content, but since Saturn's has not been investigated by a probe, astronomers do not know exactly what it contains and at what altitude. The biggest mystery on Saturn, though, is its winds. They are the fastest in the solar system and have a unique circulation pattern.

ATMOSPHERIC MAKEUP

Symbol	Name	Percentage (by number of molecules)
H2	Molecular hydrogen	97
He	Helium	3
H20	Water	Not yet measured
CH4	Methane	0.2
NH3	Ammonia	0.03
H2S	Hydrogen sulfide	Not yet measured

COLD SOUP

Saturn's atmosphere remains one of the mysteries of the solar system. But by comparing Saturn with Jupiter—whose atmosphere is better understood—and using data collected by Voyagers 1 and 2 and Pioneer 11, astronomers put the puzzle together.

The atmospheres of Jupiter and Saturn seem to be quite similar, each having clouds that encircle the planet in wide belts, parallel to the equator. Part of the reason for the banded structure is that these planets have a very rapid rotation—Saturn spins once every 10 hours 39.5 minutes—that stretches the clouds out. In addition to the banding, the clouds also exhibit an altitude dependence, existing in two or three separate and chemically distinct layers. On both planets the topmost layer is probably a cirrus-type cloud of ammonia (NH_3) ice crystals. On Saturn this may be thicker and relatively lower down than on Jupiter, giving Saturn's underlying cloud decks a washed-out appearance quite unlike the vivid bands of its brightly colored neighbor. Below the ammonia there is probably a layer of frozen ammonium hydrosulfide (NH_4HS) crystals, as there is on Jupiter, or perhaps a combination of water and ammonia.

Like Jupiter with its famous Great Red Spot, Saturn's atmosphere also plays host to some vast storm systems. The more frequent and smaller of these hurricane-like storms are thousands of miles in diameter, and vary in duration from days to years. They tend to form at the boundary between two bands of clouds.

TOO WINDY FOR STORMS

Some of Saturn's atmospheric phenomena are on an altogether vaster scale. At intervals of about 30 years, the planet suffers an outbreak of bright clouds just above the equator. The last outbreak began in September 1990. It rapidly spread around a third of the planet—some 75,000 miles (120,700 km). These events seem to coincide with summer in Saturn's northern hemisphere—but no one can yet explain why.

Such storms are eventually ripped apart by the terrific winds that tear around Saturn. Astronomers believe that the winds are partly a byproduct of the planet's convection system. The theory is that Saturn's interior cools enough for helium to condense out of the upper atmosphere and rain into the interior. As this rain falls, its gravitational energy is converted into heat, setting up giant convection currents that warm the outer portions of the planet in rising cells. These rising currents, whipped up by the planet's rapid rotation, contribute to the ferocity of the vicious winds.

SPIN CYCLE

SATURN OFTEN SHOWS GREAT OUTBREAKS OF WHITE STORM CLOUDS GENERATED WHEN AMMONIA ICE CRYSTALS CONDENSE IN UPDRAFTS OF WARMER AIR. ONE SUCH OUTBREAK IN THE 1790S ENABLED WILLIAM HERSCHEL, GERMAN-BORN ENGLISH ASTRONOMER (1738–1822; RIGHT), TO MAKE THE FIRST ESTIMATE OF SATURN'S ROTATION PERIOD. BUT BECAUSE SATURN'S CLOUDS ROTATE FASTER THAN THE PLANET ITSELF, HERSCHEL'S ESTIMATE WAS SLIGHTLY SHORT.

ATMOSPHERIC MYSTERIES

Saturn (below) as seen by the Hubble Space Telescope in October, 1990. The great white storm, which recurs about every 30 years, is clearly visible. The bright clouds, visible from Earth in amateur telescopes, are thought to consist of ammonia ice crystals.

MAGNETIC LIGHT
The Hubble Space Telescope captured this image (above) of Saturn's ultraviolet auroral rings in 1998. The planet has been revealed to have an enormous and powerful magnetic field.

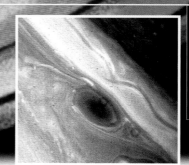

SPOT GAP
A brown spot (left) was photographed by the Voyager 2 probe in 1981. The feature is thought to have been caused by a downdraft that created a gap in the upper clouds, through which the darker clouds below were briefly revealed.

SATURN'S RINGS

Saturn's system of rings is one of the most beautiful sights in the solar system. The planet itself can be seen with the naked eye and the rings viewed through a small telescope. But to see the rings at their spectacular best, we on Earth must turn to the images returned by the Hubble Space Telescope and the two Voyager space probes. These show that instead of just the two big rings visible through a small telescope, there are thousands of narrow ringlets whose paths are guided by the gravity of nearby moons.

RING SIZE

DISTANCE OF INNERMOST (D) RING FROM SATURN	4,080 MILES (6,570 KM)
DISTANCE OF OUTERMOST (E) RING FROM SATURN	74,000 MILES (120,000 KM) (APPROX)
TOTAL SPAN OF RINGS	170,000 MILES (273,590 KM)
THICKNESS OF MAIN RINGS	100–3,000 FT (30–915 M)
NUMBER OF RINGS	7
NUMBER OF RINGLETS	10,000
WIDTH OF NARROWEST RINGLETS	TENS OF FT/M
TYPICAL SIZE RANGE OF RING PARTICLES	0.5 IN TO 20 FT (1.3 CM TO 6 M) ACROSS
ESTIMATED DISTANCE BETWEEN LARGER RING PARTICLES	30 FT (9 M)

SATURN'S GLORY

When the Italian astronomer Galileo Galilei studied Saturn in 1610, he saw what he thought were two large moons, one on each side of the planet. But in 1655, the Dutch astronomer Christiaan Huygens concluded that the "moons" Galileo had seen were actually a single, encircling ring structure. Huygens thought that this ring was solid and quite thick.

The first indication that Saturn had more than one ring came in 1676 when the Franco-Italian astronomer Giovanni Cassini observed two rings separated by a gap, rather than a single, solid ring. This gap, between what are now called the A and B rings, is named the Cassini Division. Another gap—in the outer part of the A Ring and now called the Encke Division—was discovered in 1837 by the German astronomer Johann Encke. Although he was the first to notice the gap, he thought it was a dark band.

RING STRUCTURE

Eventually, five rings—the A, B, C, D and E rings—were detected using Earth-based telescopes. A further ring, the F Ring, was discovered by the Pioneer 11 probe in 1979, and yet another, the G Ring, by the Voyager probes in 1980 and 1981.

Astronomers now believe that Saturn's rings are made up of belts of countless particles. Most of these particles range in size from minute grains of dust to snowflakes, but include some larger chunks of material that measure a few yards across. It is likely that many of the particles are ice, and studies by the Cassini spacecraft suggest they give an almost fluffy consistency.

Close-up pictures have revealed that Saturn's seven main rings are made up of thousands of thin ringlets. The "gaps" between the ringlets still contain particles, but because there are less of them, they reflect less light and so appear to be darker.

This profusion of ringlets and other mysterious structures suggests the process that causes the rings to keep their shape is extremely complex. Astronomers believe that it not only involves interactions between the ring particles themselves, but also the gravitational effects of Saturn's moons, some of which "shepherd" the rings to keep them in position.

How Saturn came to possess rings is also a mystery. Some experts believe that they are the remnants of a moon (or moons) that was unable to form because of the powerful gravitational field of Saturn itself. Another suggestion is that the rings are the result of some catastrophic impact, perhaps by an asteroid or a large comet that smashed into a moon orbiting Saturn and left broad bands of debris circling the planet. Yet another theory proposes that the rings are the icy remains of a giant comet that passed close enough to Saturn to be torn apart by the planet's gravity. We may never know for sure.

RING SHADOW

THE RINGS OF SATURN DO NOT EMIT LIGHT OF THEIR OWN, THEY MERELY REFLECT LIGHT FROM THE SUN. FOR THIS REASON, WHEN THEY ARE BACKLIT BY THE SUN, THEY APPEAR DARK. THE RINGS CONTAIN ENOUGH MATERIAL TO CAST A CLEARLY VISIBLE SHADOW ON SATURN. IF IT WERE POSSIBLE FOR YOU TO STAND ON SATURN, YOU WOULD SEE TWO TYPES OF SUNLIGHT: UNOBSTRUCTED SUNLIGHT WHEN THE RINGS WERE NOT IN THE WAY, AND DIFFUSE, RING-FILTERED LIGHT WHEN THEY WERE.

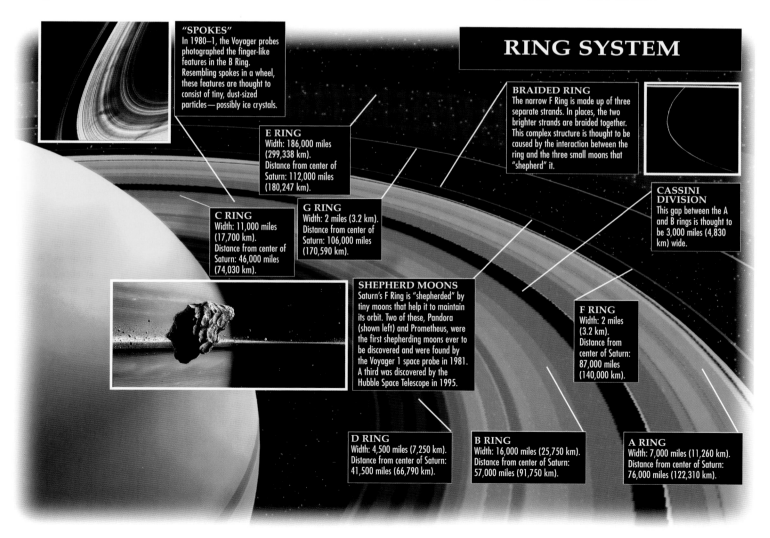

"SPOKES"
In 1980–1, the Voyager probes photographed the finger-like features in the B Ring. Resembling spokes in a wheel, these features are thought to consist of tiny, dust-sized particles—possibly ice crystals.

RING SYSTEM

BRAIDED RING
The narrow F Ring is made up of three separate strands. In places, the two brighter strands are braided together. This complex structure is thought to be caused by the interaction between the ring and the three small moons that "shepherd" it.

E RING
Width: 186,000 miles (299,338 km). Distance from center of Saturn: 112,000 miles (180,247 km).

C RING
Width: 11,000 miles (17,700 km). Distance from center of Saturn: 46,000 miles (74,030 km).

G RING
Width: 2 miles (3.2 km). Distance from center of Saturn: 106,000 miles (170,590 km).

CASSINI DIVISION
This gap between the A and B rings is thought to be 3,000 miles (4,830 km) wide.

SHEPHERD MOONS
Saturn's F Ring is "shepherded" by tiny moons that help it to maintain its orbit. Two of these, Pandora (shown left) and Prometheus, were the first shepherding moons ever to be discovered and were found by the Voyager 1 space probe in 1981. A third was discovered by the Hubble Space Telescope in 1995.

F RING
Width: 2 miles (3.2 km). Distance from center of Saturn: 87,000 miles (140,000 km).

D RING
Width: 4,500 miles (7,250 km). Distance from center of Saturn: 41,500 miles (66,790 km).

B RING
Width: 16,000 miles (25,750 km). Distance from center of Saturn: 57,000 miles (91,750 km).

A RING
Width: 7,000 miles (11,260 km). Distance from center of Saturn: 76,000 miles (122,310 km).

SATURN'S MOONS

The moons of Saturn are the most complex and fascinating group of satellites in the solar system. Dominated by mighty Titan, the family also includes the "classical" moons Mimas, Enceladus, Tethys, Dione, Rhea and Iapetus, plus at least 62 known moons.

Pictures returned by the Voyager missions in the early 1980s showed Saturn's moons to be cold, icy places that bear the scars of countless ancient impacts. But that's not to say that they are dull worlds: In fact, most of them have yet to reveal their inner secrets.

SATURN'S LARGER MOONS

Name	Diameter (miles/km)	Discovered by	Distance from Saturn (miles/km)	Name	Diameter (miles/km)	Discovered by	Distance from Saturn (miles/km)
Pan	12/19	Voyager 1, 1980	83,033/133,629	Telesto	15/24	Voyager 1, 1980	183,132/294,722
Atlas	21/32	Voyager 1, 1980	85,544/137,670	Calypso	16/26	Voyager 1, 1980	183,132/294,722
Prometheus	68/109	Voyager 1, 1980	86,607/139,380	Dione	695/1,118	J.-D. Cassini, 1684	234,516/377,417
Pandora	55/89	Voyager 1, 1980	88,067/128,855	Helene	20/32	Voyager 1, 1980	234,555/377,480
Epimetheus	75/120	Voyager 1, 1980	94,109/151,454	Rhea	951/1,530	J.-D. Cassini, 1672	327,503/527,065
Janus	118/190	Voyager 1, 1980	94,140/151,504	Titan	3,201/5,151	C. Huygens, 1655	759,385/1,222,112
Mimas	249/400	W. Herschel, 1789	115,282/185,528	Hyperion	174/280	Voyager 1, 1980	920,447/1,481,316
Enceladus	320/515	W. Herschel, 1789	147,906/238,032	Iapetus	910/1,465	J.-D. Cassini, 1671	2,212,992/3,561,353
Tethys	660/1,062	J.-D. Cassini, 1684	183,102/294,674	Phoebe	137/220	Voyager 1, 1980	8,049,720/12,954,769

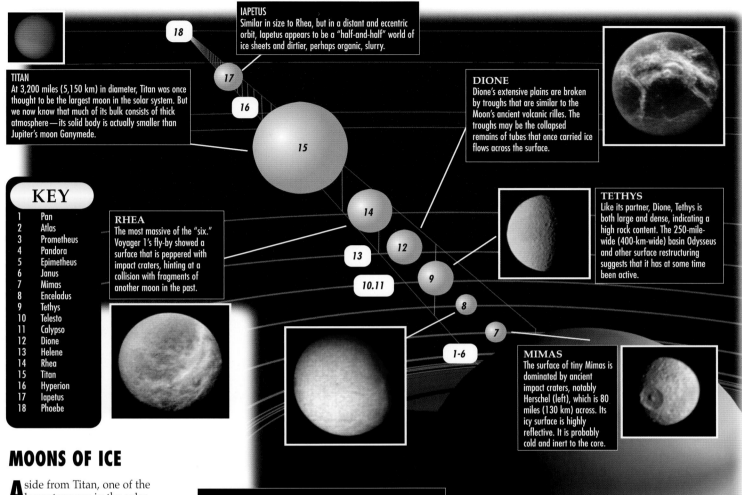

IAPETUS
Similar in size to Rhea, but in a distant and eccentric orbit, Iapetus appears to be a "half-and-half" world of ice sheets and dirtier, perhaps organic, slurry.

TITAN
At 3,200 miles (5,150 km) in diameter, Titan was once thought to be the largest moon in the solar system. But we now know that much of its bulk consists of thick atmosphere—its solid body is actually smaller than Jupiter's moon Ganymede.

DIONE
Dione's extensive plains are broken by troughs that are similar to the Moon's ancient volcanic rilles. The troughs may be the collapsed remains of tubes that once carried ice flows across the surface.

KEY

1	Pan
2	Atlas
3	Prometheus
4	Pandora
5	Epimetheus
6	Janus
7	Mimas
8	Enceladus
9	Tethys
10	Telesto
11	Calypso
12	Dione
13	Helene
14	Rhea
15	Titan
16	Hyperion
17	Iapetus
18	Phoebe

RHEA
The most massive of the "six." Voyager 1's fly-by showed a surface that is peppered with impact craters, hinting at a collision with fragments of another moon in the past.

TETHYS
Like its partner, Dione, Tethys is both large and dense, indicating a high rock content. The 250-mile-wide (400-km-wide) basin Odysseus and other surface restructuring suggests that it has at some time been active.

MIMAS
The surface of tiny Mimas is dominated by ancient impact craters, notably Herschel (left), which is 80 miles (130 km) across. Its icy surface is highly reflective. It is probably cold and inert to the core.

SATURN'S COURT

MOONS OF ICE

Aside from Titan, one of the largest moons in the solar system, Saturn's most interesting satellites are its "classical" moons—those discovered by the astronomers Jean-Dominique Cassini and William Herschel in the 17th and 18th centuries. These six moons form three pairs each of roughly equal size, and all of them bear the scars of ancient impacts that hint at the Saturn family's violent past. Consisting mostly of water and other ices, they are dark, frozen worlds where surface temperatures plummet below –300°F (–149°C).

Yet in spite of their uninviting and lifeless appearance, there are signs that some of these classical moons were once geologically active—and perhaps still are today. Pictures returned by the Voyager probes reveal evidence of fault lines that appear to have been plugged by fluid material from the satellites' interiors. Some of the moons also exhibit lava-like plains, similar to the mare on our own Moon, that appear to have flowed across the surface and covered up the more ancient impact craters.

The puzzle is how bodies that consist mostly of ice could display such apparently volcanic characteristics. In their search for an answer, astronomers have looked to the process that stops a car's radiator from freezing in winter. Just as antifreeze keeps water flowing at well below its normal freezing point, so the large amounts of ammonia thought to be locked up in Saturn's moons may have caused their ices to form a kind of frozen slurry.

VOLCANIC SLUSH

At the incredibly low temperatures that exist on Saturn's moons, icy slurry might behave like basalt lava. Requiring only minimal heat to get it moving, it could well up through cracks in the crust or creep across the surface like a giant glacier.

But where would the heat come from? Saturn's moons—like our own Moon—must have long since cooled down from the superhot maelstrom that formed them. On Earth, volcanism is driven by the heat of radioactive decay, which helps to keep the interior molten. But we have yet to find evidence of such decay among Saturn's moons—indeed, as far as the less dense bodies are concerned, it is questionable whether there is any rocky material under the ice at all.

A more likely explanation is that on some moons, the heat generated by impacts triggered the process now known as icy volcanism. Another possibility, especially on the inner moons, is that they were wrenched apart and heated by the tidal effects of Saturn's massive gravity, like Io—Jupiter's moon. The latest findings show amazing fissures at the south pole—the now famous "Tiger Stripes"—out of which shoot geysers of icy particles.

LUCKY BREAK

THE FRENCH-ITALIAN ASTRONOMER JEAN-DOMINIQUE CASSINI (1625–1712), DISCOVERER OF THE CLASSICAL MOONS IAPETUS, RHEA, TETHYS AND DIONE, FOUND HIS WAY INTO STARGAZING WHEN HE WAS HIRED TO WORK IN THE OBSERVATORY OF A WEALTHY NOBLEMAN, GATHERING INFORMATION FOR ASTROLOGICAL PREDICTIONS. ARMED WITH THE FINEST INSTRUMENTS OF THE DAY, PLUS A DESIRE TO PROVE THAT ASTROLOGY WAS NONSENSE, CASSINI BEGAN HIS OWN GROUND-BREAKING STUDY OF THE SKIES.

URANUS AND NEPTUNE

The solar system's two outer giants are near-identical twins, but with some major differences in their orbits. Uranus lies twice as far out as Saturn, and Neptune farther still. Both planets are sometimes called "ice giants"—considerably smaller than Jupiter and Saturn, they consist of a mix of chemical compounds such as methane, and their interiors are thought to take the form of slushy "ices" made up of these various compounds. Their composition also gives them their distinctive blue-green colour (though Neptune is significantly bluer). Aside from these similarities, the planets are very different. Uranus orbits the Sun "on its side," with its axis tilted so far from the vertical that parts of the planet experience days and nights lasting more than 40 years. Perhaps because of this, Uranus shows far less activity than Neptune, despite receiving far more heat from the Sun. Both planets have ring systems and large families of satellites, the largest of which is Neptune's giant icy moon Triton.

This computer-generated montage shows Neptune as it would appear from a spacecraft approaching Triton, Neptune's largest moon. Triton's surface is mostly covered by nitrogen frost mixed with traces of condensed methane, carbon dioxide, and carbon monoxide.

URANUS

The giant blue-green globe of Uranus is big enough to swallow the Earth 64 times over. It has a strong magnetic field, a family of at least 27 moons and, after Saturn, the most impressive system of rings in the solar system. Beneath its smooth-looking, almost featureless exterior, Uranus is essentially a fluid world. An atmosphere rich in hydrogen thickens imperceptibly, with no discernible break between gas and liquid, into a world-wide ocean where water and methane predominate.

URANUS PROFILE

URANUS		EARTH
31,673 MILES (50,973 KM)	DIAMETER	7,973 MILES (12,831 KM)
97° 55'	AXIS TILT	23° 27'
30,685 DAYS	LENGTH OF YEAR	365 DAYS
17 HOURS 14 MINUTES	LENGTH OF DAY	24 HOURS
1.78 BILLION MILES (2.86 BILLION KM)	DISTANCE FROM SUN	93.5 MILLION MILES (150 MILLION KM)
−365°F (−185°C) (CLOUD TOPS)	SURFACE TEMPERATURE	59°F (15°C)
0.92 G	SURFACE GRAVITY	1 G
HYDROGEN (82%), HELIUM (15%), METHANE (2%)	ATMOSPHERE	NITROGEN (80%), OXYGEN (19%)
0.1 MILLIBAR (CLOUD TOPS)	ATMOSPHERIC PRESSURE	1,000 MILLIBARS
WATER, AMMONIA, METHANE, MOLTEN ROCK, HYDROGEN, HELIUM	COMPOSITION	SILICON (60%), ALUMINUM (15%)
27	NUMBER OF MOONS	1

GREEN GIANT

Uranus is a giant planet—four times the diameter of the Earth—but it is so far away that it is all but invisible to the naked eye. So although the planets in the solar system out to Saturn have been known since antiquity, Uranus was not discovered until 1781. Its discovery doubled the dimensions of the known solar system, but astronomers knew little of this huge world until the Voyager 2 probe passed within 51,000 miles (82,077 km) of it on January 24, 1986—almost two centuries after its discovery.

The images sent back by Voyager were somewhat surprising. No surface details of Uranus can be seen from Earth, but even close up, Voyager could see only a featureless blue-green globe. The planet has none of the strikingly colored atmospheric bands typical of Saturn and Jupiter, even though, like these two worlds, its atmosphere is composed almost entirely of hydrogen and helium.

Voyager 2 did show that the atmosphere on Uranus has a band-like structure, but it can only be seen clearly in high-contrast false-color images. Uranus is so cold that its clouds form very low down, their colors hidden from view by the blue-green atmosphere above them.

LIQUID GAS

The interior of Uranus is also unlike those of Saturn and Jupiter, which consist mainly of hydrogen. Its density is higher, a sign that heavier gases and liquids are present. Although Uranus is often called a gas giant, its actual composition is almost certainly mainly liquid—hydrogen makes up only 15 percent of the planet's mass, compared with more than 80 percent of Jupiter's, and almost all of it is in the atmosphere. Uranus probably has a rocky core surrounded by an ocean of water, liquid methane and liquid hydrogen. The ocean—hot, under the prevailing pressure—gradually blends into the atmosphere. Like all the other gas giants, Uranus has no distinct surface to separate the point at which "air" becomes "ground."

The rings of Uranus were first seen in 1977 when the planet passed in front of a background star. The star appeared to flicker as it went behind the planet, a sign that something was blocking its light. Earth-bound telescopes detected a total of nine rings; the Voyager 2 mission found two more. They are all very narrow and dark, typically as black as coal; and like those of Saturn, the material they are made of ranges in size from dust specks to rocky lumps up to 30 ft (9 m) across. The innermost ring, designated 1986U2R by astronomers, is about 24,000 miles (38,620 km) from the center of Uranus. The outermost and brightest ring—Epsilon—is around 6,000 miles (9,650 km) farther out.

DISCOVERY

URANUS WAS DISCOVERED IN 1781 BY SIR WILLIAM HERSCHEL, A BRITISH MUSICIAN OF GERMAN ORIGIN. HE NAMED THE NEW FIND GEORGIUM SIDUS ("GEORGE'S STAR") FOR HIS PATRON, KING GEORGE III, BUT THE NAME WAS WIDELY CHALLENGED. GERMAN ASTRONOMER JOHANN BODE SUGGESTED THAT THE NEW PLANET BE CALLED URANUS, AND THIS NAME WAS OFFICIALLY ADOPTED IN 1850.

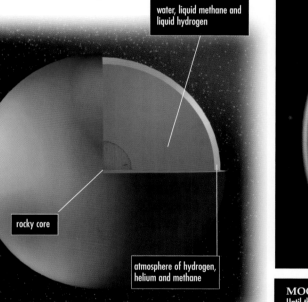

water, liquid methane and liquid hydrogen

rocky core

atmosphere of hydrogen, helium and methane

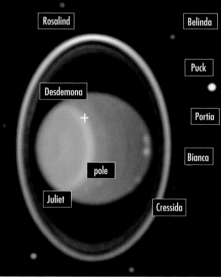

Rosalind

Belinda

Puck

Desdemona

Portia

Bianca

pole

Juliet

Cressida

MOONS
Until the Voyager 2 encounter with Uranus, only five moons of Uranus were known; two were found in 1787 (Titania and Oberon), two in 1850 (Ariel and Umbriel), and the last as recently as 1948 (Miranda). Most are named after characters from the works of William Shakespeare. Voyager 2 found another 10 (of which eight are visible in this false-color picture), and in 1997, Earth-based telescopes found 12 more, bringing the total up to 27.

RINGS
Uranus has 11 rings, nine of which were detected from Earth. The other two were discovered in 1986 by Voyager 2. This probe also found 10 new moons, two of which act as "shepherd moons" and keep the outer ring, Epsilon, in position.

URANUS: ITS RINGS AND MOONS

URANUS'S ATMOSPHERE

Aspace traveler hurtling by Uranus would see nothing but an inscrutable blue-green billiard ball: Without any surface markings, the planet wouldn't even appear to be rotating. But viewed through color filters at close range, or through the Hubble Space Telescope, atmospheric features such as racing wind bands and lethal clouds of methane gas begin to show themselves. Voyager 2's fly-by revealed that Uranus has certain similarities with its previous targets, Jupiter and Saturn—but also some important differences.

URANIAN ATMOSPHERE FACTS

THICKNESS	.4,500 MILES (7,242KM)
COMPOSITION	.HYDROGEN (83%) HELIUM (15%) METHANE AND OTHERS (2%)
WIND SPEEDS	.UP TO 400 MPH (644 KM/H)
MEAN SURFACE TEMPERATURE	.AROUND −320°F (−160°C)
MEAN SURFACE PRESSURE	.14.5 LB (6.6 KG) PER SQUARE IN (6.5 SQUARE CM)
PRESSURE AT AMMONIA CLOUD LAYER	.116 LB (32 KG) PER SQUARE IN (6.5 SQUARE CM)
PRESSURE AT WATER CLOUD LAYER	.1,740 LB (790 KG) PER SQUARE IN (6.5 SQUARE CM)
TEMPERATURE AT AMMONIA CLOUD LAYER	.AROUND −200°F (−93°C)
TEMPERATURE AT WATER CLOUD LAYER	.AROUND 35°F (1.6°C)
AVERAGE PLANETARY DENSITY	.0.047 LB PER CUBIC IN (0.0021 KG PER 6.5 CUBIC CM) (1.3 TIMES AS DENSE AS WATER)

COSMIC ICEBOX

Despite being classed as a "gas giant," Uranus bears little resemblance to those mighty gas-balls Jupiter and Saturn. Although the Uranian atmosphere is mainly hydrogen and helium—like all the gas giants— only part of the planet is composed of gas at all. Beneath Uranus' 4,500-mile (7,240-km)-thick gassy shroud, scientists believe there is a liquid mantle—a vast, scalding-hot ocean of methane, ammonia and water—and an Earth-sized rocky core. As a result, Uranus is sometimes described as a hybrid planet, partway between a gas giant and a rocky world like Earth. Of all the planets in the solar system, only Neptune closely resembles it.

As well as hydrogen and helium, the relatively thick atmosphere contains smaller amounts of methane and ammonia. The methane absorbs red wavelengths from the sunlight that shines on the outer atmosphere, which is what gives the planet its distinctive blue-green color.

During Voyager 2's encounter with Uranus in 1986, different colored filters were used on each of its eight cameras. This made it possible to photograph Uranus in more detail, and revealed icy clouds and fast winds. Uranus has three cloud decks, which include an upper one of methane ice, a middle layer of ammonia and a lower one of water ice. The lower two are permanently hidden by the methane layer. There is also a high-altitude haze layer above the methane clouds. Racing clouds showed that the winds blow mostly in the same direction as the planet rotates, but vary with latitude. Faint bands were also indicated, yet Voyager found no evidence of raging storms. Unless maelstroms of the type seen on Jupiter and Saturn are buried deep within the atmosphere where they can't be seen, we must assume that Uranian weather is fairly calm, probably due to the temperature.

Uranus is as chilly as Neptune, even though Neptune is 1.6 times farther from the Sun. Both planets have an average temperature of just –353°F (–178˚C). The only explanation for Uranus' mysterious lack of warmth is that, unlike the other gas giants, the planet generates little or no internal heat. On Jupiter, storms are thought to be powered by plumes of hot gas that rise from the interior, but Uranus seems to lack the means to stir up storms in this way.

Uranus also has unusual seasons. Because the planet is tipped on its side, it rolls around the Sun like a beer barrel rather than spinning like a top. During its 84-year-long orbit, the poles point at the Sun for a period of 42 years at a time. But its sunlit regions are actually colder than the night side—in the upper atmosphere, at least. The reasoning is complex, but scientists suspect that Uranus may behave like a giant refrigerator in which the Sun's energy somehow sets up flows of material within the planet's interior that cause it to lose heat. It is one of many oddities of Uranus that remain unexplained.

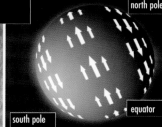

NOW VOYAGER

THE VOYAGER 2 FLYBY IN 1986 GAVE US VAST AMOUNTS OF DATA ON URANUS — MORE THAN HAD BEEN GATHERED IN OVER 200 YEARS OF GROUND-BASED OBSERVATION. VOYAGER DETECTED THE FIRST CLOUDS AND WINDS AND STUDIED THE PLANET'S COMPOSITION AND TEMPERATURES. THE PROBE ALSO DISCOVERED AURORAE ON THE NIGHT SIDE AND A MYSTERIOUS "ELECTROGLOW" (RIGHT) ON THE DAY SIDE THAT SCIENTISTS STILL DO NOT FULLY UNDERSTAND.

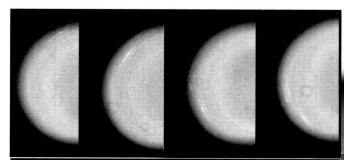

CLOUD SPOTTING
In the warmest latitude bands, where the atmospheric layers are penetrated by sunlight, Voyager 2 discovered the first direct evidence of Uranian weather—a top layer of clouds composed of methane ice crystals (white smudges on the above images). Voyager also found evidence of clouds in its Radio Science experiment. As Uranus passed between the probe and Earth, the radio signals sent to Earth were weakened by the methane in the planet's atmosphere. The signals dipped twice during the probe's transit, so scientists deduced that the probe had flown over methane clouds on either side of the planet.

THE HEART OF THE MATTER

According to data collected by Voyager 2, the gaseous Uranian atmosphere envelopes a planet containing more solid material. Gas flows with the atmosphere driven by the heat of the Sun may account for the surprisingly low temperatures.

GASEOUS ATMOSPHERE
Composed mainly of hydrogen and helium, plus methane, ammonia and water, it is estimated to be around 4,500 miles (7,240 km) thick.

LIQUID MANTLE
A vast ocean of boiling ammonia, methane and water mingled with rocky deposits that is kept liquid by massive gravitational pressures.

PREVAILING WINDS
Prevailing wind directions on Uranus vary according to latitude—as do wind speeds. Some of the fastest winds are found on or around 60°S of the equator, where they race at up to 220 yards (200 m) per second—faster than the planet's rotational speed.

PURPLE HAZE
This image, taken by Voyager 2 with colored filters later enhanced by color contrast, shows Uranus' sunlit south pole shrouded in haze or smog. This is believed to be made up of acetylene and other chemicals generated by the action of sunlight on the methane in the atmosphere.

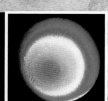

ROCKY CORE
Thought to be around 3,000 miles (4,830 km) in diameter and about the same mass as the Earth.

north pole

equator

south pole

RINGS OF URANUS

The rings of Uranus are the darkest objects in the entire solar system—so dark that they went unnoticed for two centuries after the discovery of the planet itself. Even then, the ring system was found by accident, and only some clever detective work revealed the full extent of the narrow, dusky bands. Astronomers are still not sure exactly what Uranus' rings are made of. But one thing is certain: They could not be more different in appearance from the bright rings of Uranus' neighbor, Saturn.

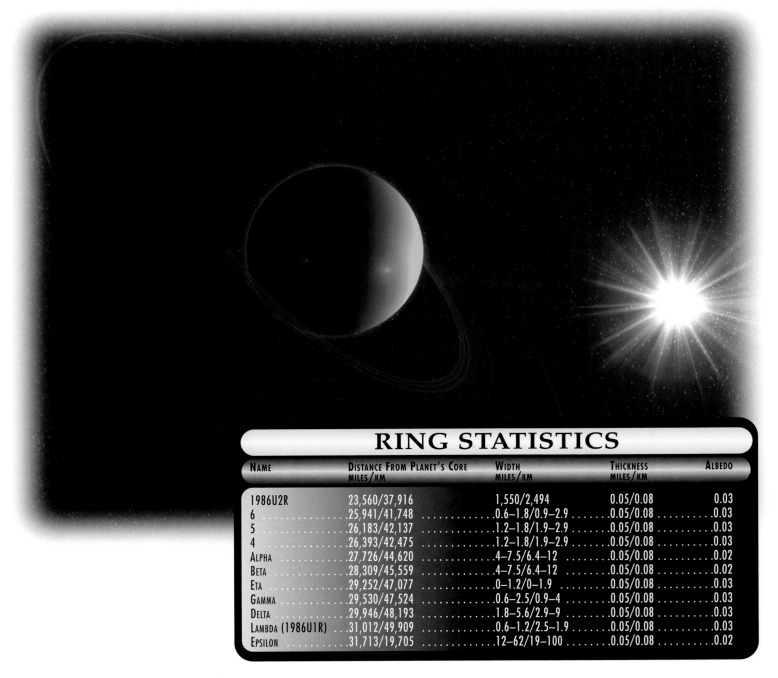

RING STATISTICS

Name	Distance From Planet's Core miles/km	Width miles/km	Thickness miles/km	Albedo
1986U2R	23,560/37,916	1,550/2,494	0.05/0.08	0.03
6	25,941/41,748	0.6–1.8/0.9–2.9	0.05/0.08	0.03
5	26,183/42,137	1.2–1.8/1.9–2.9	0.05/0.08	0.03
4	26,393/42,475	1.2–1.8/1.9–2.9	0.05/0.08	0.03
Alpha	27,726/44,620	4–7.5/6.4–12	0.05/0.08	0.02
Beta	28,309/45,559	4–7.5/6.4–12	0.05/0.08	0.02
Eta	29,252/47,077	0–1.2/0–1.9	0.05/0.08	0.03
Gamma	29,530/47,524	0.6–2.5/0.9–4	0.05/0.08	0.03
Delta	29,946/48,193	1.8–5.6/2.9–9	0.05/0.08	0.03
Lambda (1986U1R)	31,012/49,909	0.6–1.2/2.5–1.9	0.05/0.08	0.03
Epsilon	31,713/19,705	12–62/19–100	0.05/0.08	0.02

BLACK ON BLACK

When 18th-century astronomer William Herschel discovered Uranus, he effectively doubled the size of the solar system. The seventh planet is 1.78 billion miles (2.86 billion km) from the Sun, in an orbit twice as far from the Sun as the sixth planet, Saturn. From Earth, astronomers can discern Uranus as little more than a tiny, indistinct blue-green circle. Because of the planet's great distance from the Earth, its rings were only revealed in 1977, and then merely indirectly. Astronomers took to NASA's Kuiper Airborne Observatory to analyze light from a star as it crossed behind Uranus. Their aim was to find out more about the planet. What they found came as something of a surprise—evidence for a series of narrow rings. These rings formed only the second planetary ring system that has been confirmed since Saturn's rings were found almost four centuries earlier. Yet, after Pioneer 11 flew past Jupiter in 1974, astronomers suspected that Jupiter, too, had rings. This was not confirmed until two years after the disclosure of the Uranian rings.

The revelation was a scientific triumph, but it brought up problems. When Uranus crossed in front of another star in 1978, nine rings showed up. All but the outermost of these were extremely thin and narrow, measuring only a few miles across. How this distinctive state could be maintained was a mystery. Over time, individual circling particles in a ring are bound to collide and, after just a few decades, the rings should start to spread outward.

The outermost and largest of Uranus' rings, dubbed Epsilon, is the closest in appearance to a Saturnian ring, but it too is mysterious. Varying in width between 12 and 62 miles (19 and 100 km) across, the rings are composed of particles that reflect less light than coal dust.

Baffled astronomers wanted to take a closer look at these thin, enigmatic rings and find out what keeps them together. They were in luck. The Voyager 2 spacecraft was launched the same year as the Uranian rings were uncovered. Taking advantage of a rare conjunction of the outer planets, the probe took a gravitational hitch-hike through the solar system to reach Uranus in late 1985. The rings were a high observational priority of the mission.

The experience of photographing Saturn's rings had given NASA mission control some expertise in keeping the spacecraft stable enough to take long exposures. This capability was essential in the low light of the Uranian system, 19 times as far from the Sun as the Earth is. The images Voyager 2 returned showed two additional rings, entirely invisible from Earth, which brought the total of Uranus' rings to 11 at least. They also revealed a number of incomplete ring arcs, as narrow as 160 ft (50 m) across. These arcs, made up of faint dust, suggest that the Uranian rings are relatively new and still evolving, perhaps only a few million years old.

Voyager 2 spent only a few months in the vicinity of Uranus and there are no plans for another mission there until at least 2020. But the Hubble Space Telescope's Wide Field and Planetary Camera has managed to resolve the rings of Uranus from Earth orbit. Hubble's new technology provides researchers with the opportunity to check whether the rings undergo any major changes in structure over time, as well as to attempt analysis of their still unknown chemical make-up.

Currently, the leading theory is that the rings are formed out of methane ice that has been cooked into tar-like chains of carbon, hydrocarbons or a mixture of both through long exposure to cosmic radiation. Still, as yet, nobody knows for sure.

IN A BLINK

On March 10, 1977, the star SAO 158687 was due to pass behind Uranus. At the time, a team of Cornell University astronomers were 40,000 ft (12,000 m) above the Earth in the Kuiper Airborne Observatory (right), which carried a 3 ft (91 cm) telescope with a light-sensitive photometer. They analyzed the light emitted by the star before and after the eclipse. The distinctive way the star blinked before Uranus crossed in front of it could only be explained by the presence of a ring system.

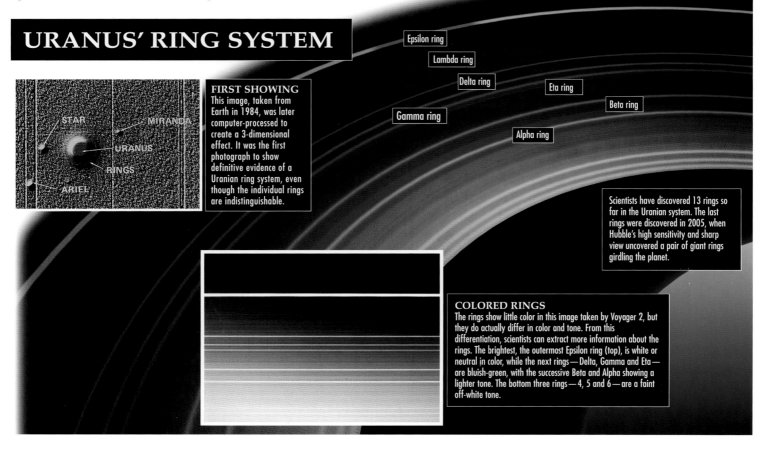

URANUS' RING SYSTEM

Epsilon ring

Lambda ring

Delta ring

Eta ring

Gamma ring

Beta ring

Alpha ring

FIRST SHOWING
This image, taken from Earth in 1984, was later computer-processed to create a 3-dimensional effect. It was the first photograph to show definitive evidence of a Uranian ring system, even though the individual rings are indistinguishable.

STAR · MIRANDA · URANUS · RINGS · ARIEL

Scientists have discovered 13 rings so far in the Uranian system. The last rings were discovered in 2005, when Hubble's high sensitivity and sharp view uncovered a pair of giant rings girdling the planet.

COLORED RINGS
The rings show little color in this image taken by Voyager 2, but they do actually differ in color and tone. From this differentiation, scientists can extract more information about the rings. The brightest, the outermost Epsilon ring (top), is white or neutral in color, while the next rings—Delta, Gamma and Eta—are bluish-green, with the successive Beta and Alpha showing a lighter tone. The bottom three rings—4, 5 and 6—are a faint off-white tone.

NEPTUNE

Remote Neptune, the eighth and farthest planet in the solar system, was unknown until a century and a half ago. Its year is so long that it has still not completed a full orbit of the Sun since it was discovered. Earth-bound observers knew almost nothing about Neptune until the NASA Voyager 2 probe passed by the planet in 1989 and returned spectacular views of this mysterious blue world. But although Voyager established that the planet shares many family characteristics with Jupiter, Saturn and Uranus, Neptune has yet to give up its greatest secret: the source of the unimaginable heat that rises from the planet's center to drive the violent winds and storms in its atmosphere.

NEPTUNE PROFILE

NEPTUNE		EARTH
30,775 MILES (49,528 KM)	DIAMETER	7,973 MILES (12,831 KM)
28°19'	AXIS TILT	23°27'
164.79 EARTH YEARS	LENGTH OF YEAR	365 DAYS
16.11 HOURS	LENGTH OF DAY	24 HOURS
2,794 MILLION MILES (4,497 MILLION KM)	DISTANCE FROM SUN	93.5 MILLION MILES (150.5 MILLION KM)
−326°F (−163°C)	SURFACE TEMPERATURE	59°F (15°C)
1.12 G	SURFACE GRAVITY	1 G
HYDROGEN (80%) HELIUM (19%) METHANE (1%)	ATMOSPHERE	NITROGEN (78%), OXYGEN (21%), ARGON (1%)
1,000–3,000 MILLIBARS	ATMOSPHERIC PRESSURE	1,000 MILLIBARS
HYDROGEN (80%) HELIUM (19%) METHANE (1%)	COMPOSITION	MAINLY IRON AND NICKEL

THE BIG BLUE

The blue-green globe of Neptune keeps a silent watch over the outer reaches of the solar system as it follows its leisurely 168-year orbit around the Sun. Little Pluto, its rocky partner Charon and a host of unknown comets lie beyond, but Neptune is the last of the orderly pattern that comprises the four inner rocky planets—Mercury, Venus, Earth and Mars—and the four outer gas giants—Jupiter, Saturn, Uranus and Neptune itself.

Neptune is so far away from the Sun—about 2.8 billion miles (4.5 billion km) on average—that it is too dim for the naked eye to see. Even the most powerful Earth-based telescopes reveal hardly any details of the surface. To find out more, NASA dispatched the Voyager 2 mission to take a closer look. The spacecraft hurtled past the planet in 1989, closing to within about 3,000 miles (5,000 km) of the cloud-tops of Neptune's thick, hazardous atmosphere.

The Neptunian atmosphere accounts for most of the planet's bulk. It is constantly tormented by winds that blow at up to 1,500 mph (2,400 km/h) and by giant, fast-moving storms like the Great Dark Spot that was identified by the Voyager 2 probe.

Atmospheric activity on this scale requires colossal amounts of energy, but the source of this energy is one of the Blue Planet's greatest mysteries. On Earth, our weather is driven by heat from the Sun. Neptune's remote orbit is 30 times farther out from the Sun, which causes solar radiation to dwindle to less than one nine-hundredth of Earth levels. Neptune is also farther from the Sun than Uranus, yet astronomers know that it is warmer. So where does the energy come from?

CRUSHED HEAT

Neptune's heat can only be generated from within the planet itself. The most popular theory is that materials of different densities within the interior have yet to fully separate out—that the planet's gravity is still dragging heavier matter toward the core, creating friction that in turn generates heat.

Scientists have speculated that such enormous heat and pressure would cause the methane at Neptune's core to separate into its component elements—hydrogen and carbon—and that the pressure might compress the carbon into a form familiar to us all: Diamonds.

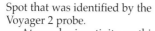

SHOT IN THE DARK

EARLY 19TH-CENTURY ASTRONOMERS FOUND THAT URANUS WAS NOT FOLLOWING ITS PREDICTED ORBIT. THEY GUESSED THAT ANOTHER PLANET WAS PULLING ON IT AND CALCULATED WHERE THIS PLANET WOULD BE. IN 1846, GERMAN ASTRONOMER JOHANN GOTTFRIED GALLE (1812–1910) POINTED A TELESCOPE IN THAT DIRECTION AND FOUND NEPTUNE: THE PREDICTIONS WERE CORRECT.

NEPTUNE'S RING

AS THE VOYAGER PROBES VISITED JUPITER, SATURN, URANUS AND NEPTUNE, THEY SHOWED THAT RINGS ARE A FAMILY CHARACTERISTIC OF THE GAS GIANT PLANETS. NEPTUNE HAS AT LEAST FOUR NARROW, FAINT RINGS OF DARK DUST THAT ARE BELIEVED TO BE THE DEBRIS FROM IMPACTS OF TINY METEOROIDS ON ITS MOONS. THE OUTER RING IS UNUSUAL IN THAT IT HAS BRIGHT PATCHES WHERE THE DUST PARTICLES APPEAR TO BE MORE DENSELY CLUSTERED AND THUS REFLECT MORE SUNLIGHT. THE CLUSTERS SUGGEST THAT THE RING IS RELATIVELY YOUNG AND HAS YET TO "THIN OUT" AROUND NEPTUNE. THE CLUSTERS MAY BE THE DEBRIS OF A SMALL MOON THAT HAS DISINTEGRATED WITHIN THE PAST FEW THOUSAND YEARS.

ATMOSPHERE
This makes up most of the planet's bulk and is roughly 80 percent hydrogen and 19 percent helium. It is a violently energetic environment, almost certainly due to the heat radiating from the core.

DARK SPOT
Voyager 2 revealed a giant storm system (right), dubbed the Great Dark Spot, Neptune's southern hemisphere. The Spot was estimated to be about the same size as the Earth and rotated counter-clockwise. Above the Spot drifted feathery white clouds that resembled the cirrus clouds in the Earth's atmosphere.

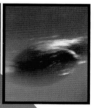

MISSED

THE ITALIAN SCIENTIST GALILEO GALILEI (1564–1642) ALMOST CAPPED HIS DISCOVERY OF JUPITER'S MOONS WITH THE FIRST SIGHTING OF NEPTUNE. IN 1612, GALILEO (RIGHT, CENTER) NOTICED AN OBJECT NEAR JUPITER, EXACTLY WHERE NEPTUNE WOULD HAVE BEEN AT THE TIME. A MONTH LATER, IT HAD MOVED — BUT HE NEVER FOLLOWED UP ON THE CLUE.

THE SCOOTER
Voyager 2 sent back pictures of a small, bright, eastward-moving cloud that scientists dubbed "the Scooter" (above). True to its name, the cloud scooted around Neptune every 16 hours, blown by the planet's strong winds. Small streaks within the Scooter constantly caused its appearance to change.

MOLTEN CORE
In common with most of the gas giants, Neptune may have a small, molten core consisting of mainly iron and silicon compounds. The temperature near the core is thought to be over 12,000°F (6,649°C).

CLOUDS
Neptune's wispy clouds consist of frozen methane crystals high in the atmosphere. The planet's blue-green color is due to the presence of methane in the thicker cloud layers below. These layers also contain crystals of ammonia and hydrogen sulfide, and display banding similar to the clouds on Jupiter and Saturn.

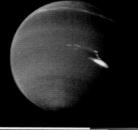

GIANT OCEAN
Scientists speculate that beneath the Neptunian atmosphere lies a planet-wide ocean of water, liquid ammonia and methane. Even at "sea level," its temperature is a staggeringly hot 4,000°F (2,204°C). It is the enormous pressure of Neptune's atmosphere that keeps the ocean liquid.

NEPTUNE INSIDE AND OUT

NEPTUNE'S ATMOSPHERE

Little was known about conditions on Neptune until the Voyager 2 probe flew by in 1989, on its closest approach to a planet since it was launched 12 years earlier. Voyager discovered that the blue gas giant has some of the wildest weather found in the solar system. Jet streams generated by an unknown internal energy source race around the equator and massive storms spin at supersonic speed. Since Voyager, Hubble Space Telescope images have verified that Neptune's atmosphere is as variable as it is turbulent.

ATMOSPHERIC STATISTICS

MEAN CLOUD SURFACE TEMPERATURE	−360°F (−182°C)
ALBEDO (SOLAR RADIATION REFLECTED)	41%
WIND SPEED RANGE	0–1,200 MPH (0–1930 KM/H)
ATMOSPHERIC AEROSOLS	AMMONIA ICE, WATER ICE, AMMONIA HYDROSULFIDE, METHANE ICE
ATMOSPHERIC GASES	PERCENTAGE OR PARTS PER MILLION
HYDROGEN	80%
HELIUM	19%
METHANE	1.5%
HYDROGEN DEUTERIDE	192PPM
ETHANE	1.5PPM

RACING WINDS

On August 25, 1989, the Voyager 2 craft passed near Neptune's north pole at an altitude of 3,000 miles (4,828 km). Nearly 3 billion miles (4.8 billion km) away on Earth, observers were able to take their first detailed look at the planet's atmosphere.

Neptune, the outermost of the gas giants, has an atmosphere several thousand miles deep, composed mainly of helium and hydrogen. A small amount of methane absorbs red light—and gives the planet its deep blue color. Because Neptune is so far from the Sun, it receives barely one-thousandth of the solar radiation that drives the weather on Earth. Many scientists assumed that its atmosphere would therefore be featureless.

Instead, Voyager 2 revealed one of the most dynamic weather patterns in the solar system. High in Neptune's frozen atmosphere, streaky bands of methane ice crystals cast shadows on the main cloud layer. This cloud layer displays distinctive zones and features moving at different speeds and in opposite directions.

Along the planet's equator, the clouds blow westward at 900 miles per hour (1,450 km/h)—three times faster than the winds in the strongest tornado on Earth. Farther north or south, at latitudes equivalent to the U.S.–Canadian border or the southern tip of South America, the winds slow down slightly, then pick up again toward the poles to reach 500 miles per hour (805 km/h), this time circling eastward.

About 10° south of the equator, Voyager 2 measured even stronger winds—1,200 miles per hour (1,930 km/h). These winds race past a dark oval area as large as the Earth that rotates counterclockwise. Dubbed the Great Dark Spot, it seems to be a gigantic Neptunian hurricane produced by gases that well up from inside the atmosphere. Voyager's observations revealed that both the Great Dark Spot and the bright cirrus-like clouds fringing it changed size and shape between one rotation and the next.

Where Neptune gets the energy to power such a remarkable weather system is unclear. Neptune has the same surface temperature as Uranus, which is 1 billion miles (1.6 billion km) closer to the Sun. Scientists have suggested that a vast amount of heat escapes from Neptune's core, which can reach 8,500°F (4,700°C), creating convection currents, in which warm gas rises and is replaced by cooler gas from beneath. Temperature readings by Voyager indicate that gases rise from the planet's mid-latitudes. Cooling, they drift toward the equator and the poles, where they sink and warm again.

This vertical flow of gases extends to great heights, helping to keep Neptune's upper atmosphere saturated with methane. Turbulent updrafts carry methane to the base of the stratosphere. Here the Sun's ultraviolet radiation converts it to a smog of ethane and acetylene particles, which descends and condenses into ice.

Next falling into the lower and warmer troposphere, the ice evaporates into gases and mixes with hydrogen. This reaction regenerates the methane content, which is then returned to the stratosphere by this ongoing cycle of convection.

THE SCOOTER

Due south of the Great Dark Spot, Voyager found a bright, irregularly shaped atmospheric feature (circled), whizzing eastward and completing one circuit every 16 hours. Nicknamed "the Scooter," the feature was probably a plume of cloud rising from a lower atmospheric layer.

LAYERS OF BLUE

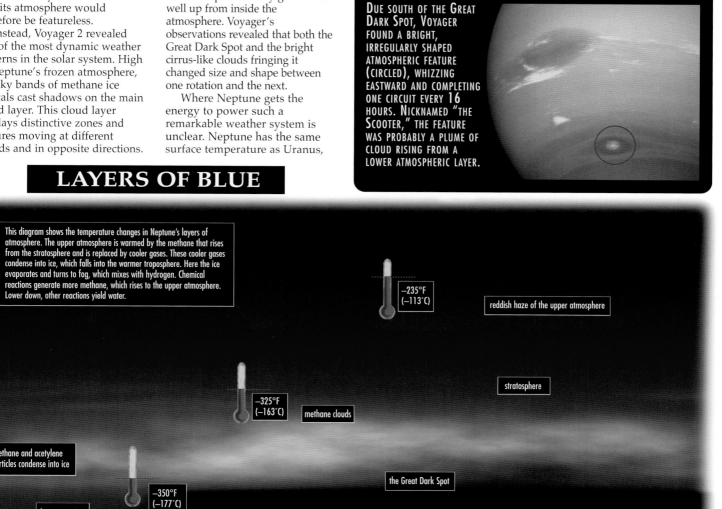

This diagram shows the temperature changes in Neptune's layers of atmosphere. The upper atmosphere is warmed by the methane that rises from the stratosphere and is replaced by cooler gases. These cooler gases condense into ice, which falls into the warmer troposphere. Here the ice evaporates and turns to fog, which mixes with hydrogen. Chemical reactions generate more methane, which rises to the upper atmosphere. Lower down, other reactions yield water.

−235°F (−113°C)

reddish haze of the upper atmosphere

stratosphere

−325°F (−163°C)

methane clouds

ethane and acetylene particles condense into ice

−350°F (−177°C)

the Great Dark Spot

ice evaporates into gases

water

−315°F (−157°C)

NEPTUNE'S RINGS

When signs of Neptune's delicate ring system emerged in the 1980s, the existence of rings around all four gas-giant planets was finally confirmed. But the rings looked different from those of the other planets: Neptune's rings seemed to be no more than fragments. Then images from Voyager 2 showed that the rings were complete. Denser segments of material—ring arcs—existed within otherwise extremely thin rings. Now scientists are puzzled about how such curious structures could have formed.

NEPTUNE'S RINGS

Name	Distance*	Radial Width
Galle	26,000 miles (41,800 km)	9 miles (14 km)
LeVerrier	33,000 miles (53,100 km)	68 miles (109 km)
Lassell	33,000–37,000 miles (53,100– 59,500 km)	25,000 miles (40,233 km)
Arago	36,000 miles (57,900 km)	62 miles (100 km)
Adams	39,100 miles (62,900 km)	31 miles (50 km)

Ring Arcs	Length
Fraternity	6,200 miles (10,000 km)
Equality	2,500 miles (4,000 km)
Liberty	2,500 miles (4,000 km)

* from Neptune's center to ring's inner edge

SPOT THE RINGS

By the early 1980s, the hunt was on for rings around Neptune. This presented astronomers with a real challenge, since the rings are completely invisible from the Earth. Only by observing stellar occultations—the eclipsing of a star by another body—could the rings be found. So between 1981 and 1989, various teams of astronomers lined up to observe 50 stellar occultations of Neptune. As many as 100 observations were made. As astronomers watched, a star would pass behind Neptune and become dimmer. But what they were really looking for was a star that dimmed three times—once slightly before, once during and once slightly after passing behind the planet. Only then would a planetary ring have been found. To the amazement of all involved, what some of the teams in fact found was a star that dimmed just twice. The unexpected result made it look as though Neptune had ring fragments rather than complete rings.

The discovery that there was at least some ring matter circling Neptune was well timed: Voyager 2 was scheduled to fly past Neptune in 1989. The spacecraft was put on a new trajectory because the extent of Neptune's upper atmosphere was unknown and it was feared that the craft might collide with the ring material. As Voyager flew past the planet, it took the first and only photographs of Neptune's rings—rings that proved to be complete after all. In fact, the Voyager images revealed that Neptune has five complete rings.

STRANGE ARCS

Neptune's outermost ring is known as the Adams ring. This ring contains at least three arcs of denser material, which astronomers have named Liberty, Equality and Fraternity. It is thought that the strange arcs are dragged into clumps by the gravity of Galatea, a moon that orbits Neptune just inside the Adams ring. Next comes the thin Arago ring and, after this, the Lassell ring—an immense "plateau" of material about 2,500 miles (4,020 km) wide. Moving closer toward the planet is the narrow LeVerrier ring and, finally, another wide ring, the innermost Galle ring.

The composition of Neptune's rings is still unknown. They are dark, probably dusty, possibly reddish in color and extremely sparse. Beyond this information, scientists know very little.

The origins of the rings are equally open to speculation, although there are a number of theories. We know that if a large rocky body comes close enough to a gas giant, the body can be torn to shreds by the planet's immense gravity. As a result, many ring theories involve moons that stray too close to the planet and break up, or comets that pass by and suffer the same fate.

Then there are the impact theories, where two small moons collide to create a swarm of debris that spreads around the planet. The debris from the impact is unable to reaccrete (clump back together again) if these moons are inside the planet's Roche limit—the theoretical boundary around a planet, inside which a body is subject to potentially fatal gravitational forces.

Whichever theory is right, Neptune's enormous gravity can certainly be destructive. It probably ripped apart some ancient cosmic bodies, leaving the remains scattered in a spinning disk around its equator. Close proximity to a gas giant can be dangerous—turning large bodies into nothing more than dispersed matter, running rings around the planet.

BOTH SIDES NOW

Two photographs taken by Voyager 2 are put together to form a complete picture of Neptune's ring system. Only three of Neptune's rings are clearly visible here—the outermost Adams ring, the LeVerrier ring (the brightest in this image) and the faint, innermost Galle ring.

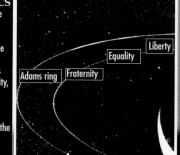

ADAMS' ARCS
This image shows the three arcs—bright clumps of ring material—that make up part of Neptune's Adams ring. The arcs were named Fraternity, Equality and Liberty because they were discovered in the bicentennial year of the French revolution.

Liberty

Equality

Adams ring Fraternity

NEPTUNE'S RINGS REVEALED

A total of five rings, traveling in circular orbits around Neptune's equator, have come to light so far. All the rings have been named after astronomers involved in the discovery of Neptune or its moons.

Galle ring

LeVerrier ring

Lassell ring

Arago ring

Adams ring

TRITON

With a surface temperature of –391°F (–199°C), the coldest ever recorded in the solar system, Triton is possibly the last place you would expect to find volcanic activity. Yet this, the largest of Neptune's eight moons, is far from dead. The eerie, pinkish-hued surface is strewn with sheets of what appears to be frozen liquid mixed with gases that has erupted from deep within the moon's core. Even stranger, Triton's unique terrain boasts giant columns of gas and dust that are driven up to six miles (10 km) into the sky by an unknown and, as yet, unexplained source of energy.

TRITON FACTS

COMPOSITION	75% ROCK; 25% FROZEN WATER, NITROGEN, AMMONIA AND METHANE
DIAMETER	1,680 MILES (2,704 KM)
MASS	0.29 MOON MASSES
DISTANCE FROM NEPTUNE	220,438 MILES (369,245)
TIME TO ORBIT NEPTUNE	5 DAYS, 21 HOURS
INCLINATION	157° (TO EQUATORIAL PLANE OF NEPTUNE)
ECCENTRICITY OF ORBIT	ZERO (IT IS PERFECTLY CIRCULAR)
ATMOSPHERE	99% NITROGEN, TRACES OF METHANE
SURFACE PRESSURE	0.0007 EARTH ATMOSPHERES
SURFACE TEMPERATURE	–391°F (–199°C)
SURFACE GRAVITY	0.08 G
ESCAPE VELOCITY	3,240 MPH (5,214 KM/H)

LAND OF PINK SNOW

Triton is the seventh-largest planetary satellite in the solar system and is easily Neptune's largest moon. It was discovered in 1846, only 17 days after Neptune itself, by the British brewer and amateur astronomer William Lassell (1799–1880). Yet although we have been aware of Triton for over 150 years, almost all of what we know about it comes from a single flyby of the Voyager 2 space probe in 1989.

Voyager 2 revealed that Triton is a unique world. Much of the terrain—the coldest in the known solar system—appears a striking salmon pink, probably due to a covering of frozen water, methane and nitrogen mixed with dust. There are vast plains that resemble the maria or "seas" on our own Moon but are made of ice, not rock. Other areas contain ridges that resemble the skin of a melon.

The most interesting feature of Triton is that it shows signs of volcanic activity, in the form of giant geysers of gas and dust that erupt miles into the sky. No one is sure what causes these "ice volcanoes." The most likely explanation is that sunlight penetrates the transparent parts of Triton's surface and melts the ice from below, causing local pressure buildups of gas. But since we know that beneath the layers of ice Triton has a rocky core, it is also possible that the pressure buildups are caused by heat generated internally—as is the case on Earth.

UNANSWERED QUESTIONS

Voyager showed that Triton, like Pluto, has an atmosphere consisting mainly of molecular crystals of nitrogen and some methane. This "air" is so thin that the atmospheric pressure at the surface is 70,000 times less than that on Earth. Triton is also about the same size as Pluto, and has a similar composition and density—around 25 percent ice around a rocky core. This, along with Triton's strange orbit, suggests that the two bodies share a common origin.

Triton not only orbits Neptune in the opposite direction to most moons; its orbit is also steeply inclined, at nearly 157° to the equatorial plane of its parent planet. This results in an 80-year "summer" that lasts for around half of the 164-year orbit around the Sun. It also suggests that we may have to wait for many faces of Triton reveal themselves.

DOOMED MOON

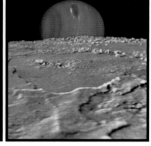

TRITON IS DOOMED, PARTLY BECAUSE OF THE MOON'S STRONG TIDAL INTERACTION WITH NEPTUNE, AND PARTLY BECAUSE IT ORBITS THE "WRONG WAY": ITS DECAYING ORBIT IS TAKING IT EVER CLOSER TO ITS PARENT PLANET. IN LESS THAN 100 MILLION YEARS, TRITON WILL BE ONLY A FEW THOUSAND MILES FROM NEPTUNE AND WILL BE TORN APART BY TIDAL FORCES. SOME OF THE PIECES WILL CRASH INTO THE PLANET; OTHERS MAY FORM A NEW SYSTEM OF RINGS.

SURFACE FEATURES

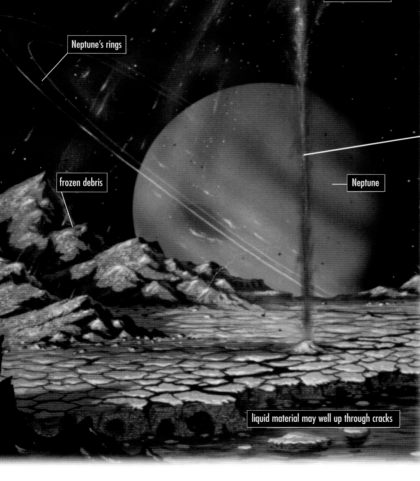

SURFACE VIEW
The most striking features on Triton are the "ice volcanoes" that regularly erupt from beneath the surface and frozen debris they leave behind. It seems that any impact craters like those found on other moons in the solar system have long since been filled in.

Neptune's rings

frozen debris

jets blown horizontally by molecular "wind"

Neptune

liquid material may well up through cracks

FROZEN "SEAS"
This Voyager 2 picture shows one of the many plains on Triton that resemble the "seas" on the Moon. The plains seem to be the result of liquid material, probably a mixture of water and ammonia, that has welled to the surface and frozen following meteorite impacts. This could also explain the apparent lack of craters.

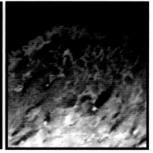

ICE VOLCANOES
Many of Voyager's pictures show geyser-like jets of what appear to be gas, dust and ice particles. These jets erupt several miles into the sky before being blown almost horizontally by Triton's powerful molecular "winds." The eruptions are probably caused by pressure buildups of gas beneath the frozen surface.

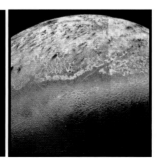

RIDGE FORMATION
Triton has little surface relief and few high mountains. But, in places, the terrain is green-tinged, with depressions and ridges that resemble the skin of a melon. Due to the absence of craters elsewhere, scientists think that the formations are more likely to be the result of subsurface activity than meteorite impacts.

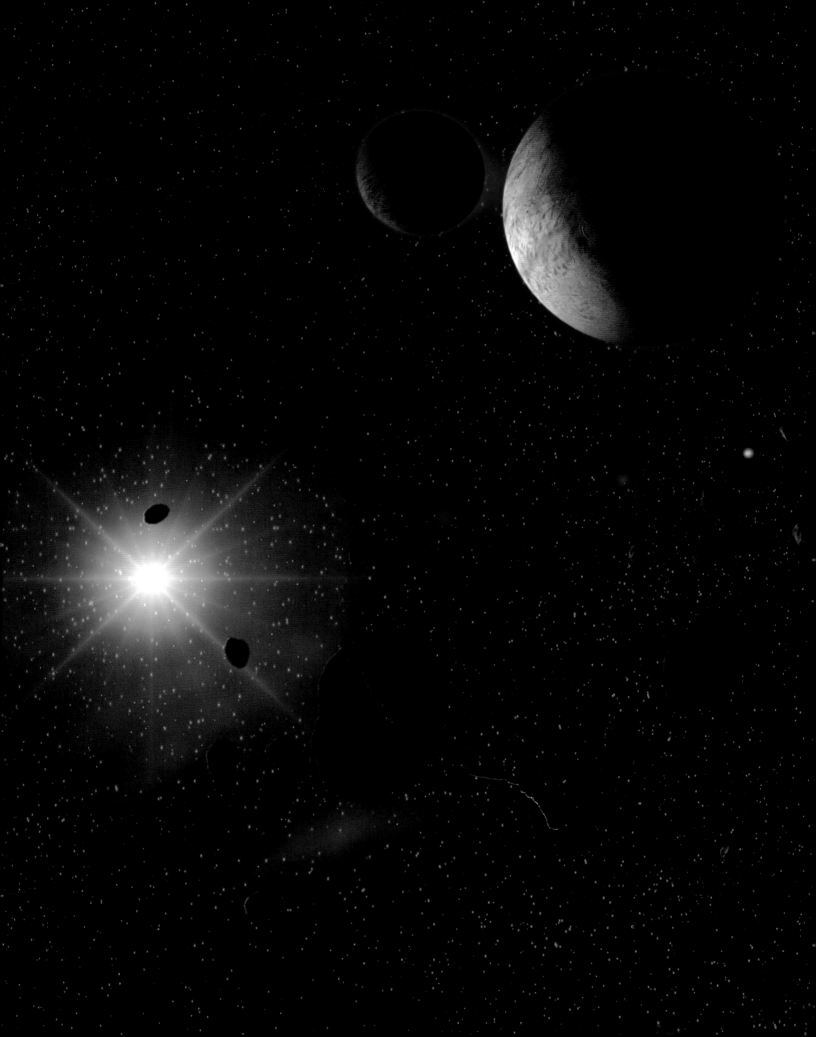

PLUTO AND BEYOND

The outer reaches of the solar system are still shrouded in mystery, but astronomers have begun to learn more about them in recent decades. Tiny Pluto, discovered in 1930 after a deliberate search for a "Planet X" whose gravity affected Neptune, orbits the Sun in an elongated, tilted orbit that sometimes brings it within the orbit of Neptune. However, even with its giant satellite Charon, Pluto is too small for its gravity to have an affect on Neptune, and it now seems that the wobbles in Neptune's orbit can be explained without another giant planet. Pluto remained a "loose end" at the far reach of the solar system until the 1990s, when astronomers began to find other objects at the same distance from the Sun. These objects form the "Kuiper Belt," an outer region of icy "minor planets," with Pluto as its largest member. Further out still lies the Oort Cloud, a giant spherical shell of dormant comets, expelled from the region around Neptune early in the solar system's history. Pluto was designated as the ninth planet in the solar system until 2006, when it was downgraded to a dwarf planet.

A computer-generated impression of the view from the Kuiper Belt, a distant zone of icy rocks and minor planets between 4.4 billion miles (7 billion km) and 90 billion miles (145 billion km) from the Sun, which includes Pluto and many other newly discovered "minor planets."

PLUTO AND CHARON

Pluto, the outermost known planet in the solar system—reclassified as a dwarf planet in 2006—orbits the Sun once every 248 years at a distance of up to 4.6 billion miles (7.4 billion km). Its largest moon, Charon, is so similar in size that together they make up the solar system's only double planet, but they are so far from Earth that very little surface detail has been discovered. Despite the lack of data, astronomers know that Pluto is an icy, rocky world and even—at times—has an atmosphere. But there is still much to learn.

PLUTO AND CHARON

PLUTO		CHARON	
DIAMETER	1,485 MILES (2,390 KM)	DIAMETER	730 MILES (1,175 KM)
AXIS TILT	122.5°	DISTANCE FROM PLUTO	12,204 MILES (19,640)
LENGTH OF YEAR	247.7 EARTH YR	TIME TO ORBIT PLUTO	6.39 EARTH DAYS
LENGTH OF DAY	6.39 EARTH DAYS	ROTATION PERIOD	6.39 EARTH DAYS
DISTANCE FROM SUN	2.9–4.6 BILLION MILES (4.7–7.4 BILLION KM)	SURFACE TEMPERATURE	–364°F (–184°C)
SURFACE TEMPERATURE	–364°F (–184°C)	SURFACE GRAVITY	APPROX. 0.02G
SURFACE GRAVITY	0.04G	ANGLE OF ORBIT TO PLUTO'S EQUATOR	98.8°
ANGLE OF ORBIT TO ECLIPTIC	17.148°	ATMOSPHERE	POSSIBLY METHANE, NITROGEN AND CARBON MONOXIDE
ATMOSPHERE	POSSIBLY METHANE, NITROGEN AND CARBON MONOXIDE	COMPOSITION	ROCK, ICES
COMPOSITION	ROCK, ICES		

DISTANT ICEBALLS

Astronomers know very little about Pluto. It is simply too far away, not to mention too small, for even space-based telescopes to reveal much, and it is the only planet yet to be visited by a space probe. But even with the scant information available, it is clear that the dwarf Pluto is the oddball of the solar system.

Pluto is easily the smallest of the known planets. It is just one-fifth the diameter of Earth and smaller than the solar system's seven largest planetary satellites, including the Earth's own Moon. In fact, Pluto is so tiny that many astronomers originally thought that it was really an escaped moon that had once orbited Neptune. Further evidence for the escaped-moon theory came from Pluto's orbit around the Sun, which is quite unlike that of any other planet and suggests that Pluto entered its present orbit long after the other planets settled into theirs.

Pluto's orbit is the most elongated ellipse of any of the planets. At its most distant from the Sun—4.6 billion miles (7.4 billion km)—Pluto is almost 2 billion miles (3.2 billion km) farther out than when it is at its closest, at which point it passes nearer to the Sun than its neighbor Neptune does. Stranger still, Pluto's orbit is tilted at an angle of some 17° to the orbits of all the other planets.

But in 1978, the discovery that Pluto had a satellite cast doubt on the "escaped moon" theory. As an alternative, some astronomers have suggested that Pluto, and its largest companion Charon, originated in the Kuiper Belt—the distant ring of rocky and icy debris that extends beyond the orbit of Neptune.

NEVER FAR APART

Pluto and Charon are sometimes labeled the "dwarf double planet" because their sizes are closer together than most planet-moon combinations, and the distance between them is far less. Charon is more than half the diameter of Pluto—making it the largest moon in relation to its parent planet—and it orbits its parent at a distance of only about eight Pluto diameters. By comparison, in the Earth/Moon system, the Moon is just over a quarter of the Earth's diameter and separated by 31 Earth diameters.

Pluto's surface is probably covered in frozen nitrogen, methane and carbon monoxide, which vaporize to form a very thin atmosphere when the planet moves closest to the Sun. Charon, by contrast, may have water ice on its surface. But we will not know for sure until the double planet is visited by a space probe—the New Horizons probe is scheduled to fly past Pluto in 2015.

PLUTO AND CHARON

DISCOVERY OF CHARON
Charon was discovered on July 2, 1978, by James Christy with the 61-in (1.54-m) telescope at the U.S. Naval Observatory in Flagstaff, Arizona. Officially, Charon is named for the figure in Greek mythology who ferried the souls of the dead across the River Styx into the underworld, which was ruled by Hades—known also as Pluto. Unofficially, Jim Christy also named the moon Charon to honor his wife, Charlene.

THE MOON
Charon is over half the size of Pluto and probably consists of about 70 percent water ice and 30 percent rock, with an ice-covered surface.

PLUTO'S ATMOSPHERE
Astronomers first realized that Pluto has an atmosphere in 1980, when the planet passed across a background star. The light from the star diminished as Pluto approached it and increased again as the two separated. From this, astronomers deduced the presence of an atmosphere that is very thin, but extends a long way. It is at least as deep as Pluto's diameter and may even stretch all the way to Charon, which would give the two bodies a shared atmospheric "envelope" (below). Methane seems to be the principal gas, but nitrogen and carbon monoxide may also be present. The atmosphere is probably created by frozen gas that thaws when Pluto is at its closest to the Sun.

THE SEARCH FOR PLUTO

DWARF OR NOT, PLUTO IS THE MOST RECENTLY DISCOVERED PLANET. ITS EXISTENCE WAS FIRST SUGGESTED IN THE 19TH CENTURY TO EXPLAIN SLIGHT WOBBLES IN THE ORBIT OF URANUS, AND EARLY IN THE 20TH CENTURY AMERICAN ASTRONOMERS PERCIVAL LOWELL (1855–1916) AND WILLIAM PICKERING (1858–1938) EACH TRIED TO PREDICT ITS POSITION. IN 1929, CLYDE TOMBAUGH (1906–97, ABOVE) STARTED WORK AT THE LOWELL OBSERVATORY IN FLAGSTAFF, ARIZONA, WITH A TEAM OF ASTRONOMERS HEADED BY VESTO SLIPHER (1875–1969). THEY CARRIED OUT AN EXHAUSTIVE PHOTOGRAPHIC SEARCH FOR THE PLANET, AND ON FEBRUARY 18, 1930, THE 24-YEAR-OLD TOMBAUGH DISCOVERED PLUTO CLOSE TO WHERE LOWELL'S CALCULATIONS HAD SAID IT WOULD BE.

THE PLANET
Pluto is thought to consist of about 70 percent rock and 30 percent water ice, with patches of frozen nitrogen, methane and carbon monoxide gases on its surface.

BEYOND PLUTO

Fifty years ago, at the beginning of the space age, Pluto was routinely described as the most distant object in the solar system. But not any more: Recent discoveries and theories suggest that the planets occupy just the inner heart. Four probes have now traveled to about twice the distance of Pluto, into the realm of the comets, with others likely to follow. Eventually, all these probes will travel through the solar system's outer reaches, where lonely comets orbit the Sun—three-quarters of the way to the nearest star.

NEW HORIZONS SCHEDULE

JANUARY 2006	Launched
APRIL 2006	Mars
JUNE 2008	Saturn
MARCH 2011	Uranus
JULY 2015	Pluto/Charon (estimated)
2015–2020	first Kuiper Belt encounters
2020 onwards	possible extended mission

TO THE EDGE

Astronomers are eager to establish the boundaries to the Sun's empire. There are two possible answers. One depends on the extent of the Sun's electromagnetic influence, the other on its gravitational reach. The electromagnetic influence—the solar wind, as it is called—gradually fades as it encounters the dust, gas and radiation that make up the incredibly tenuous "atmosphere" between the stars, known as the interstellar medium. Pioneer 10 and Voyager 1, both at almost twice Pluto's distance, report that the intensity of cosmic rays from other stars increases by 1.3 percent every 100 million miles (160 million km). At that rate, like the light of a lighthouse dying away in fog, the Sun's radiation should finally fade out at about four times Pluto's distance.

Meanwhile, Pioneer 10 and Voyager 1—along with Voyager 2, now 5.5 billion miles (8.9 billion km) away—have entered the domain of the comets. Astronomers believe that the cometary sources form two regions, one that reaches to 25 times the distance of Pluto from the Sun and a second stretching out to 5,000 times that distance.

INTO COMET COUNTRY

The first comet store, the source of short-period comets, is named after Dutch-American astronomer Gerard Kuiper (1905–73), who suggested its existence in 1951. He proposed that the belt stretched from Neptune's orbit to 25 times Pluto's distance from the Sun, lying in the same plane as the planets. Until 1992, the Kuiper Belt was mere theory. But then David Jewitt and Jane Luu of the University of California spotted a minute object about 200 miles (320 km) across, orbiting beyond Neptune—the first Kuiper Belt Object (KBO). Since then, some 60 objects have been found. Astronomers theorize that there should be anything from one billion to 6.7 billion of them. Voyager 1, Voyager 2 and Pioneer 10 are in the Kuiper Belt now. Slight shifts in their path may allow scientists to calculate the combined gravity of the comets and estimate their numbers.

The second comet "sink" is the source of long-period comets, a cloud named for Dutch scientist Jan Oort (1900–92), who suggested its existence in the 1940s. This halo of the solar system, ranging from 6,000 to 200,000 times the distance

of Earth to the Sun, may contain as many as six trillion comets. If the Voyager and Pioneer probes survive long enough to enter the Oort cloud, it will be as dead objects in 2,000 years. They will probably continue their journey unscathed, leaving the Oort Cloud—and the solar system—some 65,000 years later.

ANOTHER PLANET?

IN JANUARY 2005, ASTRONOMERS MICHAEL BROWN, CHAD TRUJILLO AND DAVID RABINOWITZ AT THE MOUNT PALOMAR OBSERVATORY IN CALIFORNIA DISCOVERED AN OBJECT BEYOND THE ORBIT OF NEPTUNE WHICH SEEMED TO HAVE A RADIUS OF AROUND 1,420 MILES (2,300 KM). THIS WOULD MAKE IT AROUND THE SAME SIZE AS PLUTO. OFFICIALLY NAMED 2003 UB313, THIS "10TH PLANET" WAS POPULARLY DUBBED XENA AFTER THE "WARRIOR PRINCESS" TV CHARACTER. IT WAS NOT UNTIL 2003 UB313 WAS CLASSIFIED AS A DWARF PLANET IN 2006 THAT IT WAS RENAMED ON SEPTEMBER 13, 2006, AFTER THE GREEK GODDESS "ERIS", WHICH STANDS FOR STRIFE OR DISCORD.

COMET FARM

THE KUIPER BELT (RIGHT) MAY CONSIST OF UP TO ABOUT 6 BILLION OBJECTS, OF WHICH SOME 70,000 ARE PLANETESIMALS BETWEEN 60 AND 475 MILES (97 AND 764 KM) ACROSS LYING IN A BAND STRETCHING 30 TO 50 AU, 200 MILLION ARE IN THE 6- TO 12-MILE (10- TO 19-KM) SIZE RANGE AND THE REST ARE UNDER A MILE ACROSS. ANY ONE OF THEM COULD BE NUDGED FROM ITS ORBIT AND BECOME A COMET. DESPITE THEIR NUMBERS, THE DISTANCES BETWEEN THEM ARE IMMENSE — ABOUT ONE LARGE OBJECT EVERY 100 MILLION MILES (160 MILLION KM).

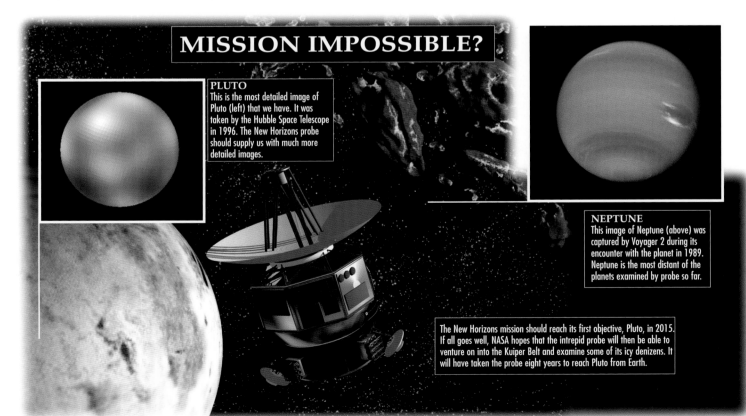

MISSION IMPOSSIBLE?

PLUTO
This is the most detailed image of Pluto (left) that we have. It was taken by the Hubble Space Telescope in 1996. The New Horizons probe should supply us with much more detailed images.

NEPTUNE
This image of Neptune (above) was captured by Voyager 2 during its encounter with the planet in 1989. Neptune is the most distant of the planets examined by probe so far.

The New Horizons mission should reach its first objective, Pluto, in 2015. If all goes well, NASA hopes that the intrepid probe will then be able to venture on into the Kuiper Belt and examine some of its icy denizens. It will have taken the probe eight years to reach Pluto from Earth.

KUIPER BELT

Late in 1992, astronomers David Jewitt and Jane Luu discovered a tiny world just 150 miles (240 km) across and over 3 billion miles (4.8 billion km) from the Sun. This lump of ice and rock was the first direct proof of the existence of the Kuiper Belt, a zone of space debris out beyond the orbit of Neptune. Until then, the Kuiper Belt had been just a theoretical possibility, but astronomers now believe that it contains thousands of small objects and is the source of many comets. Some day, it could also provide interstellar travelers with vital supplies. Missions to explore the Kuiper Belt are underway.

MAJOR KUIPER BELT OBJECTS

Name	Discovered	Diameter	Perihelion (au)	Aphelion (au)
2003 UB313	2005	1,600 miles (2,575 km)*	38.2	97.6
Pluto	1930	1,440 miles (2,317 km)	29.5	49.3
2004 DW	2004	930 miles (1,497 km)*	30*	50*
Sedna	2003	<930 miles (<1,497 km)*	76	990
Charon	1978	795 miles (1,279 km)	29.5	49.3
2005 FY9	2005	780 miles (1,255 km)*	38.7	52.6
2003 EL61	2005	745 miles (1,199 km)*	35.2	51.5
Quaoar	2002	740 miles (1,191 km)*	40*	44*
Ixion	2001	660 miles (1,062 km)*	29*	47*
Varuna	2000	560 miles (901 km)*	39*	44*
2002 AW197	2002	550 miles (885 km)*	68.5	76.4

* APPROX

OUT ON THE EDGE

Far out in the gloom of deep space, beyond the orbit of Neptune, lies a zone of debris left over from the birth of the solar system. The debris takes the form of cold, dark chunks of ice and rock that orbit the Sun in a broad, flat ring called the Edgeworth-Kuiper Belt, or known simply as the Kuiper Belt.

At an average distance of around 3 billion miles (4.8 billion km) from the Sun, so-called Kuiper Belt Objects (KBOs) are so faint that astronomers didn't detect them until 1992. But occasionally, a KBO turns itself into one of the most visible objects in the night sky: The Kuiper Belt is a fertile source of comets.

The existence of the Kuiper Belt was predicted long before the first KBOs were discovered. In 1943, the Irish astronomer Kenneth Essex Edgeworth (1880–1972) suggested that certain comets must come from a region beyond the known planets. And in 1951, the same idea was put forward independently by

Gerard Pieter Kuiper (1905–73), a Dutch-born American astronomer.

The Kuiper Belt came into existence shortly after the planets and their moons formed out of the swirling cloud of gas and dust that orbited the young Sun. Some leftover material settled into what is now the asteroid belt between the orbits of Mars and Jupiter, having failed to form a planet due to Jupiter's massive gravitational pull. Much of the rest was flung far beyond the orbit of Neptune by the gravity fields of the two large outer planets. There, the material formed the huge number of orbiting planetesimals—small rocks mixed with water ice and frozen gases—that comprise the Kuiper Belt.

The vast majority of the planetesimals has stayed in the belt ever since and will remain there for as long as the solar system survives. But from time to time, one of them is dragged out of its regular orbit by Neptune's gravity and propelled toward the inner solar system to become what is known as a short-period comet.

All short-period comets travel in the ecliptic, the plane in which the planets move, unlike long-period comets, which can enter the inner solar system from any direction. It was this fact that prompted Edgeworth and Kuiper to suggest that there must be a "reservoir" of icy cometary bodies somewhere beyond Neptune.

THE SEARCH FOR KBOS

The first serious search for KBOs, which are so dimly lit by the distant Sun that they are very hard to see, got under way in 1987, when astronomers David Jewitt and Jane Luu began scanning the skies with the 7 ft 2-in (2.2-m)

telescope of the University of Hawaii. The pair took multiple pictures of different parts of the sky, then used computers to compare the pictures and look for objects that appeared to have moved. On August 30, 1992, they found an object that had moved exactly the right distance to be in orbit beyond Neptune. This small, reddish rocky body, called 1992 QB1, is 176 miles (283 km) across. It moves in an almost circular orbit that is 44 times farther from the Sun than the Earth and farther than the average distance of Pluto. Jewitt and Luu found a second object beyond Neptune in March 1993. Further sightings of KBOs followed rapidly, and within five years of the first discovery, 60 were known to exist.

KBO HUNTER

JANE LUU, CO-DISCOVERER OF THE FIRST KBO, WAS BORN IN SAIGON (NOW HO CHI MINH CITY), VIETNAM, IN 1963. SHE CAME TO THE U.S. AT THE AGE OF 12, AND AFTER GRADUATING FROM STANFORD UNIVERSITY, SHE STUDIED AT THE MASSACHUSETTS INSTITUTE OF TECHNOLOGY. SHE THEN WORKED AT HARVARD UNIVERSITY AND IS NOW A SENIOR SCIENTIST AT MIT.

THE KUIPER BELT

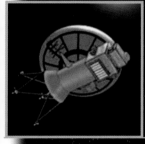

KUIPER PROBE
The Pluto-Kuiper Belt New Horizons probe (left) will arrive at Pluto in about 2015 and then travel on to explore the Kuiper Belt.

PLUTO AND ITS MOONS
Pluto and its five moons orbit the Sun in a path that takes them within the orbit of Neptune. This unusual orbit has led astronomers to propose that they came from the Kuiper Belt.

FAINT SUN
Seen from the Kuiper Belt, the Sun is 1,000 times fainter than it appears from Earth. The belt's inner edge lies about 2.8 billion miles (4.5 billion km) from our parent star; the outer edge is at least 4.4 billion miles (7 billion km), and perhaps over 90 billion miles (145 billion km), from the Sun.

KUIPER BELT OBJECTS
The Kuiper Belt lies beyond the orbits of Neptune and Pluto. It contains many thousands of small objects, including perhaps more than 35,000 that are larger than 60 miles (97 km).

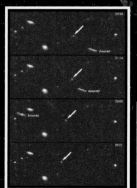

THE FIRST KBO
This sequence of pictures, taken by David Jewitt and Jane Luu, revealed the first KBO to be discovered, 1992 QB1. During the time interval covering these pictures, the faint object (arrowed) moved steadily across the sky while the background stars remained stationary.

MINOR MEMBERS OF THE SOLAR SYSTEM

Between the major planets orbit millions of smaller objects—asteroids, comets, and countless other pieces of space debris. Most of the larger objects—the asteroids or minor planets that never grew large enough to become substantial worlds in their own right—are confined to a belt between the orbits of Mars and Jupiter, held there by Jupiter's enormous gravity. A few asteroids stray out into more eccentric orbits, including some that occasionally cross Earth's own orbit, known as Near-Earth asteroids. Comets are usually less substantial than asteroids, being composed of a mixture of dust and ice. They originate in the icy reaches of the outer solar system, but occasionally fall into orbits that bring them past the Sun at high speeds, burning off their icy material to form spectacular tails as they do so. Dust particles left behind by these visitors are spread throughout the inner solar system, and form meteors or shooting stars when they enter Earth's atmosphere. Larger chunks from asteroids or other planets occasionally reach our planet's surface as meteorites.

Comet Hale-Bopp, photographed in March 1997 as it made its closest approach to the Sun. Hale-Bopp became visible to the naked eye in the summer of 1996, and in March 1997 a solar eclipse in Mongolia and eastern Siberia allowed observers there to see the comet in the daytime.

ASTEROID BELT

The asteroid belt—a broad band between the orbits of Mars and Jupiter—is home to thousands of small, rocky bodies that orbit the Sun. These asteroids, also called "minor planets," are thought to be the remains of a larger planet that tried to form in the early days of the solar system but was prevented from doing so by the powerful gravitational influence of the giant planet Jupiter. Despite their sinister reputation, the combined mass of the asteroids in the belt is still less than one percent of the Earth's mass.

ASTEROID SIZE

ASTEROID NUMBERING
WHEN AN ASTEROID'S ORBITAL DETAILS HAVE BEEN ESTABLISHED, ASTRONOMERS GIVE IT A NUMBER THAT IS WRITTEN BEFORE THE NAME. ASTEROIDS ARE RARELY SPHERICAL. THE SIZES GIVEN BELOW ARE MAXIMUMS.

LARGE ASTEROIDS
ASTEROIDS LARGER THAN 100 MILES (160 KM) ACROSS	.26
ASTEROIDS LARGER THAN 300 FT (90 M) ACROSS	.POSSIBLY 1 MILLION
TOTAL MASS OF ASTEROIDS IN BELT	.LESS THAN 15% OF THE MOON

VERMIN OF THE SKIES

At the end of the 18th century, astronomers began to search for a "missing" planet that they were convinced must exist in the extra-large gap between the orbits of Mars and Jupiter. Among these astronomers was a group that called itself the "Celestial Police."

This group scanned the skies systematically for a dot of light that could be seen to move in relation to the stars. But they were cheated of their quarry. Other astronomers established that the gap between Mars and Jupiter was filled with a number of tiny asteroids rather than the full-sized planet that the Celestial Police hoped to find. The first of these asteroids was discovered on January 1, 1801 by the Italian astronomer Giuseppe Piazzi. He named the new body Ceres, for the Roman goddess of agriculture. A second, Pallas, was found by German astronomer Heinrich Olbers in March 1802.

In the following years, more of these miniature worlds were found. Astronomers now think that there are probably tens of thousands of asteroids—one called them "vermin of the skies"—and over 8,500 have now been cataloged. Hundreds of new asteroids are added to the record every year.

MAVERICK ORBITS

The orbits of most asteroids lie between those of Mars and Jupiter, but there are some asteroids that travel in what are called maverick orbits. Some of these pass closer to the Sun than the Earth, some extend way beyond Jupiter,

and others—the Trojan asteroids— travel in the same orbit as Jupiter.

Asteroids have too little gravity to support atmospheres, or even to draw themselves into a spherical shape; most resemble shapes like lumpy potatoes. The majority are also too close to the Sun to have retained any water or methane in frozen form.

Nearly all known asteroids are pitted with craters—the scars of impacts with meteoroids or other asteroids. Most of this probably happened when the solar system was forming and space was more crowded. More recent cratering could be due to a much larger asteroid that broke up.

LAGRANGE

THE TROJAN ASTEROIDS TRAVEL IN TWO GROUPS IN THE ORBIT OF JUPITER, ONE 60° AHEAD OF THE PLANET, THE OTHER 60° BEHIND IT. THESE POSITIONS ARE TWO OF WHAT ARE KNOWN AS THE LAGRANGE POINTS OF THE ORBIT. THESE POINTS, AT WHICH SMALL OBJECTS CAN SAFELY REMAIN IN A LARGER OBJECT'S ORBIT, ARE NAMED FOR THE FRENCH ASTRONOMER JOSEPH LAGRANGE (1736–1813), WHO CALCULATED THEIR EXISTENCE MATHEMATICALLY.

ASTEROID MOON
Dactyl, the moon of asteroid 243 Ida, was the first satellite of an asteroid to be discovered. It was first imaged by the Galileo spacecraft in 1993. Ida is about 36 miles (58 km) long; Dactyl is just a mile (1.6 km) long.

CERES
This image of 1 Ceres was taken by the Hubble Space Telescope. Ceres, the first and largest asteroid to be discovered, is almost spherical—unlike any of the other known asteroids. Ceres was also classified as a dwarf planet in 2006, but is still otfen called an asteroid.

MATHILDE
An image of 253 Mathilde, built from four separate images taken by the NEAR (Near-Earth Asteroid Rendezvous) probe in 1997 from a distance of 1,500 miles (2,414 km). The central shadow is a crater thought to be six miles (10 km) deep.

NO IMPACT

SCIENCE FICTION WRITERS, BELIEVING THAT ASTEROIDS MUST BE CROWDED TOGETHER IN SPACE, HAVE OFTEN PORTRAYED THE ASTEROID BELT AS A PLACE OF DANGER FOR SPACE TRAVELERS. SOME HAVE EVEN SPECULATED THAT SPACECRAFT ENTERING THE REGION WOULD BE BATTERED BY "ASTEROID STORMS." THE ASTEROID BELT IS CERTAINLY CROWDED, BUT ONLY BY COMPARISON WITH THE REST OF THE SOLAR SYSTEM, WHICH IS A VERY EMPTY PLACE INDEED. THE 2 PIONEER AND 2 VOYAGER PROBES THAT VISITED THE OUTER PLANETS FLEW THROUGH THE ASTEROID BELT WITHOUT ANY CLOSE ENCOUNTERS.

THE ASTEROID BELT

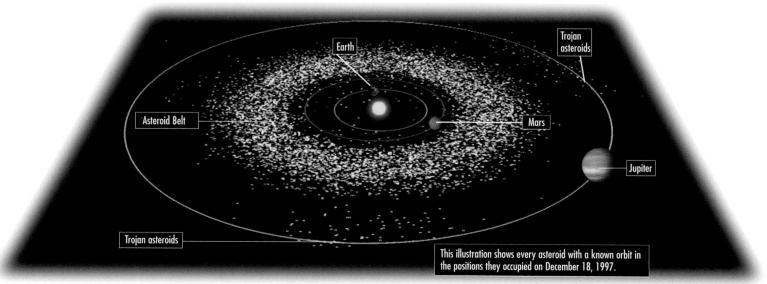

This illustration shows every asteroid with a known orbit in the positions they occupied on December 18, 1997.

KILLER ASTEROIDS

Earth-crossing asteroids—lumps of stray matter whose orbits cross that of the Earth—are not just the invention of disaster movies: Asteroid strikes are a real possibility, and have actually happened in the past. The chances of a collision in our lifetime are small. But if an asteroid were to hit us, there is a strong possibility that it would occur without warning. And if the asteroid were large enough, it could cause enough damage to signal the end of life on Earth as we know it.

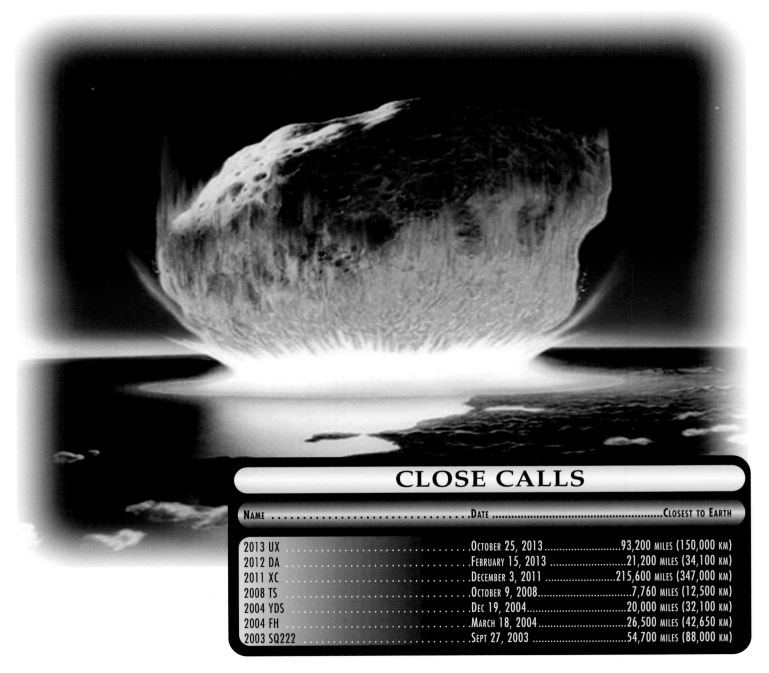

CLOSE CALLS

Name	Date	Closest to Earth
2013 UX	October 25, 2013	93,200 miles (150,000 km)
2012 DA	February 15, 2013	21,200 miles (34,100 km)
2011 XC	December 3, 2011	215,600 miles (347,000 km)
2008 TS	October 9, 2008	7,760 miles (12,500 km)
2004 YDS	Dec 19, 2004	20,000 miles (32,100 km)
2004 FH	March 18, 2004	26,500 miles (42,650 km)
2003 SQ222	Sept 27, 2003	54,700 miles (88,000 km)

DOOMSDAY STRIKE

Every night, thousands of shooting stars appear in the night sky, evidence of the huge quantity of space matter that is constantly bombarding the Earth's atmosphere. Most of these objects are small meteors that burn up harmlessly before they reach the surface. However, out in space there are some very large objects, some a mile or two (up to 3.2 km) across. And between the small rocks and the really large ones lie many more, too small to spot, yet big enough to cause considerable damage if they hit the Earth.

Such impacts have occurred in uninhabited areas several times over the last century. Scientists are warning that it is only a matter of time before there is a major asteroid disaster.

CLOSE SHAVE

Asteroids exist mostly in orbit around the Sun between Mars and Jupiter, in a vast ring known as the asteroid belt. Occasionally, though, an asteroid will leave its secluded orbit, and veer off into the inner solar system. This sudden change may be caused by an impact with another asteroid, or by the gravitational pulls of Jupiter or Mars.

In recent years, astronomers have chanced on rocks a few hundred yards in diameter hurtling near to Earth. Records for the closest recorded approach are constantly changing as astronomers detect even smaller objects—often when they have already passed the Earth.

Each year, other asteroids are spotted coming almost as close, and it seems that the harder astronomers look, the more they find. It is now estimated that there are over 1,000 near-Earth asteroids roughly a mile (1.6 km) in size. And although there is no known body due to hit the Earth, there are many asteroids out there that we don't know about.

Perhaps it is time to start putting more effort into searching for Earth-crossers. One may not strike for a thousand years, or it may hit us tomorrow.

SIBERIAN STRIKE

THE BIGGEST IMPACT FOR 100 YEARS TOOK PLACE IN SIBERIA, RUSSIA, ON JUNE 30, 1908. WHILE STILL 4 MILES (6.5 KM) FROM THE GROUND, THE OBJECT SHATTERED WITH A FORCE AROUND 2,000 TIMES THAT OF AN ATOM BOMB AND FLATTENED THOUSANDS OF SQUARE MILES OF FOREST. THE ASTEROID WAS PROBABLY A 100,000-TON (90,700-TONNE) ROCK THE SIZE OF A LARGE HOUSE. THIS PHOTOGRAPH SHOWS SCIENTISTS LOOKING FOR PIECES OF THE DEBRIS. THE ARROW INDICATES A FRAGMENT WEIGHING 660-LB (300 KG).

LOCAL DAMAGE
1

Size of body:
Up to 600 ft (183 m) in diameter.
Rate of impact:
One to 10 per century.
Impact over land:
May explode in the air, causing a multi-megaton blast that flattens the area below for hundreds of miles. Could cause extensive local damage, but no lasting environmental effects.
Impact over sea:
If it does not break up and is close to shore, could cause a small tsunami (tidal wave) with localized flooding. If in deep ocean, probably no effects.

WIDESPREAD DEVASTATION
2

Size of body:
600 ft to 1 mile (183 m to 1.6 km) in diameter.
Rate of impact:
One every 10,000–1 million years.
Impact over land:
Could blast a crater up to 10 miles (16 km) wide, with devastation on a national scale around the area of impact. Worldwide environmental effects (for example, loss of a season's crops), resulting in large-scale famine, collapse of the world's financial markets, and serious economic depression.
Impact over sea:
A worldwide tsunami that could flood all land below 200 ft (60 m) above sea level (including New York, Washington and most of Holland).

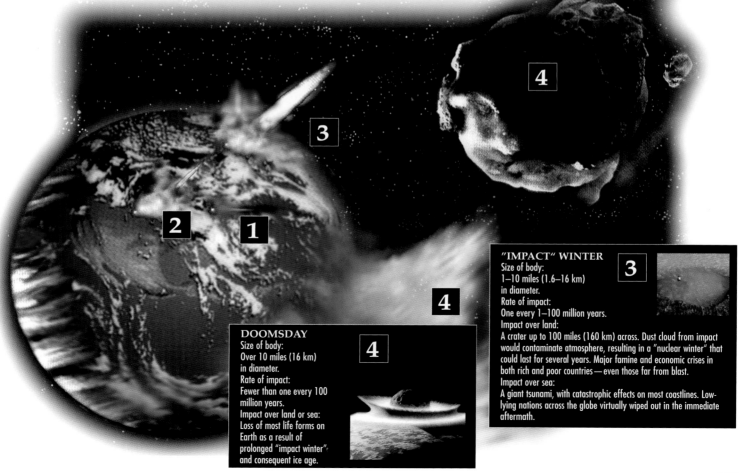

"IMPACT" WINTER
3

Size of body:
1–10 miles (1.6–16 km) in diameter.
Rate of impact:
One every 1–100 million years.
Impact over land:
A crater up to 100 miles (160 km) across. Dust cloud from impact would contaminate atmosphere, resulting in a "nuclear winter" that could last for several years. Major famine and economic crises in both rich and poor countries—even those far from blast.
Impact over sea:
A giant tsunami, with catastrophic effects on most coastlines. Low-lying nations across the globe virtually wiped out in the immediate aftermath.

DOOMSDAY
4

Size of body:
Over 10 miles (16 km) in diameter.
Rate of impact:
Fewer than one every 100 million years.
Impact over land or sea:
Loss of most life forms on Earth as a result of prolonged "impact winter" and consequent ice age.

COMETS

Comets are really nothing more than small, dirty balls of ice, dust and rock that swoop around the solar system in elongated, elliptical orbits. In deep space, they are inert; but as they near the inner solar system, the Sun's heat brings them to life. The ice melts, and the dust and gas boil off to form great glowing tails that can stretch tens of millions of miles through space. For thousands of years, comets were thought to herald great events—or, opposingly, ones foretelling doom. Now, some scientists study their composition with interest as they believe comets may harbor the seeds of life itself.

SOME RECENT COMETS

Name	Closest Approach to Sun (million miles/million km)	Date of Closest Approach	Period
Kohoutek	.13.1/21	.December 28, 1973	.6.67
Kobayashi-Berger-Milon	.39.6/63.7	.September 9, 1975	.Not periodic
West	.18.3/29.4	.February 25, 1976	.Not periodic
Encke	.31.6/50.9	.August 17, 1977	.3.3
Halley	.54.8/88	.February 9, 1986	.76.0
Hyakutake	.21.4/34.4	.May 1, 1996	.Not periodic
Hale-Bopp	.84.9/136.6	.April 1, 1997	.2,380
Lovejoy	.36.8/59.3	.September 7, 2013	.6,300

DIRTY SNOWBALLS

Comets were formed along with the rest of the solar system around 4.6 billion years ago. These fragile lumps of ice and frozen gas could never have coalesced anywhere close to the Sun or they would have been quickly evaporated by its heat. Instead, they were probably born much farther out, in the cold vicinity of the orbits of Uranus or Neptune. There, the comets would have been strongly affected by the gravitation of these two planets. Many of them would have been slung far from the planetary realm to form the Oort Cloud—a spherical region of inert comets that surrounds our solar system and reaches perhaps halfway to the nearest star.

Even at that distance, comets remain in orbit around the Sun—although they may take millions of years to complete their long, elliptical journey. A few—classified by astronomers as short-period comets—make a full orbit in less than 200 years. All the rest are grouped together as long-period comets. Often, they

approach from the Oort Cloud at a steep angle to the plane of the planets, and many of them may be on their first visit to the inner solar system. The human race could well be extinct before some of these voyagers return—if they ever do make the journey towards Earth.

Whatever its orbital period, though, every comet spends most of its existence as an insignificant speck of deep-frozen cosmic debris that is invisible even to the most powerful of telescopes. But as the comet begins its approach to the Sun, the growing warmth triggers a miraculous transformation.

COMET STRUCTURE

At the heart of a comet is a nucleus, at most only tens of miles across. Often called a "dirty snowball," it is largely made of ice, sometimes with a rocky core of a few miles across. The ice consists of layers of frozen gas—hydrogen, nitrogen, oxygen, carbon dioxide and carbon monoxide—as well as water. Dust and pockets of unfrozen gas are mixed in, and everything is encased in a thick crust of frozen dust as dark as coal.

As the comet approaches the Sun, it begins to warm up. Near the

orbit of Jupiter, the Sun's heat is enough to turn its ices into gas, which leaks through cracks in the crust and surrounds the nucleus in a vast halo called the coma. As the comet plunges still closer to the Sun, this material spreads out behind it in the two enormous tails that make comets so spectacular. One is slightly curved and made of dust, which glows yellow-white as it reflects sunlight. The other tail—straight, often blue and always pointing away from the Sun—is made of a thin scattering of gas pushed out millions of miles by the pressure of solar radiation.

HALLEY'S COMET

EDMUND HALLEY WAS THE FIRST PERSON TO REALIZE THAT COMETS ORBIT THE SUN AND SO ARE PERIODIC VISITORS TO OUR SKIES. HE ANALYZED THE ORBITS OF COMETS SEEN IN 1531, 1607 AND 1682, CONCLUDED THAT THEY WERE THE SAME OBJECT, AND PREDICTED THAT IT WOULD REAPPEAR IN 1758. SADLY, HALLEY DID NOT LIVE TO SEE THE REAPPEARANCE OF THE COMET THAT NOW BEARS HIS NAME (RIGHT), BECAUSE HE DIED IN 1742.

INSIDE A COMET
In deep space, a comet is an inert lump of dust and frozen gas. But as the comet approaches the Sun, the gas begins to boil off. It forms a thick "coma" that obscures the original lump, which now becomes the nucleus of the developing comet. Sometimes, the Sun heats pockets of gas trapped beneath the still-frozen surface. Eventually, they burst through, releasing jets of hazy debris that will form the comet's tails. Repeated passes of a comet around the Sun will in time rob it of anything that can still evaporate. Only a rocky core—if the comet has one—will remain, quietly orbiting the Sun as a tiny asteroid.

coma

exploding gas pockets

loose fragments

rocky core

HALLEY'S NUCLEUS

WHEN HALLEY'S COMET APPROACHED THE SUN IN 1986, THE SPACE PROBE GIOTTO FLEW THROUGH ITS COMA. SCIENTISTS WERE EXPECTING TO FIND THAT THE COMET WAS MADE OF MINERAL ELEMENTS SUCH AS IRON, CARBON, CALCIUM AND SILICON. INSTEAD, GIOTTO FOUND HYDROGEN, NITROGEN AND ORGANIC MOLECULES. THE NUCLEUS ITSELF WAS MAINLY ICE.

Hale-Bopp, one of the brightest comets of the 20th century, was prominent in the night sky in the spring of 1997.

inert comet nucleus

ices begin to melt

Jupiter

tails die away

Sun

gas tail

fully formed comet

dust tail

LIFE OF A COMET
Far out in its orbit, the comet is nothing but a frozen nucleus. When it nears the orbit of Jupiter, it starts to thaw. Ice melts, and tails of gas and dust begin to form. As the comet continues inward to the Sun, the tails may expand to a spectacular length. They gradually die away after the comet swings around the Sun and heads off again to the cold fringes of the solar system.

COMETS IN HISTORY

Throughout history, even to the present day, comets have provoked strange reactions in human observers. Often thought to foretell the deaths of rulers, comets have always been seen as bad news. Ignorance has made them history's most feared omen. It was not until the Renaissance that astronomers discovered that comets are not atmospheric phenomena—an idea that had survived since before the birth of Christ. And despite our present-day knowledge of comets, they can still surprise and alarm us.

GREAT COMETS IN HISTORY

Comet	Year	Magnitude	Closest approach to Earth (million miles / million km)
(No name)	1577	−4	94/151
De Cheseaux	1743	−7	125/201
Donati	1858	−1	80/129
Great Southern Comet	1882	−10	148/238
Daylight Comet	1910	−4	130/209
Ikeya-Seki	1965	−10	21/34
Hale-Bopp	1997	−1.5	193/311

CHAPTERS IN COMET HISTORY

DAMNED
The comet of 1456 caused just as much alarm as that of 1066. This was again Comet Halley on a return visit. The comet was declared an agent of the devil by Pope Calixtus III and was officially excommunicated.

EXHALATIONS
IN THE 4TH CENTURY B.C., ARISTOTLE THOUGHT OF THE UNIVERSE AS COMPOSED OF CELESTIAL SPHERES, WITH THE EARTH AT THE CENTER. COMETS, HE THOUGHT, WERE BELOW THE MOON IN THE LOWEST SPHERE AND FLEW IN THE EARTH'S UPPER ATMOSPHERE. HE BELIEVED THAT THEY WERE "EXHALATIONS" FROM THE EARTH — GASSY EMISSIONS FROM FISSURES OR VOLCANOES. ABOVE THE MOON, HE BELIEVED, THE PLANETS AND STARS WERE SUBJECT TO NO CHANGE BUT THEIR CIRCULAR MOTION.

CENTURY'S END
Comet Hale-Bopp over the Little Ajo Mountains, Arizona. One of the most spectacular comets of the century, Hale-Bopp was at its brightest in 1997. Its appearances close to the millennium prompted a slew of extreme religious cults.

BATTLE STAR
The appearance of a comet in 1066 was thought to have foretold the demise of King Harold of England in the Battle of Hastings that took place later that year. It appears in the famous Bayeux Tapestry (above). We now know the fiery omen was Comet Halley.

GREAT COMET
The Great Comet of 1843 as seen from Paris, France. Blazing away at magnitude –7, the tail of this comet stretched across the sky. Estimated to have been over 200 million miles (320 million km) long, it was the longest comet tail ever recorded.

BAD OMENS

The history of comets begins with the Chinese. Between about 1400 B.C. and 1600 A.D., they noted at least 338 cometary appearances, and kept remarkably accurate records, such as the Mawangdui textbook. Dating from about 300 B.C., the book contains reports on 29 comets, illustrated and classified with great care.

However, until the Renaissance, not even the Chinese had any idea what comets were. The view of the 4th-century-B.C. Greek philosopher Aristotle that they were atmospheric phenomena was the most commonly held opinion among scientists. The first person to contradict Aristotle and suggest that comets were celestial bodies was the Roman philosopher Seneca. Unfortunately, Seneca's ideas were not widely accepted.

Aristotle's version was only really overturned by the Danish astronomer Tycho Brahe (1546–1601). In 1577, Brahe used the parallax method of measuring stellar distances, to measure the distance of a comet. He found that it was moving far beyond the Moon, certainly not in Earth's upper atmosphere. With Aristotle's universe dismissed, astronomers needed a new comet theory.

NEW THEORIES

English astronomer Edmond Halley (1656–1742) next worked out the orbits of 24 comets that had been observed between 1337 and 1698. With one he found a regular pattern. The comets of 1531, 1607 and 1682 appeared to be the same object, returning at approximately 76-year intervals. Halley predicted that it would return again in 1758. It did, and was named after Halley in recognition of his achievement.

The next great leaps in comet science were not taken until the 1950s when American astronomer Fred Whipple worked out that comets are lumps of dirty ice.

WHAT IF?
...A COMET CHANGED HISTORY?

How would we cope with the coming of a huge comet?

Imagine that a comet is observed, making a close approach to the Sun. Space agencies work feverishly to launch a small armada of space probes to study the comet.

Then the world gets nervous. Church attendance soars, the media announces the end of the world. Panic ensues and the stock market fluctuates madly. As McCoy-Alvarez continues to swell, the riots starts and spreads like wildfire. In the general confusion, hardly anyone notices that McCoy-Alvarez is receding. The comet has done no harm to the Earth this time—at least, not directly.

METEORS

Gaze upward on a clear night and sooner or later you will see streaks of light that race across the sky for up to a few seconds. Sometimes the streaks give off what look like sparks, or leave a glowing trail. You might even see a storm of streaks, all of which seem to radiate from a fixed point. The objects in question are meteors—natural fireworks displays that are put on by small particles of cometary debris called meteoroids as they fall through space and burn to a cinder high up in the Earth's atmosphere.

METEOR SHOWER CALENDAR

Shower name	Maximum Intensity	Duration (min.)	Visual Strength	Associated Comet
Quadrantids	January 3	5	Medium	Not Known
Lyrids	April 22	5	Irregular	Thatcher
Eta Aquarids	May 4	5	Weak	Halley
Delta Aquarids	July 29	8	Medium	Not Known
Capricornids	July 30	3	Medium	Not Known
Perseids	August 12	6	Strong	Swift-Tuttle
Andromedids	October 3	11	Weak	Biela
Draconids	October 9	1	Irregular	Giacobini-Zinner
Orionids	October 21	2	Medium	Halley
Taurids	November 3	30	Weak	Encke
Leonids	November 17	2	Irregular	Tempel-Tuttle
Geminids	December 14	4	Strong	Asteroid 3200 Phaethon
Ursids	December 22	7	Weak	Tuttle

SPACE TRAILS

To the ancients, the fiery trails of meteors must have looked very much as though a star had come adrift from the heavens and blazed its way across the sky. But the term "shooting star" for a meteor is misleading: Meteors are not stars, but the glowing tracks left by small particles called meteoroids that enter the Earth's atmosphere at high speed and burn up as they do so.

Meteoroids are particles of dust from comet tails that crossed our part of the solar system thousands of years ago. They orbit the Sun at speeds of many miles per second, and if they happen to encounter Earth's atmosphere, their speed increases from between 7 and 45 miles per second (11–72 km/sec).

At such speeds, the particles rapidly find themselves plunging through increasingly dense layers of the atmosphere. Although they weigh no more than a tiny fraction of an ounce, they carry more kinetic energy than a bullet from a gun. Within a fraction of a second, friction heat causes their outer layers vaporize, throwing atoms into the atmosphere.

The atoms cause the surrounding air molecules to become ionized and they begin to glow brightly. The meteoroid itself soon breaks up, but not before it has left a trail of glowing air several yards wide and maybe 20 miles (32 km) long. On the ground, 50 miles (80 km) below,

anyone looking upward during the night hours will see this trail of destruction as the brief appearance of a shooting star.

Within seconds, the meteor is gone and the trail fades. Sometimes, however, the passage of the meteoroid releases so much energy that a train of glowing gas remains for several minutes.

SAME TIME

The Earth's part of the solar system is full of interplanetary debris that results in sporadic meteors. But far more interesting are the regular streams of meteoroids that give rise to meteor showers. These appear without fail on certain dates of the year when the Earth plows through a cloud of debris that has spread out in the wake of a comet's orbit probably within the past few hundred years.

From the ground, the meteors give the impression that they are radiating away from a particular point in the sky, known as the radiant. Simply the perspective, the view is like how parallel lanes of a highway seen from a bridge seem to radiate away from a single point on the horizon.

These meteor showers are named after the constellation in which the radiant appears. The Perseids, for example, regularly produce 60 to 100 meteors an hour around August 12, and appear to come from a point in Perseus. Some showers give rise to true meteor storms, in which hundreds of meteors appear.

WHAT IF?
...THE EARTH PASSED THROUGH A COMET'S TAIL?

Almost all of the regular meteor showers that happen at various times of the year take place when the Earth crosses the orbit of a comet and sweeps up the debris it leaves behind. Most of this debris tends to be scattered evenly around the comet's orbit. But some of the debris may be concentrated at one point in the orbit, and when the Earth crosses such a point, the resulting meteor shower can be spectacular. A good example is the Leonid shower, which revisits once every 33 years.

If the Earth were to pass through the actual tail of a comet, which contains still greater concentrations of debris (freshly swept off the comet by the effects of radiation from the Sun at close range), the result would be not a shower but a storm. Countless billions of cometary meteoroids would be swept up by the atmosphere, and the particles that create noticeable

meteor trails would be present in colossal numbers. Scientists can only speculate what kind of display this concentration of meteoroids would put on, but it would make the average fireworks display seem tame.

The chances of any of these cometary meteoroids reaching ground level would be very slim, so the storm, although dramatic, would not present any physical danger to the Earth's inhabitants. The danger would be if the Earth were hit by the comet's head—or even by just a part of it. The impact of separate fragments of comet Shoemaker-Levy 9 on Jupiter in 1994 clearly demonstrated the potential destructive power of a comet impact on a planet.

The Earth is thought to have been hit by just such a cometary fragment on June 30, 1908, when an object devastated some 850 square miles (2200 square km) of forest in the Tunguska region of central Siberia in Russia.

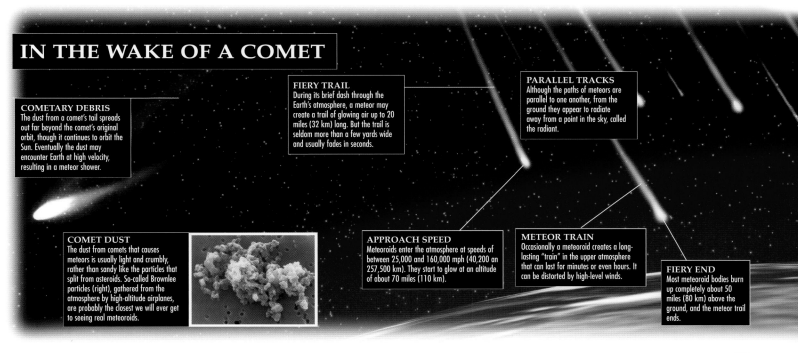

IN THE WAKE OF A COMET

COMETARY DEBRIS
The dust from a comet's tail spreads out far beyond the comet's original orbit, though it continues to orbit the Sun. Eventually the dust may encounter Earth at high velocity, resulting in a meteor shower.

FIERY TRAIL
During its brief dash through the Earth's atmosphere, a meteor may create a trail of glowing air up to 20 miles (32 km) long. But the trail is seldom more than a few yards wide and usually fades in seconds.

PARALLEL TRACKS
Although the paths of meteors are parallel to one another, from the ground they appear to radiate away from a point in the sky, called the radiant.

COMET DUST
The dust from comets that causes meteors is usually light and crumbly, rather than sandy like the particles that split from asteroids. So-called Brownlee particles (right), gathered from the atmosphere by high-altitude airplanes, are probably the closest we will ever get to seeing real meteoroids.

APPROACH SPEED
Meteoroids enter the atmosphere at speeds of between 25,000 and 160,000 mph (40,200 an 257,500 km). They start to glow at an altitude of about 70 miles (110 km).

METEOR TRAIN
Occasionally a meteoroid creates a long-lasting "train" in the upper atmosphere that can last for minutes or even hours. It can be distorted by high-level winds.

FIERY END
Most meteoroid bodies burn up completely about 50 miles (80 km) above the ground, and the meteor trail ends.

METEOR
STREAMS

Meteor streams, the icy trails of debris left in the wake of comets as they pass close to the Sun, are among the most elusive phenomena in the solar system. For most of the time, apart from the odd dent they leave in spacecraft, these clouds of tiny, dark particles might as well not exist—after all, we cannot see them. But when the Earth's orbit crosses their path and they rain down through the atmosphere, burning up as they go, the result is a meteor shower—one of the most dazzling spectacles in the night sky.

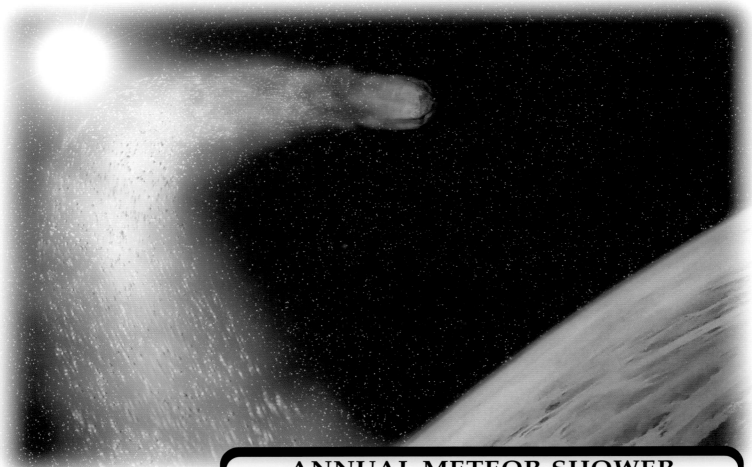

ANNUAL METEOR SHOWER

Name	Date at maximum intensity	Number of meteors per hour	Parent comet
Quadrantids	Jan. 4	110	unknown
Perseids	Aug. 12	68	Comet 1862 III
Orionids	Oct. 21	30	Comet Halley
Leonids	Nov. 17	10	Comet P/Tempel-Tuttle
Geminids	Dec. 14	58	3200 Phaethon

TRAIL BLAZERS

As a comet nears the Sun, its icy outer layer begins to evaporate and it sheds tiny particles, or meteoroids, in its wake. This trail of debris is a known as a meteor stream. The particles in the stream move in roughly the same direction as the comet, but at different speeds. Over time, many of them come to lag far behind their parent body, while others race ahead.

Each time a comet reaches perihelion, its closest point to the Sun, it adds to the trail of meteoroids left behind on its previous visit—for example, Halley's Comet loses around 300 million tons (272 million tonnes) of material on each pass. In this way, the comet steadily shrinks while the meteor stream behind it continues to build up.

In time, the meteor stream becomes strewn across the comet's path—denser in some places than in others, because the comet does not shed material at an even rate. Eventually, the stream may spread all the way around, and slightly beyond, the comet's orbit. By this stage, the comet that created it may well have "died"—its ice having evaporated to leave a dark, dusty core that no longer sheds material to produce a fiery tail. With no fresh dust to replenish it, the meteor stream, too, will gradually melt away to nothing.

SHOWER FORECASTING

Comets can be one of the brightest and most beautiful objects in the night sky, but the meteor streams that they leave behind are completely invisible from Earth. The particles within them are simply too small to be detected, even through the most powerful telescopes. We only become aware of a meteor stream's existence when its path crosses the Earth's orbit around the Sun. At this point, some of the particles pass through the atmosphere, where they reveal themselves as a meteor shower. By comparing the intensity of the shower with the orbit of the stream's parent comet, we can begin to picture how it is distributed across outer space.

The Earth collides with around 10 significant meteor streams each year, producing roughly the same number of regular meteor showers. Not all are spectacular, or even

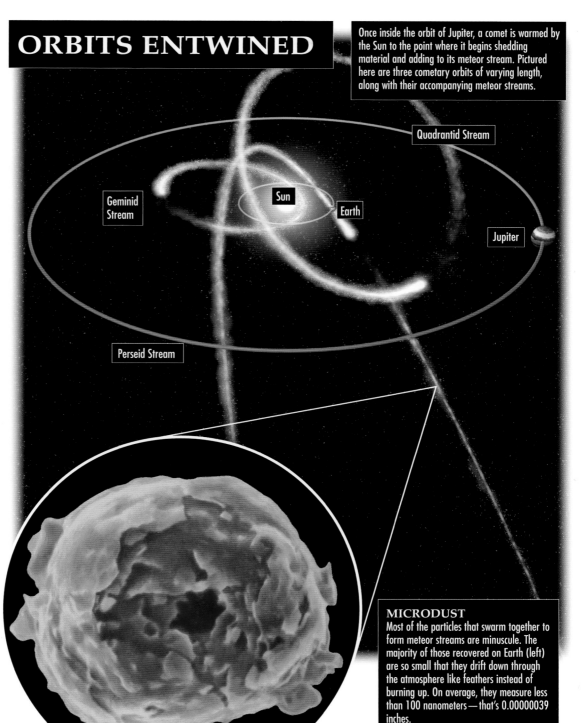

ORBITS ENTWINED

Once inside the orbit of Jupiter, a comet is warmed by the Sun to the point where it begins shedding material and adding to its meteor stream. Pictured here are three cometary orbits of varying length, along with their accompanying meteor streams.

Quadrantid Stream

Geminid Stream

Sun

Earth

Jupiter

Perseid Stream

MICRODUST
Most of the particles that swarm together to form meteor streams are minuscule. The majority of those recovered on Earth (left) are so small that they drift down through the atmosphere like feathers instead of burning up. On average, they measure less than 100 nanometers—that's 0.00000039 inches.

visible to the naked eye. But, on very rare occasions, the Earth runs into an especially dense part of a meteor stream. When this happens, the result is a spectacular meteor "storm" in which the sky becomes ablaze with thousands of fiery streaks.

We may not be able to see a meteor shower approaching, but its return can usually be predicted.

Only a close encounter with a giant planet like Jupiter will drag the meteor stream away from its regular path and cause it to miss the Earth completely. But even if the stream returns, there is still no guarantee of an impressive fireworks display because many comets leave little or no stream beyond their immediate vicinity. The Leonids are a good example.

Around November 17 every year, the Earth crosses the Leonid meteor stream. But only once every 33 years can we expect a really great display—that is, when the Earth crosses the stream just ahead of, or behind, its parent comet, Comet P/Tempel-Tuttle. The 1833, 1866, and 1966 returns of Tempel-Tuttle resulted in some of the most spectacular meteor showers ever seen. The 1999 return also saw spectacular showers in some parts of the world.

METEORITES

Every year the Earth receives thousands of visitors from space. They are meteorites—pieces of rocky debris that have crossed the Earth's path through space to produce spectacular fireballs as they plunge into the atmosphere. Most meteorites simply fall into the sea and are lost. But some are recovered on land, especially in Antarctica, where they lie preserved in the ice. And meteorites are more than just lumps of rock: Many are as old as the solar system itself and offer important clues to the formation of the Earth.

METEORITE CRATERS

Location	Diameter	Age (MILLIONS OF YEARS)
1 Aouelloul, Mauritania	0.23 miles (0.37 km)	3.1
2 Brent, Ontario, Canada	2.4 miles (3.9 km)	450
3 Clearwater Lake, Quebec, Canada	14 miles (23 km)	290
4 Kara, Russia	31 miles (50 km)	57
5 Meteor Crater, Arizona, U.S.	0.75 miles (1.2 km)	0.1 or less
6 Popigay, Russia	62 miles (100 km)	39
7 Ries, Germany	15 miles (24 km)	15
8 Taban Khara Obo, Mongolia	0.8 miles (1.3 km)	30 or less

HARD RAIN FALLING

Most of the pieces of space debris known as meteoroids that streak across the sky are dust grains from comet tails. When these tiny specks of matter hit the atmosphere, the heat generated by friction vaporizes them. But sometimes a much larger and more solid object makes it through the Earth's protective shroud and hits the ground. No longer a meteoroid, its arrival on Earth has earned it the name of meteorite.

Some meteorites originate on the Moon or Mars, where they were once dislodged by ancient asteroid impacts, and a few even began life in the heads of comets. But the majority of meteorites appear to come from the asteroid belt—the ring of debris, possibly the remains of a planet that failed to form, that orbits the Sun between Mars and Jupiter.

When two asteroids collide within the belt, the energy of the impact sends pieces flying. Sooner or later, some of these fragments find themselves on a collision course for Earth. And if a fragment is big enough—at least 4 ounces (100 g) in weight, but more often a pound (500 g) or more—it creates a spectacular fireball as it arrives.

After its scorching descent through the atmosphere, the meteorite reaches the surface as a burned and blackened lump of rock. Yet despite its atmospheric roasting, a meteorite found soon after landing is often coated with frost. This is because, like a cosmic Baked Alaska, its interior remains at the freezing cold temperature of outer space.

HISTORY LESSONS

Meteorites come in two distinct classes. Iron meteorites are composed of a near-pure nickel-iron alloy. Stony meteorites are made from a range of minerals, including some iron. Many stony meteorites have a complex, grainy structure that is quite different from any other known rocks. Scientists believe that these so-called chondrites may have condensed directly from the original dusty nebula that formed our solar system.

Older than any rocks on Earth, chondrites are time capsules from an age before our planet existed and, as such, provide a unique source of information from an era of which we know little. One subgroup, the carbonaceous chondrites, may even yield insights into the origins of life. Formed at the same time as other chondrites, they contain carbon-based organic matter, including amino acids—the fundamental building blocks from which all living things are made. People have even suggested that carbonaceous chondrites were the seeds from which all life on Earth first sprang.

Iron meteorites usually survive weathering on Earth better than their stony companions, which in any case are often mistaken for ordinary Earth rocks. An iron meteorite is noticeably heavier than a stone or rock of the same size. But any recently fallen meteorite is characterized by a black, sooty crust—sometimes covered with ripples—that signifies its fiery arrival in the vicinity of our planet.

Michael Aponte shows what a space rock did to his girlfriend's car. The offending meteorite (inset) was later sold—earning enough for a new car.

STONES FROM SPACE

SENT FROM ALLAH?

REPUTEDLY AMONG THE WORLD'S MOST FAMOUS METE-ORITES IS THE BLACK STONE THAT RESIDES WITHIN THE ANCIENT TEMPLE OF KA'ABA IN THE MOSLEM HOLY CITY OF MECCA. THE STONE IS SAID TO HAVE BEEN GIVEN TO ABRAHAM, FATHER OF THE TRIBE OF ISRAEL, BY THE ARCHANGEL GABRIEL.

1 COLLISION
Asteroids collide infrequently. But when they do, the impact yields a large amount of debris. Fragments from the collision scatter in all directions at various speeds.

2 TARGET EARTH
The speed of asteroid fragments relative to the Earth depends on whether our planet is heading toward them or away from them. Closing speeds can reach 45 miles per second (72 km/sec).

HOT METAL

BEFORE HUMANS LEARNED HOW TO SMELT IRON FROM ITS NATURAL ORES, METEORITES WERE THE ONLY SOURCE OF THIS IMPORTANT METAL. THE ANCIENT EGYPTIANS (RIGHT) USED IT SPARINGLY, ONLY FOR SPECIAL WEAPONS AND EXOTIC JEWELRY.

3 ARRIVAL
The fragments, now called meteoroids, enter the Earth's atmosphere. Air friction slows them down with fiery abruptness and leaves bright trails that can last for several minutes.

GROUNDED
In cross-section, an iron meteorite (right) has a crystallized, shiny surface. Carbonaceous chondrites (far right) are rich in carbon and organic chemicals.

THE STARS IN THE SKY

Humans have seen patterns in the sky since before recorded history, and many of the star groups and constellations we know today probably date back to these times. At first, constellations were merely the pictures formed by joining certain stars together, but after the invention of the telescope astronomers began to allocate faint stars that fell in no pattern to their nearest constellation. Eventually, in the early 20th century, the constellations were formalized as 88 distinct regions of the sky with well-defined boundaries. This means that every object in the sky now lies inside a particular constellation. The precise stars we see in our night sky depend on our location on Earth and the time of year—our view of them changes as the Earth orbits the Sun and spins on its own axis, and the Earth itself always blocks our view of half the great "celestial sphere." The Star Atlas pages that follow show the general layout of the constellations and the positions of interesting objects, while many newspapers, magazines, and websites publish monthly maps showing specific locations of the sky in more detail.

NASA's Hubble Space Telescope can gaze deep into the universe to pick out a menagerie of galaxies. Located within the same tiny region of sky are spiral, elliptical, and irregular galaxies. Some are big, some are small, a few are relatively nearby, but most are almost unimaginably distant from our galaxy.

STAR ATLASES

Astronomers have been trying for thousands of years to make accurate maps of the night sky. Their efforts have resulted in countless different ways of representing the heavens and nearly as many systems for labeling individual stars, so it is hardly surprising that many star atlases appear confusing to the untrained eye. In fact, the principles of a modern star atlas are really quite simple: Once you get used to the dots, lines and strange symbols, you'll find that they are indispensable guides to turning our cluttered skies into clear and fascinating areas of study.

POPULAR STAR ATLASES

Atlas Name	Faintest Star Magnitude	Scale (degrees per in)	Number of Stars	Number of Maps
Norton's 2000.0	6.5	7.250	8,400	16
Sky Atlas 2000.0	8.5	3.120	80,000	26
Uranometria	9.5	1.400	332,000	518
Millennium Star Atlas	11.0	0.705	1,058,000	1,548

MAPPING THE HEAVENS

Star maps and atlases can range from small diagrams in newspapers to large volumes that show hundreds of thousands of stars. But all share one difficulty: how to represent the night sky on a flat sheet of paper when we see it as the inside of a sphere. For a small area this is not too hard, but over a large section of the sky, distortion inevitably creeps in.

Other problems stem from the fact that only half of the celestial sphere is visible from a particular place at any one time, and that the actual part of the sky on view is constantly changing. There is no perfect solution, and there are various ways to divide up the sky. Most are shown here.

Star atlases show the whole sky, section by section, with a reference map to show which part of the sky is visible from the observer's location at each time of the year.

Popular star maps often have lines joining many of the stars. These lines have a double purpose: They show the main star patterns, like the Big Dipper, and they link stars in a particular constellation. Unfortunately, there is no official agreement on where the lines should be placed, and maps can quickly become confusing if they include too many of them.

ONE STAR, SEVERAL NAMES

Stars usually have several different names, most of them provided by the great star catalogs of Johann Bayer (1572–1625) and John Flamsteed (1646–1719). The German Bayer labeled the prominent stars of each constellation with Greek letters in order of brightness: Alpha Centauri, for example, is the brightest star in Centaurus. English astronomer Flamsteed numbered the stars in each constellation from west to east, so 61 Cygni is the 61st star in the Cygnus constellation. A third cataloger, the Frenchman Charles Messier (1730–1817), confined his work to star clusters, nebulae and other deep-space objects now known to be distant galaxies: M31, for example, is Messier's label for the great galaxy in Andromeda. Most star atlases use the names and numbers provided by all three systems, together with more modern labels for very faint stars.

HEMISPHERIC MAPS

THE SECTION OF SKY VISIBLE FROM EACH PART OF THE EARTH VARIES SLIGHTLY FROM MONTH TO MONTH. HEMISPHERIC MAPS TAKE THIS INTO ACCOUNT AND PROVIDE MONTHLY STAR POSITIONS FOR SPECIFIC LOCATIONS. THEY ARE OFTEN PUBLISHED IN NEWSPAPERS AT THE BEGINNING OF EACH MONTH.

LOOKING BACK

SOME EARLY STAR MAPS TOOK THE FORM OF GLOBES AND WERE ILLUSTRATED WITH THE MYTHICAL FIGURES THAT THE CONSTELLATIONS ARE NAMED FOR. BUT MOST OF THEM SHOWED THE HEAVENS FROM THE OUTSIDE LOOKING IN, SO THE STAR PATTERNS WERE MIRROR IMAGES OF WHAT IS ACTUALLY SEEN IN THE SKY.

BIG ORANGE
The celestial sphere is "peeled" like an orange to create six different map sections.

CIRCULAR SKY
From Earth, the sky appears in the form of a giant sphere.

STAR CATALOG
M-numbers denote Messier-cataloged objects. M36, M37 and M38 are all open star clusters in the Auriga constellation.

SKY GRID
The grid used to mark star positions is equivalent to the Earth's longitude and latitude.

ZOOM IN
Star atlases often include magnifications of interesting areas, such as the Scorpius constellation, shown here.

NO GAPS
Each map section overlaps with its neighbors, so that objects do not fall between them.

SQUASHED STARS
Star positions are distorted as the sphere becomes a sheet.

PEELING BACK THE SKY

HARD EVIDENCE

GLOBE CUTTING
A simple way to convert the celestial globe into flat maps is to divide the sky into north and south, using the two poles as center points. The resulting circular maps (far right) show the limit of view at the edge of the circle and the sky directly overhead at the center. The diagram at near right shows how each section of three-dimensional sky is squeezed onto the two-dimensional map.

Star maps in hemispheres have a disadvantage. It is hard to include much detail without making the maps too large to use practically.

STAR POSITIONS

To find the position of a star or any other celestial object, you need only two coordinates—declination and right ascension, roughly the same as the latitude and longitude of a place on Earth. But the sky appears to rotate daily, which adds a complication, and there are movements of stars to take into account. All this means that star maps, unlike their terrestrial cousins, grow out of date every 50 years or so. In the distant future, our descendants will gaze up at skies quite different from those familiar to us today.

BRIGHTEST STARS

NAME	RIGHT ASCENSION	DECLINATION
SIRIUS	06 HR 45 MIN	−16°43′
CANOPUS	06 HR 24 MIN	−52°42′
ALPHA CENTAURI	14 HR 40 MIN	−60°50′
ARCTURUS	14 HR 16 MIN	+19°11′
VEGA	18 HR 37 MIN	+38°47′
CAPELLA	05 HR 17 MIN	+46°00′
RIGEL	05 HR 15 MIN	−08°12′
PROCYON	07 HR 39 MIN	+05°13′
ACHERNAR	01 HR 38 MIN	−57°14′
BETELGEUSE	05 HR 55 MIN	+07°24′

ALL POSITIONS ARE GIVEN FOR THE EPOCH 2000.0

HEAVENS ABOVE

The sky appears to us as the inside of a globe, which astronomers call the celestial sphere. As the Earth spins on its axis, the celestial sphere seems to rotate in the opposite direction. But the axis remains fixed throughout the year; any star in particular traces out the same circle around the Earth every day, and passes over the same points on Earth.

The sky has its equivalent of the latitude and longitude we use to mark positions on Earth. Celestial latitude is called declination. Stars with a declination of 0° travel along the celestial equator—directly above the Earth's equator; those with declinations of +90° or –90° are always above the Earth's North and South poles respectively.

To measure longitude in the sky, you need a fixed starting point. This can be anywhere you like, so long as everyone else agrees. On Earth, "longitude zero" is set arbitrarily on Greenwich in London, England; on the celestial sphere, astronomers have chosen the point where the Sun crosses the celestial equator in March.

Known as the first point of Aries, this point marks zero in the sky's longitude system, which astronomers call right ascension. The scale is measured in hours and minutes. The star Regulus, for example, has a right ascension of 10 hours and eight minutes. So 10 hours and eight minutes after "zero" has passed above an observer, the sky's rotation will bring the star into view.

CHASING STARS

Like latitude on Earth, declination is measured as an angle: 15° of declination covers 15° of sky. Right ascension is trickier. Because of the direction the sky appears to move in, the scale runs from right to left (from west to east); 24 hours of right ascension cover 360° of the sky. Just as the Earth's lines of longitude vary in their distance apart depending on their latitude, so the size of the sky-circle described by right ascension varies with the declination. On the celestial equator, where the imaginary lines of right ascension are farthest apart, one hour covers a vast area of sky. But near the celestial poles, where the lines

of the sky's "longitude" converge, one hour is able to take in far less space. In each case, though, an hour of right ascension matches 15° of a circle, as well as an hour of real time.

There is another complication. Because the Earth is moving in its orbit, the planet's rotation relative to the stars is slightly faster than its rotation relative to the Sun. In fact, the stars take 23 hours 56 minutes to rotate in the sky, rather than the 24 hours of our solar day. If you time a star crossing your meridian—that is, a north-south line drawn through your position—on one night, the

star will cross it four minutes earlier the night after.

Because of this four-minute difference, astronomers have to employ a separate timescale, called sidereal time, to keep track of star movements. Just as there is a local time for every point on Earth measured by the apparent movement of the Sun, so there is a sidereal time based on the apparent movement of the stars.

Despite these measurements, star maps are only accurate for about 50 years as star positions are subject to an unpredictable and gradual shifting. Stars move through space with their own speeds and in their own directions. Slow variations in the Earth's orbit also affect accuracy.

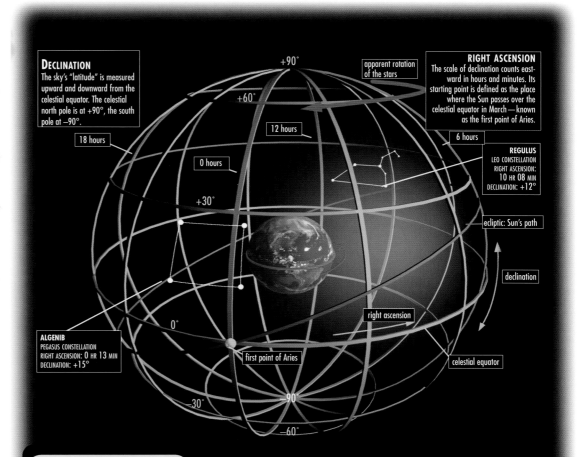

DECLINATION
The sky's "latitude" is measured upward and downward from the celestial equator. The celestial north pole is at +90°, the south pole at –90°.

+90°
+60°
12 hours
18 hours
0 hours
+30°

apparent rotation of the stars

RIGHT ASCENSION
The scale of declination counts eastward in hours and minutes. Its starting point is defined as the place where the Sun passes over the celestial equator in March—known as the first point of Aries.

6 hours

REGULUS
LEO CONSTELLATION
RIGHT ASCENSION:
10 HR 08 MIN
DECLINATION: +12°

ecliptic: Sun's path

declination

right ascension

ALGENIB
PEGASUS CONSTELLATION
RIGHT ASCENSION: 0 HR 13 MIN
DECLINATION: +15°

0°

first point of Aries

celestial equator

–30°
–90°
–60°

THE CELESTIAL SPHERE

HOT TIP

UNTIL RECENTLY, OBSERVATORIES USED A SEPARATE CLOCK SET TO RUN FOUR MINUTES PER DAY SLOWER THAN NORMAL. THE CLOCK KEPT TRACK OF SIDEREAL TIME, WHICH ASTRONOMERS NEED TO KNOW IN ORDER TO POINT THEIR TELESCOPES ACCURATELY. TODAY, ELECTRONIC EQUIPMENT HAS MADE THE SIDEREAL CLOCK OBSOLETE.

HARD EVIDENCE

STAR CRUISER
The fastest-moving star across the sky is the faint Barnard's Star (right), visible in small telescopes. It moves 10.3 arc seconds per year—a Moon diameter every 150 years. Like many local stars, Barnard's is a red dwarf, smaller and dimmer than our Sun. Its speedy apparent motion is due to its proximity. Only six light-years away, Barnard's Star is the third-closest star to Earth, after the Sun and Alpha Centauri.

PRECISE DANE

THE 16TH-CENTURY DANISH ASTRONOMER TYCHO BRAHE MEASURED THE POSITIONS OF HUNDREDS OF STARS TO AMAZING ACCURACY BY EYE ALONE, AS THE TELESCOPE HAD NOT YET BEEN INVENTED. HE USED A MURAL QUADRANT—A SCALE OF DEGREES FIXED TO A SOUTH-POINTING WALL. AMONG TYCHO'S OTHER CLAIMS TO FAME WAS HIS NOSE. AFTER THE ORIGINAL WAS CUT OFF IN A DUEL, HE REPLACED IT WITH A GOLD AND SILVER REPLICA.

MAGNITUDE SCALE

From blazing Sirius to the dimmest members of the Little Dipper, the night sky is littered with stars of different brightnesses. Ancient observers plotted these celestial beacons, taking notice of each light's position, intensity and color. With the advent of the telescope, many other less-brilliant objects were revealed. More recently, digital cameras and giant optics have plumbed the depths of space, bringing into view stars and galaxies millions of times fainter than those familiar to us in the night sky.

KEY DATES FOR MAGNITUDE

HIPPARCHUS PRODUCES HIS STAR CATALOG	129 B.C.
PTOLEMY'S ALMAGEST IS PUBLISHED	137 A.D.
GALILEO GALILEI DISCOVERS NEW STARS	1610
NORMAN POGSON'S LOGARITHMIC SCALE	1856
PALOMAR 200-IN (5-M) TELESCOPE SEES TO MAGNITUDE 20	1947
MAGNITUDE −22 FIREBALLS OBSERVED	1993
HUBBLE IMAGES 30TH-MAGNITUDE GALAXIES	1995

LIGHT GAUGE

Around 130 B.C., the Greek astronomer Hipparchus (c. 180–125 B.C.) categorized the brightest stars as "first magnitude." This was the first step in creating a system to rank stars in order of brightness. Lesser stars, which were still quite bright, were called 2nd and 3rd magnitude. Combined, these stars made up many of the familiar asterisms of the sky. Fainter stars, scattered throughout the heavens, were similarly rated: 4th and 5th magnitude points in decreasing brightness. Finally, 6th magnitude stars lay at the outer limit of visibility.

After its inclusion in the Egyptian astronomer Ptolemy's (c. 90–168 A.D.) star atlas, the Almagest, the system was adopted unchanged through the Middle Ages—until Galileo turned his telescope toward the heavens and discovered stars fainter than the ones seen with the naked eye. The brightest of these he termed "seventh magnitude."

The current scale encompasses objects with brightness differences of almost 60 magnitudes. The brightest, our Sun, is a blinding magnitude –26.7; the dimmest galaxies glimpsed in long-exposure images captured by the Hubble Space Telescope are estimated to approach magnitude +30. This span represents a huge disparity in brightness—the distant galaxies are some 100 billion trillion times fainter than the Sun.

Fully dark-adapted eyes can see as far down as magnitude 6.5, which encompasses all the planets out to Saturn. A pair of 50-millimeter binoculars reveals 9th magnitude objects, bringing Uranus and Neptune into view; and a 6-in (152-mm) reflector telescope detects magnitude 13, so Pluto is just visible (if you know just where to look). An amateur with a modest telescope fitted with a CCD (charge coupled device) can see objects down to magnitude 20, a domain long reserved for observatories.

All these magnitudes represent an object's brightness as seen from Earth—its apparent magnitude. This gives no clue to an object's intrinsic brightness: A dim star nearby could have the same apparent magnitude as a bright star that is far away. To compare the real brightness of objects, astronomers use absolute magnitude—a measure of brightness as seen from a standard distance of 32.6 light-years. At that range, our Sun would glow feebly at magnitude 4.85. But the giant star Rigel in the constellation of Orion would shine at –8, rivaling the brightness of the quarter Moon.

Today, devices called photometers can measure to hundredths of a magnitude and can detect subtle changes in a star's output and tiny changes in a planet's albedo (how much sunlight is reflected off the surface), or compare the brightnesses of comets. These precise measurements can give vital clues to the inner structure and workings of the object.

HARD EVIDENCE

WORK IT OUT
You can use a calculator to estimate the brightness difference between our Sun and a given star. First, look up the star's magnitude in a sky atlas and subtract the star's magnitude from –27 (the Sun's magnitude). Then tap in 2.512 and raise it to the power of the difference. For example, a 3rd-magnitude star is 30 magnitudes dimmer than the Sun. Raise 2.512 to the power of 30 and you get a 1 with 12 zeros after it, or a trillion. The star appears a trillion times dimmer than the Sun in the sky.

WHAT IF?
...WE COULD SEE FARTHER?

A giant space telescope operated from a permanent space station could glimpse objects at vast distances— and thus events that took place billions of years ago.

Ever since the advent of the telescope, astronomers have been intent on seeing farther and fainter objects in the depths of space. For two centuries, observers used larger and larger mirrors to probe the cosmos. By the end of the 19th century, photography had boosted the telescope's light grasp. The 20th century saw an instrumentation explosion with the introduction of giant telescopes, smart drives, adaptive optics, CCDs (charge coupled devices) and computer-enhanced imaging. And by the end of the same century, the orbiting Hubble Space Telescope, flying above the atmospheric distortion, had reached down to magnitude +30 by scanning a barren patch of sky for 35 hours straight.

Every time the magnitude barrier is broken and scientists exceed the earlier limit of detection, discoveries are made and insights are gained about the processes that drive the universe. And so the quest for ever fainter objects goes on.

The future promises exciting developments. Further miniaturization of silicon chips—the same process that drives the performance gains of computers—will push the technological limits of digital imaging. Upgraded CCDs attached to the larger replacement for the Hubble Space Telescope will provide further increases in sensitivity, capturing objects a few magnitudes dimmer than currently possible.

Perhaps before the end of the 21st century we will see telescopes reaching down to magnitudes as dim as +50. One future development might be that of the ultimate space observatory. With a limiting magnitude of +50, it is hard to imagine what could be dredged up by this enormous eye on the sky. Beneath its gaze would lie planets in other star systems and distant protogalaxies. Perhaps we could see to the edge of the universe—and to the beginning of creation.

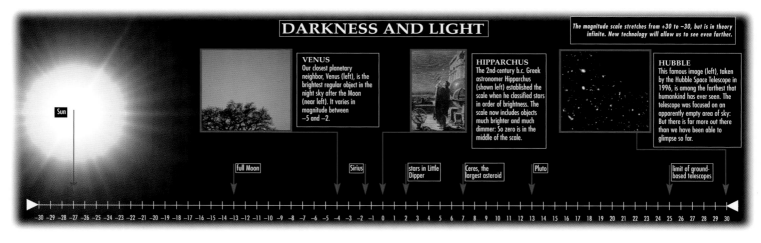

DARKNESS AND LIGHT

The magnitude scale stretches from +30 to –30, but is in theory infinite. New technology will allow us to see even farther.

Sun

VENUS
Our closest planetary neighbor, Venus (left), is the brightest regular object in the night sky after the Moon (near left). It varies in magnitude between –5 and –2.

HIPPARCHUS
The 2nd-century b.c. Greek astronomer Hipparchus (shown left) established the scale when he classified stars in order of brightness. The scale now includes objects much brighter and much dimmer: So zero is in the middle of the scale.

HUBBLE
This famous image (left), taken by the Hubble Space Telescope in 1996, is among the farthest that humankind has ever seen. The telescope was focused on an apparently empty area of sky: But there is far more out there than we have been able to glimpse so far.

full Moon | Sirius | stars in Little Dipper | Ceres, the largest asteroid | Pluto | limit of ground-based telescopes

–30 –29 –28 –27 –26 –25 –24 –23 –22 –21 –20 –19 –18 –17 –16 –15 –14 –13 –12 –11 –10 –9 –8 –7 –6 –5 –4 –3 –2 –1 0 1 2 3 4 5 6 7 8 9 10 11 12 13 14 15 16 17 18 19 20 21 22 23 24 25 26 27 28 29 30

STAR ATLAS 1

To use a star atlas, it helps to imagine that the stars are fixed to the inside of a transparent sphere around the Earth. A star atlas divides this sphere into six sections: one each for the regions around the north and south celestial poles, and four that divide the equatorial regions like the segments of an orange. This section covers the sky from the north celestial pole to a declination of 40° N, describing features that are visible all year from latitudes above 40° N (north of Philadelphia, Pennsylvania, or Madrid, Spain).

SIGHTS IN THE NORTHERN SKY

	Right Ascension	Declination	Apparent Magnitude	Angular Separation		Right Ascension	Declination	Apparent Magnitude	Angular Separation
BRIGHT STARS					**STAR CLUSTERS**				
Capella	07H 17M	+46°00'	0.08	N/A	Double Cluster	02H 20M	+57°08'	6.00	N/A
Deneb	20H 41M	+45°17'	1.33	N/A					
					GALAXIES				
DOUBLE STARS					M 81	09H 56M	+69°04'	6.90	N/A
Mizar	13H 24M	+54°56'	2.22	14"	M 82	09H 56M	+69°41'	8.40	N/A
Nu Draconis	17H 32M	+55°10'	4.90	62"	M 51 (Whirlpool)	13H 30M	+47°12'	8.40	N/A
VARIABLE STARS									
Mu Cephei	21H 44M	+58°47'	3.4–5.10	N/A					
Delta Cephei	22H 29M	+58°25'	3.5–4.40	N/A					

NORTHERN LIGHTS

Featuring prominently in the northern sky is the group of seven stars that make up the Big Dipper—actually a part of the constellation Ursa Major. Two stars in the bowl of the Dipper, Merak and Dubhe, point to the north pole star, Polaris. On the opposite side of Polaris from the Big Dipper lies the distinctive W-shape of the constellation Cassiopeia.

Because Polaris lies very close to the sky's north pole, the rest of the sky appears to turn counterclockwise around it. The orientation of this map therefore depends on when you look at it. A good tip is to find north, then look around you, halfway up the sky, until you come to Polaris. Follow by searching for either the Big Dipper or Cassiopeia, and turn the map to match the positions of these constellations.

The brightest star in the northern part of the sky is Capella in the constellation of Auriga, with Deneb, in Cygnus, in second place. The Milky Way, which runs through Cassiopeia, is almost overhead on winter evenings.

KEMBLE'S CASCADE

With binoculars, look for a shaft of starlight in the constellation of Camelopardalis (the Giraffe). Kemble's Cascade consists of a chain of about 20 stars, the brightest of which is 5th magnitude, and spans five Moon widths. Canadian astronomer Lucian Kemble described it in 1980 as "a beautiful cascade of faint stars, tumbling from the northeast down to the open cluster NGC 1502." To find it, begin at the bright stars of Perseus and hop north from star to star until you see the 5th magnitude star at the Cascade's center.

M 81 AND M 82

A pair of contrasting galaxies are within range of small telescopes in the northern part of Ursa Major, about a third of the way from the bowl of the Big Dipper to the Pole Star. M 81 is a beautiful, symmetrically shaped spiral galaxy. It covers nearly half the area of the full Moon, but is tilted at an angle to us so that its outline appears almost elliptical. Half a degree to the north of it is situated M 82, smaller and fainter but still

The map covers areas of the sky around the celestial north pole (below, shaded).

detectable in binoculars on a good night. M 82 is also elliptical, and is at right angles to M 81. M 82 is thought to be interacting with a large cloud of dust, which can give it a strange appearance on long-exposure photographs.

POLARIS

Contrary to popular myth, the North Pole Star, Polaris, is not especially bright. In fact, it is an ordinary-looking star of 2nd magnitude that is special only because it happens to lie within a degree of the north celestial pole. Small telescopes show that Polaris is the brightest member of a roughly circular chain of stars, like a necklace, about one full Moon width wide. Polaris is actually classified as a Cepheid variable, but its brightness changes are so slight that they are not noticeable with the naked eye.

Magnitude Scale

⬤	0
⬤	1
●	2
●	3
•	4
·	5

Numbers around the edge of the map are hours of right ascension. Numbers in the middle are degrees of declination.

STAR ATLAS 2

This section covers the region of sky between declination 50° N and 50° S, and from right ascension 21 hours to three hours. Running vertically through the center of this area is the line marking zero-hours right ascension, the sky's equivalent of the Greenwich meridian. The zero line runs from the celestial poles through the point where the Sun crosses the celestial equator from south to north each year. The stars in this part of the sky are visible in the evening from September through to December.

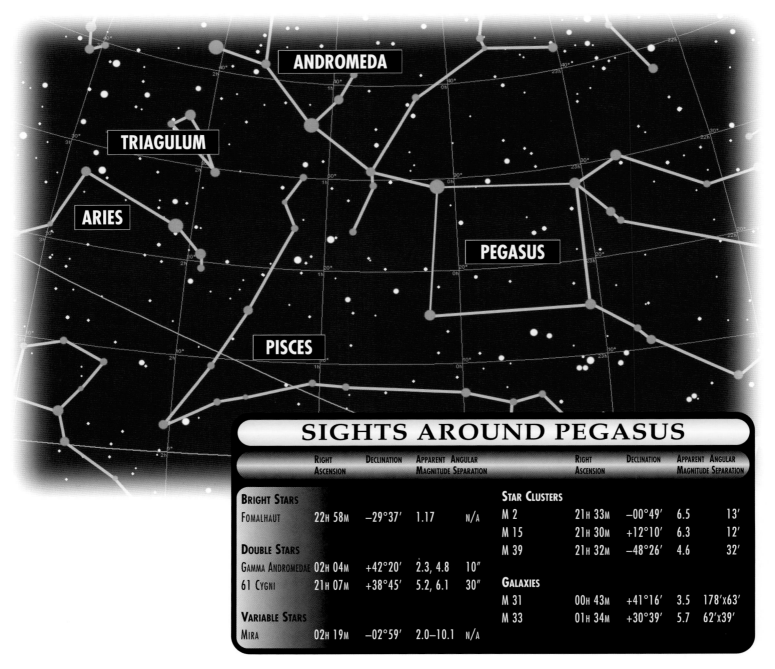

SIGHTS AROUND PEGASUS

	RIGHT ASCENSION	DECLINATION	APPARENT MAGNITUDE	ANGULAR SEPARATION		RIGHT ASCENSION	DECLINATION	APPARENT MAGNITUDE	ANGULAR SEPARATION
BRIGHT STARS					**STAR CLUSTERS**				
FOMALHAUT	22H 58M	−29°37′	1.17	N/A	M 2	21H 33M	−00°49′	6.5	13′
					M 15	21H 30M	+12°10′	6.3	12′
DOUBLE STARS					M 39	21H 32M	−48°26′	4.6	32′
GAMMA ANDROMEDAE	02H 04M	+42°20′	2.3, 4.8	10″					
61 CYGNI	21H 07M	+38°45′	5.2, 6.1	30″	**GALAXIES**				
					M 31	00H 43M	+41°16′	3.5	178′x63′
VARIABLE STARS					M 33	01H 34M	+30°39′	5.7	62′x39′
MIRA	02H 19M	−02°59′	2.0–10.1	N/A					

NORTHERN FALL SKIES

This area of sky is strangely bereft of bright objects. The only 1st magnitude star is Fomalhaut, in the constellation Piscis Austrinus. Dominating this area is the Square of Pegasus, which stands astride the zero-hour line of right ascension. The Square is a block of sky with a moderately bright star at each corner. From mid-northern latitudes, the Square stands high in the south on November evenings. A line southward from the western edge of the Square leads to Fomalhaut. Northwest of the Square is Cygnus, a summer constellation now departing the evening sky.

Draw a line northward from the eastern side of the Square and you will come to the W-shape of stars that marks the position of the constellation Cassiopeia and, in the north-eastern corner, her daughter Andromeda.

NGC 253

The constellation of Sculptor contains the south pole of our Galaxy, the point that lies at 90° south of the plane of the Milky Way. In this direction, we can see out into deep space without interruption from stars, gas or dust clouds in our own galaxy. The most prominent galaxies in Sculptor are NGC 55, on its southern border, and NGC 253 (inset), almost on its northern border with Cetus. Both are spiral galaxies tilted to us at such an angle that they appear elongated. NGC 253, the brighter of the two, can be picked up in binoculars under favorable conditions. Moderate-size telescopes show that NGC 253 has a mottled appearance, which was caused by dust clouds in its arms.

NGC 891

A galaxy of interest in the constellation of Andromeda is NGC 891 (top inset), a spiral seen almost exactly edge-on. Lying near the border with Perseus, it can be glimpsed in moderate-size telescopes as a hazy 10th-magnitude band of light one-third the apparent diameter of the Moon. Larger telescopes—with apertures of 12 in (300 mm) or more—may show a dark lane of dust that runs across the galaxy, but this feature is best seen on long-exposure photographs.

M 39

The large open star cluster M 39 can be found high in the sky in the eastern edge of Cygnus (at the top right of the main map). It is bright enough to be glimpsed with the naked eye under clear conditions. Binoculars show its most prominent members (inset), of 7th magnitude, while through small telescopes about two dozen stars can be seen, with the same apparent width as the full Moon. M 39 lies 950 light-years away.

ARABIAN NIGHTS

Many civilizations in history have had their own star myths and constellation figures, with the present system only accepted in 1930. Although most constellations are Greek in origin, many stars have Arabic names, showing that Arabic astronomy was once dominant.

As most of Europe entered the so-called Dark Ages—when much of the knowledge built up by the Greeks and Romans was lost—the nations of Islam became the center of astronomical knowledge.

Perhaps the most influential Arabic astronomer was Abd al-Rahman al-Sufi (903–986), known as Azophi. Around 964 a.d., he produced an Arabic edition of the Greek star atlas the Almagest, in which he introduced many star names. Some came from tribes, but others were Arabic versions of Ptolemy's descriptions. As Arabic influence spread into Spain from the 10th century onward, the works of Ptolemy (90–168), the author of the Almagest, were reintroduced to European scholars. Greek and Arab books were translated from Arabic into Latin, the scientific language of the day.

By this roundabout route, we now have constellations of Greek origin bearing Latin titles and containing stars with Arabic names.

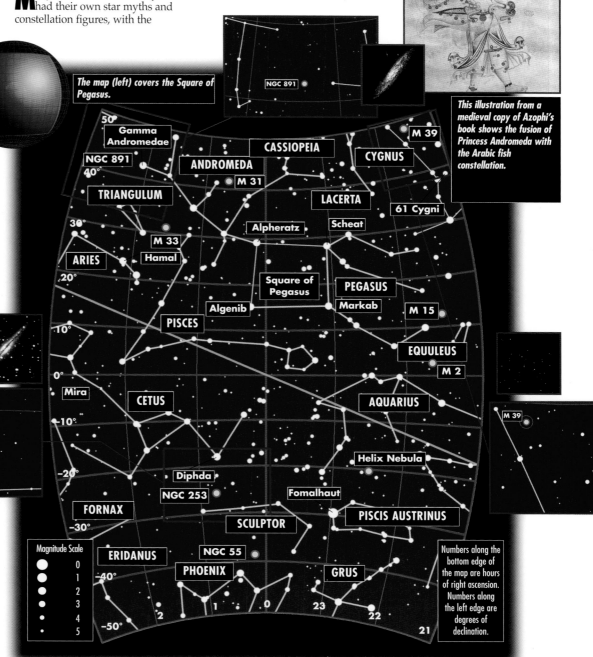

The map (left) covers the Square of Pegasus.

This illustration from a medieval copy of Azophi's book shows the fusion of Princess Andromeda with the Arabic fish constellation.

Magnitude Scale
0
1
2
3
4
5

Numbers along the bottom edge of the map are hours of right ascension. Numbers along the left edge are degrees of declination.

169

STAR
ATLAS 3

This section covers the region of the sky from three hours to nine hours right ascension, and between declination 50° north and 50° south. Running down the center of this area from north to south is the six-hour line of right ascension, which passes just to the east of the bright star Betelgeuse. The Sun crosses this six-hour line at the June solstice each year. This part of the sky is visible in the evening from December to March—making it winter in the northern hemisphere and summer in the southern hemisphere.

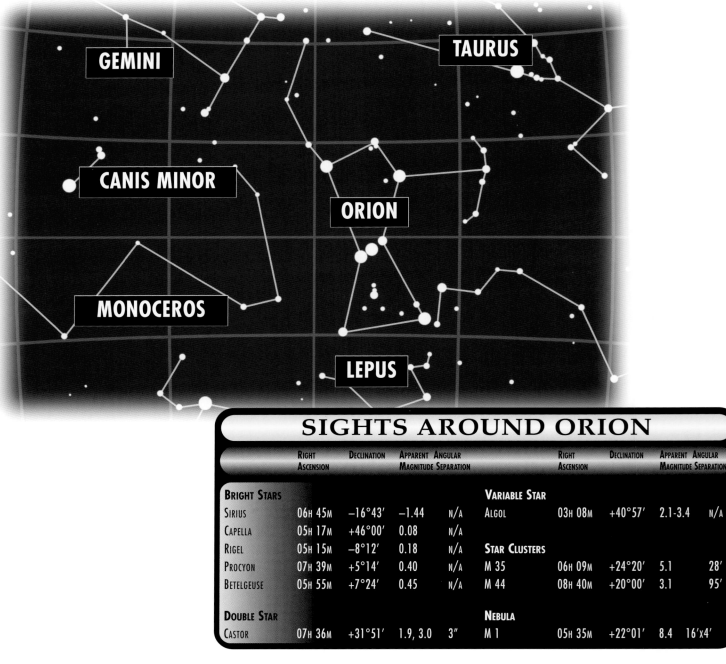

SIGHTS AROUND ORION

	Right Ascension	Declination	Apparent Magnitude	Angular Separation		Right Ascension	Declination	Apparent Magnitude	Angular Separation
Bright Stars					**Variable Star**				
Sirius	06H 45M	−16°43′	−1.44	N/A	Algol	03H 08M	+40°57′	2.1-3.4	N/A
Capella	05H 17M	+46°00′	0.08	N/A					
Rigel	05H 15M	−8°12′	0.18	N/A	**Star Clusters**				
Procyon	07H 39M	+5°14′	0.40	N/A	M 35	06H 09M	+24°20′	5.1	28′
Betelgeuse	05H 55M	+7°24′	0.45	N/A	M 44	08H 40M	+20°00′	3.1	95′
Double Star					**Nebula**				
Castor	07H 36M	+31°51′	1.9, 3.0	3″	M 1	05H 35M	+22°01′	8.4	16′x4′

ORION'S CONSORT

Straddling the celestial equator, the constellation Orion takes center stage, surrounded by Taurus, Auriga, Gemini and Canis Major. This is one of the most glorious areas of the sky, containing five of the 10 brightest stars in the heavens: Sirius, Capella, Rigel, Procyon and Betelgeuse. South of the three stars of Orion's belt is a complex of stars and gas clouds that form his sword, most notably the Orion Nebula. Follow the line of Orion's belt to the northwest and you will come to the V-shaped Hyades star cluster in Taurus. To its southeast the belt points to Sirius in Canis Major, the brightest star in the entire night sky. Northeast of Orion is Gemini, with its brightest stars Castor and Pollux, while north of Orion lies Auriga and its leading star Capella. To the southwest of Orion the long constellation of Eridanus, the river, meanders into the southern sky.

THE TRAPEZIUM

At the heart of the Orion Nebula is a multiple star known as Theta Orionis, popularly called the Trapezium because its four brightest stars are arranged in a trapezium shape (an irregular quadrilateral). Actually a small cluster of stars, Theta Orionis (below) was born from the gas of the Orion Nebula within the past few million years, and the light of the newborn stars makes the nebula glow. Small telescopes show the four brightest components of Theta Orionis, of magnitudes 5.1, 6.7, 6.7 and 7.9, but a telescope with a 4-in (100-mm) aperture or larger also reveals two others. Nearby lies Theta-2 Orionis.

M 78

Attention on nebulosity in Orion often focuses on the glorious Orion Nebula and the faint but fascinating Horsehead Nebula to its north. Consequently, the patch of nebulosity known as M 78 (below) is often overlooked. Unlike most bright nebulae, it is not composed of glowing gas, but is lit up by starlight reflected off dust. In moderate apertures it resembles the head of a comet with a short tail. A 10th-magnitude double star appears at the "comet's" head.

M 79

The beautiful globular cluster M 79 is notable for its unusual position. Most globular clusters are situated close to the center of the galaxy. But M 79 (below) lies in the opposite hemisphere of the sky from the Galactic Center. This is because the cluster is actually beyond us from the perspective of the Galactic Center: It is about 41,000 light-years from us, but about 60,000 light-years from the Galactic Center.

STARS OF HISTORY

To the ancient Greeks, Orion was a great hunter, but other cultures saw the constellation differently. In ancient Egypt, Orion represented Osiris, god of the underworld, who was killed by his brother before becoming immortal.

In China, Orion was seen as the leading warrior appointed by the local farmers to defend their food against raiders during the winter. For Hindus, the three belt stars formed an arrow, shot by the deer slayer, Lubdhaka, whose bow is represented by Sirius and nearby stars. Native Peruvians saw the three stars of Orion as a criminal held by the arms, with the four stars outlining the body of Orion as vultures about to tear him apart.

This map covers the area of sky around the constellation of Orion

50°
40°
30°
20°
10°
0°
-10°
-20°
-30°
-40°
-50°

PERSEUS
Capella
Algol
AURIGA
M 38
Castor
Pollux
GEMINI
M 35
M1
Pleiades star cluster
TAURUS
Aldebaran
Hyades star cluster
CANCER
M 44
Ecliptic
CANIS MINOR
Betelgeuse
Procyon
ORION
HYDRA
M 78
Orion Nebula
Orion's Belt
MONOCEROS
Rigel
Sirius
LEPUS
M 41
M 79
ERIDANUS
CANIS MAJOR
PUPPIS
COLUMBA
CAELUM
HOROLOGIUM

Magnitude Scale
0
1
2
3
4
5

Numbers along the bottom edge of the map are hours of right ascension. Numbers along the left edge are degrees of declination.

8 7 6 5 4 3

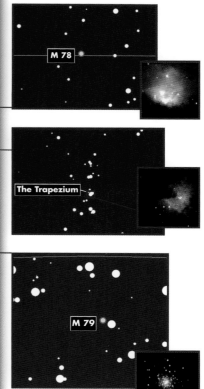

M 78

The Trapezium

M 79

STAR ATLAS 4

This section covers the region of the sky from right ascension nine hours to 15 hours, and between declination 50° north and 50° south. Running north to south through the center of this area is the 12-hour line of right ascension, which brushes the tail of Leo before heading into the southern celestial hemisphere. The Sun crosses this 12-hour line at the September equinox each year. This part of the sky is visible from March until June—spring in the northern hemisphere and fall in the southern hemisphere.

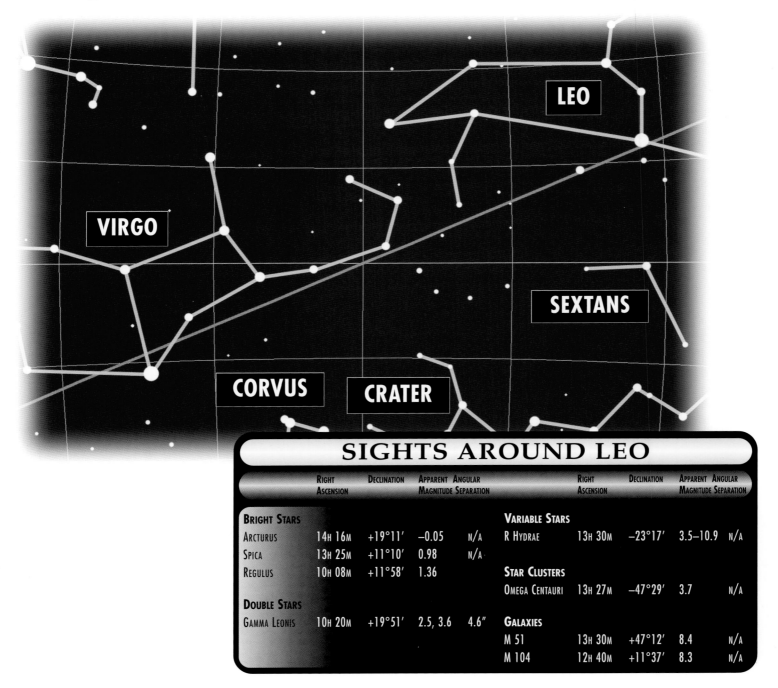

SIGHTS AROUND LEO

	Right Ascension	Declination	Apparent Magnitude	Angular Separation
Bright Stars				
Arcturus	14H 16M	+19°11'	−0.05	N/A
Spica	13H 25M	+11°10'	0.98	N/A
Regulus	10H 08M	+11°58'	1.36	
Double Stars				
Gamma Leonis	10H 20M	+19°51'	2.5, 3.6	4.6"

	Right Ascension	Declination	Apparent Magnitude	Angular Separation
Variable Stars				
R Hydrae	13H 30M	−23°17'	3.5–10.9	N/A
Star Clusters				
Omega Centauri	13H 27M	−47°29'	3.7	N/A
Galaxies				
M 51	13H 30M	+47°12'	8.4	N/A
M 104	12H 40M	+11°37'	8.3	N/A

LION'S DEN

This area of sky is ruled by Leo, its head marked by a sickle-shape of stars with the brightest, Regulus, at the base. Blue-white Regulus is at the apex of a long, thin triangle of stars completed by Arcturus in Boötes and Spica in Virgo. The orange-colored Arcturus, harbinger of spring, also helps form another pattern: a large starry "Y," made up of Epsilon Boötis (Izar) in the middle, Alpha Coronae Borealis (Alphecca) at top left and Gamma Boötis (Seginus) at top right.

South of Leo, the constellation of Hydra, the Water Snake, slithers across 100° of sky from its head, adjoining Cancer and Canis Minor, to the tip of its tail, next to Libra.

Beneath the tail of Hydra, lies the Centaurus, the Centaur, boasting the largest and brightest globular cluster in the sky, Omega Centauri.

M 68

To find this 8th-magnitude globular cluster, draw a line southward from Delta through Beta Corvi to reach a 5th-magnitude double star. M 68 is about a Moon's width away. Visible as a fuzzy star in binoculars, it shows up in small telescopes at about 10 times the diameter of Jupiter. This extremely rich globular contains over 100,000 stars, and would appear far more impressive were it not over 30,000 light-years away. Some of its outlying stars appear to be in loops, but apertures of at least 4 in (100 mm) are needed to see this.

M 84 AND M 86

Near the heart of the Virgo cluster lie two of its main members. M 84 is classed as an elliptical galaxy, but it may in fact be a lenticular galaxy, class S0—halfway between an elliptical and a spiral. M 86, an elliptical galaxy, is the larger of the pair, with a more distinct edge than the hazier M 84. Both M 84 and M 86 can be seen through a 3-in (76-mm) telescope, and is surrounded with faint galaxies.

M 105

Galaxy hunters will be familiar with the pairings of M 65 and M 66, and M 95 and M 96. The latter duo has a third companion which is often overlooked: M 105, a 9th-magnitude elliptical galaxy that appears almost perfectly rounded and featureless except for its star-like core. Small telescopes will show it, while somewhat larger apertures will also detect two fainter galaxies with which it forms a triangle, NGC 3384 and—faintest of the trio—NGC 3389. All these galaxies are thought to be members of a related group.

A DIFFERENT STORY

To modern-day observers, the stars of Leo outline the shape of a lion, but other civilizations saw them differently. For example, about 4,000 years ago, the ancient Babylonians interpreted the stars of Leo as a huge dog, representing the ferocious guard dogs they used for protection. Elsewhere, the sickle of Leo has been seen as a figure, such as in Siberia, where the shape of a sleeping woman was seen in its arc of stars, with the top of the sickle her head and Regulus her knees. In China, the arc of the sickle was extended to the north to complete the Rain Dragon, an effigy of which was carried at times of drought. In another Chinese grouping, the star at the root of Leo's tail, Denebola, represented the Chinese Royal Prince, and the surrounding stars were his extensive retinue of advisors and guards.

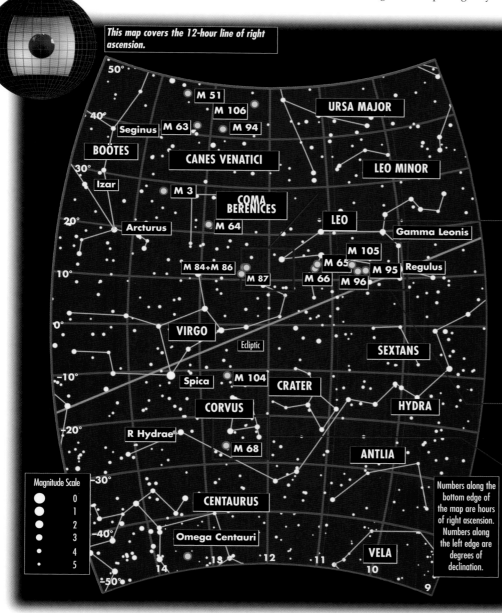

This map covers the 12-hour line of right ascension.

Numbers along the bottom edge of the map are hours of right ascension. Numbers along the left edge are degrees of declination.

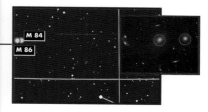

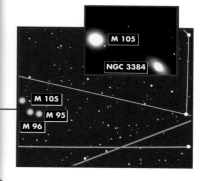

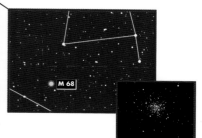

STAR ATLAS 5

This atlas covers the sky from right ascension 15 hours to 21 hours, and between declinations 50° north and 50° south. Running vertically straight through the center of this area is the 18-hour line of right ascension, which the Sun crosses at the December solstice each year, when it is at its farthest south of the celestial equator. This part of the sky is visible in the evening from the months of June until September—during summer in the northern hemisphere and winter in the southern hemisphere—and also includes the brightest and richest parts of the Milky Way.

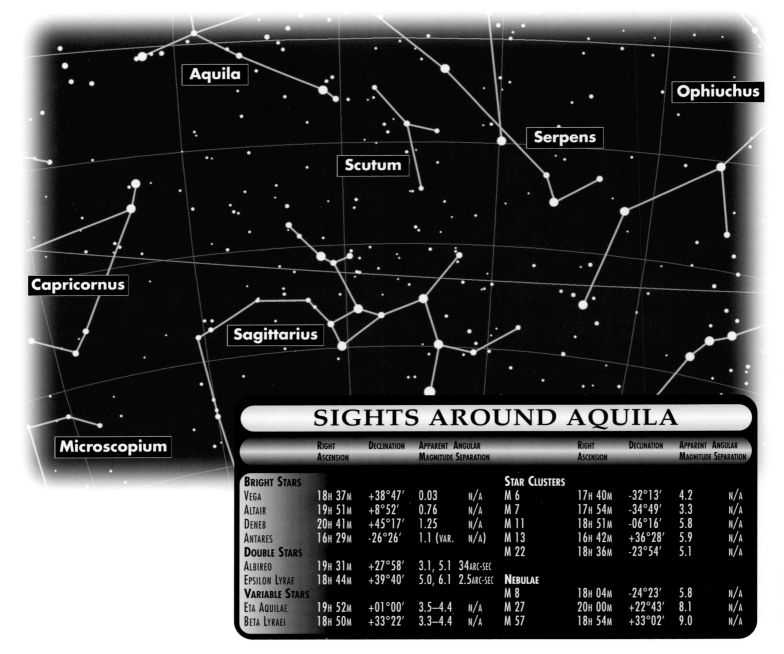

SIGHTS AROUND AQUILA

	Right Ascension	Declination	Apparent Magnitude	Angular Separation		Right Ascension	Declination	Apparent Magnitude	Angular Separation
Bright Stars					**Star Clusters**				
Vega	18h 37m	+38°47'	0.03	N/A	M 6	17h 40m	-32°13'	4.2	N/A
Altair	19h 51m	+8°52'	0.76	N/A	M 7	17h 54m	-34°49'	3.3	N/A
Deneb	20h 41m	+45°17'	1.25	N/A	M 11	18h 51m	-06°16'	5.8	N/A
Antares	16h 29m	-26°26'	1.1 (var.)	N/A	M 13	16h 42m	+36°28'	5.9	N/A
Double Stars					M 22	18h 36m	-23°54'	5.1	N/A
Albireo	19h 31m	+27°58'	3.1, 5.1	34arc-sec					
Epsilon Lyrae	18h 44m	+39°40'	5.0, 6.1	2.5arc-sec	**Nebulae**				
Variable Stars					M 8	18h 04m	-24°23'	5.8	N/A
Eta Aquilae	19h 52m	+01°00'	3.5–4.4	N/A	M 27	20h 00m	+22°43'	8.1	N/A
Beta Lyrae	18h 50m	+33°22'	3.3–4.4	N/A	M 57	18h 54m	+33°02'	9.0	N/A

NORTHERN SKIES

Two giants stand head-to-head in the summer sky: Hercules and Ophiuchus. The constellation Hercules represents the Greek demi-god famous for undertaking 12 nearly impossible tasks to free himself from servitude. Ophiuchus is less well-known, representing the Greek god of medicine. In the sky he is visualized with a huge snake wrapped around him, in the form of the constellation Serpens. Serpens is divided into two halves, one representing the head (Serpens Caput) and the other its tail (Serpens Cauda), but the snake is a single constellation.

A different sort of giant in this part of the sky is the giant trio of stars known as the Summer Triangle: Vega in Lyra, Deneb in Cygnus and Altair in Aquila. Vega, the brightest, is a blue-white star that is the first to come into view as the sky darkens. A summer treat is to scan this area with binoculars, picking out the deep-sky objects.

LAGOON NEBULA

The Lagoon Nebula in Sagittarius, also known as M 8, is an elongated cloud of gas visible to the naked eye on clear nights and easily seen in binoculars. One half of the nebula contains the open cluster NGC 6530, composed of about two dozen stars of 7th magnitude and fainter, while in the other half burns the hot 6th-magnitude blue supergiant 9 Sagittarii, one of the main stars that lights up the nebula.

M 56

Lying nearly halfway between Beta Cygni (Albireo) and Gamma Lyrae, this globular cluster in Lyra is one of the fainter deep-sky objects listed by Charles Messier. It is not difficult to find, but at 8th magnitude it is beyond the range of most binoculars. Small to moderate-size telescopes show a hazy patch elongated north-south, without the strong central condensation common in many globulars. Larger apertures and higher powers resolve individual stars, shown as chains and arcs.

NGC 6572

This 8th-magnitude planetary nebula can be seen in a 3-in (75-mm) telescope, lying in a fairly barren area in the north of Ophiuchus near the border with Serpens Cauda. Its disk is small—about 8 arcseconds wide, twice the apparent size of Uranus, and with a similar blue-green color. It lies at the end of a chain of faint stars.

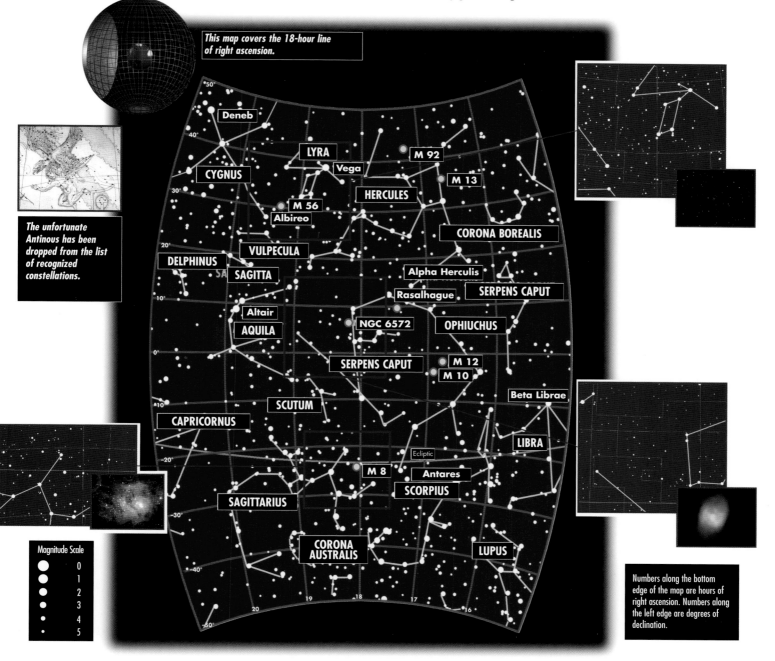

This map covers the 18-hour line of right ascension.

The unfortunate Antinous has been dropped from the list of recognized constellations.

Deneb

LYRA
Vega
M 92
CYGNUS
M 13
HERCULES
M 56
Albireo
CORONA BOREALIS
VULPECULA
DELPHINUS
Alpha Herculis
SAGITTA
SERPENS CAPUT
Rasalhague
Altair
NGC 6572
OPHIUCHUS
AQUILA
SERPENS CAPUT
M 12
M 10
Beta Librae
SCUTUM
CAPRICORNUS
LIBRA
Ecliptic
M 8
Antares
SAGITTARIUS
SCORPIUS
CORONA
AUSTRALIS
LUPUS

50°
40°
30°
20°
10°
0°
-10°
-20°
-30°
-40°
-50°
20   19   18   17   16

Magnitude Scale
0
1
2
3
4
5

Numbers along the bottom edge of the map are hours of right ascension. Numbers along the left edge are degrees of declination.

175

STAR ATLAS 6

his section covers the sky from declination 40° S to the south celestial pole, an area that is mostly invisible from the United States, although regions at the edge of the map can be seen from the southern states. This area contains the second- and third-brightest stars in the night sky, Canopus and Alpha Centauri, which is also the closest naked-eye star to the Sun. Other great naked-eye sights include the Southern Cross and the Magellanic Clouds, two small irregular galaxies that are satellites of our Milky Way.

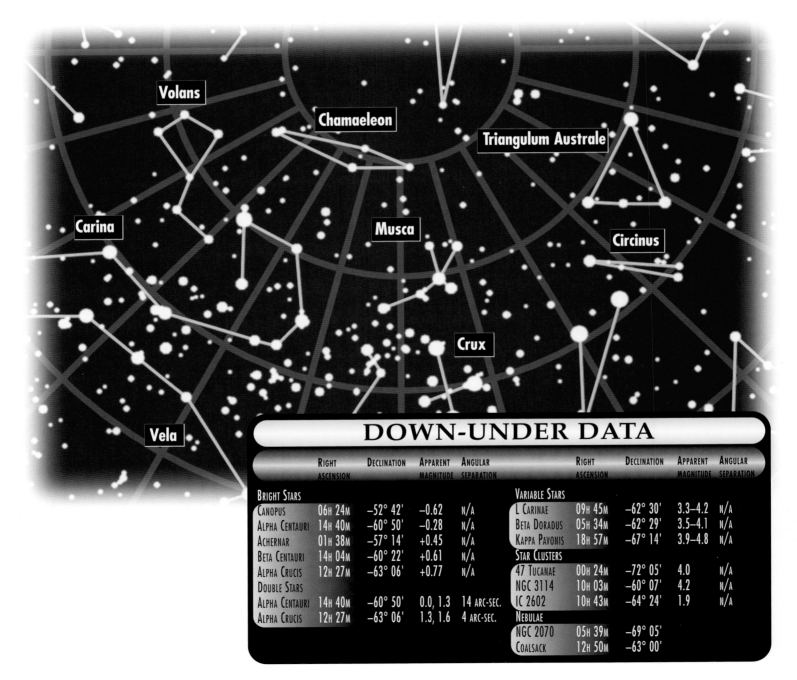

DOWN-UNDER DATA

	Right Ascension	Declination	Apparent Magnitude	Angular Separation		Right Ascension	Declination	Apparent Magnitude	Angular Separation
Bright Stars					**Variable Stars**				
Canopus	06h 24m	−52° 42'	−0.62	N/A	L Carinae	09h 45m	−62° 30'	3.3–4.2	N/A
Alpha Centauri	14h 40m	−60° 50'	−0.28	N/A	Beta Doradus	05h 34m	−62° 29'	3.5–4.1	N/A
Achernar	01h 38m	−57° 14'	+0.45	N/A	Kappa Pavonis	18h 57m	−67° 14'	3.9–4.8	N/A
Beta Centauri	14h 04m	−60° 22'	+0.61	N/A	**Star Clusters**				
Alpha Crucis	12h 27m	−63° 06'	+0.77	N/A	47 Tucanae	00h 24m	−72° 05'	4.0	N/A
Double Stars					NGC 3114	10h 03m	−60° 07'	4.2	N/A
Alpha Centauri	14h 40m	−60° 50'	0.0, 1.3	14 arc-sec.	IC 2602	10h 43m	−64° 24'	1.9	N/A
Alpha Crucis	12h 27m	−63° 06'	1.3, 1.6	4 arc-sec.	**Nebulae**				
					NGC 2070	05h 39m	−69° 05'		
					Coalsack	12h 50m	−63° 00'		

SOUTHERN BEAUTIES

The symbol of the southern skies is Crux, the constellation of the Southern Cross, which is depicted on several national flags. It contains four bright stars arranged in cruciform shape with a fifth, fainter star just off-center. The brightest, Alpha Crucis, is actually a sparkling double star, easily seen by a small telescope. It is also the closest 1st-magnitude star to the southern pole. Two other bright stars, Alpha and Beta Centauri, point toward Crux. Alpha Centauri, the third-brightest star in the sky, is another easy double for small telescopes.

The long axis of the Southern Cross points toward the south celestial pole. On the opposite side of the pole from Crux lie the large and small Magellanic Clouds (LMC and SMC), two small satellites of our own Galaxy. Binoculars show many clusters and nebulae within them: The most prominent is the Tarantula Nebula in the LMC.

NGC 3114

This large and scattered open cluster in Carina, of similar apparent size to the full Moon, is visible to the naked eye in dark skies. Its brightest members, of 6th magnitude and fainter, can easily be seen in binoculars. Small telescopes, with wide field and low magnification, show its stars to be arranged in curving arms somewhat like a very sparse spiral galaxy.

NGC 6752

At 6th magnitude, this globular cluster in Pavo can be seen in binoculars and is close enough to us—about 15,000 light-years away—for its brightest stars to be resolvable in telescopes of three in (76 mm) in aperture. The condensed central part appears about four times larger than the disk of Jupiter, while its scattered outlying stars extend over half the apparent diameter of the Moon.

COALSACK

The best-known and most prominent of all dark nebulae, the Coalsack is a cloud of dust and gas about 600 light-years away in the local spiral arm of our Galaxy. The Coalsack blots out light from the stars behind. Its prominence is due to it being silhouetted against a particularly rich backdrop of the Milky Way near the stars of Crux. Easily visible with the naked eye, the Coalsack is shaped like an almond and spans the width of a dozen full Moons.

NEW INVENTIONS IN THE SKIES

Most of the area of sky around the south celestial pole was unknown to European astronomers prior to the 15th century, when European seamen ventured into the southern hemisphere, crossing the Atlantic to South America, and around the southern tip of Africa. They returned with reports of new celestial sights such as the two satellites now known as the Magellanic Clouds, after the Portuguese round-the-world explorer Ferdinand Magellan.

But the southern stars were not grouped into new constellations until around 1600, when two Dutch navigators, Pieter Dirkszoon Keyser and Frederick de Houtman, introduced 12 figures named mostly after exotic animals.

The first comprehensive southern sky survey was made around 150 years later by a Frenchman, Nicolas Louis de Lacaille. From the Cape of Good Hope in southern Africa between 1751 and 1752, Lacaille cataloged nearly 10,000 stars (Keyser and de Houtman had charted only about 300 of the brightest stars), introducing 14 new constellations to fill in the gaps between Keyser and de Houtman's figures.

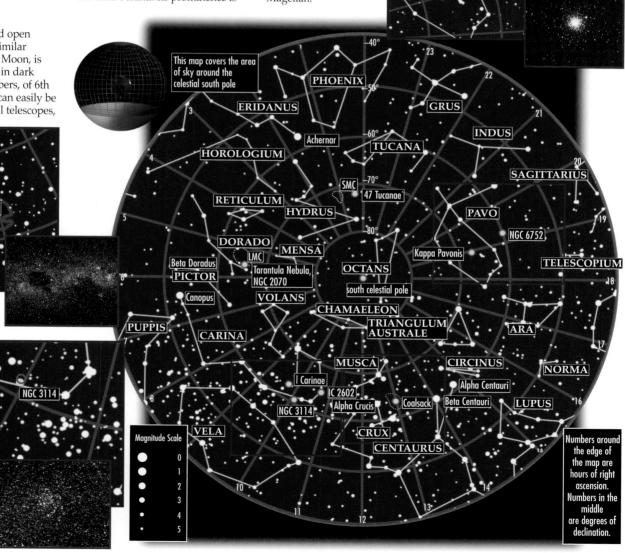

This map covers the area of sky around the celestial south pole

Magnitude Scale
0
1
2
3
4
5

Numbers around the edge of the map are hours of right ascension. Numbers in the middle are degrees of declination.

STUDYING THE STARS

part from the Sun, all the stars lie so far away that they only appear as points of light through even the most powerful telescopes. In order to understand the physical properties of stars, and explain how and why they differ from one another, astronomers must use every technique at their disposal to extract information from starlight. They observe not just in visible light, but at a variety of other wavelengths of radiation —in parts of the spectrum where objects cooler or hotter than the Sun may shine. Radio waves and infrared are emitted by some of the coolest objects in the universe, while ultraviolet, X-rays and gamma rays, with far more energy than the Sun's surface. By splitting the radiation from celestial objects into a spectrum of different wavelengths, astronomers can determine the elements that emit the radiation, and can even measure the motions of individual stars. All this information ultimately allows them to model the true physical properties of stars, and to find patterns in these properties that are the key to understanding stellar evolution.

The Hubble Space Telescope floats against the background of Earth after a week of essential repair and upgrade by Space Shuttle Columbia astronauts in 2002. Astronauts also installed a new camera—the Advanced Camera for Surveys— which doubled Hubble's field of view.

MESSAGES IN STARLIGHT

The starlight that twinkles from a clear night sky has reached the end of a journey that may have taken thousands of years— and the light bears the marks of its passage. It has been dimmed, colored and distorted during its trip through space. In recompense, though, starlight is crammed with information. It can tell scientists much about the star that created it. And for those who can read the code, starlight also tells tales of the molecules, atoms and magnetic fields it has encountered since its birth.

HISTORY OF STARLIGHT

1836 . . British astronomer John Herschel and German physicist Karl August von Steinheil independently devise instruments to compare the brightnesses of stars.

1864 . . William Huggins and Angelo Secchi independently begin the study of stellar spectra.

1868 . . William Huggins measures speed at which Sirius is moving away from us by the Doppler shift in its spectrum.

1868 . . Spectrum of hitherto unknown element discovered in sunlight. The element is named helium (from the Greek *helios*, meaning "sun") and is discovered on Earth in 1895.

1904 . . Existence of interstellar gas discovered from absorption lines in star spectra.

1929 . . Hubble discovers the expansion of the universe from the red-shifts of light from galaxies.

1930 . . Robert Trumpler discovers the extent of interstellar light absorption by observing globular clusters.

1969 . . First organic molecule, formaldehyde, discovered in interstellar gas from its spectral lines.

1970 . . Molecular hydrogen observed in space by its spectrum (radio astronomers had already mapped hydrogen in the form of single atoms).

SPECTRAL STORIES

Starlight is born in the core of a star. At temperatures of millions of degrees and pressures of hundreds of billions of atmospheres, nuclear reactions release photons of intensely energetic gamma rays. As these fight their way outward through the star—a journey that can take millions of years—they are constantly absorbed and re-emitted, usually at a lower energy level. Lastly, at the stellar surface, where the temperature is measured only in thousands or tens of thousands of degrees, the photons begin their trip through space. No longer gamma rays, most of them appear as heat and pressure.

The color of that light is the first important message that it bears. The hotter the star's surface, the shorter the wavelength. The star Rigel, for example, looks distinctly blue: It has a temperature of 20,000°F (11,000°C). The red color of Betelgeuse indicates a surface temperature of only 6,000°F (3,300°C), and stars with temperatures close to that of the Sun, about 10,000°F (5,500°C), appear white.

Astronomers gain far more information when they examine the spectrum of the starlight. Split rainbow-style into its component colors, the light reveals its history. Dark lines on the spectrum mark where certain very precise wavelengths are missing. These wavelengths were present when the light left the surface of the star, but were absorbed by atoms in the cooler, thinner gases of the star's atmosphere, above the surface. The dark absorption lines amount to a description of the star's atmosphere, of which hydrogen and helium are the main elements.

COSMIC FINGERPRINTS

As well as the marks of absorption, spectra also include so-called emission lines. These are peaks in brightness at very specific frequencies, which represent energy given off by a particular element. Like absorption lines, emission lines serve as cosmic fingerprints that identify the origins of the light beam that includes them.

Starlight also reveals the motion of its source. Light from a star that is moving toward the Earth will be blue-shifted—that is, all the wavelengths in its light will be shortened slightly, so that a dark absorption line that normally shows in the yellow part of its spectrum appears toward the blue end. Light from a star that is moving away from the Earth is red-shifted, so the same absorption line will be a corresponding distance toward the red.

The same effect gives clues to the temperature and density of a star's atmosphere. The denser the gas, the more atoms are present, and the higher the temperature, the faster the atoms are moving—in all directions. The result is a series of random red- and blue-shifts. Absorption lines that are normally thin and sharp are stretched into thickened, fuzzy blurs.

Even after it has escaped into space, starlight is still gathering information. Clouds of gas and dust fill the spaces between the stars. The clouds are very sparse— far thinner than the best vacuum on Earth—but even so, the gas leaves telltale absorption lines in the starlight spectrum. Dust dims the starlight—around 40 percent might be lost over 1,500 light-years, and far more in dusty regions of the galaxy. The dust scatters shorter-wavelength blue light, whereas the longer reddish wavelengths pass freely. So red-tinged starlight may be from a star masked by light-years of dust.

REVEALING COLORS

STARLIGHT STRAIGHT
As light leaves a star, its spectrum contains telltale emission and absorption lines. This simplified spectrum shows only the the emission lines of hydrogen, the most abundant element in the universe.

HEAT AND PRESSURE
The clear, sharp spectral lines are smeared into thick blurs by temperature and pressure, which agitate the atoms that emit them. But the hydrogen lines remain in their characteristic position in the spectrum.

INTERRUPTION
Between the star and observers on Earth, starlight passes through a cloud of interstellar gas. The gas—hydrogen is again pictured—absorbs light at specific frequencies, leaving a dark gap in the spectrum.

RECEDING
If the star is moving away from the Earth, the frequency of its light is shifted toward the red end of the spectrum. The hydrogen lines have all moved together in that direction—but retain their pattern, which amounts to the gas's signature.

APPROACHING
If the star is moving toward the Earth, its light is squeezed to a slightly higher frequency— toward the blue end of the spectrum. Hydrogen's spectral fingerprint reveals the blue-shift, and allows astronomers to calculate the speeds involved.

LIGHT ANALYSTS

GERMAN SCIENTISTS ROBERT BUNSEN (RIGHT; 1811–99) — OF BUNSEN BURNER FAME — AND GUSTAV KIRCHHOFF (1824–87) INVENTED THE SPECTROGRAPH, AN INSTRUMENT THAT ANALYZED LIGHT. THEY WENT ON TO DEVELOP TECHNIQUES OF SPECTRAL ANALYSIS STILL NAMED FOR THE TWO PIONEERS. IN 1859, KIRCHHOFF FIRST SPECULATED THAT DARK LINES IN THE SUN'S SPECTRUM WERE CAUSED WHEN SPECIFIC GASES IN THE SUN'S ATMOSPHERE ABSORBED LIGHT AT CERTAIN VERY PRECISE WAVELENGTHS.

CLASSIFYING THE STARS

Faced with the chaos of 5,000 visible stars, astronomers have always reacted by organizing. Ancient stargazers created the signs of the Zodiac. Modern astronomers can see many more stars and tell different stories from new groupings. Where the ancients painted heroes and animals on the sky, astronomers today turn starlight into science. "Classifying the stars is the greatest problem to be presented to the human mind," according to American astronomer Annie Jump Cannon. She should know—she has classified an incredible 400,000 of them in total.

STARS THAT DO NOT FIT

ASTRONOMERS CANNOT CLASSIFY EVERY STAR. THEY BRAND SOME ODDBALLS WITH A "P," FOR "PECULIAR."

NONSTANDARD STARS

VERY HOT WOLF-RAYET STARS HAVE PROBABLY LOST THEIR ATMOSPHERE. CARBON STARS ARE COOL AND RED AND FUSE ELEMENTS HEAVIER THAN HYDROGEN TO MAKE CARBON.

TECHNICALLY SPEAKING, SOME ARE NOT STARS AT ALL, SINCE THEIR CORES ARE TOO COLD TO BURN HYDROGEN: WHITE DWARFS' CORES ARE COLD BECAUSE THE STARS ARE TOO OLD; T-TAURI STARS ARE TOO YOUNG; BROWN DWARFS ARE TOO SMALL.

PLANETARY NEBULAE—ONCE CONFUSED WITH STARS—ARE ONLY STELLAR REMAINS. NOVAE ARE EXPLODING STARS.

WHERE ASTRONOMERS PUT THEM

ASTRONOMERS GIVE NEW CLASSIFICATION LETTERS TO SOME. WOLF-RAYET STARS HAVE BECOME GROUP "W," ABOVE "O." CARBON STARS BECOME THE "C" CLASSIFICATION, A HYBRID OF STARS IN GROUPS "K" AND "M." VERY COOL STARS ARE "L" AND "S." WHITE DWARFS' LETTER CLASSIFICATIONS ARE "DA," "DB" AND "DC."

STARS WITHOUT A LETTER CLASSIFICATION—T-TAURIS, FOR INSTANCE—CAN STILL BE PLOTTED ON A COLOR-LUMINOSITY GRAPH. THEY SIMPLY LIE AWAY FROM THE MAIN GROUPS OF STARS.

CHAOS TO CLARITY

To the untrained eye, stars all look similar. But the astronomers who assembled the famous Harvard University star catalog were eager to simplify and organize, and seized on small—but crucial—differences to tell them apart.

Their work—published mostly between 1918 and 1924—relied on an instrument called a spectrograph that splays visible light into a rainbow or spectrum of the light's component colors. But a spectrum of starlight contains more than a band of colors. It also has black lines crossing the band at particular points. These lines help astronomers work out what each star is made of.

To a scientist, the colors of the spectrum mean nothing more than electromagnetic radiation of specific wavelengths. The Danish physicist Niels Bohr (1885–1962) discovered that the dark and bright spectral lines are both created by the unique characteristics of atoms and molecules. If light travels through a substance, the electrons will absorb certain wavelengths, leaving gaps in a spectrum that show up as characteristic dark absorption lines. If a substance becomes hot enough to emit light, the electrons of its constituent atoms give off photons of light at those same wavelengths. An astrophysicist can measure these wavelengths by analyzing the light's spectrum and use them to identify the substances in a star.

Sometimes, though, the signature is unreadable. Above a certain temperature, atoms vibrate so much that they knock electrons out of orbit completely—so they do not absorb or emit any photons at all. Therefore, very hot stars often have weak spectral lines.

MULTIPLYING MESSAGES

Harvard astronomers first tried to classify the stars by spectral lines alone, but soon realized it would be more meaningful to classify them by temperature. Using a theory about energy emission by the German physicist Max Planck (1858–1947) with observations of starlight at different wavelengths, they could estimate a star's temperature from its color.

But as soon as they had begun reclassifying stars, another complication arose. Within a single temperature range, some stars had far thinner spectral lines. The astronomers realized that there was more data to be had from starlight: The width of the lines implied differences in size, density and brightness as well.

In dense stars, atoms are relatively close together and so collide more frequently than the average. This has the effect of thickening spectral lines. Stars with narrow spectral lines are less dense but tend to be bigger. And given the same temperature, bigger stars are more luminous, since they have more surface area from which to radiate light.

In response to these insights, astronomers William Morgan and Philip Keenan devised a classification known for them as the "MK" system. It adds a scale of luminosity to the Harvard temperature scale so that astronomers can differentiate between stars with the same temperature—and therefore the same spectral class—but sometimes hugely different sizes, such as red dwarfs and red giants. The MK system uses five basic classes: supergiant, bright giant, giant, subgiant and dwarf. In addition, the position of spectral lines yields information about the composition of a star, whether it is young and hydrogen-rich or old, riddled with heavy elements and perhaps likely to go supernova. With details of this kind, the data wrung out of a shaft of starlight can bring the mysterious points of light in the sky vividly to life.

FIRST LADY

PIONEER ASTRONOMER ANNIE JUMP CANNON SAW IT ALL. SHE SINGLE-HANDEDLY CLASSIFIED ALMOST EVERY ONE OF THE 225,000 STARS IN THE HARVARD COLLEGE OBSERVATORY STAR CATALOG.

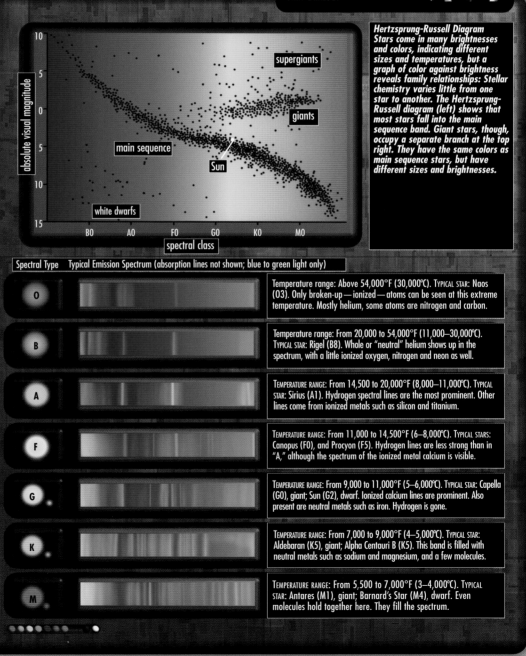

Hertzsprung-Russell Diagram Stars come in many brightnesses and colors, indicating different sizes and temperatures, but a graph of color against brightness reveals family relationships: Stellar chemistry varies little from one star to another. The Hertzsprung-Russell diagram (left) shows that most stars fall into the main sequence band. Giant stars, though, occupy a separate branch at the top right. They have the same colors as main sequence stars, but have different sizes and brightnesses.

Spectral Type	Typical Emission Spectrum (absorption lines not shown; blue to green light only)	
O		Temperature range: Above 54,000°F (30,000°C). TYPICAL STAR: Naos (O3). Only broken-up—ionized—atoms can be seen at this extreme temperature. Mostly helium, some atoms are nitrogen and carbon.
B		Temperature range: From 20,000 to 54,000°F (11,000–30,000°C). TYPICAL STAR: Rigel (B8). Whole or "neutral" helium shows up in the spectrum, with a little ionized oxygen, nitrogen and neon as well.
A		TEMPERATURE RANGE: From 14,500 to 20,000°F (8,000–11,000°C). TYPICAL STAR: Sirius (A1). Hydrogen spectral lines are the most prominent. Other lines come from ionized metals such as silicon and titanium.
F		TEMPERATURE RANGE: From 11,000 to 14,500°F (6–8,000°C). TYPICAL STARS: Canopus (F0), and Procyon (F5). Hydrogen lines are less strong than in "A," although the spectrum of the ionized metal calcium is visible.
G		TEMPERATURE RANGE: From 9,000 to 11,000°F (5–6,000°C). TYPICAL STAR: Capella (G0), giant; Sun (G2), dwarf. Ionized calcium lines are prominent. Also present are neutral metals such as iron. Hydrogen is gone.
K		TEMPERATURE RANGE: From 7,000 to 9,000°F (4–5,000°C). TYPICAL STAR: Aldebaran (K5), giant; Alpha Centauri B (K5). This band is filled with neutral metals such as sodium and magnesium, and a few molecules.
M		TEMPERATURE RANGE: From 5,500 to 7,000°F (3–4,000°C). TYPICAL STAR: Antares (M1); giant; Barnard's Star (M4), dwarf. Even molecules hold together here. They fill the spectrum.

THE COLOR
OF STARS

Although almost all stars appear white to the naked eye, a closer look reveals that starlight is tinged with hues of red, orange, yellow and blue. Astronomers have discovered that the distribution of these colors relates directly to the temperature at a star's surface: Cool ones are reddish, while those that are very hot appear a shade of light blue. And since a star's temperature reveals much about its composition, its age and the workings of its core, the color of starlight has become a valuable long-distance tool for observing the universe and informing us about its stars.

IF COLORS WERE HEAT...

ASTRONOMERS MEASURE STAR COLORS BY TEMPERATURE, RATHER THAN THEIR APPARENT COLOR, ACCORDING TO MAX PLANCK'S THEORY OF RADIATION. BASED ON THEORETICAL VALUES, THESE "COLOR-TEMPERATURES" ARE RARELY WHAT YOU MIGHT EXPECT.

CLEAR BLUE SKY	25,000	WHITE	"DAYLIGHT" FLUORESCENT TUBE	7,300	DEEP ORANGE
ELECTRONIC FLASH	11,500	PALE YELLOW	TUNGSTEN LAMP (500 WATTS)	5,300	REDDISH ORANGE
XENON ARC LAMP	10,500	BRIGHT YELLOW	"WARM WHITE" FLUORESCENT TUBE	5,000	BRIGHT RED
FLASHCUBE OR MAGICUBE	9,500	BRIGHT YELLOW	PROJECTION LAMP (750 WATTS)	4,750	BRIGHT RED
SUMMER SUNLIGHT (9 A.M. TO 3 P.M.)	9,500	BRIGHT YELLOW	HOUSEHOLD LAMP (100 WATTS)	4,500	BRIGHT RED
WHITE FLAME CARBON ARC LAMP	8,500	DEEP YELLOW	CANDLE FLAME	2,300	DULL RED

TRUE COLORS

Astronomers in the 19th century described star colors with equally colorful language. One 1887 book described the double stars of Beta Cygni as "yellow and sapphire blue" while those of Epsilon Boötis were apparently "pale orange and sea green." Clearly, describing and measuring star colors with the naked eye was an imprecise business.

Many of the star colors described by early stargazers are now thought to be false. For example, astronomers now believe that to the naked eye, green stars appear white—and that the "green" stars seen by 19th-century observers were optical illusions created by the color contrast between double stars. To guard against such mistakes, modern astronomy classifies the color of stars using a scientifically measured index. This is done by passing the starlight through filters that admit only certain wavelengths of light and then comparing the star's brightness as seen through each filter.

The reason for such painstaking work is that a star's true color reveals so much about its inner workings. In fact, analyzing the color of the light from a distant star yields far more information than a close-up black and white image of the same star ever could.

It was the German physicist Max Planck (1858–1947) who first came up with the idea that a star's color could reveal its temperature. Planck's theory states that as the temperature of an object increases, so does the frequency of the radiation that it emits. For example, when a metal rod is heated, it begins by glowing red, then turns to orange, followed by white and eventually blue. The same applies to stars: Where the most light that is radiated from the star's surface falls in the visible spectrum bears a direct relationship to its temperature—

which can be anything between 3,000°F (1,650°C) and 360,000°F (200,000°C).

Planck's theory also explains why there are no green stars. A heated metal bar emits not just one frequency (and hence, color) of light, but a whole range. One way to imagine this is as a "hill" of radiation of different wavelengths in which the intensity falls away to either side of a "hilltop" that represents the dominant color.

Stars tend to be either reddish and bluish because these are the colors at the two ends of the visible spectrum: When one or the other is dominant, there are relatively few other colors able to interfere with it. Green, by contrast, sits in the middle of the visible spectrum. So even when the temperature of a star makes green the dominant color, the many colors on either side of it tend to wash the green out, causing the star to appear white to the naked eye instead.

TRUE BLUE

IRONICALLY, ASTRONOMERS FIRST TOOK AN INTEREST IN STAR COLORS WHEN THEY BEGAN TO TAKE BLACK AND WHITE PHOTOGRAPHS. PHOTOGRAPHIC PLATES OF THE LATE 19TH CENTURY WERE MOST SENSITIVE TO ORANGE AND RED. IN A 19TH-CENTURY VERSION OF THIS MODERN TRIPLE-EXPOSURE OF (CLOCKWISE FROM TOP) CAPELLA, VEGA AND BETELGEUSE, BETELGEUSE WOULD HAVE BEEN BRIGHTEST, FOLLOWED BY CAPELLA, THEN VEGA. FROM THE DIFFERENCES BETWEEN THE PLATES AND WHAT THEY THEMSELVES SAW, ASTRONOMERS DEDUCED THAT STARS MUST BE DIFFERENT COLORS.

WHAT IF?
...WE FOUND A VIVID STAR?

Even the most vibrant stars in the universe are relatively washed-out. Although a reddish-looking star emits mostly red, orange and yellow light, it also radiates light at all other frequencies in the visible spectrum that dilutes the colors.

It would therefore would be a shock if an intensely colored jewel was discovered in the sky. The first reaction would be that it was not a star at all, but some kind of heavenly body—perhaps an undiscovered planet or unknown comet. The possibility that the object was an alien spacecraft would also be considered, since for a star to be a single color would overturn cosmological theory of the last 300 years. As far a we know, the core nuclear reactions that generate a star's radiation cannot produce light of just one frequency.

One possible explanation for such a vivid object is that it is a normal star surrounded by gas and dust that filters out all but a single frequency of its light. Different kinds of matter absorb wavelengths of radiation at different frequencies. So could a gas or dust cloud ever produce such an effect?

Although the idea is plausible, it is unlikely to occur in reality. Some of the most distant galaxies are quasars, whose radiation travels billions of light-years to reach us. Even though this radiation passes through many thousands of galaxies on its way to Earth, it remains largely intact. Therefore, it is almost unthinkable that the elements needed to absorb so many frequencies of radiation would be present in the same place along the path of just one electromagnetic wave.

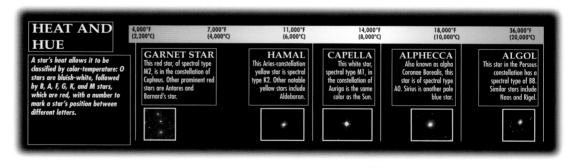

HEAT AND HUE

A star's heat allows it to be classified by color-temperature: O stars are bluish-white, followed by B, A, F, G, K, and M stars, which are red, with a number to mark a star's position between different letters.

4,000°F (2,200°C)	7,000°F (4,000°C)	11,000°F (6,000°C)	14,000°F (8,000°C)	18,000°F (10,000°C)	36,000°F (20,000°C)
GARNET STAR This red star, of spectral type M2, is in the constellation of Cepheus. Other prominent red stars are Antares and Barnard's star.	**HAMAL** This Aries-constellation yellow star is spectral type K2. Other notable yellow stars include Aldebaran.	**CAPELLA** This white star, spectral type M1, in the constellation of Auriga is the same color as the Sun.	**ALPHECCA** Also known as alpha Coronae Borealis, this star is of spectral type A0. Sirius is another pale blue star.	**ALGOL** This star in the Perseus constellation has a spectral type of B8. Similar stars include Naos and Rigel.

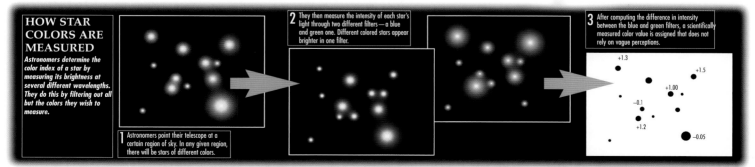

HOW STAR COLORS ARE MEASURED

Astronomers determine the color index of a star by measuring its brightness at several different wavelengths. They do this by filtering out all but the colors they wish to measure.

1 Astronomers point their telescope at a certain region of sky. In any given region, there will be stars of different colors.

2 They then measure the intensity of each star's light through two different filters—a blue and green one. Different colored stars appear brighter in one filter.

3 After computing the difference in intensity between the blue and green filters, a scientifically measured color value is assigned that does not rely on vague perceptions.

+1.3 +1.5 +1.00 −0.1 +1.2 −0.05

STAR DISTANCES

How do you find the distance to an unreachable star? Even the nearest stars are so remote that they appear only as pinpoints of light, and there is no immediate hope of traveling to them, let alone of stretching some hypothetical tape measure all the way out there. Yet astronomers speak confidently of the distances of stars thousands of light-years away. The method they use is simple in principle, and recent measurements from space using the Hipparcos satellite have improved its accuracy.

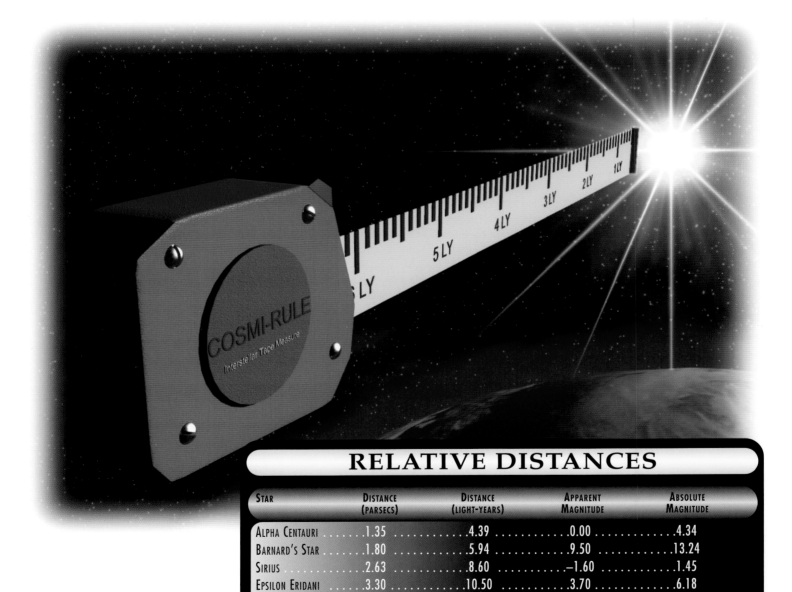

RELATIVE DISTANCES

STAR	DISTANCE (PARSECS)	DISTANCE (LIGHT-YEARS)	APPARENT MAGNITUDE	ABSOLUTE MAGNITUDE
ALPHA CENTAURI	1.35	4.39	0.00	4.34
BARNARD'S STAR	1.80	5.94	9.50	13.24
SIRIUS	2.63	8.60	−1.60	1.45
EPSILON ERIDANI	3.30	10.50	3.70	6.18
61 CYGNI A	3.40	11.36	5.20	7.49
TAU CETI	3.60	11.90	3.49	5.68
ALTAIR	5.00	16.77	0.80	2.20

NEAR MISS

THE FIRST STAR DISTANCE (FOUR LIGHT-YEARS TO ALPHA CENTAURI) WAS MEASURED IN **1833** BY THOMAS HENDERSON (RIGHT) IN SOUTH AFRICA. BUT HE SAT ON THE RESULTS FOR SIX YEARS, SO THE CREDIT FOR THE FIRST MEASUREMENT WENT TO GERMAN ASTRONOMER F.W. BESSEL, WHO PUBLISHED THE DISTANCE TO **61 CYGNI** IN **1838**.

...AND THE UNKNOWN
A more distant star, D, with a similar spectrum to A, will be of the same type and therefore the same true brightness. Astronomers compare its apparent brightness with that of A to estimate its distance.

VIEW FROM Y
From this side of Earth's orbit, star A appears closer to star B. In practice, the shift in position is minute.

VIEW FROM X
From one side of the Earth's orbit, nearby star A appears to be closer to star C than to star B.

THE KNOWN...
A star's spectrum shows dark lines caused by material in the star's atmosphere. Each type of star has characteristic lines. Since the distance to star A has been measured directly, astronomers can calculate its true brightness.

GETTING FROM A TO D

SUN

A

B   D

C

The distance of star A can be measured from Earth using the parallax method, based on its apparent shift in position relative to B and C when viewed from X and Y. Once the much more distant star D is identified as having a similar spectrum to A, its distance can be estimated based on its apparent brightness.

HIPPARCOS

THE HIPPARCOS SATELLITE, DESIGNED TO MEASURE STAR DISTANCES ACCURATELY, WAS ALMOST A FLOP. A FAULTY ROCKET LEFT THE SPACECRAFT IN A HIGHLY ELLIPTICAL ORBIT THAT PASSED THROUGH THE VAN ALLEN BELTS OF RADIATION AROUND THE EARTH. BUT THE SATELLITE SURVIVED AND THE MISSION WAS REPLANNED TO ALLOW FOR THE NEW ORBIT.

HOW FAR'S THAT STAR?

The system that astronomers use to measure star distances is little more than an extension of the way we judge distances with our eyes—the method of parallax. Each eye sees from a slightly different viewpoint, and our brains use the difference to gauge distances to nearby objects. For a more distant object, such as a far-off mountain peak, the few inches between our eyes are not enough. So map-makers often begin their work by pacing out a baseline, after which they can measure the angles from the ends of the baseline to their target object and work out the object's distance using the branch of math known as trigonometry.

The stars are so far off that astronomers need the longest baseline they can possibly find—the orbit of the Earth around the Sun. This allows them to make measurements, six months apart, that are separated by 186 million miles (300 million km). The parallax—which is the shift in the star's apparent position when viewed from these two points—reveals its distance.

For example, the nearest bright star—Alpha Centauri—shifts only about 1.5 arc seconds as seen from either side of the Earth's orbit. Though the angle is tiny—equivalent to the gap between a car's headlights in Philadelphia as seen from New York City—in the case of Alpha Centauri, it translates as a distance of 26 trillion miles (42 trillion km). Because such large numbers rapidly become unmanageable, astronomers have their own units of measurement for star distances. Professional astronomers use parsecs, that is, the distance that a star would have to be for its angle of parallax (as measured across the 93-million-mile (150m km) radius of the Earth's orbit) to be exactly one arc second. Expressed in these units, Alpha Centauri is 1.347 parsecs from Earth.

Many people prefer to think of interstellar distances in terms of the time light would take to reach us from the star. Light travels at 186,000 miles (300,000 km) per second, and in a year it covers about 6 trillion miles—or one light-year. There are 3.26 light-years in a parsec. Most stars that are visible to the naked eye are within a few hundred light-years.

BREAKING THE BLUR BARRIER

Star parallaxes are complicated by the fact that stars are not stationary but moving through space. It takes several years of measurement to disentangle a star's parallax from its proper motion. The Earth's turbulent atmosphere, which blurs star images, is another barrier to accurate measurement. In fact, only about 100 stars are close enough for their distances to be measured by parallax from Earth-based telescopes.

Greater accuracy is possible from space, which is why the Hipparcos satellite was launched in 1989. As a result, the distances of over 7,000 stars are now known within five percent. But although Hipparcos can provide reliable data within 500 light-years of the Earth, the number of stars whose parallax can be measured directly is a tiny proportion of the total number of stars in our galaxy.

In the case of more distant stars, astronomers use a less accurate method. First they compare the star's brightness and spectrum—its signature—with those of nearby stars whose distance is known. Astronomers then assume that two stars with similar spectra will be of similar true brightness, which allows them to place the more distant of the two stars by measuring the apparent difference in brightness between them.

WEIGHING STARS

Astronomers have a scale that can weigh the stars: Gravity. Their technique relies on very precise observations that measure how much the gravitational pull of one star affects a near companion and, hence, just how much mass has done the pulling. Such observations give accurate data for only a few dozen stars. But because astronomers know how mass is linked to brightness, they can estimate the mass of many more stars—and learn more about how they live and die.

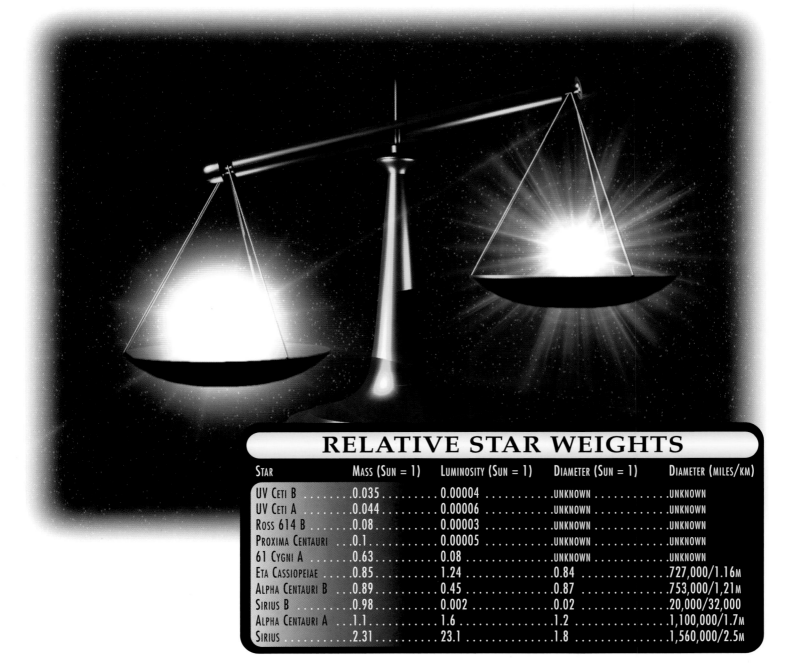

RELATIVE STAR WEIGHTS

STAR	MASS (SUN = 1)	LUMINOSITY (SUN = 1)	DIAMETER (SUN = 1)	DIAMETER (MILES/KM)
UV Ceti B	0.035	0.00004	UNKNOWN	UNKNOWN
UV Ceti A	0.044	0.00006	UNKNOWN	UNKNOWN
Ross 614 B	0.08	0.00003	UNKNOWN	UNKNOWN
Proxima Centauri	0.1	0.00005	UNKNOWN	UNKNOWN
61 Cygni A	0.63	0.08	UNKNOWN	UNKNOWN
Eta Cassiopeiae	0.85	1.24	0.84	727,000/1.16m
Alpha Centauri B	0.89	0.45	0.87	753,000/1,21m
Sirius B	0.98	0.002	0.02	20,000/32,000
Alpha Centauri A	1.1	1.6	1.2	1,100,000/1.7m
Sirius	2.31	23.1	1.8	1,560,000/2.5m

GRAVITY'S SCALES

How on Earth do you weigh a star? The answer is surprisingly simple: You use the same, universal force of gravity that allows you to weigh things on Earth. When you stand on a bathroom scale, the scale measures the tug of gravity—and displays your weight. The same force of gravity holds the Earth in its orbit around the Sun and grips every star in every galaxy throughout the universe.

The first star anyone weighed was the Sun, which involved a relatively straightforward procedure. The distance from the Earth to the Sun was known, as was the length of the Earth's orbital period of exactly one year. The equations of orbits and gravity worked out by Johannes Kepler and Sir Isaac Newton back in the 17th century did the rest. Calculation showed the Sun was 333,000 times the mass of the Earth.

Unfortunately, other stars are far too distant from Earth to have any measurable gravitational effect. But the stars are not necessarily distant from each other. Unlike the Sun, most of the galaxy's stars are binaries, pairs of stars that orbit each other around a common center of mass. If astronomers can find a binary's orbital period and measure the distance that separates the two stars, they can use gravitational equations to calculate the combined mass of the pair.

SEEING THE LIGHT

Some nearby binary stars show clearly in telescopes. They can be seen orbiting each other, taking from days to years to do so. In these cases, astronomers can find the masses of the stars using the same equations that they use to find the Sun's weight. The masses of about 50 binary stars can be found by this method. But for other binary stars, too distant to be made out individually, astronomers use the techniques of spectroscopy. Spectroscopy involves splitting a star's light into a rainbow of color, or a spectrum. Within the rainbow are thin lines that correspond to gases in the star's atmosphere, which absorb light at a very specific frequency and leave a dark gap in the spectrum. The exact position of the lines shows whether a star is moving toward or away from Earth. If receding, the spectral lines

move toward the red end of the spectrum. If it is approaching, they move toward the blue.

For a pair of stars, the lines from them are seen to separate each time one star is moving toward us and one is moving away. Regular observations yield both the period of rotation and the speeds of the stars. After making an assumption about whether the stars are more or less edge-on or face-on, astronomers can feed the data into the equations and get values for the star's masses.

Using information gleaned from well-observed double stars, astronomers can link the mass of a star with many of its other properties, especially its true brightness. Given a star's spectrum and brightness, they can confidently assign it a mass—which means that they can now estimate the masses of most of the stars they can see in the sky. Even so, most of our knowledge of star masses is still based on precise observations of just 50 stars that are near to us.

SIRIUS B

THE FIRST STAR TO BE DISCOVERED BY ITS GRAVITATIONAL PULL WAS SIRIUS B (RIGHT), THE FAINT COMPANION OF SIRIUS, THE BRIGHTEST STAR IN THE SKY. SIRIUS B WAS PREDICTED IN 1844, FROM AN OTHERWISE INEXPLICABLE WOBBLE IN THE MOTION OF ITS BRIGHT COMPANION. THE TINY STAR, A WHITE DWARF, WAS FIRST SEEN IN A TELESCOPE 18 YEARS LATER.

HARD EVIDENCE

SPECTRAL CLUES

Both light waves and sound waves are affected by the movement of their source. In the case of sound waves, the shift is audible—as in the change of note of a car as it dashes past you. Light changes wavelength, which shows up in its spectrum. At left are two spectra of a faint binary star, taken at different times. The dark lines, which indicate silicon in the primary star, show up clearly. In the top picture, the fainter or secondary star of the pair was moving toward us, so its silicon lines are to the left of the main lines (blueshifted). On the lower picture the star was moving away, so its spectral lines have slipped to the right of those of the primary star (redshifted).

DARKER LINES INDICATE SILICON IN PRIMARY STAR.

FAINTER LINES SHOW SILICON IN SECONDARY STAR.

BINARY IN BALANCE

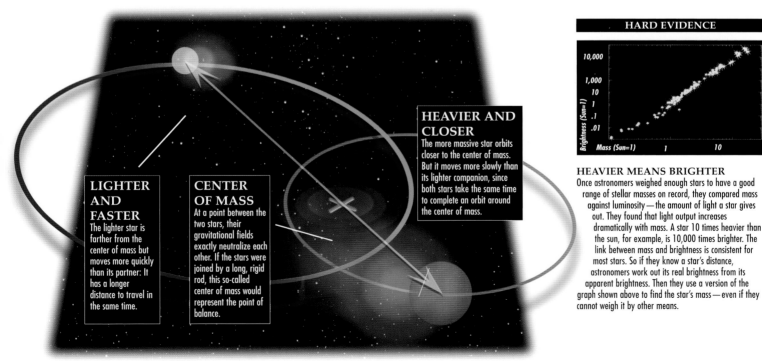

LIGHTER AND FASTER

The lighter star is farther from the center of mass but moves more quickly than its partner: It has a longer distance to travel in the same time.

CENTER OF MASS

At a point between the two stars, their gravitational fields exactly neutralize each other. If the stars were joined by a long, rigid rod, this so-called center of mass would represent the point of balance.

HEAVIER AND CLOSER

The more massive star orbits closer to the center of mass. But it moves more slowly than its lighter companion, since both stars take the same time to complete an orbit around the center of mass.

HARD EVIDENCE

HEAVIER MEANS BRIGHTER

Once astronomers weighed enough stars to have a good range of stellar masses on record, they compared mass against luminosity—the amount of light a star gives out. They found that light output increases dramatically with mass. A star 10 times heavier than the sun, for example, is 10,000 times brighter. The link between mass and brightness is consistent for most stars. So if they know a star's distance, astronomers work out its real brightness from its apparent brightness. Then they use a version of the graph shown above to find the star's mass—even if they cannot weigh it by other means.

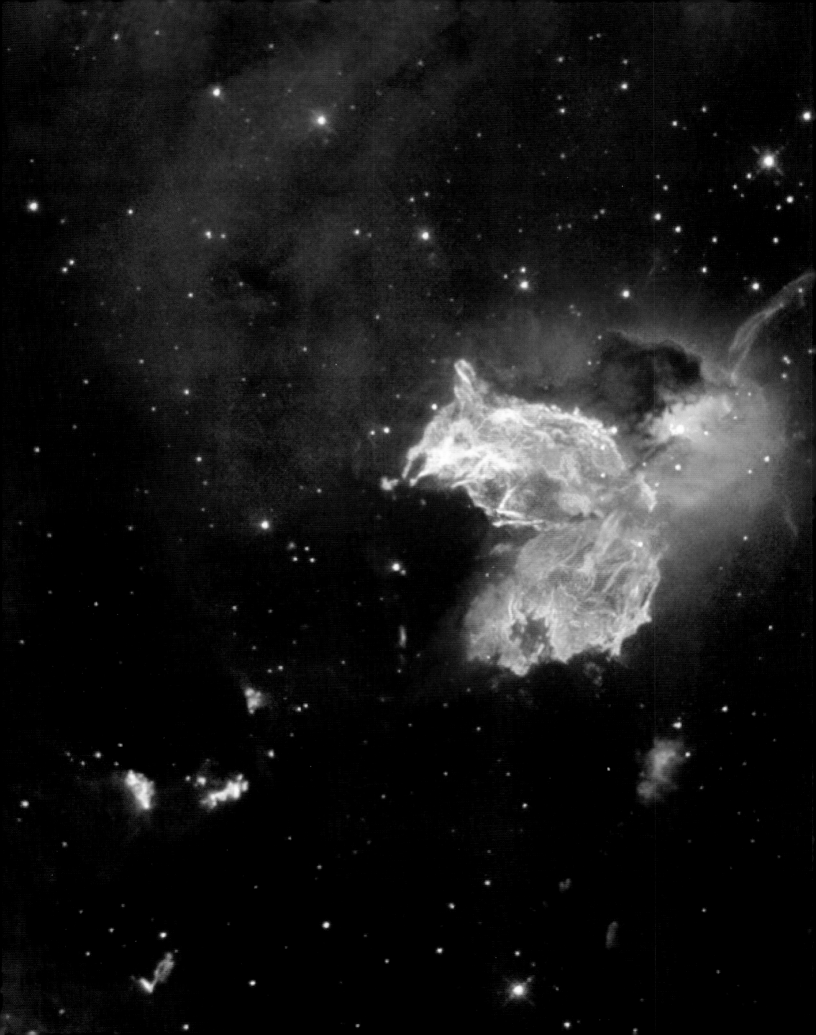

STELLAR LIFE CYCLES

All stars begin life in a similar way, as clouds of gas and dust collapsing and condensing under their own gravity to form protostars. The exact conditions within the protostellar nebula, however, are key to the star's later life story. Some stars are able to grow unfettered, pulling in enormous amounts of material and reaching many times the mass of the Sun. Some have their supply of material cut off when they are still small, and form dwarf stars far fainter than the Sun. Eventually, all stars reach an equilibrium in which they spend most of their lives, converting hydrogen to helium in fusion reactions at their core. But as the core fuel supply runs out, the differences between stellar life stories becomes more marked. Stars like the Sun end their lives in a relatively sedate way, ballooning to form red giants and then shedding their outer layers as beautiful planetary nebulae, but the most massive stars are destroyed in spectacular supernova explosions. This process forms stellar remnants—among some of the strangest objects in the universe.

A violent and chaotic-looking mass of gas and dust is seen in this Hubble Space Telescope image of a nearby supernova remnant. Denoted N 63A, the blazing object is the remains of a massive star that exploded, spewing its gaseous layers out into an already turbulent region of space.

BIRTH OF A STAR

The birth of a star takes much too long for any one person to witness, although on a cosmic timescale it is a relatively rapid process—it "only" takes millions of years. The process begins when a vast expanse of gas and dust known as a "dark cloud" begins to contract and heat up, causing the center of the cloud to become so dense and hot that it then blows away the surrounding layers. Then what remains of the cloud contracts still further, triggering the nuclear fusion reactions that cause a new star to begin to shine in the night sky.

SITES OF STAR FORMATION

NAME	DISTANCE (LIGHT-YEARS)	CONSTELLATION
ORION NEBULA	1,500	ORION
OMEGA NEBULA	5,000	SAGITTARIUS
LAGOON NEBULA	5,200	SAGITTARIUS
TRIFID NEBULA	5,200	SAGITTARIUS
EAGLE NEBULA	7,000	SERPENS

A STAR IS BORN

A star begins its life as a cold, dark cloud of gas and dust that begins to contract and collapse in on itself. But scientists still cannot say for certain under what conditions this process is triggered. One cause seems to be the gravitational pulls of neighboring stars in the galaxy, which at times may squeeze and stretch a dark cloud. Another trigger could be shock waves—either from other stars in the process of forming, or from giant stars that have recently "died" in supernova explosions. This would explain why star formation appears to have a snowball effect and why new stars often emerge in clusters.

Eventually a dark cloud contracts to the point where it starts to collapse under its own weight. As it does, it gets denser, and the resulting friction generates heat in increasingly vast amounts.

PROTOSTAR

A t this point the temperature rises rapidly and the cloud becomes what astronomers call a protostar— a "potential" star. Although shrouded in dust and gas, it is a big source of infrared radiation. As the temperature at the core of a protostar reaches around 20 million °F (11 million °C), a nuclear fusion reaction begins in which hydrogen atoms in the core turn into helium atoms, giving off energy as they do so. The protostar flares up to become a full-fledged star. A violent "stellar wind" blows away the remaining outer layers of gas and dust, giving rise to jet flows that can be seen over great distances. In the case of a star measuring the approximate size of our Sun, the birth process takes around 50 million years. Within the star's interior, the inward pull of gravity is precisely balanced by the outward flow of energy, and the star settles down to a lifetime of steady burning that lasts billions of years.

STAR CHILD

Each of us can truly be called a star child, made out of stardust. All the atoms in our bodies, except for hydrogen, were forged in distant stars long before our solar system was born.

FOUR STAGES OF STAR FORMATION

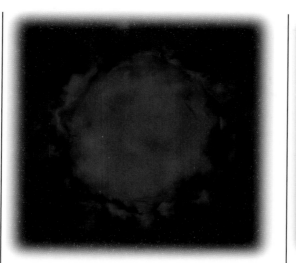

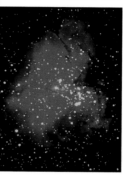

1 TRIGGER

Star formation begins when a dark cloud of dust and gas is disturbed by outside pressures and begins to collapse in on itself. Such disturbances may result from gravitational forces met while passing through a spiral galaxy. They may also be due to cosmic shock waves—such as those from other newly formed stars, or from giant stars that "die" in a supernova explosion, such as SN 1987A (left), first seen in 1987.

2 COLLAPSE

Once the collapse of a dark cloud has been triggered, it continues under its own momentum. Gravity forces draw the dust particles and gas molecules toward the core at an ever increasing rate. It was by this process that the Eagle nebula (left) in the constellation of Serpens—which is 7,000 light-years from Earth—changed from an invisible interstellar dust cloud into a bright and active region of star formation.

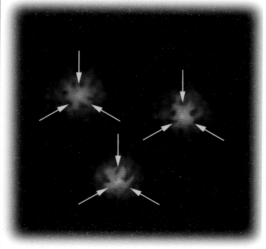

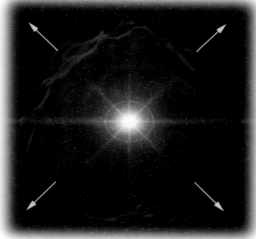

3 SMALL CLOUDS

As the collapsing cloud contracts, it heats up and becomes what is known as a protostar. The temperature climbs to millions of degrees, then nuclear fusion reactions begin and the star flares into life. A forceful "stellar wind" sweeps away the surrounding material and lights up nearby gas clouds. Sometimes the "stellar wind" is channeled into jets of gas known as Herbig-Haro jets.

4 NEW STAR

After the gas streams expelled by the newborn star have blasted away the surrounding gas and dust, the star finally emerges from its nursery. New stars often form in clusters such as the Trapezium group (left) in the Orion nebula. The majority of stars are not single, but have one or more other stars in orbit around them. The Sun is unusual in not having such a companion.

BROWN DWARFS

rown dwarfs are stars that never quite made the grade. By planetary standards, they are immense—up to 80 times the size of Jupiter—but even this incredible size is not massive enough to sustain the nuclear fusion reactions that burn at the heart of real stars.

These stellar failures glow so dimly that astronomers have only recently been able to detect them. Yet brown dwarfs may represent a missing link in theories of star and planet formation: Though hard to see, they could be more numerous than the stars themselves.

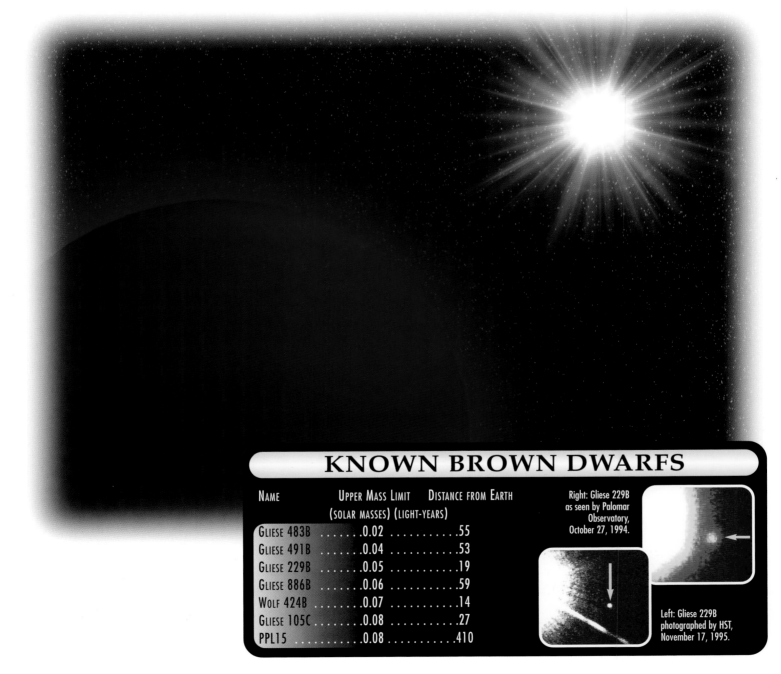

KNOWN BROWN DWARFS

Name	Upper Mass Limit (Solar Masses)	Distance from Earth (Light-years)
Gliese 483B	0.02	55
Gliese 491B	0.04	53
Gliese 229B	0.05	19
Gliese 886B	0.06	59
Wolf 424B	0.07	14
Gliese 105C	0.08	27
PPL15	0.08	410

Right: Gliese 229B as seen by Palomar Observatory, October 27, 1994.

Left: Gliese 229B photographed by HST, November 17, 1995.

FAILED STARS

A brown dwarf begins life in the same way as all successful stars—as a lump of matter condensing from a swirling cloud of hydrogen. But its birth cloud is too small, and the brown dwarf never quite makes the grade.

Regular stars come in all sizes, from red dwarfs that are half the radius of the Sun to supergiants a thousand times larger. All of these bodies, though, have at least several hundred times more mass than even the heaviest known planets, and it is this mass that turns them into stars. Under the crushing pressure at the core, temperatures rise above 5 million°F (2.7 million °C)—enough to fuse the hydrogen atoms into helium. The energy released in this process not only makes the star shine brightly, but creates an outward gas pressure that balances the inward pull of gravity and holds the star together.

If a star in the process of forming cannot amass sufficient bulk—about 8 percent of the mass of the Sun—its core never reaches the critical fusion temperature and it becomes a brown dwarf instead.

With no internal energy source to balance its gravity, the failed star slowly collapses inward. The collapse itself generates some heat and the brown dwarf shines after a fashion—but less brightly and for less time than even the faintest fusion-powered star.

Compared with most real stars, the active life of a brown dwarf is short. Its only heat source is the energy released by shrinking under its own gravity, and after a few hundred million years the dwarf's core becomes so dense that even gravity cannot compress it any further. At this point, the brown dwarf—by now crushed to perhaps half of its initial diameter—quietly peters out. Very slowly its residual heat leaks away into space and it begins to fade into darkness.

DIM RED LIGHT

D espite their name, brown dwarfs are not actually brown. A brown dwarf with 5 percent of the Sun's mass, for example, would have a surface temperature of around 4,000°F (2,200°C), causing it to glow deep red. But in appearance, such an object would be hard to tell apart from a far-off red dwarf, the smallest of the true stars.

Because brown dwarfs are so cool by stellar standards, most of their energy is infrared. So although astronomers predicted their existence as far back as 1963, they had to wait for 1990s equipment, including space-based infrared telescopes, before they could be observed. The first brown dwarf was detected in 1994, 19 light-years away in the Lepus constellation. Astronomers now think that brown dwarfs may be more common than stars in our galaxy—but we may only ever see the brightest and the nearest ones.

DULL COMPANION

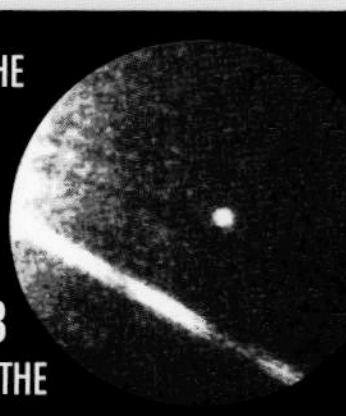

THE FIRST BROWN DWARF EVER OBSERVED—SHOWN AT RIGHT IN THE CENTER OF A HUBBLE SPACE TELESCOPE IMAGE—IS KNOWN ONLY BY ITS CATALOG NAME OF GLIESE 229B. THE OBJECT HAS ABOUT THE SAME DIAMETER AS JUPITER, BUT HAS 50 TIMES MORE MASS. THE SURFACE TEMPERATURE IS 1,300°F (700°C), COMPARED WITH THE 9,750°F (5,400°C) OF OUR OWN SUN. GLIESE 229B ORBITS A FAINT RED DWARF JUST 19 LIGHT-YEARS FROM EARTH, IN THE CONSTELLATION LEPUS. IT WAS DISCOVERED IN 1994.

PLEIADES DWARF

THE PLEIADES IS A CLUSTER OF YOUNG STARS SOME 410 LIGHT-YEARS AWAY THAT MAY HARBOR SEVERAL BROWN DWARFS. ONE OBJECT, CALLED PPL15, HAS ONLY 6 TO 8 PERCENT OF THE SUN'S MASS. IN 1996, ASTRONOMERS DISCOVERED THAT ITS LIGHT SPECTRUM CONTAINS LITHIUM, AN ELEMENT THAT IS USUALLY DESTROYED BY ATMOSPHERIC HEAT IN REGULAR STARS.

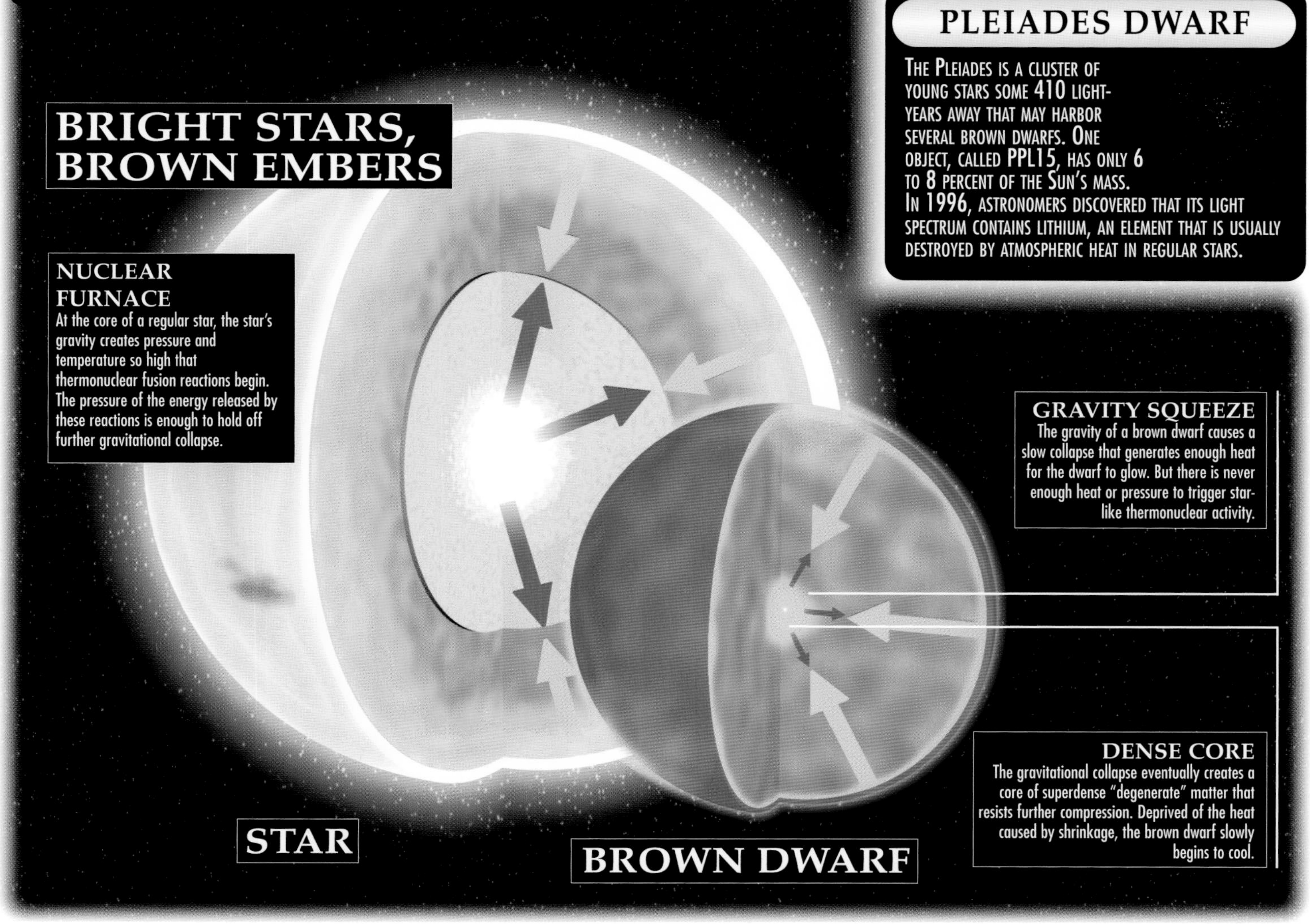

BRIGHT STARS, BROWN EMBERS

NUCLEAR FURNACE

At the core of a regular star, the star's gravity creates pressure and temperature so high that thermonuclear fusion reactions begin. The pressure of the energy released by these reactions is enough to hold off further gravitational collapse.

GRAVITY SQUEEZE

The gravity of a brown dwarf causes a slow collapse that generates enough heat for the dwarf to glow. But there is never enough heat or pressure to trigger star-like thermonuclear activity.

DENSE CORE

The gravitational collapse eventually creates a core of superdense "degenerate" matter that resists further compression. Deprived of the heat caused by shrinkage, the brown dwarf slowly begins to cool.

STAR

BROWN DWARF

THE MAIN SEQUENCE

When stars are plotted according to their color (temperature) and brightness (absolute magnitude) on a graph known as a Hertzsprung-Russell diagram, the vast majority of them show up as a curving diagonal band that astronomers refer to as the main sequence. Such stars are all in the stable, middle-aged phase of their long lives. These stars neither expand nor contract, and they consistently convert hydrogen into helium at a steady rate. The Sun is safely on the main sequence—otherwise, life on Earth would be impossible—and so are about 90 percent of the stars in the universe.

ON SEQUENCE

Star	Spectral Class	Distance (light-years)	Apparent Magnitude
Acrux	B3	320	0.8
Regulus	B7	85	1.4
Sirius	A1	8.6	-1.5
Formalhaut	A3	22	1.2
Alpha Centauri	G2	4.3	0.0
Sun	G2	0.000016	-26.7
Tau Ceti	G8	11.9	3.5
Epsilon Eridani	K2	10.5	3.7
61 Cygni A	K5	11.4	5.2
Lalande 21185	M2	8.3	7.5

GOING STEADY

A star is born in the whirl of a collapsing cloud of gas. When pressures and temperatures at the star's core rise high enough, nuclear fusion begins. Hydrogen—which makes up around 75 percent of most new stars—is converted into helium at a remarkably steady rate. The star shines, and the radiation pressure from its nuclear-burning heart keeps it from collapsing under its own gravity.

Once those hydrogen fires have ignited, the star begins its career on what astronomers call the main sequence. So long as there is hydrogen to burn, the star will remain there. And how long that will be depends on just one thing: the star's mass. Massive stars burn their fuel quickly, and glow brightly. Because of their high surface temperatures, their light is blue. Within a few million years, their hydrogen is gone, and they move out of the main sequence into the next stage of their evolution. Low-mass stars burn slowly. Much cooler than the blue giants, they glow a dim red. But they keep on glowing for many billions of years.

There are top and bottom limits at each end of the main sequence scale. Stars larger than 60 times the mass of the Sun are unstable—they blow themselves apart before their main sequence life can begin. And stars with less than eight percent of the Sun's mass never become hot enough at their cores for hydrogen fusion to start. In between those limits, main sequence stars can range from ferociously hot blue giants down to dim red dwarfs.

GRAPHIC UNDERSTANDING

E arly in the 20th century, astronomers Ejnar Hertzsprung and Henry Norris Russell discovered an interesting pattern. When they plotted the temperatures of stars—in effect, their colors—against their luminosity, the resulting graph showed that 90 percent of them fell into a diagonal line from the top left to the bottom right. This so-called Hertzsprung-Russell (HR) diagram turned out to be a great step forward in understanding the stars.

The stars at the top left are hot, blue, big and young. Those at the bottom right are cool, red, small and old—possibly almost as old as the universe. Somewhere in between lies our own Sun, technically a yellow dwarf star with a main sequence life of around 9 billion years, half of which still remains before it.

The HR diagram also tells much about the remaining 10 percent of stars—those not on the main sequence. As stars age, they drift gently across the diagram. The Sun, for example, will eventually consume its hydrogen. It will cool down, but also expand greatly in size. So it will become redder and more luminous, and its HR position will move upward and to the right. Later, its fires will dim as it shrugs off its outward layers. As a white dwarf, the Sun will sink toward the bottom left of the HR diagram. It will still glow dimly—because it is hot—but its nuclear furnaces will be extinct.

STAR PLOTTERS

THE HERTZSPRUNG-RUSSELL DIAGRAM WAS NAMED AFTER TWO ASTRONOMERS, EJNAR HERTZSPRUNG AND HENRY NORRIS RUSSELL (RIGHT). THEY INDEPENDENTLY DISCOVERED THAT MOST STARS FALL ONTO A DIAGONAL BAND WHEN THEIR LUMINOSITY IS PLOTTED AGAINST THEIR TEMPERATURE. HERTZSPRUNG PRESENTED HIS DIAGRAM IN 1911 AND RUSSELL TWO YEARS LATER IN 1913. THEY LATER COLLABORATED TO IMPROVE IT.

HARD EVIDENCE

QUICK COUNT
The mass of a star determines how much fuel it contains and how fast the star will burn it, so there is a simple relationship between mass and lifetime on the main sequence. Astronomers usually calculate by comparing the mass of the star in question with that of the Sun. A star 10 times as massive as the Sun, for example, will spend just 100 million years on the main sequence. A small star of 0.1 solar masses—Gliese 623B is shown here—may stay there for a trillion years.

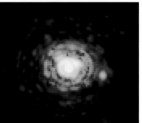

MIDDLE-AGE SPREAD

On a graph that plots the surface temperature of stars against their luminosity, most appear in a diagonal line called the main sequence: They are quietly getting on with their adult lives.

The luminosity axis on this Hertzsprung-Russell diagram shows the real brightness of stars on a scale where the Sun measures 1. The temperature—which dictates a star's color—is measured in degrees Kelvin above absolute zero. The Sun is a G-type star.

HOT BLUE
Blue giant stars in the constellation of Orion blaze furiously. But within 100 million years they will be extinct—blasted off the main sequence by the supernova explosions that will destroy them.

YELLOW DWARF
The Sun is technically a yellow dwarf, although as this true color picture shows, our nearest star is actually white. It should remain on the main sequence for another 5 billion years.

DIM RED
The red dwarf star Gliese 105 and its tiny companion star consume fuel so slowly that they will stay on the main sequence for billions of years. They may already be more than 10 billion years old.

RED GIANTS

When a star has exhausted its store of hydrogen fuel, it does not simply fizzle out. Instead, the star's core collapses and its outer layers begin to expand enormously. The result, at least for a time, is the large, luminous but relatively cool star known as a red giant. Although red giants eventually go on to die in different ways—the exact circumstances depend on their mass and chemical composition—all stars will eventually pass through the red giant stage, including our own Sun.

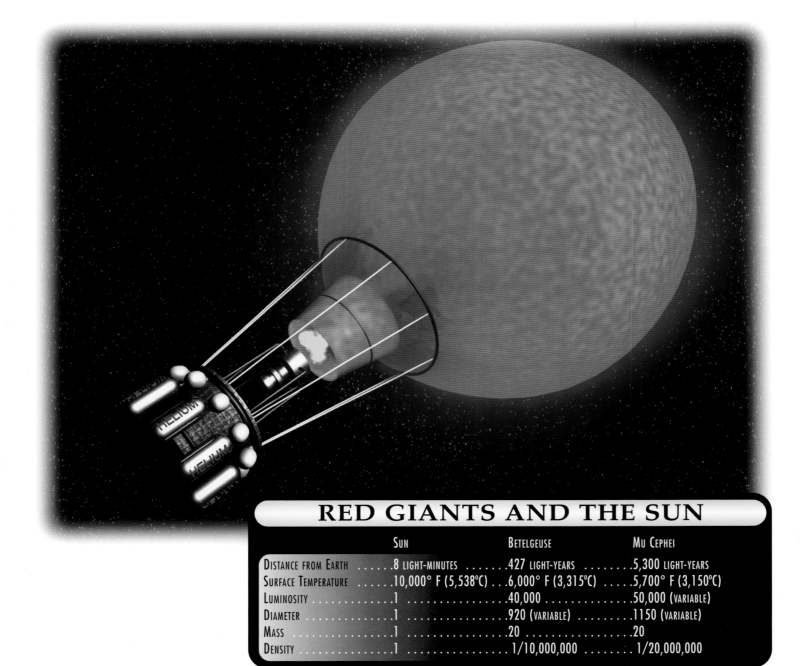

RED GIANTS AND THE SUN

	SUN	BETELGEUSE	MU CEPHEI
DISTANCE FROM EARTH	.8 LIGHT-MINUTES	.427 LIGHT-YEARS	.5,300 LIGHT-YEARS
SURFACE TEMPERATURE	.10,000° F (5,538°C)	.6,000° F (3,315°C)	.5,700° F (3,150°C)
LUMINOSITY	.1	.40,000	.50,000 (VARIABLE)
DIAMETER	.1	.920 (VARIABLE)	.1150 (VARIABLE)
MASS	.1	.20	.20
DENSITY	.1	.1/10,000,000	.1/20,000,000

SWOLLEN STARS

Most stars are so far away that even the largest telescope shows them only as a point of light. But a few stars are so big that careful observations from Earth reveal their true disks despite their distance. These are the red giants. They are not especially massive—their mass may be similar to the Sun's—but they are so swollen that the whole of the Earth's orbit could fit inside one. Yet red giants are no stellar freaks. Once, they were typical stars, producing a steady stream of energy. Now, they are nearing the end of their lives.

When a star has burned most of its hydrogen fuel, the core of helium "ash" collapses under its own weight. The star contracts by 98 percent and compression makes it heat up until hydrogen starts burning to helium in a thin shell around the core. As the zone of hydrogen fusion migrates away from the center, the core grows denser and hotter until eventually its energy sends the star's outer layers billowing into space. In only a few hundred million years, the star's diameter increases by more than a hundredfold, cooling to about half its previous temperature.

The temperature drop means that the star's light becomes much redder, like the cooling embers of a fire. But the vast increase in the star's surface area ensures that the actual energy output is now much greater than before. Red giant stars are among the most luminous that can be seen in the sky.

Meanwhile, the core continues to contract until the helium is so tightly compressed that its nuclei and electrons are crushed together. Eventually, the core reaches a temperature high enough to fuse the helium to carbon, but because the core material is so densely packed, it behaves more like molten metal than a gas. Instead of expanding, it simply gets hotter. Fusion accelerates until, at a temperature of 180,000,000° F (100,000,000°C), the core abruptly reverts to a gas and explodes.

But when the central helium fuel runs out, the core collapses again. This time, energy generated swells the star into a red supergiant so spread out that gravity has only a tenuous hold on its outer layers.

At this stage many supergiants begin to pulsate, as violent core explosions alternate with cooling and contraction. The precise behavior of each star depends on its mass. Huge stars, such as Betelgeuse in the constellation of Orion, may flicker erratically. Lighter stars, such as Mira in Cetus, can cycle from bright to faint over a period of months. For the lighter stars, helium is the last usable power source. Eventually nuclear burning will cease. The star will throw off its outer layers to become a planetary nebula. More massive stars may end their lives more spectacularly in the dramatic explosions known as supernovae.

AILING GIANTS

STEADY BURN
For most of its life, a star converts hydrogen to helium in its core (blue). Outward pressure from nuclear fusion balances the force of gravity that pulls inward. This "main sequence" lasts for about 10 billion years.

EXPANSION
After all the available hydrogen has been consumed, nuclear fusion ends and the star collapses under its own weight. As the core contracts, the outer layers expand and cool, radiating red light. This stage may last for a few hundred million years.

HELIUM FLASH
The helium core—heated to 180 million°F (100 million°C)—explodes, and thrusts the star's outer clouds farther. The explosion ignites two separate nuclear fires: In the inner core (blue) helium fuses into carbon, and in the cooler middle shell, hydrogen is fused into helium. Depending on the star's mass, it may only have a few thousand years left to live.

HARD EVIDENCE

T-6,000,000,000
The Sun has been stable for more than 4 billion years, converting hydrogen into helium at a steady 400 million tons (363 million tonnes) per second. Over time, the concentration of helium in the Sun's core has risen from 27 to 62 percent. When it reaches 100 percent—about six billion years from now—the Sun will become a red giant.

LONG SHOT

In 1933, the organizers of the second Great Exposition in Chicago had a bright idea. To mark the 40 years since the previous Exposition, they used rays from the red giant Arcturus—thought to be 40 light-years away—to turn on the lights. They collected starlight with a telescope and focused it on a newfangled photocell switch. It worked. Sadly, according to later measurements, Arcturus is 37 light-years away.

A CENTURY OF PROGRESS
1833 1933
COME!
CHICAGO
WORLD'S FAIR

BLUE SUPERGIANTS

Hotter than any other stars, blue supergiants are the most powerful stars known. These stellar monsters are at least 10 to 20 times the diameter of the Sun, as well as being much brighter, and some emit more energy than hundreds of thousands of smaller, normal stars. In some cases, the radiation emitted by these stars is powerful enough to take some of a blue supergiant's outer layers with it, to form a vast gaseous envelope around the giant star. As a result of such fierce activity, these stars have some of the shortest known stellar lives—lasting only a million years or so.

SOME BLUE SUPERGIANTS

NAME	LOCATION	SPECTRAL CLASSIFICATION	DISTANCE	VISUAL MAGNITUDE	ABSOLUTE MAGNITUDE
ALPHA CAMELOPARDALIS	CAMELOPARDALIS	O.95 Ia	6,940 LIGHT-YEARS	4.29	−6.2
ZETA ORIONIS	ORION	O.95 Ib	820 LIGHT-YEARS	1.68	−5.9
EPSILON ORIONIS (ALNILAM)	ORION	B0 Ia	1,340 LIGHT-YEARS	1.62	−6.2
KAPPA CASSIOPEIAE	CASSIOPEIA	B1 Ia	4,130 LIGHT-YEARS	4.21	−6.6
NU SCORPII	SCORPIUS	B2 Iv	440 LIGHT-YEARS	4.00	−5.7
ETA CANIS MAJORIS	CANIS MAJOR	B5 Ia	3,200 LIGHT-YEARS	2.42	−7.0
BETA ORIONIS (RIGEL)	ORION	B8 Ia	770 LIGHT-YEARS	0.19	−7.1
SIGMA CYGNI	CYGNUS	B9 Ia	4,530 LIGHT-YEARS	4.27	−7.1

BRIEF LIVES

By human standards, the Sun is unimaginably powerful. But our star cannot come close in comparison with the blue supergiants, the most powerful stars in the universe. These stellar heavyweights outdo the Sun in every respect. Blue supergiants are hotter than our star, more massive, larger and much brighter, and they live much faster lives.

Blue supergiants are stars of spectral class O or B: To astronomers, this is a code meaning that these stars have surface temperatures that range from 20,000°F (11,000°C) to more than 100,000°F (55,500°C). Such high temperatures give these stars their bright blue-white color, and no stars are hotter than those classified as class O.

In terms of mass, blue supergiants are among the heaviest stars known. Typically, they range from five to 25 solar masses, and in some extreme cases outweigh more than 100 Suns. But it is because of their luminosity that these stars really stand out.

All hot objects, including stars, radiate energy at a rate that depends on their surface area and on the fourth power of their temperature. Thus, if the temperature of an object doubles, then the output of energy increases 16 times. Blue supergiants have the highest stellar temperatures, and their diameters are at least 20 times that of the Sun. As a result, they are exceptionally luminous. Even a modest blue supergiant is brighter than 10,000 Suns, and the most brilliant would outshine several hundred thousand Sun-like stars put together.

FAST WORKERS

Such power comes at a price, though. And the blue supergiants pay for their supremacy with a lifetime only one-thousandth that of our Sun. These stars are so massive that, in order to counterbalance their tendency to collapse under their own weight, their cores have to produce an enormous amount of outward pressure.

As in all stars, that pressure is generated by nuclear reactions—in blue supergiants, the conversion of helium into carbon. But because the cores of blue supergiants are under so much more stress than in lesser stars, the nuclear reactions in blue supergiants must work faster in order to generate pressure and prevent collapse. So these blue stars consume their nuclear fuel at phenomenal rates, and use up that fuel far more quickly than a star like the Sun.

This high luminosity has other implications. Photons—particles of light and all other forms of electromagnetic radiation—can exert a pressure like a hail of bullets. The higher the temperature, the greater the photon energy, and the higher the luminosity, the more photons per second a star emits. So a high temperature and luminosity combine to produce a very powerful radiation pressure.

In the case of a blue supergiant, the star's own emitted radiation as it leaves the surface can literally push atmospheric gas away and blast it into space. The result is a star that slowly evaporates: The star creates a nebulous shell of gas around it, as happens with the Wolf-Rayet stars.

Blue supergiants are exceedingly rare. In a typical region of the Milky Way, only 0.1 percent of the stars will be blue supergiants, and most will be of class B. O-type stars are even more uncommon, numbering less than one in four million stars. But the tremendous luminosity of these stars means that, despite their scarcity, they are easy to spot in the depths of space. Some blue supergiants can even be seen individually in distant galaxies.

DOWN AT HEEL

RIGEL, ONE OF THE MOST FAMOUS STARS IN THE SKY, IS A BLUE SUPERGIANT 1,400 LIGHT-YEARS AWAY IN THE CONSTELLATION ORION, THE HUNTER (RIGHT). RIGEL IS ONE OF THE TWO BRIGHTEST STARS IN ORION — THE OTHER BEING THE RED SUPERGIANT BETELGEUSE. RIGEL MARKS THE HUNTER'S HEEL. TWENTY TIMES THE MASS OF THE SUN AND 150,000 TIMES AS LUMINOUS, RIGEL IS THE SEVENTH BRIGHTEST STAR IN THE ENTIRE SKY AND IS EASILY SEEN WITH THE UNAIDED EYE.

Orion

Rigel

Blue supergiants shrink and shed their outer layers over tens of thousands of years. In nebula NGC 6164-6165, the contracting central star has blasted out gas to form three shells.

STELLAR COMPARISON

Unlike cooler stars, the outermost layers of blue stars are not convective—they do not transfer heat outward in a cellular pattern. So these stars are unable to generate magnetic fields in their interiors. As a result, they lack the surface features—starspots—that are associated with stellar activity in cooler stars. Blue supergiants are featureless, blue-white globes.

Sun shown at same scale

The Sun is 9.73 times the size of Jupiter, which in turn is 11.2 times as large as the Earth. The blue supergiant (far left), although 20 times the diameter of the Sun, is a medium-size example.

blue supergiant

the Sun

Jupiter

Earth

R136 IN LMC
Some 160,000 light-years away in the Large Magellanic Cloud lies a spectacular cluster of giant blue stars called R136. The cluster, embedded inside the nebula known as 30 Doradus, is a tight jumble of thousands of blue stars, some as much as 50 times heavier than the Sun.

NGC 3603
This Hubble image of the galactic nebula NGC 3603 captures a blue supergiant in the process of shedding its layers into space. Called Sher 25, the star (center) is partially surrounded by a ring of gas ejected by the star as it ages.

PLANETARY NEBULAE

When 18th-century astronomers probed the skies with powerful telescopes, they found fuzzy disks unlike the pinpoints of regular stars. They called the objects planetary nebulae. But these nebulae are not planets: They are expanding clouds of gas and debris that mark the death of stars.

Illuminated by the stellar remnants within them, the intricate and beautiful nebulae are short-lived, destined to soon disperse into invisibility. The material they contain, though, will be recycled in the stars—and worlds—of the next generation, eventually being sucked toward newly forming objects.

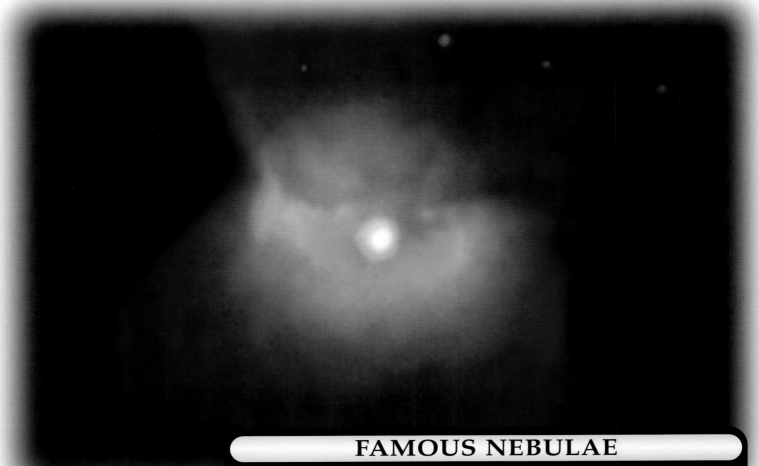

FAMOUS NEBULAE

Name	Catalog Number	Constellation	Magnitude	Distance	Size
Dumbbell Nebula	NGC 6853 (M27)	Vulpecula	8	2,000 light-years	1 light-year
Saturn Nebula	NGC 7009	Aquarius	8	3,000 light-years	1.5 light-years
Ring Nebula	NGC 6720 (M57)	Lyra	9	2,000 light-years	1 light-year
Helix Nebula	NGC 7293	Aquarius	6.5	500 light-years	2 light-years
Cat's Eye Nebula	NGC 6543	Draco	8.3	3,000 light-years	0.5 light-years
Owl Nebula	NGC 3587 (M97)	Ursa Major	11	1,500 light-years	1 light-year
Eskimo Nebula	NGC 2392	Gemini	10	3,000 light-years	0.5 light-year

THE LAST SUNSET

For most of its life, a star burns with the light of nuclear fusion as hydrogen in its core is converted into helium. The energy of the reaction creates an outward pressure that prevents the star from collapsing under its own weight. But when the hydrogen runs out, the star starts to shrink. Paradoxically, the shrinkage itself generates more light and heat, and the outer layers puff out enormously. The star becomes a red giant.

If the star is very massive, it will one day destroy itself in the spectacular blast of a supernova. Moderate-sized stars—the Sun, for example—keep expanding until their outermost layers have escaped completely into space. Only the hot core remains. But it still has enough energy to flood its neighborhood with ultraviolet radiation. This energy lights up the expanding gas. Many light-years distant, astronomers on Earth detect a planetary nebula.

The term was coined in 1785 by British astronomer William Herschel, who noted the resemblance of the objects he observed to hazy planets, though he knew they were not planets. But to find out what planetary nebulae really were, astronomers had to wait for more powerful telescopes and modern astrophysical theories.

STRANGE SHAPES

Those theories certainly account for the simplest planetary nebulae. But better telescopes have brought problems as well as solutions, by revealing that not all planetary nebulae are just expanding shells.

Most planetary nebulae have

WHAT IF?
...WE COULD WATCH WHAT HAPPENS TO NEBULAR GAS?

A planetary nebula may mark the end of a star, but not that star's material. The universe is the ultimate recycling machine and does not like waste.

As a planetary nebula expands into space, its material gets thinner. It is only visible because of the impact of ultraviolet radiation from the star's remains. This radiation has an ionizing effect: When a photon of ultraviolet light strikes an atom, it knocks away an outer electron. Shortly afterward, the electron rejoins its parent atom in a process known as recombination. When it does so, the atom gives off a photon of visible light.

As the nebula expands, its atoms grow farther apart, and their chance of encountering an ionizing photon diminishes. About 100,000 years after the planetary nebula is born, its gas has spread so widely that the ionization and recombination cease.

The nebula is now scarcely denser than the surrounding interstellar medium—the atoms and ions between stars—and it fades out into invisibility.

But this is not the end of the nebula's story. As the nebular gas drifts through space, it will one day encounter other clouds of gas and dust. As these clouds of gas collide, gravitational eddies will form within them. Some regions will have higher densities than others, and their greater mass will give them a greater gravitational attraction.

Out between the stars, dense areas grow denser as their gravity pulls in more of the surrounding material—increasing their ability to grow denser still. After a few million years, these denser regions are substantial enough to collapse under their own gravity. At the collapsing cloud's center, a new star is born from the ashes and the cycle begins afresh.

some kind of symmetry. But in many cases the structure is far more complex than a simple shell. Some are hourglass-shaped. Others appear to spout distinct jets of material, and others still have intricate elliptical patterns.

Astronomers still cannot explain how all these features arise. Probably, the stars that create the nebulae do not eject their gas into space at equal speeds and densities in every direction. The one common factor they share is the extraordinary beauty of their final expanding shrouds.

The material that constitutes planetary nebulae is very thin. Their great size—they can be up to two light-years across—means

that the star matter they contain is spread thinner than the best vacuums that scientists can create on Earth. Mostly, the nebulae are made up of hydrogen and helium. But they also contain heavier elements, notably oxygen and nitrogen. In the next round of star

formation, these extra elements will give the next generation of stars a more complex chemical structure. And some of the material, once the discarded mantle of a dead star, may wind up as part of a planet circling a new-born sun.

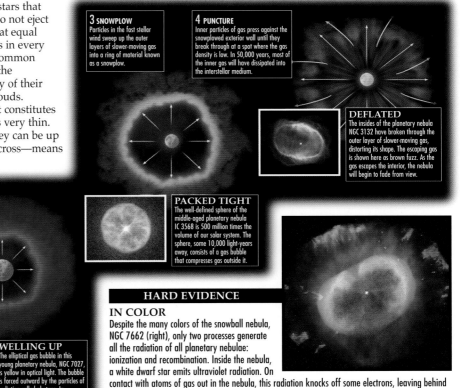

3 SNOWPLOW
Particles in the fast stellar wind sweep up the outer layers of slower-moving gas into a ring of material known as a snowplow.

4 PUNCTURE
Inner particles of gas press against the snowplowed exterior wall until they break through at a spot where the gas density is low. In 50,000 years, most of the inner gas will have dissipated into the interstellar medium.

DEFLATED
The insides of the planetary nebula NGC 3132 have broken through the outer layer of slower-moving gas, distorting its shape. The escaping gas is shown here as brown fuzz. As the gas escapes the interior, the nebula will begin to fade from view.

2 SWELLING BUBBLE
Millions of years after the first ejection, the dust clears, and the intense starlight propels a second wave of particles up to a thousand times faster than the first wave.

PACKED TIGHT
The well-defined sphere of the middle-aged planetary nebula IC 3568 is 500 million times the volume of our solar system. The sphere, some 10,000 light-years away, consists of a gas bubble that compresses gas outside it.

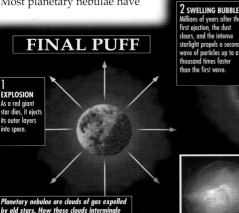

FINAL PUFF

1 EXPLOSION
As a red giant star dies, it ejects its outer layers into space.

Planetary nebulae are clouds of gas expelled by old stars. How these clouds intermingle determines their shape.

WELLING UP
The elliptical gas bubble in this young planetary nebula, NGC 7027, is yellow in optical light. The bubble is forced outward by the particles of radiation called photons. In sufficient quantities, a hail of photons gradually beats the bubble outward.

HARD EVIDENCE

IN COLOR
Despite the many colors of the snowball nebula, NGC 7662 (right), only two processes generate all the radiation of all planetary nebulae: ionization and recombination. Inside the nebula, a white dwarf star emits ultraviolet radiation. On contact with atoms of gas out in the nebula, this radiation knocks off some electrons, leaving behind positively-charged ions. Eventually, these ions will attract free-floating negatively-charged electrons. When ion and electron recombine, they emit visible light. It is this "recombination radiation" that illuminates the nebula. Recombining oxygen ions emit green light; recombining hydrogen ions, blue light; and recombining nitrogen ions, red light.

WHITE AND BLACK DWARFS

A star dies. It collapses under its own weight until its super-compressed matter occupies a sphere no bigger than an Earth-sized planet—a white dwarf. Their crowded interiors generate no new energy, so white dwarfs shine merely as the energy that has built up inside them slowly leaks through the packed interior and into space. But these objects will not shine forever. Gradually, over many billions of years, they will fade from view. The end product is a black dwarf—cool, dark, and invisible.

SOME WHITE DWARFS

Star	Location	Visual magnitude
Sirius B	Canis Major	8.5
Alpha CMa	Canis Major	8.7
40 Eri B	Eridanus	9.7
Alpha CMi	Canis Minor	10.8
Wolf 28	Pisces	12.4
V1603 Tau	Taurus	12.5
Feige 55	Canis Major	12.8
BB PSc	Pisces	14.4

STELLAR EVENING

Hydrogen and helium sustain the nuclear reactions of a star like our Sun, and produce the energy that holds it in shape despite the crushing force of its own gravity. But when the star has exhausted its supply of this material, it becomes a victim of its own immense mass. Gravity finally wins, and the star begins to shrink. The end result is a super-compressed sphere the size of a small planet but millions of times denser—an object called a white dwarf. A spoonful of typical white dwarf matter would tip the scales at several tons. No terrestrial object can ever become this dense. But white dwarfs are not made of terrestrial materials, or even of ordinary matter.

Normal matter is composed of atoms. Each atom has a nucleus surrounded by a cloud of negatively charged particles called electrons. In everyday objects, these electrons are so far apart that the material they make up is essentially just empty space. But inside a white dwarf, atoms are so tightly compressed that their electron clouds mingle. At these densities, a concept known as the Pauli exclusion principle comes into play.

This principle essentially states that there is a minimum distance separating two electrons. If there were no such limit, all atoms would collapse to become as simple as hydrogen, and complex chemistry would cease to exist. But when electrons are forced together, they repel each other with their own force, which is known as degeneracy pressure.

TO THE LIMIT

In a white dwarf, where gravity has compressed the star's atoms until the electrons are as close together as they can get, it is this degeneracy pressure—the resistance of the electrons to being any closer together—that prevents any further collapse of the star.

As far as their physical dimensions are concerned, white dwarfs share a strange property. A white dwarf with the same mass as the Sun would be 90 percent the size of the Earth. But a heavier white dwarf, with 1.2 solar masses, has a more powerful gravitational pull because of its extra mass. The force of gravity compresses the heavier star even more, shrinking its diameter to only about 60 percent of Earth's. In other words, the more massive white dwarfs are, the smaller they are—and the higher their internal pressure is.

Using this relationship, the Indian-American astrophysicist Subrahmanyan Chandrasekhar (1910–95) showed that there is a maximum possible mass for a white dwarf, and thus a minimum possible radius. The Chandrasekhar limit states that if the star contains more than 1.4 solar masses, its gravity becomes so overwhelming that even degeneracy pressure cannot support its weight. The star collapses further, until it becomes a neutron star, a tiny, superdense ball hundreds of times smaller than even a white dwarf.

CLASSIFYING DWARFS

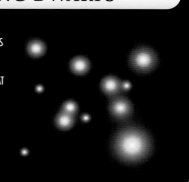

NORMAL STARS ARE CLASSIFIED BY THEIR DIFFERENT COLORS (RIGHT). WHITE DWARFS USED TO BE CLASSIFIED IN A SIMILAR WAY. BUT IN 1983, U.S. ASTRONOMER ED SION PROPOSED A NEW CLASSIFICATION THAT CONSISTED OF THREE CAPITAL LETTERS. THE FIRST LETTER, D, STANDS FOR "DEGENERATE," THE SECOND IS A CODE THAT DESCRIBES THE SPECTRUM OF THE STAR AND THE LAST LETTER DESCRIBES WHETHER THE SMALL STAR HAS ANY PECULIAR FEATURES, SUCH AS A STRONG MAGNETIC FIELD.

HARD EVIDENCE

NEBULAE
When a star like the Sun dies, it swells into a red giant and then puffs off its tenuous gas envelope to expose its core. The core is so hot that it energizes the discarded gas that surrounds it and makes it glow brilliantly to form a bright shell—a planetary nebula, like the Dumbbell nebula (right). These objects are common in the galaxy. In many cases, the central star—that is, the core of the original dying star—is either a white dwarf, or is well on the way to becoming one.

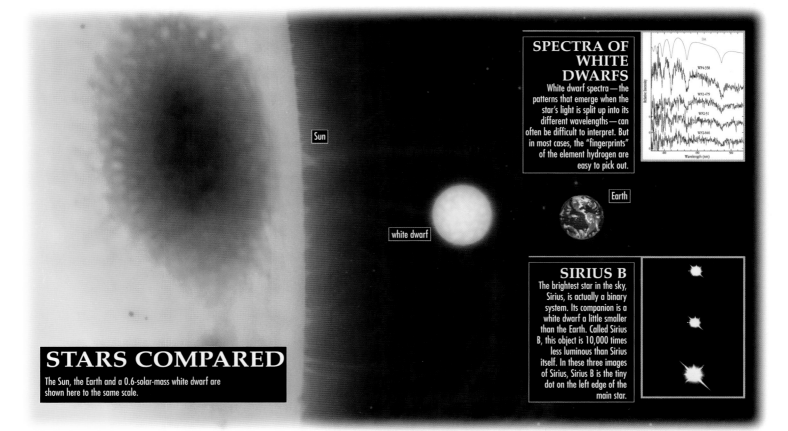

Sun

white dwarf

Earth

SPECTRA OF WHITE DWARFS
White dwarf spectra—the patterns that emerge when the star's light is split up into its different wavelengths—can often be difficult to interpret. But in most cases, the "fingerprints" of the element hydrogen are easy to pick out.

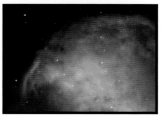

SIRIUS B
The brightest star in the sky, Sirius, is actually a binary system. Its companion is a white dwarf a little smaller than the Earth. Called Sirius B, this object is 10,000 times less luminous than Sirius itself. In these three images of Sirius, Sirius B is the tiny dot on the left edge of the main star.

STARS COMPARED
The Sun, the Earth and a 0.6-solar-mass white dwarf are shown here to the same scale.

SUPERNOVA

ot even stars live forever—and the bigger the star, the more spectacular its demise. When a star is at least eight times the size of our Sun, it can end in a detonation so powerful that it temporarily outshines every other star in its galaxy. Called a supernova, such a blast is rare:

Only six supernovae have been observed in the Milky Way during all of recorded history. Over galactic timescales, though, these catastrophes have created the elemental material from which new generations of stars, planets and even life itself have eventually been formed.

OBSERVED SUPERNOVAE

Name	Detonation Date	Discoverer	Location	Distance from Earth
The Veil Supernova	Around 18000 B.C.	unknown	Cygnus	1,600 light-years
The Vela Supernova	Around 9000 B.C.	unknown	Vela	6,000 light-years
The Crab Supernova	1054 A.D.	Chinese astronomers	Taurus	6,300 light-years
Brahe's Supernova	1572	Tycho Brahe	Cassiopeia	10,000 light-years
Kepler's Supernova	1604	Johannes Kepler	Ophiuchus	20,000 light-years
SN1987A	1987	Ian Shelton	Large Magellanic Cloud	179,000 light-years
SN1997ap	1997	Supernova Cosmology Project	Coma Berenices	9 billion light-years

SUPERNOVA EXPLOSION

PAST BANG

IN 1054 A.D., STARTLED CHINESE ASTRONOMERS RECORDED THE APPEARANCE OF A NEW STAR IN THE CONSTELLATION OF TAURUS. IN FACT, A STAR HAD DIED IN A SUPERNOVA EXPLOSION. A MILLENNIUM LATER, THE EXPANDING CLOUD OF DEBRIS IS KNOWN AS THE CRAB NEBULA.

SUPERNOVA 1987A

IN 1987, A STAR IN THE LARGE MAGELLANIC CLOUD BLEW ITSELF TO PIECES. ALTHOUGH THE EXPLOSION WAS 179,000 LIGHT-YEARS AWAY, IT WAS THE BRIGHTEST "NEARBY" SUPERNOVA IN 400 YEARS. AFTER THE BLAST, A SPHERICAL SHELL OF GAS AND DEBRIS EXPANDED INTO SPACE, CAPTURED IN THIS FALSE-COLOR IMAGE TAKEN BY THE HUBBLE SPACE TELESCOPE. IN A FEW MILLION YEARS, THE SHELL WILL BECOME SO DIFFUSE THAT IT WILL NO LONGER BE VISIBLE.

TOTAL DESTRUCTION
A few minutes after a star goes supernova, a planet at Jupiter's distance from the Sun is annihilated by an expanding cloud of debris, gas and radiation. The radiation could threaten life light-years away.

HARD CORE
A surge of energy blows the outer layers of the star away from the superdense neutron core that will survive the supernova explosion. The energy, generated by the star's gravitational collapse, creates new elements and leaves behind a neutron star only a few miles across.

DEATH OF A STAR

The titanic explosion astronomers call a supernova marks the destruction of a star that has run out of fuel—and time. Stars feed on hydrogen, the most abundant element in the universe. Nuclear reactions at a star's core fuse atoms of hydrogen together to make helium. The process generates an enormous amount of heat, as well as an outward pressure of escaping radiation that prevents the star from collapsing under its own colossal weight.

Stars big enough to turn supernova—at least eight times as massive as our Sun—have relatively short lives. Their core temperatures are very high, and they burn through their hydrogen fuel supply quickly. When their hydrogen has all fused to helium—perhaps after only 10 million years—the star has little time left. Another nuclear-fusion reaction turns the helium core into carbon, which yields enough energy to buy the star another half million years. When the helium has gone, the next reaction, carbon into neon, lasts only a few centuries. It takes only about a year to turn the neon into oxygen and around six months to burn the oxygen into silicon. The final reaction, which converts silicon to iron, runs to completion in just one day.

No further atomic reactions are possible: Iron is stable, even in the furnace of a stellar core. In addition, quite abruptly, there is no internal energy available to counterbalance the force of gravity, and the star collapses inward—within just a few seconds. As it collapses, the inner core becomes ever denser. Soon, its component atoms are squeezed so tightly together that nothing is left but the subatomic particles called neutrons, and the core can collapse no farther.

Infalling material now bounces back at speeds of up to 150 million miles (240 million km) per hour. A devastating shock wave blows the defunct star apart in an immense eruption that for a time can outshine the light from an entire galaxy. The cataclysmic energies involved in the final destructive moments are enough to break through the barrier of iron's nuclear stability—a supernova is the only place in the universe where elements heavier than iron can be made.

Only the star's core remains. This so-called neutron star may contain 20 percent of the original star's mass, squeezed into a dim cosmic tombstone only a few miles across. Meanwhile, gas, debris and radiation from the supernova spread outward. The remnants collide with preexisting interstellar gas, generating shock waves that compact the gas and often lead to the formation of new stars. Thus star death leads to star birth—and more.

During a supernova explosion, the new elements forged in the ruined star are scattered like windborne seeds throughout space. In time, these elements will make planets like our Earth and living things like ourselves.

NEUTRON STARS

Neutron stars are the collapsed remains of giant stars that ended their days in supernova explosions. By cosmic standards a neutron star is tiny—only a few miles across—and glows so dimly that it is barely visible. Yet neutron stars have their own ways to make themselves known.

Their incredible density means that just a cupful of their matter weighs more than a 2-mile (3.2 km)-wide asteroid. And although neutron stars are usually too small to be seen, their gravity has a marked effect on the orbits of nearby stars, which can make them visible through telescopes.

MATTER DENSITIES COMPARED

Object	Mass of 1 cu ft (0.02 m³)
Orion Nebula	1/1000,000,000,000 oz/2.8 x 10⁻¹¹
Earth	343.75 lb (156 kg)
Sun's core	5.125 tons (4.65 tonnes)
White Dwarf star	31,250 tons (28,350 tonnes)
Neutron star . . . . .31.25 trillion tons (28.35

TINY, HEAVY, DENSE

Forged by a supernova explosion into some of the heaviest material in the universe, a neutron star crams enough matter to build three Suns into a smooth, spinning ball that may be less than 20 miles (32 km) in diameter. At such a density, the fundamental structure of matter is altered. Atoms no longer exist: Their component electrons and protons are gone, crushed by titanic pressure into neutrons that are themselves packed together almost as tightly as they would be inside a regular atomic nucleus. Tiny by the standards of its stellar neighbors, a neutron star is really a gigantic subatomic particle.

A neutron star begins life as the core of a giant star—at least 10 times as massive as the Sun. Within the giant, the gravitational pressures are enormous. So long as the star has hydrogen to burn, the outward pressure of the radiation created by nuclear fusion counterbalances the inward pressure of the star's mass. But when the star runs out of fuel, it collapses under the force of its own colossal gravity, and the matter in the core rapidly undergoes a remarkable transformation.

In regular atoms, electrons orbit a tiny, dense nucleus that is made up of protons and neutrons. Compared with the size of the nucleus, the electrons are a vast distance away: Atoms consist mainly of empty space. But inside a star, the enormous heat and pressure separate out the atomic nuclei into ultra-dense particles that exist in a kind of electron soup—a state known as plasma.

Even in the thick plasma at the heart of a star, powerful subatomic forces keep the various particles apart; at a subatomic level, the plasma deep inside a star is still mostly empty space.

But in a dying giant star, the repulsive force between protons and electrons is overcome by the irresistible force of the star's gravitational collapse. Suddenly, squeezed together, they combine into neutrons with no space at all between them. The core of the dying star transforms itself into a new kind of matter of unimaginable density, and a new neutron star is born.

COSMIC CLUES

The first real clues to the existence of neutron stars came from their effect on other stars. When a neutron star orbits a normal companion star that is losing material as it ages, the neutron star's powerful gravity tears long ribbons of gas from its neighbor and draws it into orbit around itself. The enormous gravitational pull causes the gas to whirl around at very high speeds, which creates so much friction between its atoms that they emit easily detectable X-rays in all directions.

The neutron star also affects the orbit of its companion, causing it to "wobble" as seen from Earth. Astronomers can measure this wobble and deduce the mass and location of the invisible neutron star that is causing it. The Hubble Space Telescope has even succeeded in detecting a lone neutron star, betrayed by the X-rays that it gives off, simply because it is so incredibly hot—measuring a staggering 1.2 million°F (660,000°C).

NEUTRONIUM

A MICROSCOPICALLY THIN LAYER OF NEUTRON STAR MATERIAL WOULD MAKE IMPENETRABLE ARMOR PLATE. THE ONLY PROBLEM IS THE MATERIAL'S WEIGHT: A TANK PROTECTED WITH A SUPER-DENSE "NEUTRONIUM" COATING WOULD SINK TO THE CENTER OF THE EARTH.

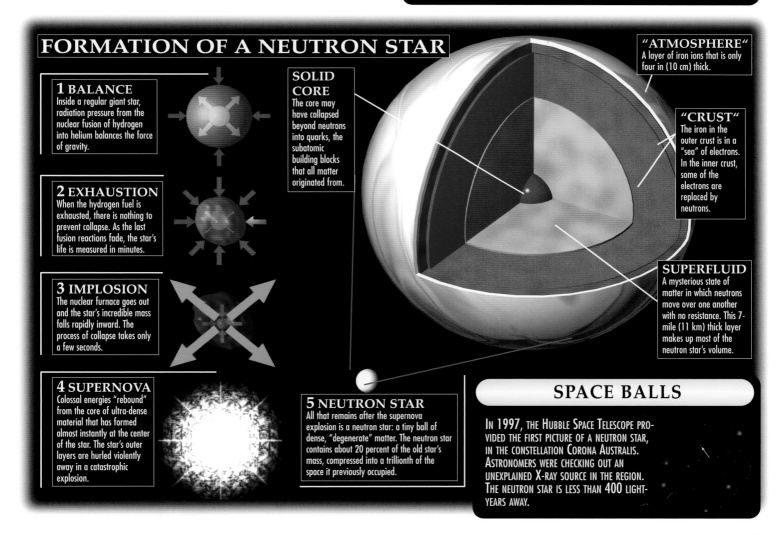

FORMATION OF A NEUTRON STAR

1 BALANCE
Inside a regular giant star, radiation pressure from the nuclear fusion of hydrogen into helium balances the force of gravity.

2 EXHAUSTION
When the hydrogen fuel is exhausted, there is nothing to prevent collapse. As the last fusion reactions fade, the star's life is measured in minutes.

3 IMPLOSION
The nuclear furnace goes out and the star's incredible mass falls rapidly inward. The process of collapse takes only a few seconds.

4 SUPERNOVA
Colossal energies "rebound" from the core of ultra-dense material that has formed almost instantly at the center of the star. The star's outer layers are hurled violently away in a catastrophic explosion.

5 NEUTRON STAR
All that remains after the supernova explosion is a neutron star: a tiny ball of dense, "degenerate" matter. The neutron star contains about 20 percent of the old star's mass, compressed into a trillionth of the space it previously occupied.

SOLID CORE
The core may have collapsed beyond neutrons into quarks, the subatomic building blocks that all matter originated from.

"ATMOSPHERE"
A layer of iron ions that is only four in (10 cm) thick.

"CRUST"
The iron in the outer crust is in a "sea" of electrons. In the inner crust, some of the electrons are replaced by neutrons.

SUPERFLUID
A mysterious state of matter in which neutrons move over one another with no resistance. This 7-mile (11 km) thick layer makes up most of the neutron star's volume.

SPACE BALLS

IN 1997, THE HUBBLE SPACE TELESCOPE PROVIDED THE FIRST PICTURE OF A NEUTRON STAR, IN THE CONSTELLATION CORONA AUSTRALIS. ASTRONOMERS WERE CHECKING OUT AN UNEXPLAINED X-RAY SOURCE IN THE REGION. THE NEUTRON STAR IS LESS THAN 400 LIGHT-YEARS AWAY.

PULSARS

Forged in the fire of a supernova explosion, a pulsar is the core of what was once a giant star. These small super-dense objects spin rapidly—typically once every second—and they are surrounded by some of the most powerful magnetic fields known to science.

As a pulsar spins, narrow beams of radio waves are emitted from its magnetic poles. If the beam is pointing in the Earth's direction, astronomers can detect the star's radio emission blinking on and off with the timekeeping precision of an atomic clock.

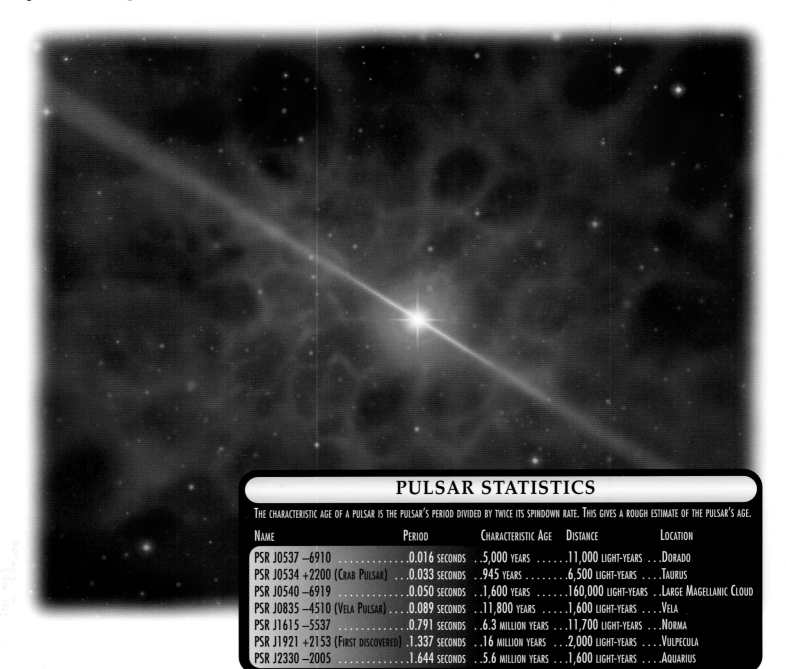

PULSAR STATISTICS

THE CHARACTERISTIC AGE OF A PULSAR IS THE PULSAR'S PERIOD DIVIDED BY TWICE ITS SPINDOWN RATE. THIS GIVES A ROUGH ESTIMATE OF THE PULSAR'S AGE.

NAME	PERIOD	CHARACTERISTIC AGE	DISTANCE	LOCATION
PSR J0537 −6910	0.016 SECONDS	5,000 YEARS	11,000 LIGHT-YEARS	DORADO
PSR J0534 +2200 (CRAB PULSAR)	0.033 SECONDS	945 YEARS	6,500 LIGHT-YEARS	TAURUS
PSR J0540 −6919	0.050 SECONDS	1,600 YEARS	160,000 LIGHT-YEARS	LARGE MAGELLANIC CLOUD
PSR J0835 −4510 (VELA PULSAR)	0.089 SECONDS	11,800 YEARS	1,600 LIGHT-YEARS	VELA
PSR J1615 −5537	0.791 SECONDS	6.3 MILLION YEARS	11,700 LIGHT-YEARS	NORMA
PSR J1921 +2153 (FIRST DISCOVERED)	1.337 SECONDS	16 MILLION YEARS	2,000 LIGHT-YEARS	VULPECULA
PSR J2330 −2005	1.644 SECONDS	5.6 MILLION YEARS	1,600 LIGHT-YEARS	AQUARIUS

COSMIC CLOCKS

Was a radio source that flashed on and off regularly—once every 1.33730119 seconds exactly—the first sign of alien intelligence? English graduate student Jocelyn Bell of Cambridge University chanced upon the source in 1967. She and her colleagues realized that the signal they had detected was not local—it was not, say, a satellite. This regular signal had to be from space. Within a few weeks, three more such objects with comparable periods were discovered. This strange radio source was an entirely new natural phenomenon. Bell's research group named these objects pulsating radio sources, or pulsars.

At first, astronomers thought that the modulations were emanating from white dwarf stars—the highly condensed remains of the cores of dead stars—that changed their radius very rapidly with strict periodicity. But some pulsars had periods too small to be explained as pulsating white dwarfs—the stress of such a rapid oscillation would break a white dwarf apart.

Therefore, pulsars had to be even smaller and denser objects. The only objects that would fit the bill were neutron stars, extremely small super-dense objects created when a massive dying star implodes under its own gravity. But when the first pulsars were discovered in 1967, nobody had ever seen a neutron star. Although the existence of neutron stars was predicted by Swiss astronomer Fritz Zwicky (1898–1974) in the 1930s, many astronomers in the 1960s still saw these objects as conjectural.

IN A SPIN

In 1968, the Crab Nebula—a supernova remnant whose light explosion was observed on Earth in 1054—was found to contain a pulsar. This pulsar, like some others, had a period much too small to be explained by a pulsating white dwarf. It had to be a neutron star. So, if pulsars were neutron stars, the next problem was to explain the pulsations.

Pulsars do not actually pulsate. The modulations are caused by rapid rotation. Just as ice skaters spin faster by pulling in their arms, so a star's core spins more rapidly as it shrinks to a 10-mile (16-km) wide neutron star. No white dwarf could rotate this quickly without flying apart. The shrinking also squeezes the star's original

magnetic field into a much smaller space, increasing it by factors exceeding a billion. A combination of rapid rotation and a powerful magnetic field strength creates a dynamo action that generates an equally intense electric field that surrounds the neutron star. This electric field tears away charged particles—electrons—from the fabric of the neutron star. The electrons move upward near the

magnetic poles, where the magnetic field accelerates them away from the polar regions along the magnetic field lines. Magnetism forces these electrons to adhere to the polar field lines in a narrow cone.

A steady flow of radio emissions rises from the poles in parallel jets as the electrons emit radio waves in the direction of their motion. Because the magnetic axis is tilted in relation to the spin axis, these jets

sweep across space like a cosmic lighthouse—but emit radio rather than light waves. If the magnetic axis is within the line of sight from Earth, then each time a pole comes into sight, we can detect a jet. Our galaxy, the Milky Way, may contain as many as 100,000 active pulsars at any given time—but many are invisible to us because their magnetic axes are pointing away from the Earth.

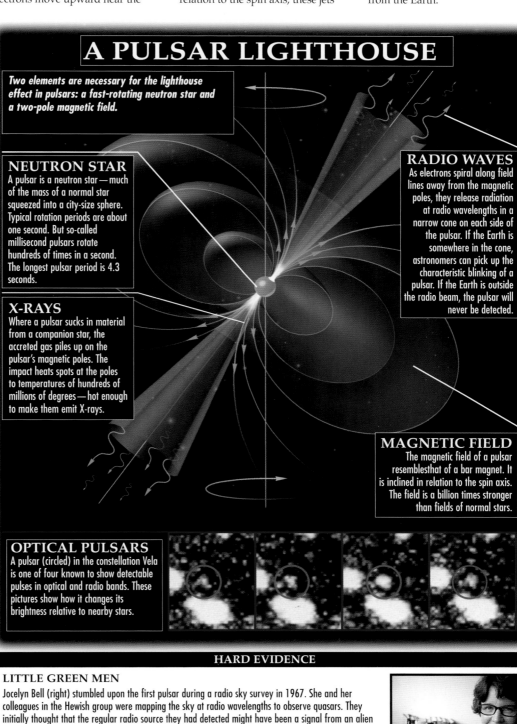

A PULSAR LIGHTHOUSE

Two elements are necessary for the lighthouse effect in pulsars: a fast-rotating neutron star and a two-pole magnetic field.

NEUTRON STAR
A pulsar is a neutron star—much of the mass of a normal star squeezed into a city-size sphere. Typical rotation periods are about one second. But so-called millisecond pulsars rotate hundreds of times in a second. The longest pulsar period is 4.3 seconds.

X-RAYS
Where a pulsar sucks in material from a companion star, the accreted gas piles up on the pulsar's magnetic poles. The impact heats spots at the poles to temperatures of hundreds of millions of degrees—hot enough to make them emit X-rays.

RADIO WAVES
As electrons spiral along field lines away from the magnetic poles, they release radiation at radio wavelengths in a narrow cone on each side of the pulsar. If the Earth is somewhere in the cone, astronomers can pick up the characteristic blinking of a pulsar. If the Earth is outside the radio beam, the pulsar will never be detected.

MAGNETIC FIELD
The magnetic field of a pulsar resemblesthat of a bar magnet. It is inclined in relation to the spin axis. The field is a billion times stronger than fields of normal stars.

OPTICAL PULSARS
A pulsar (circled) in the constellation Vela is one of four known to show detectable pulses in optical and radio bands. These pictures show how it changes its brightness relative to nearby stars.

HARD EVIDENCE

LITTLE GREEN MEN
Jocelyn Bell (right) stumbled upon the first pulsar during a radio sky survey in 1967. She and her colleagues in the Hewish group were mapping the sky at radio wavelengths to observe quasars. They initially thought that the regular radio source they had detected might have been a signal from an alien intelligence. The group lightheartedly suggested that the source should be named LGM-1, in which the letters LGM stood for Little Green Men. The object is now known as CP1919.

BLACK HOLES

A black hole is an object whose gravitational pull is so great that nothing—not even light—can escape from it. At one time, black holes were entirely theoretical. But now their existence, both in our own galaxy and elsewhere in the universe, has been confirmed. A black hole forms when a massive star dies and collapses under its own mass. Some black holes, billions of times more massive than the Sun, lie at the centers of distant galaxies. Others may have been forged in the first fiery moments during the creation of the universe.

BLACK HOLES LARGE & SMALL

OBJECT	MASS	RADIUS OF EVENT HORIZON
V404 CYGNI	12 SUN MASSES (24,000 TRILLION TRILLION TONS)	24 MILES (38 KM)
CYGNUS X-1	20 SUN MASSES (40,000 TRILLION TRILLION TONS)	40 MILES (64 KM)
CENTER OF MILKY WAY	1 MILLION SUN MASSES (2 BILLION TRILLION TRILLION TONS)	2M MILES/3.2M KM (ABOUT 10 LIGHT-SECONDS)
CENTER OF M 106	36 MILLION SUN MASSES (72 BILLION TRILLION TRILLION TONS)	72M MILES/116M KM (THE RADIUS OF VENUS' ORBIT OF THE SUN)
CENTER OF M 87	3 BILLION SUN MASSES (6 TRILLION TRILLION TRILLION TONS)	6 BILLION MILES/9.6 BILLION KM (60 TIMES THE RADIUS OF THE EARTH'S ORBIT OF THE SUN)
MINI BLACK HOLE*	ABOUT 100 MILLION TONS	THE SIZE OF AN ATOMIC NUCLEUS

...AND IF OUR EARTH AND SUN WERE BLACK HOLES, HOW BIG WOULD THEY BE?

OBJECT	MASS	RADIUS OF EVENT HORIZON
THE EARTH	7 BILLION TRILLION TONS	ABOUT A THIRD OF AN INCH (8 MM)
OUR SUN	300,000 EARTH MASSES (2,000 TRILLION TRILLION TONS)	2 MILES (3.2 KM) * EXISTENCE NOT PROVED

INTO THE HEART OF DARKNESS

Throw a ball into the air and gravity will bring it back down to Earth. But throw the ball fast enough—around 25,000 mph (40,000 km/h)—and it will escape from the Earth's gravity into space. Objects that are more massive than the Earth have stronger gravitational fields that demand higher escape velocities (EVs); the Sun's EV, for example, is about 100 times the Earth's.

Black holes are bodies so massive and dense that their theoretical EV is greater than the speed of light itself. This means that not even light can escape from such bodies, rendering them effectively invisible—hence the name.

A black hole is formed when a very large star—at least 30 times the mass of the Sun—dies and collapses under its own weight. It shrinks down to an infinitely dense point known as a singularity, at which point conventional mathematics can no longer cope. Around the singularity is an imaginary circle called the event horizon, beyond which all light from the object is turned back by the force of its own gravity. And since Einstein proved that gravity can not only capture light, but can also distort time and space, inside the event horizon space and time completely break down.

You could never see a person actually fall into a black hole: as they approached the event horizon, time would slow to the point where it would take infinitely long to reach it! In the meantime, the black hole's gravitational pull on light would make them appear to fade away. As for the person, who knows? All we know for sure is that in a black hole, reality as we know it ceases to exist.

LIMITED LIFE

BLACK HOLES ARE NOT COMPLETELY BLACK. ENGLISH PHYSICIST STEPHEN HAWKING (RIGHT) HAS SHOWN THAT BLACK HOLES GIVE OFF FAINT RADIATION, WHICH IMPLIES THAT EVENTUALLY THEIR MASS MUST EVAPORATE IN A HAZE OF SUBATOMIC PARTICLES.

HOW STARS BECOME BLACK HOLES

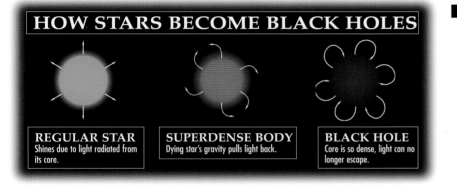

REGULAR STAR
Shines due to light radiated from its core.

SUPERDENSE BODY
Dying star's gravity pulls light back.

BLACK HOLE
Core is so dense, light can no longer escape.

STELLAR HOLES
Many black holes have similar masses to regular stars. They are too dark to be seen directly, but astronomers infer their presence by monitoring their gravitational effects on nearby bright stars. Sometimes, a black hole's gravitational pull "captures" material from a companion star (right). This material becomes agitated and heats up, causing it to emit X-rays that astronomers can also detect. So far, the best candidate for a stellar-mass black hole is V404 Cygni, discovered in 1989.

INSIDE A BLACK HOLE

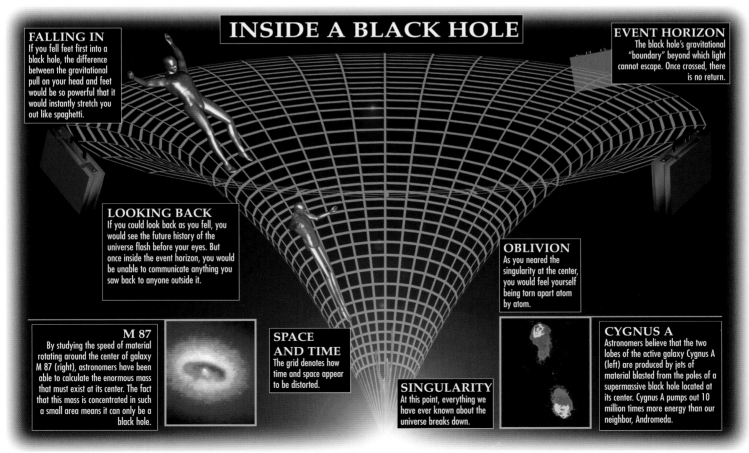

FALLING IN
If you fell feet first into a black hole, the difference between the gravitational pull on your head and feet would be so powerful that it would instantly stretch you out like spaghetti.

EVENT HORIZON
The black hole's gravitational "boundary" beyond which light cannot escape. Once crossed, there is no return.

LOOKING BACK
If you could look back as you fell, you would see the future history of the universe flash before your eyes. But once inside the event horizon, you would be unable to communicate anything you saw back to anyone outside it.

OBLIVION
As you neared the singularity at the center, you would feel yourself being torn apart atom by atom.

M 87
By studying the speed of material rotating around the center of galaxy M 87 (right), astronomers have been able to calculate the enormous mass that must exist at its center. The fact that this mass is concentrated in such a small area means it can only be a black hole.

SPACE AND TIME
The grid denotes how time and space appear to be distorted.

SINGULARITY
At this point, everything we have ever known about the universe breaks down.

CYGNUS A
Astronomers believe that the two lobes of the active galaxy Cygnus A (left) are produced by jets of material blasted from the poles of a supermassive black hole located at its center. Cygnus A pumps out 10 million times more energy than our neighbor, Andromeda.

OUR GALAXY

The Milky Way we see in the sky is merely a side-on impression of the great star system in which we belong. The Milky Way galaxy is an enormous cosmic spiral containing some 200 billion stars, and vast amounts of gas, dust and other matter. Within the Milky Way, young stars are found in brilliant clusters, while around it orbit vast globular balls of older stars. The gas and dust form nebulae—great clouds of matter within which stars are born, and which may be illuminated spectacularly by the fierce radiation of the young stars within them. The entire system is maintained by the slow turning of the Milky Way itself, triggering episodes of collapse that turn its spiral arms into regions of continuous starbirth. At the center of the system lies an enormous hub of old red and yellow stars, concealing a violent region that contains a dormant, supermassive black hole, with the mass of several million stars lying at its heart.

This bizarre formation is actually an innocuous pillar of gas and dust. Called the Cone Nebula (NGC 2264)—so named because it has a conical shape in ground-based images—this giant pillar resides in a star-forming region of our galaxy.

STAR CLUSTERS

A s well as being a beautiful sight to behold of contrasting colors and sizes, open star clusters give astronomers the chance to study a single family of stars simultaneously and to compare the differences between them. What has become apparent is that star clusters, just like human families, go through many ups and downs during the course of their existence. Some individuals are brilliant but spendthrift, while others are more sensible with their resources. And, in time, members of even the closest family unit can drift apart.

FAMOUS STAR CLUSTERS

Cluster	Constellation	Distance (light-years)	Diameter (light-years)	Features
M 6/NGC 6405, the Butterfly	Scorpius	2,000	20	About 80 stars
M 7/NGC 6475, Ptolemy's cluster	Scorpius	800	18	A spectacular cluster with over 80 stars
M 11/NGC 6705, the Wild Duck	Scutum	6,000	24	Approximately 2,900 stars
M 44/NGC 2632, Praesepe, or the Beehive	Cancer	577	16	At least 200 stars; shares movement with Hyades and may have been formed with it
M45, the Pleiades, or Seven Sisters	Taurus	380	13	More than 500 stars, spread over an area of sky about twice the diameter of the full moon
NGC 869, NGC 884, the Double cluster	Perseus	7,100/7,400	62/62	NGC 869 has about 400 stars, NGC 884 has about 300
NGC 4755, the Jewel Box	Crux	7,600	22	About 7 million years old, with three blue giants and a red supergiant among its brightest stars
Hyades	Taurus	151	80+	Shares movement with Praesepe

Numbers with the prefix "M" refer to Messier catalog numbers; those with the prefix NGC refer to listings in the New General Catalog.

BRIGHT YOUNG THINGS

Star clusters are among the most beautiful sights to be seen through a telescope and often contain dozens of brilliant stars in contrasting colors. One of the most famous lies in the constellation of the Southern Cross, where a bright red supergiant star set among blue and white neighbors has earned it the name of the Jewel Box.

Loose groups such as this are called open clusters. They can have hundreds of members and are to be found in the main disk of our galaxy. It is no accident that the stars in such clusters are so close, since they were all were born together at roughly the same time from a single cloud of gas. In their youth, the stars formed a tightly knit group, perhaps only a light-year apart, and shared the same motion through space as they orbit the galaxy.

Yet there are forces at work to separate the sibling stars, including the gravitational pull of other stars and clusters and mutual encounters between members of the same cluster. Over millions of years, these forces conspire to cause even the largest clusters to disperse. As clusters age, the stars within them also undergo a transformation. The most massive stars squander their fuel so rapidly that they cool into red supergiants within only a few million years—a phenomenon that explains the beautiful color variations within clusters such as the Jewel Box.

The importance of star clusters to astronomers lies in their common origin. Each cluster is a snapshot of stars that were born together but have developed at different rates according to their masses. In fact, much of what we know today about the evolution of stars comes from the patient study of open clusters.

CRUCIAL STEP

THE HYADES IN TAURUS (RIGHT) IS ONE OF THE CLOSEST AND MOST IMPORTANT CLUSTERS TO ASTRONOMERS BECAUSE ITS DISTANCE CAN BE MEASURED HIGHLY ACCURATELY. SUCH MEASUREMENTS ARE THE YARDSTICKS BY WHICH THE SIZE OF THE UNIVERSE AS A WHOLE IS ESTIMATED.

HOW STAR CLUSTERS SHOW THEIR AGE

YOUNG CLUSTER

THE BRILLIANCE OF YOUTH...

A young star cluster, perhaps only a few million years old, is dominated by massive, brilliant blue stars that use up their fuel very quickly. The more sedate yellow and red dwarf stars will long outlive their flashy neighbors.

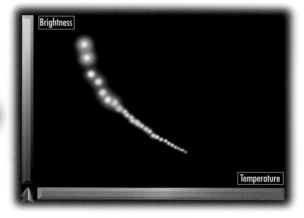

...BIG, BRIGHT AND BLUE

When the stars in a young cluster are plotted in order of brightness, they show a smooth transition from bright, hot and blue to dim, cool and red. In reality the cluster may also contain many smaller red stars that are just too faint to be seen from Earth.

30 Doradus, part of the Tarantula Nebula in the Large Magellanic Cloud, is among the most recently formed clusters.

The most massive of the brilliant, blue stars in the young cluster NGC 3293 has already evolved into a red supergiant.

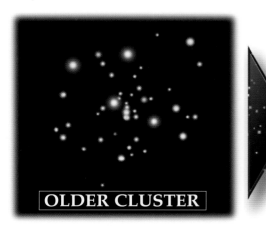

OLDER CLUSTER

OLD AGE TAKES ITS TOLL...

As a cluster ages, its most massive blue stars cool to become red supergiants and eventually explode as supernovae. The stars in the cluster may also drift apart, causing the cluster to become fainter and less clearly defined.

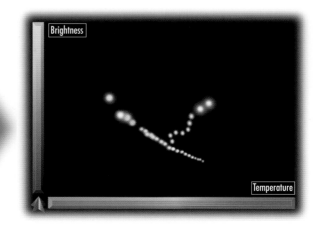

...AND THE RED STARS SHINE OUT

The brightest, hottest blue stars have gone, to be replaced by red giants of similar brightness but lower temperature. Some medium-mass stars have also begun to age, their increased brightness and redness resulting in a trail of stars toward the red-giant region.

All the bright young stars in NGC 2818 have long since exploded. This glowing planetary nebula is the remnant of such an event.

Trumpler 5 is a very old cluster, consisting only of middle-aged and low-mass stars that have drifted apart from each other.

GLOBULAR CLUSTERS

Unlike the groups of stars that make up most of the galaxies in the universe, globular clusters do not reside in the core or the arms of a galaxy. Instead, these balls of millions of stars swing around the center of the galaxy in eccentric orbits that can extend to 40,000 light-years. Because their orbits are inclined at random, the clusters appear in a spherical halo around the center of the Galaxy. The most prominent globular clusters, and the easiest to study, are the ones that orbit the Milky Way.

THE NEAREST CLUSTERS

Name	Right Ascension	Declination	Distance (light-years)	Apparent Magnitude
M 22	18:36.4	−23:54	10,100	5.10
47 Tucanae	00:24.1	−72:05	13,400	4.03
Omega Centauri	13:26.8	−47:29	16,000	3.68
M 13	16:41.7	+36:28	22,800	5.80
M 30	21:40.4	−23:11	24,800	7.20
M 80	16:17.0	−22:59	27,400	7.30
M 68	12:39.5	−26:45	32,300	7.80
M 15	21:30.0	+12:10	32,600	6.20
M 2	21:33.5	−00:49	36,200	6.50
M 72	20:53.5	−12:32	52,800	9.30

ERRANT STARS

Spherical groups of stray stars called globular clusters are found outside the most massive parts of a galaxy, known as the halo, a spherical region around a spiral galaxy. But they are not very different from the galaxy's most central stars. Both groups formed as the galaxy was coalescing. As an enormous gas cloud slowly contracted to become the galaxy, small parts of gas on the outskirts fragmented and collapsed on their own. The larger clouds of gas collapsed into globular clusters.

A typical spiral galaxy, such as the Milky Way, will today be surrounded by a few hundred globular clusters. A giant elliptical galaxy may have 10 times as many—the total of all the galactic collisions and mergers that probably form such huge galaxies.

A single globular cluster contains between 10,000 and several million stars. Usually these star-spheres are no more than a few hundred light-years in diameter, but sometimes they measure just a few dozen light-years. Globular clusters almost always contain very old stars, formed at the same time during the initial collapse of the gas cloud. These stars are known as Population II stars and were among the first to form after the Big Bang.

We know that the stars are very old because they contain few chemical elements heavier than helium. Heavy elements such as carbon and nitrogen are made in the hearts of stars and scattered into space as the stars die. New stars—called Population I stars—form from the remains of these recycled materials.

SWEPT CLEAN

Globular clusters never get to foster new stars from the gas of old ones. The clusters are regularly swept clean as they pass through the disks of spiral galaxies. The gravity of densely packed stars in the disk pulls free gas out of a cluster—in extreme cases, the disk can tear apart the whole cluster, scattering its stars in space. According to one estimate, half of the Milky Way's 160 clusters will be destroyed this way over the next 10 billion years.

Still, not every cluster is old. We have discovered globular clusters containing young stars in the nearby Large Magellanic Cloud. One of the galaxy's star-forming clouds, the Tarantula nebula, may be a cluster in the process of forming. And a similar cloud—NGC 604—has been found in the spiral galaxy M 33.

WHAT IF?
...CLUSTER STARS TOLD THE UNIVERSE'S AGE?

Globular cluster stars can be dated by comparing their color and brightness with other stars, giving values of 14—16 billion years. A more complicated method uses the universe's expansion rate to work out the time of the Big Bang, yielding an age of 10—20 billion years.

As better estimates were made of the universe's extent, its age crept toward 10 billion years. This left an impossible scenario: Globular cluster stars were older than their universe.

In the 1990s scientists uncovered evidence that the expansion of the universe has not been constant since the Big Bang, but has in fact accelerated, meaning all the old calculations of the age of the universe have been underestimates.

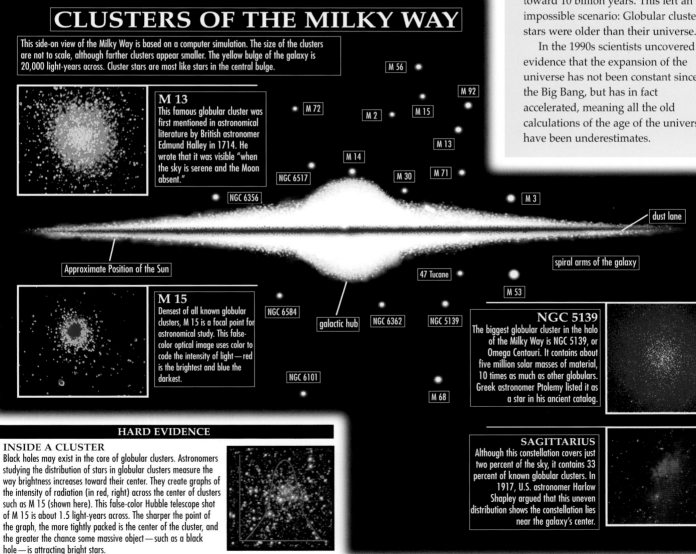

CLUSTERS OF THE MILKY WAY

This side-on view of the Milky Way is based on a computer simulation. The size of the clusters are not to scale, although farther clusters appear smaller. The yellow bulge of the galaxy is 20,000 light-years across. Cluster stars are most like stars in the central bulge.

M 13
This famous globular cluster was first mentioned in astronomical literature by British astronomer Edmund Halley in 1714. He wrote that it was visible "when the sky is serene and the Moon absent."

M 56
M 92
M 72
M 2
M 15
M 13
M 14
NGC 6517
M 30
M 71
NGC 6356
M 3
dust lane
Approximate Position of the Sun
spiral arms of the galaxy
47 Tucane
M 53

M 15
Densest of all known globular clusters, M 15 is a focal point for astronomical study. This false-color optical image uses color to code the intensity of light—red is the brightest and blue the darkest.

NGC 6584
galactic hub
NGC 6362
NGC 5139
NGC 6101
M 68

NGC 5139
The biggest globular cluster in the halo of the Milky Way is NGC 5139, or Omega Centauri. It contains about five million solar masses of material, 10 times as much as other globulars. Greek astronomer Ptolemy listed it as a star in his ancient catalog.

HARD EVIDENCE

INSIDE A CLUSTER
Black holes may exist in the core of globular clusters. Astronomers studying the distribution of stars in globular clusters measure the way brightness increases toward their center. They create graphs of the intensity of radiation (in red, right) across the center of clusters such as M 15 (shown here). This false-color Hubble telescope shot of M 15 is about 1.5 light-years across. The sharper the point of the graph, the more tightly packed is the center of the cluster, and the greater the chance some massive object—such as a black hole—is attracting bright stars.

SAGITTARIUS
Although this constellation covers just two percent of the sky, it contains 33 percent of known globular clusters. In 1917, U.S. astronomer Harlow Shapley argued that this uneven distribution shows the constellation lies near the galaxy's center.

INTERSTELLAR MATTER

The space between the stars is not empty. Aside from dark matter, whose nature is still unknown, the unimaginably large voids that make up most of the galaxy contain a strange mixture of stray atoms, molecules and microscopic dust particles known as the interstellar medium (ISM). The ISM is the ultimate in cosmic recycling. Although, by human standards, it is incredibly thinly scattered, this jumble of matter represents the ashes of dead stars—and the raw material for new ones.

NEBULAE COMPOSITION

COMPOSITION OF INTERSTELLAR GAS (PERCENTAGE OF NUMBER OF ATOMS)		COMPOSITION OF INTERSTELLAR DUST (PERCENTAGE OF NUMBER OF ATOMS)	
HYDROGEN	92	OXYGEN	52
HELIUM	8	CARBON	28
OTHER	<1	NITROGEN	8
		IRON	4
		SILICON	3
		MAGNESIUM	3
		SULFUR	2
		OTHER	<1

THIS SHOWS THAT ALTHOUGH HYDROGEN ACCOUNTS FOR MOST INTERSTELLAR GAS (AND PROBABLY MOST INTERSTELLAR MATTER IN GENERAL), INTERSTELLAR DUST CONTAINS HEAVIER ELEMENTS THAT ARE PROBABLY THE DEBRIS FROM EARLIER GENERATIONS OF STARS.

BETWEEN THE STARS

Despite its apparent emptiness, interstellar space is a rich resource. Hidden within the void between stars are vast quantities of matter that are more thinly spread than any vacuum on Earth—on average, less than 20 atoms per cubic inch (1.25 per cubic centimeter). But a lot of near-nothing adds up. This seemingly unimportant material makes up as much as 10 percent of the visible mass of the entire Milky Way—enough to make 20 billion Suns. Astronomers call it the interstellar medium (ISM).

The ISM is everywhere. In our own galaxy, it forms a 700-light-year thick disk stretching the width of the Milky Way. But the distribution within the disk is far from even. Matter clumps together in clouds called nebulae that can measure up to thousands of light-years across. At one extreme, the density of the ISM is estimated to reach 800 atoms per cubic inch with an average temperature as low as –300°F (–180°C). In other places, density falls, but the temperature rockets to a staggering 2 million°F (1.1 million°C).

GLOWING IN THE DARK

Much of the ISM, such as in the Orion Nebula, glows due to the stars within it. Other parts merely reflect the light of stars to one side. There are still other regions, like the dark, brooding Horsehead Nebula, that block out the light of background stars completely. From studying these different regions, astronomers now have a good idea of what the ISM consists of.

Virtually all of the gas in the ISM is hydrogen, which glows a distinctive red when it is superheated by nearby stars. Since hydrogen is the basic

element from which heavier elements are created inside stars, it seems likely that most of this interstellar gas is virgin material that has yet to experience the star-formation process. But there are heavier elements, too, signifying that at least some of the gas originated in earlier generations of stars. Oxygen, for example, glows a distinctive green and is seen in the shattered remains of stars that have blown apart. Elsewhere are clouds composed only of molecules, such as the hydrogen-oxygen-carbon compound alcohol.

The ISM is not all gas: There is dust, too, composed of microscopic grains of rock and ice. Though this dust accounts for only one percent of the ISM's mass, it is far better at blocking out light—especially red light, which causes stars to appear redder, and thus farther away, than they really are. In fact, it is partly thanks to these and other effects of the ISM that we know as much as we do about the structure of the universe today.

INTERSTELLAR LIGHT SHOW

Hot Gas
The background is a cloud of hydrogen gas that glows red due to the heat of stars embedded within it.

Absorbent Dust
The "horsehead" that gives the nebula its name is actually a dark cloud of gas and dust. The cloud blocks out light from the stars behind it, leaving the nebula silhouetted against the brighter background.

Foreground Stars
The stars that appear to shine most brightly are often those that lie in front of the clouds of ISM. This one is Zeta Orionis, the left-most star in the belt of Orion.

The shapes and patterns of the Horsehead Nebula reveal much about interstellar matter.

THICK AND THIN

THE CLOUDS NEAR THE STAR RHO OPHIUCHI, 700 LIGHT-YEARS AWAY, SHOW HOW PATCHY INTERSTELLAR MATTER CAN BE. IN ONE AREA, THEY ARE THIN ENOUGH TO REVEAL THE GLOBULAR CLUSTER M4, WHICH IS 5,000 LIGHT-YEARS FARTHER AWAY. BUT NEARBY LIES A STAR WHOSE LIGHT IS WEAKENED BY THE CLOUDS BY A FACTOR OF 10,000 TRILLION (10^{16})!

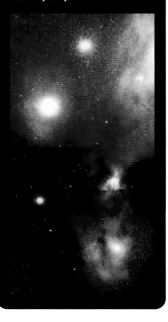

HOT GAS
Hydrogen is easily the most common component of the ISM. Much of it exists in the form of giant clouds that glow red as they absorb ultraviolet energy from neighboring stars. Often, these clouds lead to the formation of new stars.

ICE PARTICLES
Astronomers think that much of the interstellar dust that is so effective at absorbing starlight consists of nothing more exotic than tar-smeared ice particles surrounding minute specks of carbon, silicon or iron.

MOLECULES
Giant molecular clouds exist throughout interstellar space. Many are composed of single elements such as hydrogen, oxygen and carbon, but in places, these elements have combined into more complex molecules, such as alcohol.

DUST AND DIRT
The Pleiades star cluster (right) contains wisp-like nebulae that were once thought to be the remains of newly formed stars. Now, astronomers think that they are simply clouds of interstellar dust into which the cluster's stars have drifted.

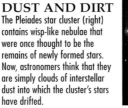

MILKY WAY

With both its name and appearance hinting at obscurity, the Milky Way has long been a source of fascination. Shrouded by interstellar dust clouds, what can be seen of the galaxy from Earth almost resembles a hazy glowing disc when viewed by the naked eye. While advances in telescopic technology have meant we know more about how the galaxy developed, many questions can still only be answered generally. For centuries, it was thought that the Milky Way was not very large and that our Sun was close to its center. It was not until the 20th century that astronomers learned that the Sun was approximately 30,000 light-years from its center, and that the Milky Way spanned across an estimated diameter of 100,000 light-years.

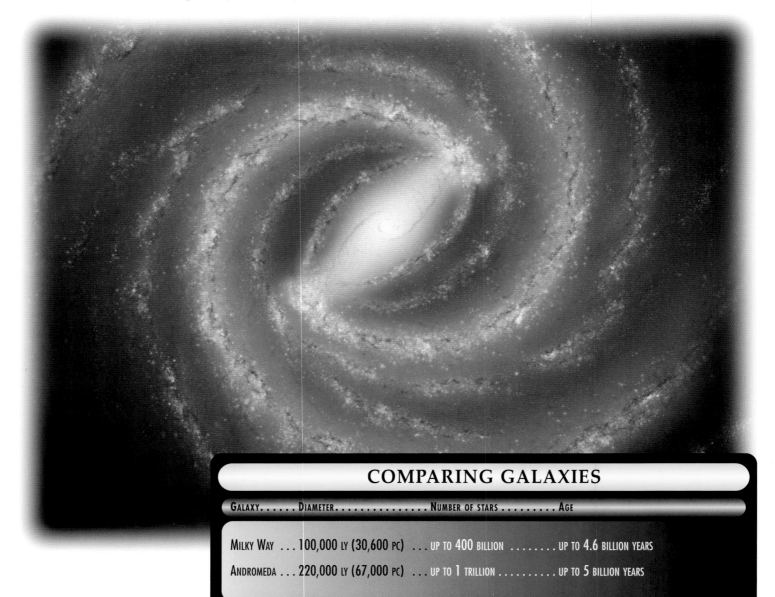

COMPARING GALAXIES

Galaxy	Diameter	Number of stars	Age
Milky Way	100,000 ly (30,600 pc)	up to 400 billion	up to 4.6 billion years
Andromeda	220,000 ly (67,000 pc)	up to 1 trillion	up to 5 billion years

EXPANDING HORIZONS

It was once thought that the Milky Way was the limit of the entire universe. For a long time, its immensity—the galaxy contains around 200 billion stars, but this figure could stretch to 400 billion in total—meant that it was hard for humans to comprehend anything bigger. Since the early 20th century, we have known that the Milky Way is only one of many galaxies. In fact, it makes up a small section of what is known as the Local Group of over twenty galaxies—or fifty if you include dwarf galaxies, which only have a few billion

propositioned in the 1990s, but not confirmed until 2005, when the Spitzer Space Telescope used infrared technology to pick out the radiation, which showed this bar to be more substantial than previously believed.

Made up of over ninety per cent dark matter, the visible part of the Milky Way makes up only around ten per cent of our galaxy. It is only with the aid of powerful infrared telescopes such as the Spitzer telescope that we were able to discover more about the structure of the Milky Way. Launched in 2003, it is in Earth's orbit in an Earth-trailing position. This means Spitzer could avoid the

extreme heat exposure of other telescopes and remain working for longer with lower amounts of coolant and costs. Since its launch, Spitzer's initial 2.5 year mission life has been extended indefinitely, with the telescope still sending back incredible information and images about the Milky Way and beyond.

NAMING THE MILKY WAY

Named for the Latin *via lactea*, meaning "road of milk," which was in turn taken from the Greek *galaxias kyklos* or "milky circle,"

the Milky Way's name resembles its hazy appearance, viewed as it is through a mist of dust, gas and debris. The milky appearance led to its name, thought to be based on a story about the goddess Hera. When Zeus fathered Heracles by a mortal female, he put his son on the sleeping Hera's breast to suckle him. On awaking, Hera realized what Zeus had done and tore the baby from her breast. Her milk shot through the night sky, becoming the Milky Way. Many celestial bodies have mythological names, but the sheer amount means that they are now often classified by letters and numbers.

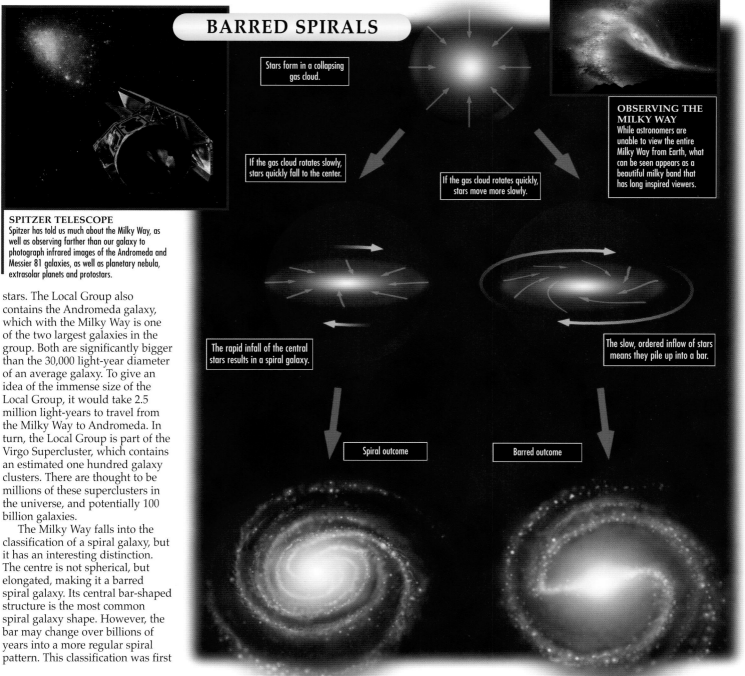

BARRED SPIRALS

Stars form in a collapsing gas cloud.

If the gas cloud rotates slowly, stars quickly fall to the center.

If the gas cloud rotates quickly, stars move more slowly.

OBSERVING THE MILKY WAY
While astronomers are unable to view the entire Milky Way from Earth, what can be seen appears as a beautiful milky band that has long inspired viewers.

The rapid infall of the central stars results in a spiral galaxy.

The slow, ordered inflow of stars means they pile up into a bar.

Spiral outcome

Barred outcome

SPITZER TELESCOPE
Spitzer has told us much about the Milky Way, as well as observing farther than our galaxy to photograph infrared images of the Andromeda and Messier 81 galaxies, as well as planetary nebula, extrasolar planets and protostars.

stars. The Local Group also contains the Andromeda galaxy, which with the Milky Way is one of the two largest galaxies in the group. Both are significantly bigger than the 30,000 light-year diameter of an average galaxy. To give an idea of the immense size of the Local Group, it would take 2.5 million light-years to travel from the Milky Way to Andromeda. In turn, the Local Group is part of the Virgo Supercluster, which contains an estimated one hundred galaxy clusters. There are thought to be millions of these superclusters in the universe, and potentially 100 billion galaxies.

The Milky Way falls into the classification of a spiral galaxy, but it has an interesting distinction. The centre is not spherical, but elongated, making it a barred spiral galaxy. Its central bar-shaped structure is the most common spiral galaxy shape. However, the bar may change over billions of years into a more regular spiral pattern. This classification was first

CENTER OF THE GALAXY

Although it is on our cosmic doorstep, just 26,000–28,000 light-years away, the center of our own galaxy remains a mystery to us. Our view of the Milky Way's core is completely hidden by bright star clouds and dark dust lanes that lie in the constellation of Sagittarius, along our line of sight toward galactic center. But in the past few years, astronomers have finally begun to discover what lies at the heart of the Milky Way, by studying it in wavelengths of light that pass straight through the dust.

GALAXY'S HEART: SGR A

DISCOVERED	.1974
DISTANCE	.26,000–28,000 LIGHT-YEARS
DIMENSIONS	.80 AU BY 150 AU (1 AU = 93M MILES/150M KM)
ESTIMATED MASS	.2.6 MILLION SOLAR MASSES
BLACK HOLE ESTIMATED DIAMETER	.9 MILLION MILES (14.5 MILLION KM)

HIDDEN HEART

The center of the Milky Way is a strange place, full of features that astronomers do not yet fully understand. Stars become much more tightly packed close to the core: Collapsing gas clouds form giant open clusters of young stars, and there are even a few ball-shaped globular clusters, containing hundreds of thousands, or even millions, of very old red stars. The closer stars get to the center, the faster they move along their orbits.

Above and below the galactic center lie towering pillars of gas called filaments, which can be anything from a few light-years to a few hundred light-years long. These filaments follow the lines of the galaxy's magnetic field, which emerges in long, curving lines above and below its center. As the charged particles within them spiral out along the field, traveling at close to the speed of light, they emit what is called synchrotron radiation at radio wavelengths.

Some 350 light-years out from the center lies a violent object known as the Great Annihilator. Two huge jets, several light-years long, burst out from above and below a massive black hole, around 100 times the mass of the Sun, that is swallowing up surrounding gas and stars. The jets are made of antimatter created around the black hole. Where they collide with normal matter, these jets are completely destroyed, releasing high-energy gamma rays with an energy 250,000 times that of visible light—the telltale sign that antimatter is present.

INTO THE CORE

The edge of the galactic center is itself marked by a ring of gas clouds of roughly 10 light-years. These gas clouds, made mostly of hydrogen molecules and helium atoms, but with some heavier and more complex molecules including ammonia (NH_3) and cyanide (CN), glow at radio wavelengths as their inner edges are heated by hot, bright stars inside them.

Within this ring of molecular clouds is a central cavity that can only be seen at infrared wavelengths. This radiation reveals that the center of the galaxy is very hot, and shows streamers of gas swirling around inside at very high speeds. This gas is being heated by some very bright, hot, mysterious objects in a cluster called IRS 16. These objects seem too bright and hot to be normal stars—they may be cannibals that have grown throughout their lives by swallowing up other stars or gas.

Close to IRS 16, at the very center of the galaxy, is an even greater mystery—a strong radio source called Sagittarius A-star, abbreviated Sgr A*. Surprisingly, Sgr A* is invisible at infrared and other wavelengths. But from the movement of stars around the galactic center, astronomers know that something at the very center of the galaxy has a mass which measures millions of times greater than the Sun, compressed into a very small point. This object is almost certainly a giant black hole, and the radio glow of Sgr A* is probably caused as material falling into the black hole is heated up and ripped apart. Why Sgr A* is such a weak source of radiation, while much smaller black holes blast out fierce X-rays, has puzzled astronomers. The black hole is probably dormant because no material has drifted into its sphere of influence recently. In the future it could flare up, allowing us to see a new X-ray source pinpointing the heart of our galaxy.

SECRETS OF THE CENTER

molecular ring of gas

STAR CLUSTERS
Giant clusters of young stars form near the galactic center because of the huge amounts of gas available. Clusters like the Quintuplet (far left) and the Arches (left) will be ripped apart by gravitational forces, but are currently the brightest clusters in the galaxy.

MINI SPIRAL
Inside the galaxy's 10-light-year-wide central cavity, the stellar winds of particles gusting from the brilliant stars of the IRS 16 cluster are blowing clouds of molecular hydrogen into three ragged spiral arms.

globular clusters

molecular ring of gas

Sgr A* within cluster IRS 16

outer lobe emitting radio waves

Although the antimatter fountain projecting from the galaxy's center is not visible to the naked eye, the rays it emits were imaged by the Compton Gamma Ray Observatory.

FILAMENTS
The Snake is a filament of ionized gas streaming out from the galactic center along a line in the galaxy's magnetic field. Unlike most filaments, however, it is not perpendicular to the galactic plane. It may run along a tangled region of magnetic field.

The central few hundred light-years of the galaxy, as revealed from Earth.

GALACTIC CENTER
At the very center of the galaxy lies IRS 16, a cluster of giant stars. Along them lies Sgr A*, a mysterious object visible at radio wavelengths only. Sgr A* is currently dormant.

HOLE TRUTH
THE PRESENCE OF A SUPER-MASSIVE BLACK HOLE AT THE GALAXY'S CENTER WAS PROVEN BEYOND DOUBT IN 1998 BY U.S. ASTRONOMER ANDREA GHEZ. BY MEASURING THE MOTIONS OF 200 STARS CLOSE TO THE CENTER OF THE MILKY WAY, GHEZ WAS ABLE TO FIND AT LEAST 20 STARS WHOSE ORBITS WERE BEING AFFECTED BY A MASSIVE OBJECT. SHE CALCULATED THAT THE OBJECT HAS A MASS 2.6 MILLION TIMES GREATER THAN THE SUN, CRAMMED INTO A SPACE JUST 1/30TH OF A LIGHT-YEAR ACROSS. WITH SUCH AN INCREDIBLE DENSITY, IT CAN ONLY BE A BLACK HOLE.

BEYOND THE MILKY WAY

Our galaxy is just one of around thirty in our immediate neighborhood—the so-called Local Group of galaxies. Most of these galaxies are dwarfs, smaller than our own, but a couple are spirals on a similar, or larger, scale. In the wider universe, there are many other types of galaxy, most importantly the ellipticals—huge balls of stars that reach gigantic proportions and may dwarf even the largest spirals. Spirals themselves are found in both normal and "barred" forms—the latter having a prominent bar of stars joining the hub to the spiral arms, of which the Milky Way is an example of. Galaxies are comparatively tightly packed for their size, so collisions and even mergers are relatively common. These and other triggers may spark violent activity in a galaxy's nucleus, and it is thought that mergers allow galaxies to slowly evolve from one type to another. On the largest scales, galaxies are pulled together by gravity to form clusters and superclusters—the biggest structures in the universe.

Similar in size and design to our own Milky Way, the majestic dusty spiral galaxy NGC 3370 is around 100 million light years away from our galaxy—just one of millions of galaxies visible with the Hubble Space Telescope.

CLASSIFYING GALAXIES

For most of history, those galaxies that were visible from Earth were nothing but faint fuzzy smears in the sky. As telescopes improved during the last century, astronomers began to be able to see detail in the smears. In 1925, American astronomer Edwin Hubble proposed a system of classifying galaxies according to their shape. Although modern astronomers have revised some of his early conclusions, today's most widely-accepted modern-day system of classification still relies on Hubble's framework.

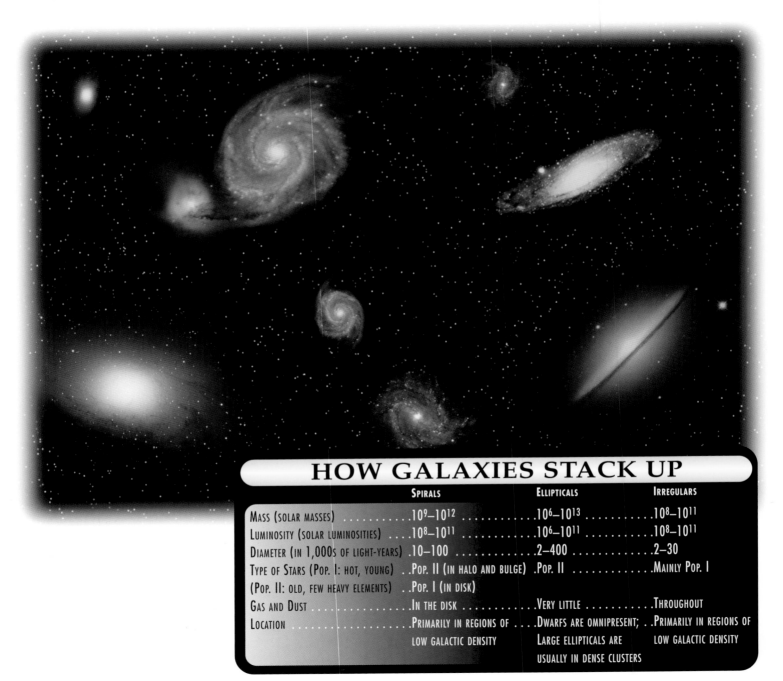

HOW GALAXIES STACK UP

	SPIRALS	ELLIPTICALS	IRREGULARS
MASS (SOLAR MASSES)	10^9–10^{12}	10^6–10^{13}	10^8–10^{11}
LUMINOSITY (SOLAR LUMINOSITIES)	10^8–10^{11}	10^6–10^{11}	10^8–10^{11}
DIAMETER (IN 1,000s OF LIGHT-YEARS)	10–100	2–400	2–30
TYPE OF STARS (POP. I: HOT, YOUNG)	Pop. II (IN HALO AND BULGE)	Pop. II	MAINLY POP. I
(POP. II: OLD, FEW HEAVY ELEMENTS)	Pop. I (IN DISK)		
GAS AND DUST	IN THE DISK	VERY LITTLE	THROUGHOUT
LOCATION	PRIMARILY IN REGIONS OF LOW GALACTIC DENSITY	DWARFS ARE OMNIPRESENT; LARGE ELLIPTICALS ARE USUALLY IN DENSE CLUSTERS	PRIMARILY IN REGIONS OF LOW GALACTIC DENSITY

TAKING SHAPE

The powerful telescopes that came into service on Mount Wilson, California, in the early decades of the 20th century allowed Edwin Hubble to open a vast new territory of astronomy. He proved that so-called spiral nebulae were in fact "island universes" or galaxies, far beyond the edges of our own Milky Way. And, as a good scientist, the first thing he did was to start classifying them. His system, published in 1925, categorized galaxies according to their shape—or, in his words, according to how much "conspicuous evidence of rotational symmetry about dominating, central nuclei" they showed. Hubble believed that the shapes revealed the life-cycle of galaxies, and represented this evolutionary system in a chart that later became known as the "tuning fork" diagram for its forked shape.

He believed that elliptical galaxies (class "E"), on the left of the diagram, were the youngest. According to his idea, diffuse and roughly spherical—globular—galaxies flatten into a lenticular or lens shape, from which they grow arms and become spiral (class "S").

The central bulge of some galaxies forms a fat finger of stars and dust—known as a "bar." "Barred spiral" galaxies given their own class of "SB." Each elliptical galaxy was given a number to describe how round or flattened it appeared: Perfectly round galaxies would be classed "E0," while very flat ones would be "E7." Hubble also used the letters "a," "b" and "c" to note how tightly wound the arms of spiral galaxies were, with "a" the tightest and "c" the loosest.

In the early 1930s, Hubble published classifications of more than 44,000 galaxies. Over the years, as more powerful telescopes were built and photographic methods advanced, the visible universe expanded farther and the astronomical catalogs swelled. Hubble's useful but rough galaxy classification gave way to more sophisticated and detailed work. His idea of evolution—that galaxies change from elliptical types to lenticular types and then to spiral types—no longer fitted the new data, and astronomers were forced to give it up. But scientists have kept Hubble's organizational scheme, for even without the evolutionary theory, his system still is the best way to organize the skies.

HUBBLE REVISITED

In 1958, U.S. astronomer William Morgan overhauled Hubble's system. He had already reorganized the field of stellar classification by coding stars by their brightness as well as their color. He rethought Hubble's system and considered how the appearance of galaxies was changed by our viewpoint on Earth. In his system, for example, he included a scale of the angle of the galaxy's tilt relative to the Earth, running from side view (1) to top view (7).

Morgan also delved inside galaxies, linking populations of stars within the galaxy to the types of light they emit. His system of galaxy classification—a, af, f, fg, g, gk or k—refers to the Harvard star classification order "O B A F G K M." Each letter stands for a different color of star, from hot blue through the rainbow to a cooler deep red. Morgan reasoned that different types of light comes from different populations of stars. Older stars in the galactic nucleus—the "Population II" stars—emit reddish light. "Population I" stars, such as the Sun, are hotter, have more heavy elements, and are spread throughout the galactic disk. Hubble classified the Andromeda galaxy, M 31, as "Sb;" Morgan called it a "kS5."

Later astronomers added new dimensions. Two years after Morgan published his new system, Canadian astronomer Sidney van den Bergh assigned a luminosity rating of I–V to individual galaxies. And at about the same time, French-born U.S. astronomer Gérard de Vaucouleurs expanded Hubble's system to take into account the three-dimensional nature of galaxies. But despite all the changes and technological advances, astronomers still swear by Hubble's original system.

HARD EVIDENCE

AN EYE OUT
Modern galaxy classification is fully automated and uses computerized image analysis. A complex program takes into account a galaxy's position, magnitude, color, shape and other characteristics. One authoritative galaxy catalog, the Sloan Digital Sky Survey, uses an 8.2-ft (2.5-m) telescope and an electronic camera high in New Mexico's Sacramento Mountains (right) to record galaxies. Each of 30 charge-coupled devices (CCDs) in the Sloan camera has four million pixels (picture elements)—twice the number of dots on a high-end computer monitor.

SPIRALS (S)
Spiral galaxies—such as M 33, an Andromeda galaxy satellite of type Sc (left)—are known for the long arms that extend from their central bulge. Hubble classified spirals by how tightly the arms wind around the bulge, from a tight-bound "a" to a loose "c."

Type Sc

Type Sb

Type SBc

Type Sa

Type SBb

GALACTIC TUNING FORK

Hubble believed that galaxies evolved along a "tuning fork" route, shown here from left to right. His theories were wrong—but his classification system is still used today.

Type S0 (lenticular)

Type SBa

Type E5

Type SBa

Type E0

ELLIPTICALS (E)
Elliptical galaxies such as M 49 (right) grade from spherical (0) to oblong (7): M 49 is an E2. They are full of stars, have little gas, and shine uniformly brightly. Hubble thought they evolved into "lenticular" galaxies.

BARRED SPIRALS (SB)
Galaxies such as NGC 1365, (above; type SBb) have a central bar of densely packed stars. These central stars can produce as much as a third of the light from a barred spiral galaxy.

MAGELLANIC CLOUDS

Our nearest galactic neighbors are easily visible to the naked eye—as long as you live in the southern hemisphere. The Magellanic Clouds are a pair of small, independent galaxies rich in unique features, from young star clusters to the brightest supernova seen in centuries. Their proximity is good news for astronomers but bad luck for the clouds themselves, as the Milky Way's gravity has already torn a chunk from them and may eventually swallow up the Magellanic Clouds completely.

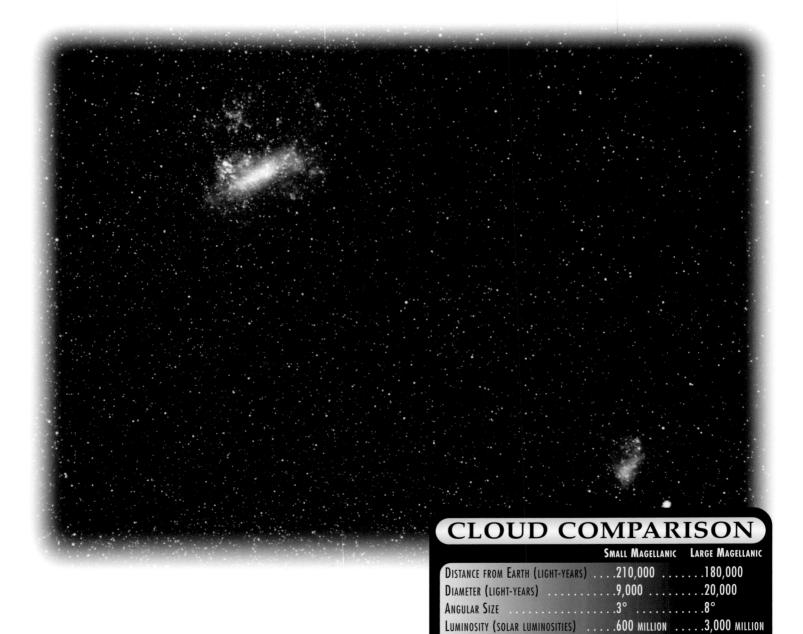

CLOUD COMPARISON

	Small Magellanic	Large Magellanic
Distance from Earth (light-years)	210,000	180,000
Diameter (light-years)	9,000	20,000
Angular Size	3°	8°
Luminosity (solar luminosities)	600 million	3,000 million
Mass (solar masses)	6 billion	25 billion

PASSING CLOUDS

As seen by the naked eye, the Magellanic Clouds are two mysterious, misty patches near the south celestial pole. In reality, the clouds are the largest in a group of about a dozen small galaxies that accompany the Milky Way through space, tethered by its gravity. To astronomers who can observe them—the clouds are too far south to be seen from the U.S.—they offer a unique opportunity to study external galaxies. The clouds may be miniatures in comparison to the giant galaxies of the distant universe, but they are practically in our backyard—less than 200,000 light-years away.

The Large Magellanic Cloud (LMC) is classed as an "irregular spiral." It is roughly bar-shaped, and with about 20 billion stars is only a tenth of the size of the Milky Way. The LMC's most dramatic feature is the glowing cloud of gas known as the Tarantula nebula, the biggest yet discovered, whose central bright region is clearly visible to the naked eye. Astronomers have also been puzzled by clusters of bluish stars, whose color suggests that they are younger than the ancient globular clusters found in most galaxies.

The Small Magellanic Cloud (SMC) is even more irregular in form than the LMC and contains fewer nebulae. The distorted, asymmetrical shape of both clouds is no accident. They are so small and diffuse that they can barely hold themselves together by gravitational attraction. Worse, their orbits around our own galaxy sometimes bring them dangerously close to it. On the last near pass, the Milky Way's gravity tore a vast plume of gas—the Magellanic Stream—from the clouds, and the SMC may be breaking up as a result. The breakup could explain its disordered appearance—and may also account for a recent burst of star formation.

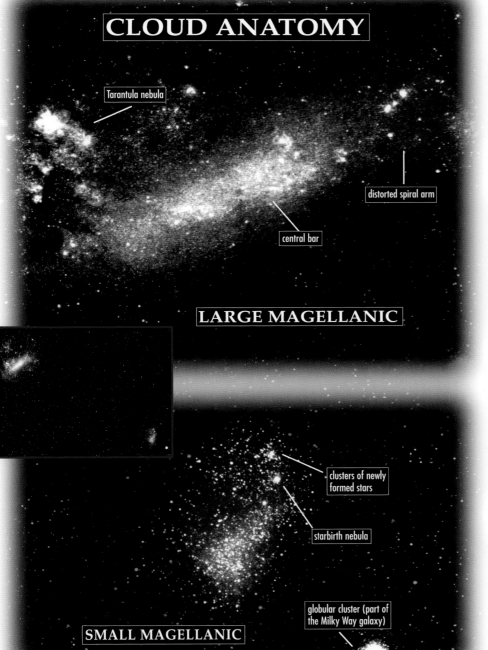

CLOUD ANATOMY

Tarantula nebula

distorted spiral arm

central bar

LARGE MAGELLANIC

clusters of newly formed stars

starbirth nebula

globular cluster (part of the Milky Way galaxy)

SMALL MAGELLANIC

ABSOLUTE LIGHT

HIRED BY HARVARD OBSERVATORY AS A HUMAN "COMPUTER" WHO WOULD CATALOG THOUSANDS OF STARS FOR A PITTANCE, HENRIETTA LEAVITT IN 1912 USED DATA FROM THE MAGELLANIC CLOUDS TO DEVISE A COMPLETELY NEW METHOD OF MEASURING STELLAR DISTANCES. HER METHOD, BASED ON THE BEHAVIOR OF VARIABLE STARS, IS STILL USED BY ASTRONOMERS TODAY.

CLOUD ATTRACTIONS

TARANTULA NEBULA
This vast cloud to one side of the LMC contains 800,000 solar masses of glowing hydrogen gas and spans 3,000 light-years. Thousands of stars are being born inside it, and at its heart lies a massive object whose nature still puzzles astronomers.

GASEOUS NEBULAE
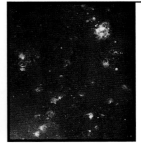
A concentration of supernova remnants (SNRs) and star forming regions (know as H II regions to astronomers) is a sign of star birth as much as star death. Heavy elements scattered by supernova destruction provide rich material for the next generation of stars.

MAGELLANIC STREAM
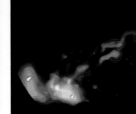
The Magellanic Stream, a long tail of hydrogen gas, stretches 300,000 light-years across space. The gas stream was pulled out by the Milky Way's gravity 200 million years ago, when the Magellanic Clouds passed close to our galaxy.

ANDROMEDA GALAXY

By intergalactic space standards, the great galaxy in the constellation of Andromeda is close to the Milky Way—it is 290,000,000 light-years away. Andromeda's majestic spiral is our own galaxy's nearest full-size galactic neighbor. It closely resembles the Milky Way in form and structure, and the distribution of chemical elements in each is so similar that astronomers refer to them together as sister galaxies. But there the similarity ends, for the Andromeda galaxy dwarfs the Milky Way in size and contains around twice as many stars.

ANDROMEDA STATISTICS

DIAMETER	.150,000 LIGHT-YEARS
NUMBER OF STARS	.400 BILLION
MASS	.320 BILLION TIMES THE MASS OF THE SUN
DIAMETER OF NUCLEUS	.25,000 LIGHT-YEARS
DISTANCE	.2.9 MILLION LIGHT-YEARS
ANGLE OF TILT	.13°
OTHER DESIGNATIONS	.M 31, NGC 224

ANDROMEDA IN FOCUS

Set among the stars of the constellation of Andromeda, the tiny, misty blur that astronomers know by the catalog number M 31 is easy to miss. Yet despite its unassuming appearance, M 31 is immensely greater than the stars that surround it. For it is an entire spiral galaxy, larger than our own.

For centuries, astronomers thought that the Andromeda galaxy was nothing more than a nebula, a cloud of light-reflective dust and gas situated within the Milky Way. Then, in the 1880s, the English astronomer Isaac Roberts used a 20-in (50 cm) telescope to take the first detailed photograph of Andromeda. For the first time, the spiral arms were revealed; but since no one could make out any individual stars, M 31 was still assumed to be a nebula. A star suddenly appeared near the center in 1885, but it barely reached naked-eye visibility. Astronomers rightly decided the new arrival was a nova—an exploding star. But they still believed the nebula hypothesis.

Ideas changed after a 100-in (2.5-m) telescope, then the world's biggest, opened on Mount Wilson near Los Angeles in 1917. The great astronomer Edwin Hubble was able to see for the first time that the outer spiral arms of the Andromeda galaxy contained individual stars. These appeared similar to many found in the Milky Way, but were much fainter. Hubble drew the logical conclusion: M 31 must be another galaxy, lying a great distance away.

Andromeda is especially important for astronomers because it is so similar to the Milky Way. Since both are spirals, with many other features in common, the pair are now described as sister galaxies. Although we can never see our own galaxy from the outside, we can observe our nearby sister instead— the next best thing. At 2.9 million light-years from Earth, Andromeda is the farthest object that can be seen with the naked eye, the distance so great that the visible light began its journey—at 186,000 miles (300,000 km) per second—long before homo sapiens evolved.

SHORTCUT TO ANDROMEDA

BLASTOFF
Earth date: Jan 1, 2050
Ship date: Jan 1, 2050

FULL THROTTLE
At very close to light-speed, relativity compresses ship time and shrinks its length with respect to the rest of the universe.

ARRIVAL
Earth date: Jan 1, 2902050
Ship date: July 4, 2091

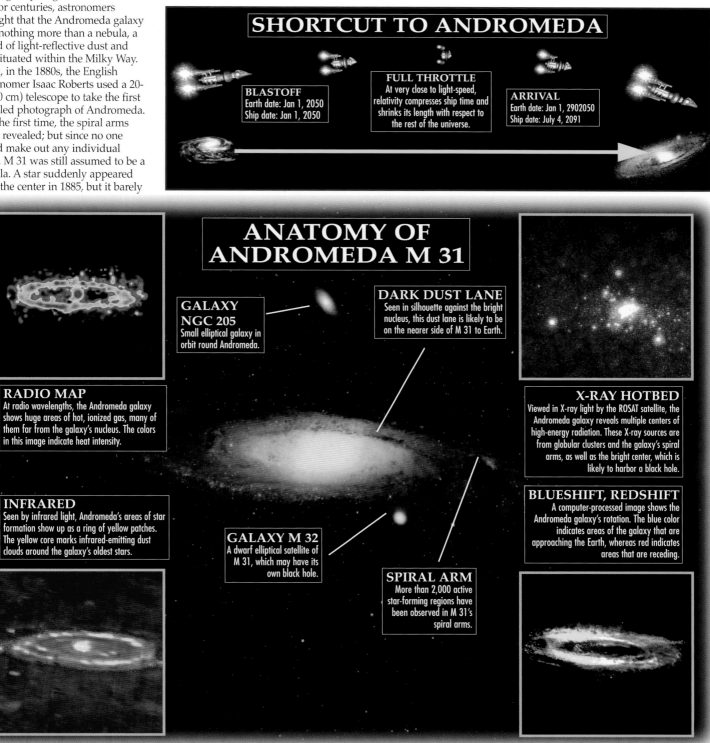

ANATOMY OF ANDROMEDA M 31

RADIO MAP
At radio wavelengths, the Andromeda galaxy shows huge areas of hot, ionized gas, many of them far from the galaxy's nucleus. The colors in this image indicate heat intensity.

GALAXY NGC 205
Small elliptical galaxy in orbit round Andromeda.

DARK DUST LANE
Seen in silhouette against the bright nucleus, this dust lane is likely to be on the nearer side of M 31 to Earth.

X-RAY HOTBED
Viewed in X-ray light by the ROSAT satellite, the Andromeda galaxy reveals multiple centers of high-energy radiation. These X-ray sources are from globular clusters and the galaxy's spiral arms, as well as the bright center, which is likely to harbor a black hole.

INFRARED
Seen by infrared light, Andromeda's areas of star formation show up as a ring of yellow patches. The yellow core marks infrared-emitting dust clouds around the galaxy's oldest stars.

GALAXY M 32
A dwarf elliptical satellite of M 31, which may have its own black hole.

SPIRAL ARM
More than 2,000 active star-forming regions have been observed in M 31's spiral arms.

BLUESHIFT, REDSHIFT
A computer-processed image shows the Andromeda galaxy's rotation. The blue color indicates areas of the galaxy that are approaching the Earth, whereas red indicates areas that are receding.

SPIRAL GALAXIES

Spirals are the most familiar form of galaxy to be seen—as well as one of the most beautiful. We can observe these vast collections of many billions of stars from every possible angle. Edge-on, they appear as flat disks built around a central bulge of old, red stars. But the fully frontal views are breathtaking, with curving arms of light, rich in young stars, gas and dust, that spiral outward from the core. Spiral galaxies also give us the opportunity to observe what we would otherwise never see—and perhaps never will: how our own Milky Way looks from the outside.

SPIRAL GALAXY FACTS

MASS	.1 billion to 1 trillion times that of the Sun
LUMINOSITY	.0.1 to 100 billion times that of the Sun
SIZE	.10,000 to 300,000 light-years across
THICKNESS	.500 to 2,000 light-years
AMOUNT OF GAS AND DUST	.5% to 15% of total mass
PROPORTION OF ALL GALAXIES	Less than 40% to 50%
NEAREST SPIRAL GALAXY	.Andromeda, 2.9 million light-years away

SPIRALING THROUGH SPACE

Hundreds of thousands of light-years across and packed with hundreds upon billions of stars, the great spirals are among the largest of all galaxy formations. They are also the most complex, with a structure that is as beautiful as it is hard to understand.

Compared with elliptical and other galaxies, a spiral galaxy is relatively flat. At its heart is a concentrated, near-spherical cluster of stars; but most of a spiral's material is distributed in a gigantic disk that is many times wider than this nucleus of stars and much flatter.

This disk is not uniform. The luminous material is arranged in two or more arms that spiral majestically from the central hub and give such galaxies their name. Overall, the proportions of a spiral galaxy are similar to a fried egg.

SPIRAL STRUCTURE

Because the stars near the center of a spiral galaxy are known to move around faster than those farther out, it was once thought that, given time, the spiral arms would coil tighter as the galaxy rotated. This also appeared to explain why some galaxies have clearly defined, open arms while others have a much tighter configuration: The tightly coiled spirals were simply older. Later, astronomers observed the spiral arms of galaxies that they knew to be old and realized that the arms were not coiling tighter with successive rotations. Something much stranger was going on.

We now know that spiral arms mark out regions of high relative density. The arms do rotate around the galactic core—but curiously, at a slower rate than the stars, gas and dust that they contain. When clouds of gas and dust drift into such a region, they are compressed; stars begin to form and the arm becomes conspicuous.

Over time, the newly formed stars pass from the front of the arm and are replaced by fresh star-forming material, which in turn forms new stars and renews the brightness of the spiral arm. The relative youth of the stars in spiral arms explains why they mainly appear blue—and why stars in the nucleus are older and redder.

Even so, there is still much to learn about spiral structures—for example, what causes the linear features that span the nuclei of so-called "barred" spirals. The Milky Way is now thought to be a barred spiral and it may be that all spiral galaxies develop bars at some stage. We may never know.

INSIDE AN OPEN SPIRAL

NUCLEUS
The central bulge containing mainly old, red stars.

STAR FORMATION
Star formation is an ongoing process in the arms of spiral galaxies such as NGC 2997 (left). In some spirals, like M 94 (above), the most active star-forming areas are in a ring around the nucleus and in the nucleus itself.

DUST LANES
Dust is always present in the arms of spiral galaxies, where it generally shows up as dark bands. The dust can be seen most clearly in edge-on galaxies such as the so-called Sombrero Galaxy (left).

SPIRAL ARM
The thin, outer part of the disk contains dust and gas clouds, and bluish, newly formed stars.

WHIRLPOOL

THIS DRAWING OF THE WHIRLPOOL GALAXY, M 51, WAS MADE IN 1845 BY LORD ROSSE OF IRELAND WITH A TELESCOPE 6 FT (1.8 M) IN DIAMETER. IT WAS THE FIRST INDICATION THAT "NEBULAE" HAD SPIRAL STRUCTURES.

LENTICULARS

SOME GALAXIES, SUCH AS THE ONE SHOWN HERE, HAVE A BULGE AND DISK BUT NO DISCERNIBLE SPIRAL ARMS, EVEN THOUGH THEY ARE CLASSIFIED AS SPIRALS. THESE ARE LENTICULAR, OR "LENS-SHAPED" GALAXIES, BECAUSE THEY RESEMBLE A LENS SEEN EDGE-ON.

TYPES OF SPIRAL GALAXIES

EDGE-ON
This view of a spiral galaxy edge-on clearly shows the remarkable flatness of these structures relative to their size. Aside from the central bulge containing old, red stars, most of the material is distributed in a disk many times thinner than the galaxy's diameter.

OPEN
Open spirals are the most easily recognizable form of spiral galaxy, with distinctive arms and a compact nucleus. This one, in the constellation of Triangulum, is a mere 3.6 million light-years away, making it a near neighbor of ours.

CLOSED
When viewed face-on, the spiral structure of a tightly wound closed spiral galaxy is not immediately obvious. The highly luminous central core is the dominant feature, with the arms compressed around it that resemble a coiled rope.

BARRED
Barred spiral galaxies are characterized by two open spiral arms linked by a relatively thick, bar-like structure running across the nucleus. Astronomers can only guess at what causes this formation and whether it is connected with a galaxy's age.

ELLIPTICAL GALAXIES

Elliptical galaxies are the retirement homes of the cosmos. They may lack the beauty of their spiral counterparts, but some contain up to 1,000 times more stars and still of much to interest astronomers. Unlike spiral galaxies that are home to stars of all ages, ellipticals contain almost no young stars—and no material to make new ones. Yet despite their aging populations, elliptical galaxies were not the first to form. They grew from collisions between earlier generations of spiral galaxies.

BRIGHTEST ELLIPTICALS

THESE ELLIPTICALS ARE SOME OF THE BRIGHTEST GALAXIES IN THE SKY. THE LOWER THE MAGNITUDE NUMBER, THE BRIGHTER THE GALAXY APPEARS. WHERE DIMENSIONS OF GALAXIES ARE MARKED ?, IT INDICATES THAT THEY ARE UNKNOWN DUE TO THE ANGLE THE GALAXIES PRESENT TO THE EARTH.

Name	Distance (light-years)	Dimensions (arc minutes)	Constellation	Magnitude
M 32	2.9 million	.8 x 6	Andromeda	8.1
M 49	.60 million	9 x 7.5	Virgo	8.4
M 110	2.9 million	17 x 10	Andromeda	8.5
M 87	.60 million	7 x ?	Virgo	8.6
M 60	.60 million	7 x 6	Virgo	8.8
M 105	.38 million	2 x ?	Leo	9.3
M 59	.60 million	5 x 3.5	Virgo	9.6
M 89	.60 million	4 x ?	Virgo	9.8

WHERE STARS RETIRE

Packed full of old, red stars, with barely a young one in sight, elliptical galaxies are less picturesque than their spiral counterparts. But the average elliptical, with its bulky, football-like shape, contains far more stars than the equivalent spiral galaxy. And ellipticals are more common, too. Some astronomers believe that 60 percent of all galaxies in the universe are elliptical, although most of them are too small to be seen from our planet.

Things were not always this way, as the Hubble Space Telescope has revealed. Since light from the farthest regions of the cosmos can take billions of years to reach us, peering deep into the universe means looking back in time, too. Hubble does this better than any Earth-based telescope, yielding important clues as to the early state of the universe in the process of its observations.

The farther back in time Hubble looks, the more spiral galaxies it sees and the closer together they appear. By contrast, distant ellipticals are rare—and the few that do exist are clearly much smaller than those close to home.

These observations allow the history of galaxy formation in the universe to be pieced together. If spiral galaxies were closer together in the past, the chances are that they collided and merged relatively often. Computer simulations have shown that mergers between several spiral galaxies can result in an elliptical galaxy. So it is reasonable to suppose that, as the universe developed, galactic collisions resulted in fewer, more widely spaced spirals and more ellipticals—exactly what we can see today.

RIDDLE OF THE CLOUDS

The collision-and-merger theory helps to explain the relatively small size of early ellipticals. In the state that we see them today, the farthest—and therefore the youngest—ellipticals have yet to experience the encounters with neighboring galaxies that will cause them to grow as large as the ellipticals situated closer to us.

The same theory may also explain another puzzling feature of elliptical galaxies—that is, why they are almost entirely devoid of gas and dust. Again, their size is a clue. Most stars survive intergalactic collisions because, within their galaxies, they are spaced relatively far apart: Like people walking through a large, empty park, their chances of bumping into each other are slim. But the gas clouds that lie between the stars are not so lucky. When galaxies collide and merge, the forces of collision trigger the collapse of their gas clouds into star-forming regions. Eventually, after generations of new stars have come and gone, the gas runs out.

It seems that what little gas is left in the galaxy is either blown away by giant stars that die suddenly in supernova explosions or is stripped away by the gas that often fills the apparent void of intergalactic space. So it is that elliptical galaxies, sometimes swollen to immense bulks by successive mergers but with no material to support new star formation, slowly live out the rest of their days.

BIG DISK

HUBBLE TOOK THIS CLOSE-UP (FAR RIGHT) OF THE CENTER OF AN ELLIPTICAL GALAXY 191 MILLION LIGHT-YEARS AWAY (RIGHT). IT SHOWS A DISK OF GAS AND DUST 3,700 LIGHT-YEARS ACROSS THAT IS SLOWLY SPIRALING TOWARD A BLACK HOLE AT THE GALAXY'S HEART. OUR VIEW OF THE GALAXY'S CENTER IS UNOBSTRUCTED BY DUST CLOUDS, AS SEEN IN SPIRALS.

HARD EVIDENCE

ELLIPTICAL SHAPES

Not all elliptical galaxies are, in fact, elliptical—or even football-shaped. But all ellipticals are more rounded in shape than spiral galaxies and are roughly uniform in brightness. Some are truly elliptical, others are spherical and still others resemble flattened soccer balls. Astronomers can never be sure of a galaxy's true shape because it can only ever be seen from one angle.

GIANT M 84

One of the largest elliptical galaxies in the nearby Virgo cluster, M 84, is 50 million light-years away. It is believed to have a black hole 300 million times the mass of the Sun at its center.

DWARF M 32

Most of the light in this galaxy comes from red giants—stars that have cooled and swollen at the end of their lives. This implies that star formation in the dwarf M 32 ended around 8 billion years ago.

M 110

Like M 32, this is a companion to Andromeda, a giant spiral less than three million light-years away. Both galaxies are tiny compared with Andromeda itself.

ANATOMY OF AN ELLIPTICAL

GALACTIC CENTER
All elliptical galaxies gradually become brighter toward the center, where the concentration of stars may be 100 million times that of the Sun's neighborhood and massive black holes may lurk unseen.

OLD AND RED
Almost all of the stars in elliptical galaxies are old and relatively cool, which means that they give off mostly red light. But paradoxically, such galaxies may be younger than some spirals, where gas is constantly being recycled to create new stars.

NO GAS OR DUST
The space between the stars in an elliptical galaxy is almost totally empty. All of the gas that was once there has been used up in star formation, blown away in supernova explosions or stripped out by intergalactic matter. Few stars are born in ellipticals.

GLOBULAR CLUSTERS
On the outskirts of many ellipticals is a vast halo that in reality is composed of swarms of globular star clusters. Like the bulk of the galaxy itself, these clusters contain mainly old stars—up to one million each.

IRREGULAR GALAXIES

About one-fourth of the galaxies in the universe appear to break the rules of galactic configuration. Spiral and elliptical galaxies have clearly defined characteristics and can usually be readily identified. But the remainder—the so-called irregular galaxies—do not seem to fit in.

These galaxies may be irregular, but they are by no means structureless. Some are flat with a pronounced bulge of cool red stars, similar to spiral galaxies, but not as symmetrical. And others are irregular because they are interacting or merging with other galaxies.

SOME IRREGULAR GALAXIES

Name	Magnitude	Distance	Diameter	Location
NGC 6822	.9	1.8 million light-years	5,000 light-years	Sagittarius
NGC 55	.8	5 million light-years	50,000 light-years	Sculptor
LMC	0.1	180,000 light-years	30,000 light-years	Dorado and Mensa
SMC	2.3	210,000 light-years	16,000 light-years	Tucana
M82	8.4	12 million light-years	30,000 light-years	Ursa Major
IC 5152	11.7	2 million light-years	7,000 light-years	Indus
IC 1613	9.2	2.9 million light-years	8,000 light-years	Cetus

COSMIC CATCH-ALL

Because of their shape, some galaxies appear to defy attempts to categorize them. These galaxies lack the majestic arms of spiral galaxies and do not have the football-shape symmetry or the scale of the ellipticals. They are simply called irregular galaxies.

Yet study shows that irregular galaxies have much in common with their spiral cousins. Spirals are disk-shaped, with a prominent central bulge from which characteristic spiral arms wind outward. They have a high gas content and their spiral arms are regions of active star formation. One form of irregular galaxy—type I irregulars—shares almost all of these features. But they differ from spirals in a number of important ways. Type I irregular galaxies have no discernible spiral structure and are highly asymmetric. And there is even more gas—with which to form new stars—in these irregular galaxies than there is found in spirals.

With its flat blue disk full of young stars and a red bulge where older stars reside, the galaxy NGC 55 resembles a spiral galaxy. But this type I irregular galaxy has no spiral arms and the bulge is not central, but displaced to one side. Some astronomers believe this galaxy is similar to the Large Magellanic Cloud, another type I irregular, that orbits the Milky Way, but which is seen more from the "side." Type I irregulars have recognizable characteristics—so, some irregular galaxies do not live up to their name. Yet the shape of other irregulars is much less ordered.

OUT OF SHAPE

Galaxies with a poorly defined structure are called type II irregulars. Like other irregulars, these galaxies have a high gas content. But the characteristic they share as a group is the lack of a typical shape. Many type II irregulars are thought to have lost their structure as a result of collision with other galaxies. Others are believed to be distorted by the gravity of nearby galaxies.

M 82, a type II irregular in Ursa Major, is highly chaotic with no central concentration. This galaxy appears to have been influenced by the gravitational forces of its neighbor, the spiral galaxy M 81. Like many type II irregulars, M 82 is mottled with bright blue regions where stars are being born. This

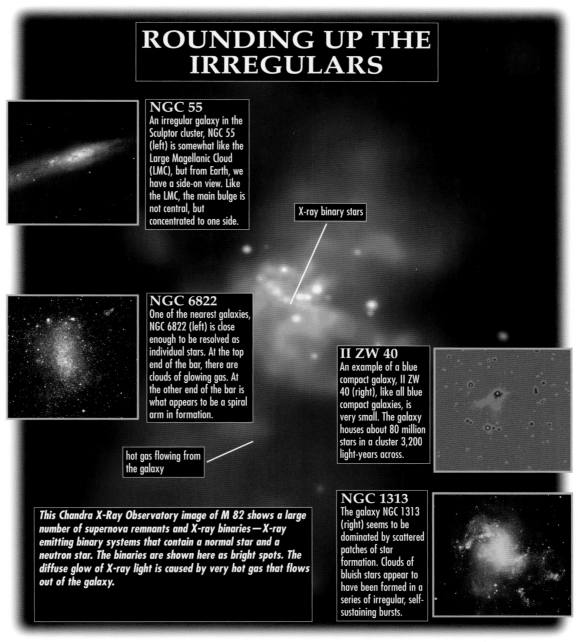

ROUNDING UP THE IRREGULARS

NGC 55
An irregular galaxy in the Sculptor cluster, NGC 55 (left) is somewhat like the Large Magellanic Cloud (LMC), but from Earth, we have a side-on view. Like the LMC, the main bulge is not central, but concentrated to one side.

X-ray binary stars

NGC 6822
One of the nearest galaxies, NGC 6822 (left) is close enough to be resolved as individual stars. At the top end of the bar, there are clouds of glowing gas. At the other end of the bar is what appears to be a spiral arm in formation.

hot gas flowing from the galaxy

II ZW 40
An example of a blue compact galaxy, II ZW 40 (right), like all blue compact galaxies, is very small. The galaxy houses about 80 million stars in a cluster 3,200 light-years across.

NGC 1313
The galaxy NGC 1313 (right) seems to be dominated by scattered patches of star formation. Clouds of bluish stars appear to have been formed in a series of irregular, self-sustaining bursts.

This Chandra X-Ray Observatory image of M 82 shows a large number of supernova remnants and X-ray binaries—X-ray emitting binary systems that contain a normal star and a neutron star. The binaries are shown here as bright spots. The diffuse glow of X-ray light is caused by very hot gas that flows out of the galaxy.

HARD EVIDENCE

FLATTENED DISK
The observations made by radio astronomers of some irregular galaxies—such as the giant irregular NGC 4449 (right)—show that the hydrogen gas within the galaxy is distributed in a flattened disk with a definite pattern of rotation. Structures of this nature are more commonly found in spiral galaxies. Yet the radio data that has been collated from the rest of the galaxy reveals that the gas dynamics are very complicated and do not conform to any obvious pattern.

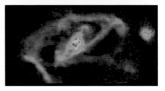

starbirth is a consequence of the many gravitational interactions that give these galaxies their truly irregular shape.

Both type I and II irregular galaxies are small compared with spirals and ellipticals. As they are so small, most irregulars are faint. Of the brightest few thousand galaxies, perhaps only 5 percent are irregular. Typically they house no more than one to 10 billion stars, between one

and 10 percent of the number in the Milky Way. But even these are giants compared to a third type of irregular—blue compact galaxies. These diminutive galaxies are little more than shapeless clouds of hydrogen gas, inside which stars constantly form.

The rate of star formation in blue compact galaxies is so high that hydrogen gas in the galaxy glows from the flood of energy from

newborn stars. The brightness makes blue compact galaxies very conspicuous for their size, despite being barely a few thousand light-years across—about 50 times smaller than a large spiral. These galaxies closely resemble the luminous star factories, known as HII regions, found in larger galaxies, but blue compact galaxies are isolated mini-galaxies in their own right.

ACTIVE GALAXIES

Every second, an active galaxy emits more energy than our Sun will radiate in 30,000 years. Yet all this power comes from a region that may be only a few light-hours across—not much larger than our solar system. Within this space sits a black hole as massive as a billion Suns. Its ferocious gravity tears nearby stars apart, then sucks the debris out of space and time. As the matter disappears forever, it gives off a gigantic flood of radiation that makes such galaxies the powerhouses of the universe.

ACTIVE GALAXIES

Name	Type	Distance (light-years)
Centaurus A	Nearest radio galaxy	16 million
Virgo A (M 87)	Radio galaxy	50 million
NGC 1068	Seyfert galaxy	65 million
NGC 1275	Seyfert galaxy	360 million
BL Lacertae	BL Lac object	870 million
Cygnus A	Radio galaxy	1 billion
3C273	Nearest quasar	2 billion

ACTIVE UNIVERSE

Active galaxies are the most powerful objects in the known universe. Each of them pours out colossal quantities of radiation, almost all of which emanates from a tiny nucleus comparable in size to the orbit of Pluto around the Sun—minute compared to the galaxy itself. Not all active galaxies look exactly the same, though. Some are mere points, others are more extended like normal galaxies, and still others have vast jets of energy that spurt from their centers. But many astronomers now believe that all active galaxies are powered in exactly the same way: By a supermassive black hole.

Even the smallest of these black holes are around a million times heavier than the Sun, whereas the largest are a thousand times bigger still. With such gigantic masses compressed into a region only light-hours across, the gravitational pull on nearby stars and gas is enormous. Stars closest to the black hole are torn violently apart. But because the galactic

center rotates, the gas and debris that remain do not fall immediately into the hole. Instead, the gas swirls around to form a vast disk-like structure. There, friction—generated as the material circulates—heats the gas to incredible temperatures. By the time the gas reaches the innermost edge of the disk and falls forever into the black hole, its temperature is so high that it gives off a flood of X-rays, which is why active galaxies are so bright.

The black-hole theory is not quite enough to account for the wide range of active galaxies observed, and astronomers have had to develop the theory further. Now, though, they are confident that they understand why some active galaxies are so different from others.

A VIEW TO THRILL

Astronomers believe that the accretion disk, perhaps three light-days across, is surrounded by a doughnut-shaped region of dense molecular gas, up to hundreds of thousands times

wider. When we view an active galaxy edge-on, this doughnut obscures the central engine, and we see what astronomers call a Seyfert galaxy. When we view from a higher elevation, though, we see the phenomenon astronomers call a quasar. And if

we are looking directly down into the throat of the black hole—parallel to the jets of hot gas blasting out from the center—we see a BL Lac galaxy.

Perhaps it is best that we are observing these displays of cosmic violence from a long way off!

FASTER THAN LIGHT?

MATTER THAT JETS FROM THE CENTER OF AN ACTIVE GALAXY SOMETIMES SEEMS TO TRAVEL FASTER THAN THE SPEED OF LIGHT, WHICH IS FORBIDDEN BY THE LAWS OF RELATIVITY. IN FACT, SUCH APPARENTLY IMPOSSIBLE SPEEDS ARE NOW KNOWN TO BE OPTICAL ILLUSIONS.

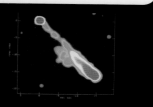

MASSIVE HOLE

THE HUBBLE SPACE TELESCOPE HAS SHOWN THAT THE GIANT ELLIPTICAL GALAXY M 87 PROBABLY HOSTS A BLACK HOLE 3 BILLION TIMES MORE MASSIVE THAN THE SUN. M 87 IS AMONG THE NEAREST ACTIVE GALAXIES—ONLY 50 MILLION LIGHT-YEARS AWAY.

CENTRAL ENGINE

GIANT TORUS
A doughnut-shaped region comprised of molecular gas that surrounds the accretion disk out to vast distances. Shown here cut away for clarity, such a torus can measure up to 1,000 light-years across—big enough to partly conceal a galactic center. Just how much the torus hides may determine what kind of active galaxy astronomers see.

JETS
Some active galaxies are spewing vast quantities of gas into intergalactic space, perhaps out to distances of millions of light-years. Astronomers are fairly sure that a galactic magnetic field is somehow responsible for these jets, but the exact mechanism is still a mystery.

ACCRETION DISK
In a vast, glowing disk, dust and star debris orbit a black hole at the galaxy's center. This accretion disk is the source of the radiation astronomers detect.

BLACK HOLE
Right at the very center of the active galaxy is a black hole that tears dust into atoms before swallowing them forever.

TYPES OF ACTIVE GALAXY

SEYFERT
Seyfert galaxies are named after the astronomer who first studied their spectra. NGC 4151 is the most famous example and the closest to our own galaxy.

BL LAC
Named for BL Lacertae, once thought to be a variable star, "BL Lacs" are members of a class of active galaxies that always appear star-like, the brightness of which varies.

QUASAR
The most distant objects we know, the name comes from "quasi-stellar," meaning star-like. A quasar looks like a star but is actually the center of an active galaxy.

QUASARS

Out on the edge of the visible universe, up to 12 billion light-years from Earth, are the mysterious powerhouses known as quasars. Seen through an optical telescope, quasars are unexceptional points of light; but in fact, every quasar is the blazing heart of an entire galaxy, fueled by the unimaginable gravitational power of a supermassive black hole. And as matter spirals inward to inevitable destruction, the quasar blasts out more radiation—in the form of X-rays, light and radio waves—than the radiation of a hundred regular galaxies put together.

REDSHIFT, SPEED & DISTANCE

Name	Redshift	Recession Velocity (as % of light-speed)	Distance (light-years)
3C273	0.16	15	3.0 billion
3C48	0.37	31	4.0 billion
3C295	0.46	36	4.7 billion
3C446	1.40	70	9.2 billion
3C9	2.00	80	10.4 billion
OQ172	3.53	90	11.5 billion
DHM0054-284	3.61	91	11.9 billion
PC1247+34	4.90	94	12.6 billion

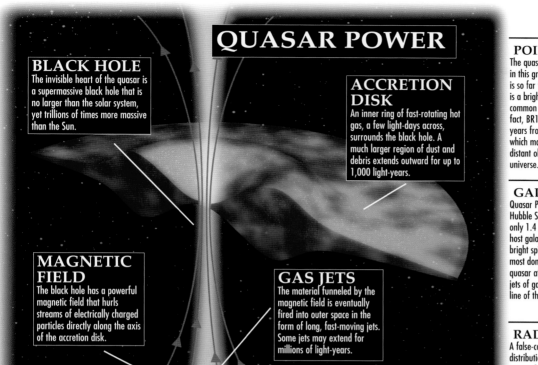

QUASAR POWER

BLACK HOLE
The invisible heart of the quasar is a supermassive black hole that is no larger than the solar system, yet trillions of times more massive than the Sun.

ACCRETION DISK
An inner ring of fast-rotating hot gas, a few light-days across, surrounds the black hole. A much larger region of dust and debris extends outward for up to 1,000 light-years.

MAGNETIC FIELD
The black hole has a powerful magnetic field that hurls streams of electrically charged particles directly along the axis of the accretion disk.

GAS JETS
The material funneled by the magnetic field is eventually fired into outer space in the form of long, fast-moving jets. Some jets may extend for millions of light-years.

THREE QUASARS

POINT OF LIGHT
The quasar BR1202-07, on the left in this ground-based optical image, is so far from us that all we can see is a bright, featureless speck—a common quasar characteristic. In fact, BR1202-07 is 12 billion light-years from the Milky Way galaxy, which makes it one of the most distant objects in the observable universe.

GALAXY CENTER
Quasar PG0052+251, at left in this Hubble Space Telescope image, is only 1.4 billion light-years away. Its host galaxy has clearly defined bright spiral arms. But the galaxy's most dominant feature by far is the quasar at its center and the telltale jets of gas that shoot out along the line of the galactic axis.

RADIO CLUES
A false-color image maps the distribution of radio energy within quasar 2355+490, shown as the red blob at the center of this picture. The companion blobs show radio waves emitted from matter that is about to be sucked out of existence into the quasar's black hole. Many quasars are strong radio emitters.

COSMIC BLASTERS

When astronomers first observed the object cataloged as 3C273, they were puzzled. This faint pinprick of light in an optical telescope was a very powerful source of radio waves, so they called it a quasar—short for "quasi-stellar [star-like] radio source." Before long, more of the strange quasars were added to a growing list.

Could they be faint, nearby stars with unusual properties? To answer the question, astronomers used a technique called spectroscopy. They split the light from the object into its component colors, then checked the resulting spectrum for the signature of important gases, such as hydrogen, which would show up as either dark or bright narrow lines in fixed positions amid the rainbow of colors.

But the spectrum from 3C273 revealed just a few bright lines, all of them in unfamiliar places. In fact, the lines were caused by ordinary hydrogen gas—but they were in the wrong place in the spectrum. They had been shifted toward the red end.

This redshift was the result of the so-called Doppler Effect and proved that quasar 3C273 was moving away from planet Earth.

Just as sound waves from a police car siren seem to produce a higher note when the vehicle approaches and a lower note as it draws away, so light waves from an approaching object are squeezed into a shorter wavelength—toward blue—if the object is approaching, and stretched into a longer wavelength—toward red—as it recedes. The extent of the shift, which occurs in light just as it does in sound, reveals how fast the object is traveling.

For many years, astronomers have used the redshifts detected in the light of distant galaxies to demonstrate that the universe is expanding. The farther away a galaxy is, the faster it moves in relation to the Earth. In this way, the quasar redshift gave astronomers not only an indication of the speed it was travelling, but also of its distance.

Quasar 3C273 was receding from the Earth at no less than 15 percent of the speed of light. Such a velocity meant that the strange object was at least 3 billion light-years away. We now know that other quasars are even more distant, some of them as much as a staggering 12 billion light-years from us. This places them not only at the very edge of the known universe, but also near the beginning of time itself.

BLACK HOLES

Their distance from us explains why many quasars show no more detail than a star. But if they are so far away, why are we able to see them at all? What makes them so bright? Only one object can yield such stupendous energy—a supermassive black hole, a billion times heavier than the Sun.

Astronomers suspect that black holes lie at the center of many, perhaps even most, galaxies, destroying stars that come too close by tearing them into clouds of dust and gas. Quasars are the doomed remnants of such stars, emitting bursts of radiation detectable from far across the universe before a black hole sucks them out of existence forever.

COLLISION

In 1995, the Hubble Space Telescope imaged the quasar called PKS2349 and found it to be surrounded by a fuzzy patch (right). But the quasar was not at the center of this patch, as had been expected. Astronomers think that PKS249 is colliding with a quasar-free galaxy. If they are right, the two galaxies will probably merge within 10 million years.

QUASAR MAN

The critical redshift measurements that proved quasars were distant, ultra-powerful objects were made by Dutch astronomer Maarten Schmidt, who was working at the California Institute of Technology. Since then, Schmidt has found that quasars are most common at extreme distances, which correspond to early stages in the formation of the universe.

GALAXY CLUSTERS

Just as stars are assembled into galaxies, so galaxies are grouped into clusters. Some clusters contain only a few galaxies, but the largest may hold many thousands—all within a few million light-years of each other. Galaxy clusters are the most massive bodies that gravity can hold together. This, and the fact that within many clusters lie clouds of searingly hot gas that reach temperatures of up to 100 million degrees, may yield important clues about the basic structure of the universe.

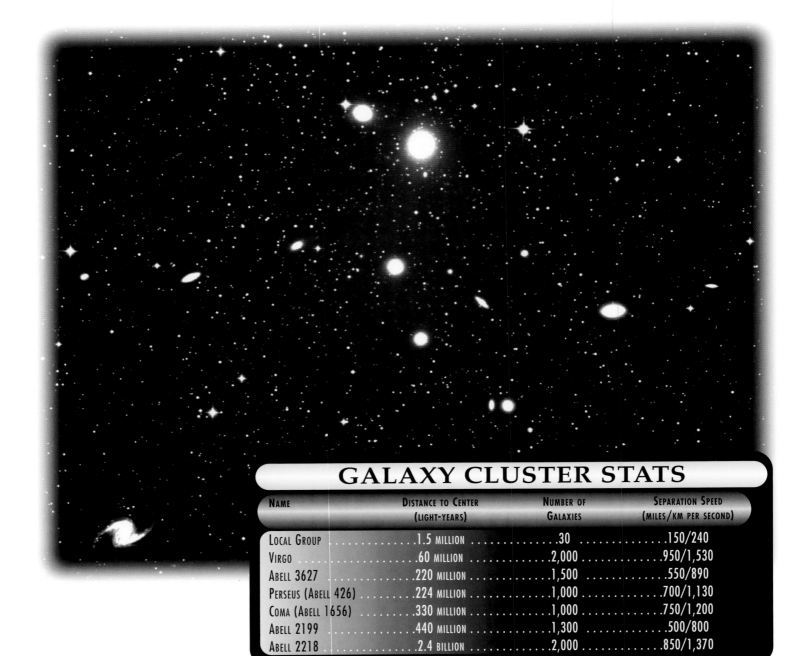

GALAXY CLUSTER STATS

Name	Distance to Center (light-years)	Number of Galaxies	Separation Speed (miles/km per second)
Local Group	1.5 million	30	150/240
Virgo	60 million	2,000	950/1,530
Abell 3627	220 million	1,500	550/890
Perseus (Abell 426)	224 million	1,000	700/1,130
Coma (Abell 1656)	330 million	1,000	750/1,200
Abell 2199	440 million	1,300	500/800
Abell 2218	2.4 billion	2,000	850/1,370

COSMIC CROWDING

Galaxies, it seems, are not scattered randomly throughout the universe. More than 60 percent of those that we know about are clustered together at remarkable densities. Individual stars within galaxies may be separated by billions of stellar diameters of space. By comparison, the galaxies themselves are packed together like football players only a few yards apart.

Cluster sizes vary greatly. The Local Group that contains our own galaxy, the Milky Way, plus around 30 others, is classed as a small cluster; it is merely a suburb of the much larger Virgo cluster, the center of which lies about 60 million light-years away. Virgo is typical of the largest galaxy clusters, gigantic structures that may include more than 2,000 individual galaxies. And that is not all they contain.

Astronomers have detected powerful X-ray sources in the largest clusters—not from the galaxies themselves, but from the space in between them. The likely source is very thin but extremely hot gas that radiates at temperatures around 100 million degrees. In some cases, this gas accounts for about 15 percent of the mass of the cluster. Much of it is what astronomers call primordial gas—the remnants of the Big Bang. The rest may have been stripped from individual galaxies within the cluster as they moved through the not-quite-empty space around them. In a process known as ram pressure stripping, super-hot gas clouds appear to rob galaxies of any spare gas, just as a gale wind strips the leaves from a tree during the fall.

CLUSTER FORMATION

Astronomers are uncertain why galaxies form clusters, but they suspect that it has something to do with the way galaxies were born in the first place.

Galaxies originated in the early universe in regions of gas that were slightly denser than the average. It is possible that the densest regions gave birth to more than one galaxy. These galaxies would have had a gravitational head start over their more scattered neighbors and would immediately have begun to draw other galaxies toward them.

If this theory is correct, it means that galaxies are in clusters because they started off in clusters and that they are rich because they were born rich. Once a cluster has formed, the laws of gravity dictate that it can only grow bigger: As its gravity pulls more and more galaxies toward it, its mass steadily increases and so does its attractiveness. This would explain why most of the galaxies that we can see appear to be heading toward the heart of a cluster.

Given time, it seems that most of the galaxies in the universe will become part of a cluster. But as the universe expands, these clusters will grow steadily more isolated—and there will always be a few galaxies that are too far away from a cluster ever to succumb to its steely gravitational embrace.

ANATOMY OF A GALAXY CLUSTER

GIANT ELLIPTICAL
NGC 1399 is the giant elliptical galaxy that dominates the Fornax I cluster of galaxies.

EDGE-ON SPIRAL
Many of the spiral galaxies in Fornax I are only visible edge-on, or have very tightly wound spiral arms.

BARRED SPIRAL
NGC 1365 is a fine example of a barred spiral galaxy, whose formation is still a mystery to astronomers.

Fornax I is a typical rich galaxy cluster whose center lies 52 million light-years from the Milky Way. Fornax I contains more spiral galaxies than most clusters—although some are only visible edge-on.

HARD EVIDENCE

HOT GAS
The gas between clusters is so thin that atoms are spaced four in (10 cm) apart. But in the vastness of space, even this can add up to a gigantic amount. The gas is invisible in ordinary light but is visible to X-ray detectors. This false-color image shows gas near the heart of a rich galaxy cluster glowing at an incredible 100 million degrees.

RICH AND POOR

A SO-CALLED RICH CLUSTER (SUCH AS THE GIANT COMA CLUSTER, PART OF WHICH IS SHOWN AT RIGHT) CONTAINS MORE THAN 30 GALAXIES PACKED WITHIN A FEW MILLION LIGHT-YEARS OF ITS CENTER—AND UP TO 3,000 MORE DISTANT GALAXIES THAT ARE DRAWN TOWARD ITS HEART. MOST GALAXY CLUSTERS ARE MORE SPARSELY POPULATED. BUT ALTHOUGH ONLY ABOUT 5 PERCENT OF ALL KNOWN CLUSTERS ARE CLASSED AS RICH, THEY PROBABLY INCLUDE MORE GALAXIES THAN ALL THEIR POOR COUSINS COMBINED.

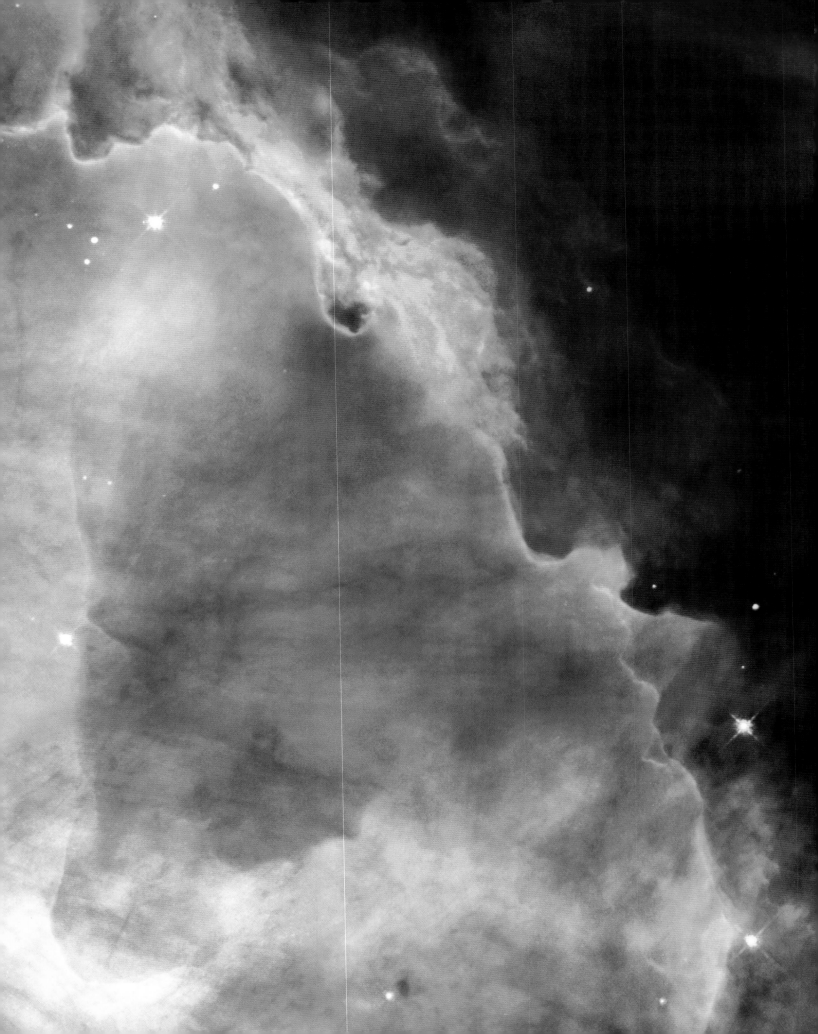

THE UNIVERSE AT WORK

The quest to understand the forces governing the universe is the work of cosmologists and theoretical physicists. Together they have made great strides in recent decades, but there are still many questions left unanswered. All matter in the universe seems to interact through just four forces—electromagnetism, gravitation, and the weak and strong nuclear forces. The structure of elements ultimately reveals that they are all composed of a relatively small handful of particles that interact through these forces, obeying on the smallest scale the laws of quantum physics. There is strong evidence that all these forces are aspects on a single "superforce" that manifests itself differently in our present-day universe. However, at the largest scales, only gravity is significant, and its behaviour is described to apparent perfection by Einstein's relativity theory. The major problem of modern physics is that quantum physics and relativity seem to be completely incompatible. Despite this, electromagnetism and gravitation theories are vital to modern physics—they describe the behaviour and evolution of the universe, the emission of radiation from stars and other sources, and commonly seen astrophysical phenomena such as jets and accretion disks.

An ocean of glowing hydrogen, oxygen, and sulfur within Messier 17, a hotbed of star formation. Our understanding of the quantum processes that work within the individual gas atoms is currently at odds with the relativity theory which currently explains the interaction between large objects such as stars and planets.

SCALES OF THE UNIVERSE

A tree may be 10 times taller than you are. The difference in scale between you and the tree corresponds to a single order of magnitude, a 10-fold increase in linear size. A difference of one order of magnitude may not seem great. But the entire known universe encompasses a range of scales that occupy only about 40 orders of magnitude. From the tiniest subatomic particles to the entire visible universe, there are just 40 steps up in scale, each 10 times larger than the previous scale and 10 times smaller than the next.

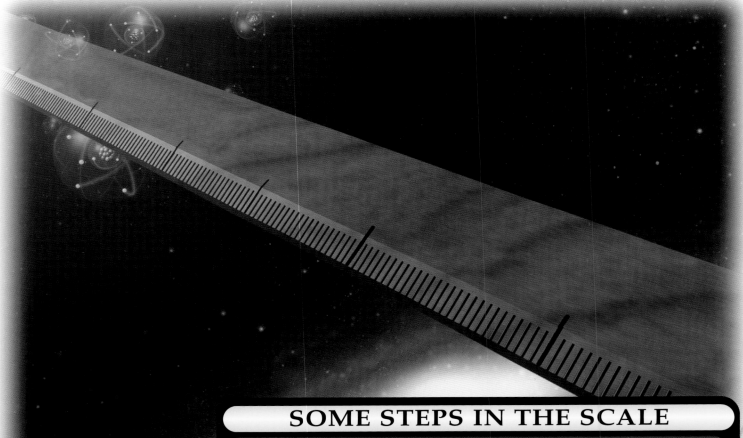

SOME STEPS IN THE SCALE

OBJECT	SIZE (IMPERIAL)	SIZE (METRIC)	SIZE COMPARED WITH PREVIOUS OBJECT
Proton	0.04 trillionths of an inch	10^{-15} m	N/A
Atom	4 billionths of an inch	10^{-9} m	100,000 times larger
DNA molecule (width)	80 billionths of an inch	2×10^{-8} m	20 times larger
Red blood cell	40 thousandths of an inch	0.01 mm	5,000 times larger
Human being	6 feet	1.8 metres	180,000 times larger
Earth (diameter)	7,928 miles	12,758 km	7,000,000 times larger
Solar System (orbit of Pluto)	7.34 billion miles	11.81 billion km	930,000 times larger
Milky Way galaxy	100,000 light-years	N/A	80,000,000 times larger
Universe	30 billion light-years	N/A	300,000 times larger

THE FORTY STEPS

Stand on a beach on a dark night and a whole range of objects is visible on many different scales. Beneath your feet are grains of sand a fraction of an inch (1 mm) across. Behind you, cliff faces may jut 100 feet (30 m) into the sky—they are 30,000 times taller than the sand grains. Overhead is the Moon, 2,160 miles (3,476 km) in diameter and 100,000 times larger than the cliffs. But there are much bigger scales in space. Most stars are hundreds of thousands of miles across, or hundreds of times the size of a planet. And stars are dwarfed by nebulae—a billion times larger and stretching for hundreds of light-years.

Telescopes reveal even larger structures. Stars and nebulae reside in gigantic galaxies, a thousand times the size of the largest nebulae. Galaxies in turn come in clusters, hundreds or thousands of times the scale of the galaxies. Clusters group into superclusters. And the largest object of all, at the end of the cosmic scale, is the universe itself. Astrophysicists estimate the universe is about 30 billion light-years from one side to the other.

While it is easy to see the very large, the very small is harder to appreciate. The universe is incomprehensibly huge compared with human bodies, but we are each made up of far more cells than there are stars in a galaxy. Each cell measures a few ten-thousandths of an inch across. Inside the cells are molecules of DNA, 5,000 times smaller.

SCALING BACK

DNA is in turn made up of atoms of carbon and hydrogen—once regarded as the most fundamental building blocks that could exist. We now know that each atom contains a number of smaller negatively charged particles called electrons, the number of which defines the chemical properties of the atom. Scientists have also discovered that electrons surround a small, positively charged core called a nucleus, on a scale 10,000 times smaller than the atom. In turn, the nucleus is seen to contain two other elementary particles—the proton and the neutron.

Over the last century, a whole "zoo" of subatomic particles has been identified. Electrons remain elemental, one of a family of fundamental particles called leptons. But protons and neutrons are now believed to be made up of smaller components known as quarks. These quarks are the smallest things in the known universe.

Starting with the smallest objects, quarks and leptons, and increasing the scale repeatedly by a factor of 10, it takes just 40 steps—or 40 orders of magnitude in scale—to encompass the entire size range in the known universe. The halfway point, 20 orders of magnitude or 10^{20} times larger than a quark or smaller than the universe, corresponds to a scale of about 500 miles (800 km)—slightly smaller than the diameter of the minor planet Ceres.

WHAT IF?
...THERE IS SOMETHING LARGER THAN THE UNIVERSE?

Better and more powerful telescopes allow astronomers to see things that are farther and farther from our corner of the universe, on larger and larger scales. So there may come a point where technology allows scientists to see to the universe's boundaries. Might they even be able to see objects outside the universe, on a still larger scale?

It is not just a question of acquiring the right technology. One reason why astronomers cannot see to the boundaries of the universe is that the very concept of the edge of space has no meaning. The universe consists not only of the matter within it but the space itself as well. The concept of something lying outside space defies logic. Scientists think of our universe as being 3-dimensional. So it is easy for us to imagine it as an enclosed entity floating around in some unknown medium that lies "outside." But our universe is not simply 3-dimensional: It is curved in another dimension we cannot experience normally.

One way to understand a universe without a boundary is to visualize the surface of a sphere. If the occupants of such an imaginary universe were to explore the cosmos, they might find something that did not fit their 2-dimensional world.

The inhabitants of this world could travel in what they would perceive to be straight lines, only to return to their starting point some time later. Their mathematicians would realize that although their universe has two dimensions, it is warped into a third that they never actually see and therefore has no boundaries, despite being finite. In the same way, our universe is probably finite in physical extent but unbounded.

THE MILKY WAY
80,000,000 times bigger than the solar system

SOLAR SYSTEM
930,000 times larger than Earth

HUMAN BEING
180,000 times larger than a red blood corpuscle

EARTH
7 million times larger than a human being

ERYTHROCYTES OR RED BLOOD CORPUSCLES
5,000 times larger than a DNA molecule

DNA MOLECULE
20 times larger than an atom

PROTON

ATOM
100,000 times larger than a proton

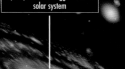

SMALL-SCALE
To study the very small, physicists use huge machines called accelerators (above). Inside an accelerator, alternating electric fields accelerate charged subatomic particles to near light-speed. Focused by magnetic fields, these elements collide with other particles. The resulting fragments reveal much about an atom's internal structure.

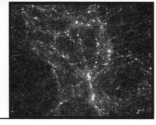

LARGE SCALE
The farther away a galaxy, the faster it is moving away from us. Using this rule, astronomers have built up an image of the universe on the largest scale. The result is a foamy structure (right): The walls of the bubbles are superclusters, while inside the bubbles are vast, relatively empty regions known as voids.

SMALLEST TO LARGEST

From the smallest objects known, quarks and leptons, to the largest objects imaginable, such as the universe itself, there are only 40 orders of magnitude.

THE FOUR FORCES

Nature is ruled by just four fundamental forces. The most familiar one is gravity—the force of attraction that exists between all matter. Gravity is by far the weakest of the four forces, yet it extends indefinitely through space. At the other extreme is nuclear force.

Trillions of times stronger than gravity, it exerts its binding power only across the tiny dimensions of an atomic nucleus. Between these two are electromagnetism, which binds atoms into molecules, and the weak nuclear force, which controls radioactive decay.

THE FAB FOUR

COMPARATIVE STRENGTH OF THE FOUR FORCES

GRAVITY	1
ELECTROMAGNETISM	1036
WEAK NUCLEAR FORCE	1025
STRONG NUCLEAR FORCE	1038

UNIVERSE UNITED

Gravity may be the weakest of all the fundamental forces, but every single particle of matter exerts a gravitational force on every other—which is why gravity has dominated the large-scale structure of the universe ever since the Big Bang. Electromagnetic (EM) force, on the other hand, is confined to charged particles, yet it is trillions of times stronger than gravity: A child's magnet, for example, can lift metal objects against the gravitational pull of the entire Earth. When charged particles vibrate, they give off photons—including the light photons we use to perceive the world around us.

Electromagnetic force is attractive between opposites: positive and negative charges, say, or the north and south poles of a magnet. In this way, it keeps atoms joined together in molecules. But EM force also repels. Positive shuns positive, and like magnetic poles push each other apart. So in order to bind together the mutually repulsive protons in an atomic nucleus, something much more powerful is needed: the strong nuclear force. Although this force acts only across the immeasurably small dimensions of the nucleus, the strong nuclear force is more than 100 times stronger than the force of electromagnetism.

The last of the four forces, the weak nuclear force, has been mathematically linked to electromagnetism. Although less powerful than either EM or the strong nuclear force, it governs the processes of radioactive decay within atoms.

QUANTUM EXCHANGE

At the subatomic level of quantum mechanics, physicists view the forces as interactions between fermions—their name for the protons, neutrons and electrons that make up matter. These protons and neutrons are in turn composed of quarks, the smallest particles currently known to exist. To interact, the fermions exchange peculiar particles called bosons, which are the force carriers of the quantum world. The most powerful carriers are gluons, which bear the strong nuclear force and hold atomic nuclei together. But gluons only exert their strength over minuscule distances, which limits the maximum size of atomic nuclei.

The bosons that carry the weak nuclear force—intermediate vector bosons—are far less powerful. Yet they are responsible for the mechanisms by which neutrons can decay into protons and electrons. The other two forces, electromagnetism and gravity, are carried by photons and gravitons respectively. Scientists have understood how photons work for the best part of a century—an understanding that underpins much electronic technology. But gravitons—at least for now—only exist in theory.

FAMILIAR FACES

1967, BERKELEY SCIENTIST STEVEN WEINBERG (LEFT) AND ABDUS SALAM, A SCIENTIST AT ENGLAND'S IMPERIAL COLLEGE, DISCOVERED THAT THE WEAK NUCLEAR FORCE SEEMED TO OPERATE THE SAME WAY AS THE FORCE OF ELECTROMAGNETISM. THEY WON THE NOBEL PRIZE FOR THEIR WORK IN 1979.

BIG BANG

BIRTH OF THE FOUR FORCES

SCHWARZ'S STRINGS

SCIENTISTS HAVE BEEN TRYING FOR YEARS TO COMBINE THE FOUR FORCES INTO A SINGLE THEORY OF EVERYTHING. ONE PROMISING APPROACH IS BEING PURSUED BY CALTECH SCIENTIST JOHN SCHWARZ (RIGHT). HE IS DEVELOPING A THEORY IN WHICH TINY ENTITIES KNOWN AS "STRINGS" DESCRIBE ALL THE PARTICLES, THEIR INTERACTIONS AND THE FORCES THAT GOVERN THEM.

GRAVITY began to emerge around 10–44 seconds after the Big Bang

STRONG NUCLEAR FORCE emerged 10–36 seconds after the Big Bang

ELECTROMAGNETISM was the final force to emerge, 10–11 seconds after the Big Bang

WEAK NUCLEAR FORCE emerged immediately from the Big Bang

Moments after the Big Bang, space was hot and dense, and each of the four forces behaved in a similar way. As the universe expanded and cooled, each force separated, adopting its own characteristics. Each force has a different strength.

GRAVITY
Gravity can keep planets orbiting around larger bodies like the Sun because the tiny attractive force in every particle all adds up to form a strong attractive force. All matter with mass exerts gravity.

STRONG NUCLEAR FORCE
The strong nuclear force is one of the forces that hold together the atom. This attracts protons and neutrons together in the nucleus. The attraction is greater than electromagnetism, which repulses them.

ELECTROMAGNETISM
Electromagnetism makes unlike charges attract each other and like charges repel. It keeps the negatively charged electrons attracted to positively charged protons in the nucleus of the atom.

WEAK NUCLEAR FORCE
The weak nuclear force impels the neutron, a nuclear particle, to split into subatomic particles. In certain elements this phenomenon is known as radioactivity.

ENERGY AND MATTER

If matter is, energy does. Matter is material: We may not always be able to see it or touch it, but we can weigh it, because it has mass. Energy makes things go, or glow: We may not be able to hold it, but we can see or feel its effects. For hundreds of years, scientists and philosophers assumed that matter and energy must be two entirely different entities that worked together to give shape and form to the universe. Then along came German theoretical physicist Albert Einstein, who showed that these entities were actually one and the same.

ENERGY CONVERSIONS

ENERGY FROM A SUGAR CUBE (ONE-TENTH OF AN OUNCE/3 GRAMS)

ACTIVITY	DOES WHAT...	ENERGY RELEASED (JOULES)
EATING IT	RELEASES CHEMICAL ENERGY	60,000
BURNING IT	RELEASES HEAT ENERGY	60,000
DROPPING IT 120 FT (36 M)	RELEASES POTENTIAL ENERGY	1
ACCELERATING IT TO 60 MPH (100 KM/H)	ADDS KINETIC ENERGY	1
RAISING ITS TEMPERATURE BY 1°	ADDS HEAT ENERGY	.7
CONVERTING ITS MASS INTO ENERGY		250 MILLION MILLION (ENOUGH TO LAUNCH 4,000 TONS/3,628 TONNES INTO SPACE)

ALTERED STATES

People used to believe that the smallest unit of matter was the atom. Then scientists discovered that atoms were composed of even smaller particles: Clouds of negatively charged electrons surrounding a more massive nucleus of positively charged protons and electrically neutral neutrons. These particles all have mass, so they count as matter, too.

When matter particles encounter different levels of energy, they change their state. Water, for example, occurs mostly in a liquid state. But if you freeze it, the atoms lose energy and the water becomes solid. Similarly, if you heat water, the atoms gain energy and the water evaporates as gas.

There is also a fourth state of matter called plasma. Rare on Earth, but commonplace in the rest of the universe, plasma is formed when atoms receive so much energy that they disintegrate into clouds of atomic nuclei and free-moving electrons. The glow from a neon streetlight comes from matter in a plasma state; so does the glow from every star that we see in the night sky.

Energy occurs in different states, too. A burning log on a fire turns chemical energy into heat and light energy. If a cinder jumps out of the fire, it means that some of the heat energy has made a further transformation into kinetic energy—the energy of movement. And if the log is perched high up on the fire, it also has potential energy—the energy that is given to it by the force of gravity.

TRADING MASS FOR ENERGY

There have been two great milestones on the road to understanding energy and matter.

The first, called the Law of Conservation of Energy, states that energy cannot be destroyed—it can only be converted from one form of energy into other forms.

The second is Albert Einstein's famous equation $e=mc^2$. This states that energy (e) and matter (m) are two versions of the same thing, and that c^2 (the speed of light times itself) governs the ratio between them. Einstein's equation shows us that there is a phenomenal amount of energy locked up in even the tiniest piece of matter—a discovery that led to the development of the atomic bomb. It also implies that matter is simply a concentrated and highly ordered form of energy—that energy came first, and matter somehow formed out of it in the first few milliseconds after the Big Bang.

Now, all over the universe, matter is decaying back into energy again. Even within the Earth, over hundreds of years, atoms of heavy elements such as uranium naturally transform themselves into lighter elements such as lead. As they do so, some of their mass reverts to energy, which is emitted in the form of heat and radiation. Much the same occurs in a nuclear power plant, except that in this case we "intercept" the energy and convert it into more usable forms, first heat and then electric power.

Even more potent is the conversion of matter into energy that takes place inside the Sun and stars. Here, at already incredibly high energy levels, atoms of hydrogen are fused into helium, releasing yet more energy as they do so. Only a tiny proportion of this energy ever reaches the Earth, yet it is what keeps us alive. If we could reproduce the fusion process in a controlled way on Earth, our energy needs would be solved forever—providing we could find the energy to start.

SOURCES OF ENERGY

ONE WAY OR ANOTHER, MOST OF OUR ENERGY COMES FROM THE SUN. AS WELL AS PROVIDING DIRECT HEAT AND LIGHT, SUNLIGHT HELPS PLANT LIFE TO GROW, WHICH IN TURN CREATES THE FOSSIL FUELS THAT WE BURN FOR POWER. BUT ENERGY COMES FROM OTHER SOURCES, TOO: NUCLEAR POWER AND GEOTHERMAL POWER TAP THE VAST AMOUNTS OF ENERGY LOCKED UP IN ALL MATTER. FOR TIDAL AND HYDROELECTRIC POWER, WE HAVE GRAVITY TO THANK.

ENERGY

Energy cannot be destroyed, only converted from one form to another. All forms of energy share what scientists call the capacity to "do work" on matter—for example by moving it, changing its state or fusing it into another type of matter altogether.

POTENTIAL ENERGY
The energy in matter that comes from gravitational attraction.

CHEMICAL ENERGY
The energy caused by the chemical interaction of matter with other matter, i.e. photosynthesis in plants.

KINETIC ENERGY
Energy acquired by acceleration; often quickly converted into heat.

MATTER

Throughout the universe matter exists in four states: solid, liquid, gas and plasma. The state of any piece of matter depends on the way its atoms respond to different energy levels, notably through changes in its temperature or to the pressure that it is under.

SOLID
The atoms of water are in a relatively low energy state; the water freezes.

LIQUID
The atoms become energized and move about, causing the ice to melt.

GAS
The atoms are energized to become highly agitated; the liquid turns to gas.

PLASMA
The atoms temporarily disintegrate into clouds of nuclei and free-moving electrons.

HARD EVIDENCE

HOW ENERGY CHANGES

1   The Sun radiates energy in the form of light.
2   Sunlight causes plants to grow.
3   Plants decay to form fossil fuels such as coal.
4   Fossil fuels supply power to build the rocket boosters that launched the Space Shuttle.
5   Gravity supplies the energy to bring the spent rocket boosters back to Earth.

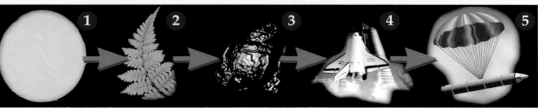

THE ELEMENTS

Elements are the purest form of matter in the universe. All elements are composed of atoms, and it is the structure of these atoms that distinguishes one element from another. The subatomic particles—protons, neutrons and electrons—that make up atoms are common to all elements. It is the variety of ways in which these particles cluster together as atoms that accounts for substances as fundamentally different as the gas hydrogen, the solid carbon and the sinister radioactive metal plutonium.

ELEMENTS COMPARED

Element	Symbol	Atomic number	Mass number	% of universe
Hydrogen	H	1	1	92.0
Helium	He	2	4	7.8
Oxygen	O	8	16	0.06
Carbon	C	6	12	0.03
Nitrogen	N	7	14	0.0085
Neon	Ne	10	20	0.0077
Iron	Fe	26	56	0.0037
Silicon	Si	14	28	0.0030
Magnesium	Mg	12	24	0.0024
Sulfur	S	16	32	0.0015

COMPLEX REACTIONS AND THE BIG BANG

Matter came into being about 13 billion years ago, during the first few fiery moments of the Big Bang. In the beginning all matter consisted of fast-moving subatomic particles. But when the universe was about three minutes old, some of these particles began to cluster into atoms, and elements were born.

The first elements were the gases hydrogen and helium. Hydrogen atoms are comprised of just two particles—a positively charged proton surrounded by a negatively charged electron. Helium atoms were rarer and more complex, with two electrons around a nucleus that included two protons and two neutrally charged neutrons.

As the universe entered its youthful phase, clouds of hydrogen condensed into the first stars. The enormous heat and pressure at their cores triggered nuclear fusion reactions, which converted hydrogen into helium. Other, more elaborate reactions also occurred, creating more complex types of atoms— and hence, more elements.

The atoms of each new element possessed one more proton, plus a corresponding electron, than the atoms of the element before it. Most of them also contained one or more extra neutrons, whose neutral charge served to hold the increasingly complex clusters of protons together. After helium atoms, with two protons and two neutrons, came atoms of the metal lithium, with three protons and four neutrons. Then came beryllium atoms with four protons and five neutrons, and so on.

Nuclear reactions within the first stars resulted in a total of 26 elements. The heaviest of these was the metal iron, whose atoms had 26 protons within their nuclei. At this point, the process stopped: There was insufficient energy within the stars to create more complex atoms and, for a time, iron was the heaviest element in the universe.

But then the process of star formation entered its second generation. When some of the early stars ran out of fuel and died, they ended their lives in cataclysmic explosions called supernovae. The energy released in these explosions was far greater than the energy generated by the fusion reactions within the stars. One of the by-products of the explosions was the forging of new and heavier elements, whose atoms had more protons and neutrons in their nuclei than iron.

UNSTABLE ELEMENTS

By the time our solar system formed, the universe had already reached its present total of 92 naturally occurring elements. Uranium, with 92 protons and more than 140 neutrons, is the heaviest of all. Why should the list of elements come to a halt at 92? In fact, it does not; but elements that are heavier than uranium are unstable and do not last for long. In a process known as radioactive decay, their nuclei split easily into atoms of two or more lighter elements. Most of these heavy elements die within seconds of being created. Even the longest-lived endure for only a few thousand years—a blink of the eye in cosmic terms.

Of the 92 durable elements, only relatively few exist on their own. Most substances on Earth are compounds of one or more elements whose atoms have joined together to form molecules.

Molecules of pure elements exist, too. A good example is the gas ozone, which consists of molecules that each contain three oxygen atoms. But by and large, elements prefer to mix with each other, and with 92 to choose from, the possible combinations are virtually endless—from the simple arrangement of hydrogen and oxygen atoms in a water molecule, to the millions of assorted atoms that make up a single molecule of the genetic code DNA.

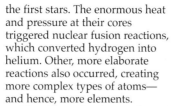

HELIUM
The nucleus of a helium atom contains two protons and two neutrons and is orbited by two electrons. Helium is a gas. Its two-electron configuration is extremely stable, so helium does not combine with other elements.

CARBON
In carbon atoms, six electrons orbit a nucleus of six protons and six neutrons. Carbon is a non-metallic solid and has a unique capacity for bonding with other elements, especially oxygen, hydrogen and nitrogen, to form highly complex molecules. All life as we know it is built from carbon-based molecules.

IRON
The metal iron has 26 protons, 26 electrons and 30 neutrons. It is the heaviest element that can be created in the core of an active star. All the elements in the universe that are heavier than iron were created in supernova explosions—when giant stars blew themselves apart.

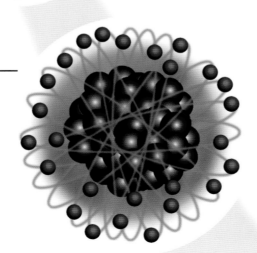

THREE ELEMENTS
All atoms have the same structure: A dense nucleus made up of protons and neutrons, surrounded by a cloud of orbiting electrons. The scale in these diagrams is greatly exaggerated. In reality, electrons have only one eighteen-hundredth the mass of protons and neutrons and are located far from the nucleus. Atoms, in fact, mostly consist of empty space.

HARD EVIDENCE
ISOTOPES
The atomic number—the number of protons in the atom's nucleus—is what defines an atom as being of a particular element. But it is possible for elements to have atoms with different numbers of neutrons. These are called isotopes of elements. Regular hydrogen, for example, has only one proton in its nucleus. But within the isotope deuterium, there is also a neutron. Isotopes of the same element all have identical chemical properties, however, because they share the same electron count.

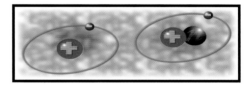

HARD EVIDENCE
RADIOACTIVITY
The neutrons and protons in an atomic nucleus must be in balance, or the nucleus will be unstable. An atom with an excess neutron may transform itself into an electron-proton pair, emitting energy in the form of radiation as it does so. This decays it into an atom of another element, but the new atom may still be unstable. The process can repeat itself several times until the nucleus reaches a stable state.

THE CURIES

IN 1898, THE PHYSICISTS MARIE AND PIERRE CURIE FOUND TWO NEW RADIOACTIVE ELEMENTS WHICH THEY CALLED POLONIUM AND RADIUM. MARIE STUDIED THESE SUBSTANCES INTENSIVELY, AND LATER REALIZED THAT THE X-RAY ENERGY THAT THEY EMITTED AS THEY DECAYED HAD APPLICATIONS IN MEDICINE— THEY COULD KILL TUMORS, FOR EXAMPLE. SADLY, MARIE CURIE LATER DIED OF LEUKEMIA DUE TO REPEATED EXPOSURE TO THE RADIATION.

ELECTROMAGNETIC RADIATION

Candles, cellphones, satellites and stars all give out electromagnetic radiation (EM)—and so does everything else in the universe. All of it travels at light-speed, though light itself is no more than the narrow band of the EM spectrum that our eyes can perceive.

Astronomers mine data from every part of that spectrum, from radio waves to energetic X- and gamma rays. Barely a century ago, humans learned how to create radio waves. Now, radio, TV and telephone transmissions flood our world in an EM deluge.

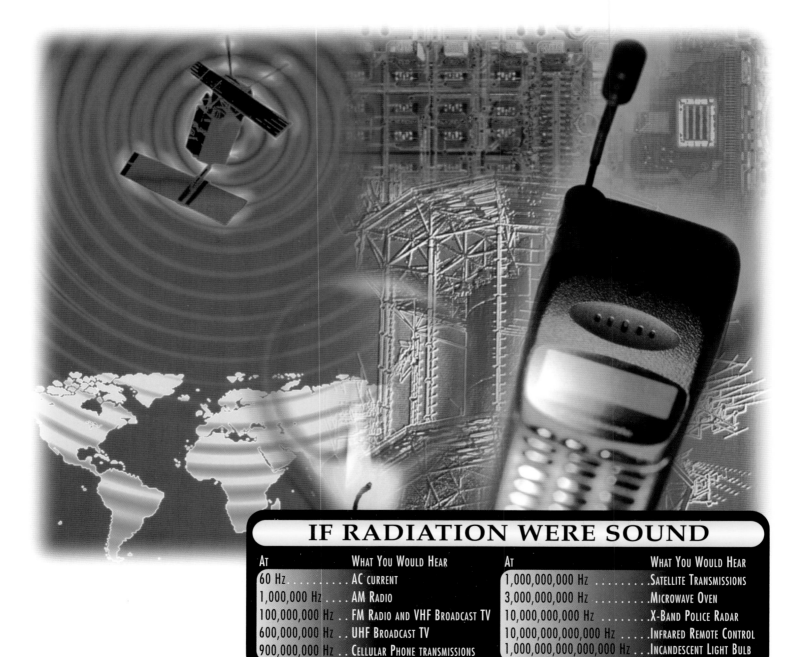

IF RADIATION WERE SOUND

At	What You Would Hear	At	What You Would Hear
60 Hz	AC current	1,000,000,000 Hz	Satellite Transmissions
1,000,000 Hz	AM Radio	3,000,000,000 Hz	Microwave Oven
100,000,000 Hz	FM Radio and VHF Broadcast TV	10,000,000,000 Hz	X-Band Police Radar
600,000,000 Hz	UHF Broadcast TV	10,000,000,000,000 Hz	Infrared Remote Control
900,000,000 Hz	Cellular Phone transmissions	1,000,000,000,000,000 Hz	Incandescent Light Bulb

WAVES OF POWER

Electromagnetic (EM) radiation is energy transferred across a distance. The light and heat from a candle is electromagnetic radiation, as are the radio beams that carry global communications and the X-rays that astronomers detect from distant galaxies.

EM radiation travels in waves of oscillating electric and magnetic fields, which spread out from their source at the speed of light. In some ways, EM waves are similar to sound waves, or to the waves that ripple through a pond disturbed by a falling stone. Like sound, EM radiation has a wavelength (the distance between peaks or troughs of successive waves) and a frequency (the number of waves per second). But the disturbances that cause EM take place inside atoms, when agitated electrons and other particles vibrate. And unlike sound, which requires a medium—air or water, for example—for its propagation, EM waves can travel through the vacuum of space. On Earth, we can see the light of a supernova explosion—but we will never hear the sound of the blast.

VIBRATION AND WAVELENGTH

The faster the vibrations that produce an EM field, the shorter the wavelength, so slowly vibrating EM fields—those of a radio transmitter, for example—produce radiation with a long wavelength. Waves must be at least as long as the vibrations of their source. In theory, the shortest EM wavelength can only be as small as the smallest subatomic particle, but EM waves can be almost infinitely long. Scientists study a small section of that possible bandwidth, from radio waves of about 3,000 cycles per second through microwaves, infrared, visible light, ultraviolet and X-rays to gamma rays, which vibrate at a million trillion times that frequency. In scientific language, cycles per second are described as hertz, in honor of the German physicist Heinrich Hertz—the first person to generate radio waves artificially. A frequency of a kilohertz means a thousand cycles per second, a megahertz a million cycles per second and a gigahertz a billion cycles per second.

The energy carried by electromagnetic radiation is directly proportional to its frequency. Radio waves, a few hundred megahertz at most, are only detectable by sensitive receivers. We experience infrared radiation as heat, and like most of Earth's animals we have evolved eyes to detect and interpret light radiation. Higher-frequency radiation has the power to knock electrons from atoms. Ultraviolet radiation bleaches paint and can cause skin cancer. X-rays and gamma rays can penetrate deeply into matter.

In the past century, new sensors have been developed to observe those parts of the EM spectrum that we cannot see. From radio waves to gamma rays, each frequency tells us more about the cosmos. In a sense, humans have just begun to open their eyes.

Stretching hundreds of miles from the Moon's surface, a giant antenna listens for broadcasts from the vastness of space.

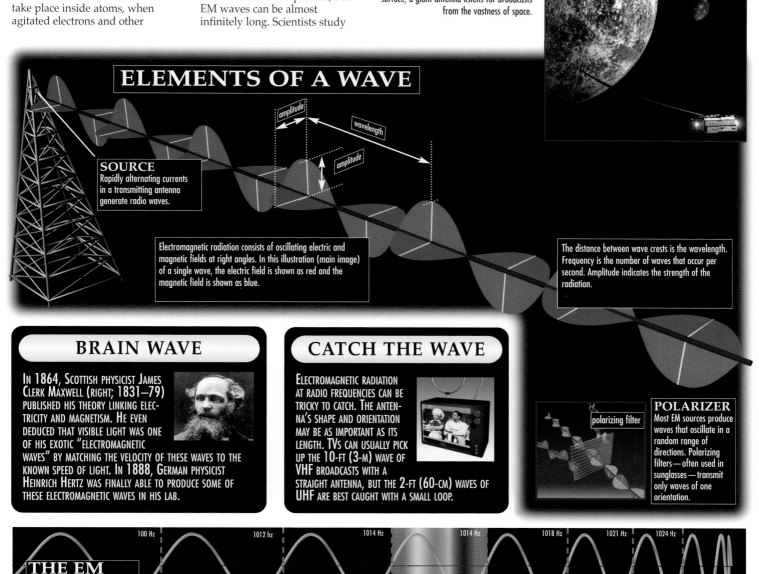

ELEMENTS OF A WAVE

amplitude

wavelength

amplitude

SOURCE
Rapidly alternating currents in a transmitting antenna generate radio waves.

Electromagnetic radiation consists of oscillating electric and magnetic fields at right angles. In this illustration (main image) of a single wave, the electric field is shown as red and the magnetic field is shown as blue.

The distance between wave crests is the wavelength. Frequency is the number of waves that occur per second. Amplitude indicates the strength of the radiation.

BRAIN WAVE

IN 1864, SCOTTISH PHYSICIST JAMES CLERK MAXWELL (RIGHT; 1831–79) PUBLISHED HIS THEORY LINKING ELECTRICITY AND MAGNETISM. HE EVEN DEDUCED THAT VISIBLE LIGHT WAS ONE OF HIS EXOTIC "ELECTROMAGNETIC WAVES" BY MATCHING THE VELOCITY OF THESE WAVES TO THE KNOWN SPEED OF LIGHT. IN 1888, GERMAN PHYSICIST HEINRICH HERTZ WAS FINALLY ABLE TO PRODUCE SOME OF THESE ELECTROMAGNETIC WAVES IN HIS LAB.

CATCH THE WAVE

ELECTROMAGNETIC RADIATION AT RADIO FREQUENCIES CAN BE TRICKY TO CATCH. THE ANTENNA'S SHAPE AND ORIENTATION MAY BE AS IMPORTANT AS ITS LENGTH. TVs CAN USUALLY PICK UP THE 10-FT (3-M) WAVE OF VHF BROADCASTS WITH A STRAIGHT ANTENNA, BUT THE 2-FT (60-CM) WAVES OF UHF ARE BEST CAUGHT WITH A SMALL LOOP.

POLARIZER
Most EM sources produce waves that oscillate in a random range of directions. Polarizing filters—often used in sunglasses—transmit only waves of one orientation.

polarizing filter

THE EM SPECTRUM

| 100 Hz | 1012 hz | 1014 Hz | 1014 Hz | 1018 Hz | 1021 Hz | 1024 Hz |

radio — infrared — visible light — ultraviolet — x-rays — gamma rays

QUANTUM THEORY

Quantum theory is weird. Even Nobel prizewinners admit they find it hard to get their heads around it. But quantum theory is also wonderful—one of the farthest-reaching achievements of the human mind. The theory rewrote the laws of physics that govern atoms and tiny subatomic particles, and overturned ideas that had held sway for more than 200 years. Without it, we would not have TV tubes, silicon chips or digital cameras. And we would never understand the way the universe really works.

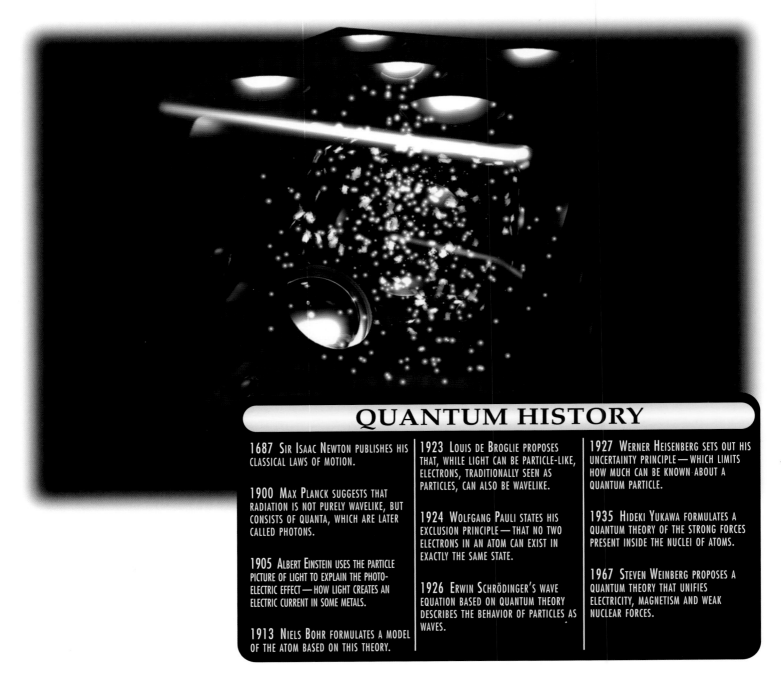

QUANTUM HISTORY

1687 Sir Isaac Newton publishes his classical laws of motion.

1900 Max Planck suggests that radiation is not purely wavelike, but consists of quanta, which are later called photons.

1905 Albert Einstein uses the particle picture of light to explain the photo-electric effect—how light creates an electric current in some metals.

1913 Niels Bohr formulates a model of the atom based on this theory.

1923 Louis de Broglie proposes that, while light can be particle-like, electrons, traditionally seen as particles, can also be wavelike.

1924 Wolfgang Pauli states his exclusion principle—that no two electrons in an atom can exist in exactly the same state.

1926 Erwin Schrödinger's wave equation based on quantum theory describes the behavior of particles as waves.

1927 Werner Heisenberg sets out his uncertainty principle—which limits how much can be known about a quantum particle.

1935 Hideki Yukawa formulates a quantum theory of the strong forces present inside the nuclei of atoms.

1967 Steven Weinberg proposes a quantum theory that unifies electricity, magnetism and weak nuclear forces.

REALITY CHECK

Quantum theory, also known as quantum physics or quantum mechanics, is the branch of physics that deals with the behavior of the very, very small: the fundamental particles of matter. And the theory insists that those particles behave in very, very strange ways.

At beginning of the 20th century, physicists noticed that light—then thought to be made up of continuous waves of electric and magnetic energy—sometimes acts instead like a swarm of tiny particles. These particles were called *quanta*—after the Latin word meaning "amount"—because they were the smallest amounts of light possible. And from *quanta* came the word quantum, as typically applied in physics.

While physicists pondered how a seemingly smooth beam of light could possibly behave like a hail of bullet-like particles, they were soon confronted with an equally perplexing, yet completely opposite, problem. They started seeing groups of electrons, which were traditionally thought of as solid particles, do things that only waves are supposed to, such as spreading out when fired through a narrow slit.

There seemed to be a paradox. How could things be both waves and particles at the same time? The emerging quantum theory eventually provided the answer. Matter and radiation can be thought of as quanta, or particles, but the positions of these particles cannot be determined exactly. Instead, the positions are given by waves of probability.

DON'T TRY TO UNDERSTAND IT

A probability wave is a bit like a crime wave: If one passes through your neighborhood then you are more likely than usual to experience a crime. Similarly, a subatomic particle's probability wave tells you where you are most likely to find the particle. But because large groups of particles cluster around the peaks of their probability waves, the group looks as if it really is a wave. And that is the source of all the confusion.

But there is still a mystery: Why does the most fundamental theory of physics only give a fuzzy, imprecise description of nature? Embarrassingly, no one knows. This missing link in scientists' grasp of the theory led Nobel Prize-winning physicist Richard Feynman to admit, "Nobody understands quantum mechanics." Scientists have had to accept that that is just the way it is. Some physicists, most notably Albert Einstein, refused to accept quantum theory and its hazy

probabilities. Scientists raised on Sir Isaac Newton's 300-year-old laws of physics, which likened particles to colliding billiard balls and predicted their positions exactly, believed that any theory to replace Newton's should also be e

Despite early doubts, quantum theory has now established itself as central to understanding everything in the microscopic world—from quarks to atoms—

and beyond. The quantum world offers insights into the physics of black holes and the birth and evolution of the universe. The theory has even found lucrative applications in industry. It has laid the foundations of semiconductor electronics—the technology that is responsible for microchips. Quantum mechanics also has applications in the technology of lasers, such as those in CD players.

Quantum theory and Einstein's theory of relativity were the greatest breakthroughs of 20th-century science. Now, physicists continue to strive to bring the two together into a single all-encompassing theory of physics to explain our universe.

WHAT IS REAL?

SCHRODINGER'S CAT

German physicist Erwin Schrödinger devised a famous thought experiment. Imagine a cat in a sealed box that contains a vial of poison gas linked to a radioactive atom, which might or might not decay. If the atom decays—a 50-50 chance—a mechanism will release the gas and kill the cat. According to quantum theory, without an observer to confirm its status, the radioactive atom must be in a "superposition" of states—it has both decayed and not decayed. So until someone opens the box and looks, the cat is both dead and not dead. But animal rights activists need not be concerned. The thought experiment has never been performed.

CORRELATION

French physicist Alain Aspect performed a curious experiment in 1982. His apparatus simultaneously emitted two photons of polarized light, in opposite directions from the same source. According to quantum theory, such polarization only exists once it has been observed—that is, the observation itself "decides" how the photon is polarized. Aspect's system of detectors discovered a bizarre fact. When he measured one photon, his measurement "decided" the nature of the other one, too—although at the point of measurement the pair were too far apart for any signal to travel between them, even at light speed. The photons were inextricably entangled—at the quantum level.

HARD EVIDENCE

electron beam

intensity pattern when both slits are open

double slit

intensity pattern when either slit is open

THE DOUBLE-SLIT EXPERIMENT
One of the most striking demonstrations of particles that act like waves is the so-called double-slit experiment. A beam of electrons is passed through two slits and onto a phosphor screen. The screen lights up where the beam hits it. When two slots are used, the double electron beam should just make two bright lines on the screen—if electrons behaved purely like particles. But electrons also behave like waves, and instead of the two bright lines, they create a so-called interference pattern of bright and dark bands. Bright bands form where two peaks, or two dips, in the waves arrive at the screen together and reinforce each other. And dark bands form where a peak from one slit arrives with a dip from the other and the two cancel each other out. The pattern observed where two slits are open differs from that where only one slit is open. The result defies common sense. But that is a human perception problem: The universe simply is the way it is.

GOD'S DICE

PERFORM AN EXPERIMENT WITH SUBATOMIC PARTICLES AND QUANTUM THEORY SAYS THAT WE CANNOT BE SURE WHAT THE OUTCOME WILL BE. INSTEAD, THE THEORY GIVES PROBABILITIES FOR EVERY POSSIBLE OUTCOME. ALBERT EINSTEIN (1879–1955)—THE CREATOR OF RELATIVITY THEORY—COULD NEVER ACCEPT THIS DISTRESSINGLY RANDOM ELEMENT OF THE QUANTUM WORLD. EINSTEIN (ABOVE) FAMOUSLY ASSERTED THAT GOD "DOES NOT PLAY DICE."

SPECIAL RELATIVITY

Travel in a spaceship at close to the speed of light, and strange things begin to happen. As observed from Earth, your watch would run slow. Your body—and your ship—would become more massive. You would appear to shrink in the direction you were moving in. Yet you would not notice any difference—although when you looked back at your friends on Earth, you would see just the same things happening to them. That's according to Albert Einstein's 1905 theory of special relativity—and experiments that have been carried out since have shown that the theory is solid.

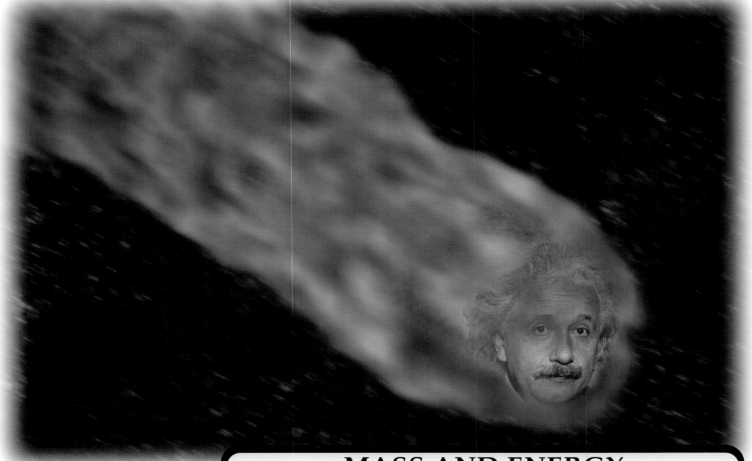

MASS AND ENERGY

SPECIAL RELATIVITY GAVE RISE TO WHAT HAS SINCE BECOME THE MOST FAMOUS EQUATION IN PHYSICS: $E=mc^2$

WHAT DO THE TERMS MEAN?

E	ENERGY IN POUNDS FEET^2 PER SECOND^2
M	MASS IN POUNDS
C	THE SPEED OF LIGHT IN FEET PER SECOND

THE EQUATION STATES THAT MASS AND ENERGY ARE EQUIVALENT. IF YOU COULD TURN THE MASS OF AN OBJECT INSTANTANEOUSLY INTO ENERGY, $E=mc^2$ GIVES THE AMOUNT OF ENERGY THAT WOULD BE RELEASED. THE EQUATION FORMS THE BASIS FOR NUCLEAR POWER AND NUCLEAR BOMBS. WHEN ATOMS FISSION OR FUSE, THE END PRODUCTS WEIGH SLIGHTLY LESS THAN THE ORIGINAL INGREDIENTS. THE MISSING MATERIAL IS CONVERTED INTO ENERGY, AND ONLY A LITTLE LOST MASS YIELDS A HUGE AMOUNT. THE BOMB THAT DESTROYED HIROSHIMA ANNIHILATED JUST 1/20 OF AN OUNCE (1.4 G) OF URANIUM.

LIMITED BY LIGHT

When Einstein (1879–1955) first published his special theory of telativity in 1905, the 20th century's most famous physicist was only a "Technical Expert, Third Class" in the Swiss patent office. But his work brought about a scientific revolution.

Special relativity is built on two fundamental principles. The first is that the laws of physics are the same for all observers, regardless of their location or velocity: Everything is relative. Before Einstein, most scientists still accepted the idea of Sir Isaac Newton (1642–1727) that motion took place against a fixed background of absolute space and time. The second principle of special relativity stipulated an entirely different absolute. Space and time are entirely relative. But speed of light is constant, regardless of an observer's viewpoint—or, as Einstein put it, the inertial frame of reference of the observer.

This absolute constancy has some very peculiar consequences. For example, an observer—Jack—on Earth sees the light from a distant star arrive at light-speed (186,000 miles per second (300,000 km/s), usually written as *c*).

Another observer—Jill—is aboard a spaceship, heading toward the star at half the speed of light. According to the old Newtonian ideas, the starlight should reach the ship at a relative speed that added *c* to the ship's own velocity—a total of 1.5 times *c*. But according to Einstein, light will reach both Jack and Jill at just *c*.

In order for *c* to be the same for Jack and Jill, space and time for one must be very different for the other. In fact, Einstein's theory showed that as Jill's speed approaches *c*, Jack will see three odd things happening to his colleague. She—and her ship—would shrink along the direction of travel. Jill's clocks would run slow compared to Jack's, an effect known as time dilation. And as her starship accelerated closer to light-speed, it would become steadily more massive. Since heavy objects are harder to accelerate than lighter ones, the faster the starship moved, the harder it would be to make it go faster still. At light speed itself, its mass would be infinite, and so would the energy required to move the ship. So nothing can go faster than light.

The extraordinary predictions of special relativity have been verified in experiments. Particle accelerators routinely collide fundamental particles of matter at very high speed in order to investigate the properties of the subatomic world. The different types of particle that fly out from these collisions each have a characteristic decay time, after which they break up into other, smaller particles. In accelerators, where particles often move at close to light-speed, decay times are longer than when the particles are stationary. The difference is exactly predicted by the time dilation effect in special relativity.

The same particle accelerators have shown that mass also increases as it moves towards light-speed, as predicted by Einstein. These huge machines can boost atomic fragments up to around 99 percent of light-speed. When the particles strike a target at such colossal velocities, the impact energies that are released are huge, just as Einstein said they would be. For all its strangeness, special relativity is one of the best-tested and most solidly confirmed theories in modern science.

ETHER EATER

THE LAWS OF SPECIAL RELATIVITY ASSUME THAT THE SPEED OF LIGHT IS CONSTANT, WHEREVER IT IS MEASURED FROM. SOME 19TH-CENTURY SCIENTISTS BELIEVED THAT LIGHT PROPAGATED THROUGH A MEDIUM KNOWN AS THE ETHER. IN THE 1880S, U.S. PHYSICISTS ALBERT MICHELSON (RIGHT) AND EDWARD MORLEY PERFORMED EXPERIMENTS TO TEST THE THEORY. THEY MEASURED LIGHT-SPEED IN TWO DIRECTIONS, AT RIGHT ANGLES TO EACH OTHER. IF THE ETHER EXISTED, THE SPEEDS SHOULD HAVE BEEN DIFFERENT — BECAUSE OF EARTH'S MOTION THROUGH THE ETHER. THE RESULTS WERE NEGATIVE: NO ETHER.

FOURTH DIMENSION

SPACE HAS THREE DIMENSIONS: UP-DOWN, LEFT-RIGHT AND FORWARD-BACKWARD. BUT THE RULES OF SPECIAL RELATIVITY CAN BE VISUALIZED BY INCLUDING TIME AS THE ADDITIONAL FOURTH DIMENSION OF SOMETHING CALLED SPACE-TIME. THE IDEA WAS FIRST SUGGESTED IN 1907 BY THE GERMAN MATHEMATICIAN HERMANN MINKOWSKI (1864–1909). MINKOWSKI (ABOVE) PROPOSED 4-DIMENSIONAL SPACE IN WHICH THREE COORDINATES SPECIFY THE POSITION OF A POINT IN SPACE AND A FOURTH MARKS THE TIME AT WHICH AN EVENT OCCURRED AT THAT POINT. SPACE-TIME FORMED THE BASIS FOR EINSTEIN'S 1915 GENERAL THEORY OF RELATIVITY.

SPEED FREAKS

WEIGHT WATCHER
The increase in the ship's mass starts very slowly and only becomes significant once it has reached a large fraction of light speed.

CLOCKED
On board the ship, an astronaut would notice nothing unusual about the passing of time. As seen from the outside universe, though, the hands of her watch would creep around more and more slowly.

As a spaceship begins to approach the speed of light, time on board slows down due to time dilation and the ship becomes more massive, shrinking along the direction of travel. If the spaceship could reach light-speed, time would stop dead and the ship would be infinitely heavy.

BIG SQUEEZE
Seen from outside, the spaceship gradually contracts along its axis of travel. As seen from aboard ship, though, it seems that the outside universe is doing the shrinking.

GENERAL RELATIVITY

Albert Einstein's general theory of relativity set out to show that the laws of physics applied everywhere in the universe. Nothing was absolute and everything was relative: The laws must hold regardless of observers' whereabouts, and whatever their speed or acceleration may be.

At the theory's heart was the idea that mass—whether in the form of a star, a planet or a miniscule pebble—was actually able to warp the very fabric of space-time. Space had contours, like a hilly landscape, and objects moved in such a way as to follow the easiest path across the universe.

STEPS TO ENLIGHTENMENT

1905	EINSTEIN PUBLISHES HIS SPECIAL THEORY OF RELATIVITY WHILE WORKING AS A "TECHNICAL OFFICER, THIRD CLASS" IN THE PATENT OFFICE IN BERNE, SWITZERLAND
1907	EINSTEIN, NOW A TECHNICAL OFFICER, SECOND CLASS, STARTS THINKING ABOUT GRAVITATION
1908–12	STILL PUZZLING OVER GRAVITATION, EINSTEIN BECOMES FIRST AN ASSOCIATE PROFESSOR AT ZURICH UNIVERSITY AND THEN A FULL PROFESSOR AT PRAGUE UNIVERSITY
1912	STRUGGLES TO LEARN THE DIFFERENTIAL GEOMETRY NEEDED TO EXPLAIN CURVED SPACE-TIME
1914–15	BECOMES PROFESSOR AT BERLIN UNIVERSITY; SHOWS HIS NEW THEORY TO COLLEAGUES — BUT THE MATH IS WRONG
1915	PUBLISHES GENERAL THEORY OF RELATIVITY

WARPED THINKING

When Albert Einstein published his special theory of relativity in 1905, he knew that much was missing. Special relativity dealt with the curious ways in which apparent constants such as length and time are altered at velocities near light-speed. But it had nothing to say about what happened when things accelerated, and it avoided the problem of gravitational fields. By 1915, after a few brilliant insights and 10 years of hard work, Einstein was ready to present general relativity.

GR, as it became known, concentrates on objects that are accelerating relative to each other. And it pays particular attention to objects accelerating due to what almost everyone had previously considered the "force" of gravity.

Einstein was inspired by what he later called "the happiest thought of my life. If a person falls freely, he will not feel his own weight." The key idea was that space and time—already linked by the special theory—were not flat. Instead, the entire continuum was curved, warped by the presence of matter. Einstein realized that this curvature was the cause of the phenomenon called gravity. Newton had explained gravity as the result of an attractive force between objects. His equations worked almost perfectly, but he was always careful to point out that he had no idea what this strange force that acted at a distance actually was. The general theory of relativity solved the problem. There was no force. Instead, objects simply followed the shortest path available to them through curved space-time.

GRAVITY THROWS A CURVEBALL

On a flat surface, the shortest possible path—known as a geodesic—is a straight line. On a spherical surface such as the Earth, a geodesic is always an arc of a circle. But in the complex curvature of space-time, a body following a geodesic might well trace out an ellipse, or a hyperbola, or any of the paths described by Newton's gravitational theory. There is no such thing as gravity: Instead, as American physicist John Wheeler later summarized, "Space tells matter how to move and matter tells space how to curve."

In fact, once Einstein had mastered the tricky mathematics necessary to describe his 4-dimensional curves, it became clear that relativity gave precisely the same solutions as Newton's 17th-century equations—except in extreme circumstances.

Those circumstances included extremes of mass, where space-time curvature became acute and Newton's equations broke down. Just such an extreme was responsible, so a jubilant Einstein realized, for observed discrepancies in the orbit of Mercury. Astronomers had long noted that the little planet's closest approach to the Sun varied from orbit to orbit—a movement inexplicable by classical gravitational theory. But the extra curvature of space near the Sun, predicted by relativity, is just enough to twist the orbit by the observed distance.

A few years later, Einstein went on to apply the field equations of general relativity to cosmology. To his dismay, the equations predicted a dynamic universe that must expand or contract, not the static universe that the science of the time took for granted. So Einstein introduced what he called a "cosmological term" to force his equations to yield a static result. "It was the biggest blunder of my life," he later recalled. Soon after this, astronomers discovered that the universe really was expanding. Relativity was right all along.

WHAT FORCE OF GRAVITY?

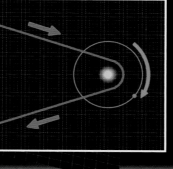

CURVED SPACE
The general theory of relativity explained gravity in terms of curved space-time. Objects simply moved in the "easiest" way through space warped by the mass of other objects. In this illustration, a planet orbits a star and a comet passes by on a hyperbolic course—neither of them due to the "force" of gravity, but to the distortions in space caused by the star's mass.

REWARDED

RELATIVITY THEORY WAS CONTROVERSIAL. ITS ELEGANCE APPEALED TO MANY SCIENTISTS — BUT OTHERS FOUND SOME OF ITS CONCEPTS HARD TO SWALLOW. SO WHEN EINSTEIN RECEIVED THE NOBEL PRIZE IN 1921, HE AND MANY OTHERS WERE A LITTLE SURPRISED: THE NOBEL COMMITTEE HAS ALWAYS DISLIKED CONTROVERSY. BUT THE TELEGRAM FROM SWEDEN WAS AT PAINS TO POINT OUT THAT THE AWARD HAD NOTHING TO DO WITH RELATIVITY. INSTEAD, EINSTEIN'S LAUREATE WAS FOR HIS WORK ON THE PHOTOELECTRIC EFFECT.

FLAT SPACE
In the old, Newtonian system, a force keeps the planet in its orbit, like a toy whirled on a string. The same force of gravity grasps a fast-moving comet and hurls it outward. For most purposes, including NASA's space probes, Newton's gravity equations are perfectly adequate — in a sense, the "flat space" picture is the same as Einstein's, with a dimension missing. But Einstein's equations can handle situations where Newton's simply do not work.

HARD EVIDENCE

PRINCIPLE OF EQUIVALENCE
Einstein thought himself into general relativity by way of what he later called the equivalence principle: the idea that the effects of gravity and of acceleration were identical. A passenger in a windowless elevator could not tell whether she was at rest on the surface of the Earth — or being accelerated through an infinitely long elevator shaft at a rate that matched the Earth's surface gravity, 32 ft (9.8 m) per second per second. For the next part of his thought experiment, Einstein put a window in the accelerating elevator and shone a beam of light through it. By the time the beam crossed the elevator, acceleration would have moved the far wall: The beam would hit it slightly lower than the level of the window — it would have been "bent" slightly downward. The equivalence principle convinced Einstein that gravity, too, would bend light. It only remained to find the experimental evidence that would prove it — and that would soon come.

GRAVITY AND THE UNIVERSE

Gravitational attraction is one of the fundamental properties of matter. It is the invisible glue that binds the universe together. The effects of gravity on Earth are felt by us all. But it took the genius of the 17th-century English mathematician Sir Isaac Newton to realize that the force that makes objects fall to the ground is the same force that raises tides in the oceans, holds the Moon in orbit around the Earth and propels the planets on their endless journey around the Sun.

NEWTON'S LAW OF GRAVITATION

$$F = G \times M_1 \times M_2 / D_2$$

"THE FORCE OF GRAVITY BETWEEN TWO OBJECTS (F) IS PROPORTIONAL TO THEIR MASSES (M1, M2) AND IS INVERSELY PROPORTIONAL TO THE SQUARE OF THE DISTANCE (D) BETWEEN THEIR CENTERS."

THE CAPITAL LETTER "G" STANDS FOR NEWTON'S GRAVITATIONAL CONSTANT — THE AMOUNT BY WHICH GRAVITY ACCELERATES THINGS ANYWHERE IN THE UNIVERSE. ITS VALUE IS STILL IN DISPUTE, BUT IS GENERALLY QUOTED (IN METRIC UNITS) AS 6.67×10^{-11} NEWTON METERS^2 PER KG^2.

NOTE "G" IS OFTEN CONFUSED WITH "g," WHICH STANDS FOR THE GRAVITATIONAL ACCELERATION ON THE SURFACE OF THE EARTH. USING NEWTON'S LAW, g = G x EARTH'S MASS / (EARTH'S RADIUS)^2. THIS WORKS OUT TO ROUGHLY 32 FT (9.8 M) PER SECOND PER SECOND.

THE FORCE

When Newton published his theory of gravity in 1687, he showed that every object in the universe exerts a gravitational force whose strength is directly related to its mass—the amount of matter in it. He concluded that gravity acts in the same way in every part of the universe. Thus, the same force that makes an apple fall to the ground also pulls on the Moon and the planets, and unites the Earth and the heavens.

Newton deduced that the gravitational pull of an object is weakened by distance. He supported this by observing the relationship between the speed at which planets orbit the Sun and their distance from it. Although Newton was able to use his simple laws to predict the movement of the planets, it took another genius—Albert Einstein—to refine these laws into the more complex theory of "relative" gravity that is generally accepted today. Even so, Newton's "classical" law of gravitation still successfully explains most of the large-scale structure of the universe.

We now know that the universe contains four fundamental forces: The strong and the weak nuclear forces that operate inside atoms; the electromagnetic force that gives matter structure; and gravity. Scientists think that at the moment of the Big Bang there was only one force (the "Unified Field"), but that gravity separated from the other three when the universe was only 10^{-43} seconds old.

Although gravity is the weakest of the four forces, its influence is the most evident on a human scale. This is partly because gravity operates over vast distances, and also because most of the matter in the universe is electrically neutral—if it were not, the electromagnetic force might dominate. The fact that gravity increases as distances diminish turns out to be its chief strength. As particles of matter are drawn toward one another, their gravitational attraction increases and they accelerate. The effect of billions of particles—each with a minute gravitational pull—speeding towards one another and picking up others along the way leads to the reactions from which matter is formed. In this way, gravity has overtaken the other forces and has become the driving force of creation.

GRAVITY WARP

ALBERT EINSTEIN (1879–1955) REFINED AND DEVELOPED NEWTON'S LAWS OF GRAVITY BY PROVING THAT GRAVITY IS MORE THAN JUST A FORCE. EINSTEIN CALCULATED THAT ALL OBJECTS WITH MASS PRODUCE "WARPS" IN SPACE-TIME WHICH MAKE THEM FALL TOWARD EACH OTHER LIKE BALLS ON A RUBBER SHEET, AND THAT WE SIMPLY PERCEIVE THE EFFECTS OF GRAVITY AS A FORCE. EVEN SO, NEWTON'S LAWS STILL HOLD GOOD FOR MOST OF THE OBSERVABLE UNIVERSE.

HARD EVIDENCE

what Hubble sees · distant quasar · galaxy · light appears to come from this direction · ring of light around galaxy · distorted light path · Hubble Space Telescope

GRAVITATIONAL LENSES
Einstein's general theory of relativity showed that gravity could act on light as well as on matter, which among other things accounts for the strange phenomenon of "gravitational lenses." When a galaxy lies between us and a distant source of light, such as a quasar, the galaxy's gravity pulls the light rays from the quasar toward it. This diverts the light rays toward Earth in much the same way as a lens focuses light in a telescope, creating a number of optical illusions. Sometimes the distorted light appears as a halo around the galaxy, as in the picture (above) taken by the Hubble Space Telescope in 1994. At other times, if the light passes through the arms of a spiral galaxy, distant single stars can appear to be doubled or even quadrupled. Scientists now believe that light is distorted in the same way by the gravitational fields of unseen black holes and dark matter.

GRAVITY AND ITS EFFECTS IN THE HEAVENS

STAR FORMATION
In the clouds of dust and gas that inhabit some regions of space, gravity pulls particles together. Once a nucleus has formed at the center, more and more material is attracted, making the object increasingly massive. When the mass becomes great enough, the force of gravity pulling the object together increases the pressure and temperature at the center to the point where nuclear reactions begin and the object becomes a star.

ORBITS
The effect of gravity in the heavens can be seen most clearly in the orbits of the Moon and the planets. The Moon, for example, is pulled toward the more massive Earth by the Earth's stronger gravitational field. But because the surface of the Earth is curved, this constant downward pull is converted into orbital motion that keeps the Moon continually circling the Earth at a more or less constant distance.

BIG CRUNCH?
All matter has a gravitational pull so the fate of the universe rests on how much matter it contains. If there is enough matter, gravity will eventually pull everything back together in a "Big Crunch"—like the Big Bang in reverse. If there is not enough, the universe will keep expanding. Many now think a Big Crunch is unlikely, since the universe has too little matter and a mysterious force called "dark energy" seems to be aiding its expansion.

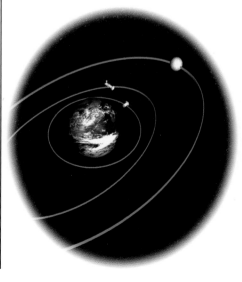

DARK MATTER

Strange as it may seem, the billions of stars burning in galaxies throughout the universe account for only a fraction of its total matter. Although some objects, such as planets, are visible thanks to the light that they reflect from nearby stars, unseen material lurks everywhere—and in some places, may have enough gravitational force to bind entire clusters of galaxies together. Is this so-called "dark matter" just the remnants of stars that failed to light up? Or is there something more mysterious out there?

THE MOUNTING DARKNESS

THE AMOUNT OF DARK MATTER IN THE UNIVERSE IS OFTEN EXPRESSED AS A "MASS-TO-LIGHT RATIO." THIS RELATES THE AMOUNT OF LIGHT EMITTED BY OBJECTS TO THE AMOUNT OF MASS INDICATED BY THE GRAVITATIONAL EFFECTS ON NEARBY BODIES. HIGHER RATIOS MEAN THE GREATER DARK MATTER.

REGION	MASS-TO-LIGHT RATIO	REGION	MASS-TO-LIGHT RATIO
SUN	1	WHOLE OF A SPIRAL GALAXY	50
SOLAR NEIGHBORHOOD	2	PAIR OF GALAXIES	100
BRIGHT PART OF A SPIRAL GALAXY	10	CLUSTER OF GALAXIES	300
WHOLE OF A SPIRAL GALAXY	50		

DARK MATTERS

Not all the matter in the universe shines like the Sun. In our own galaxy, we can see dark clouds of dust and gas because of the light that they reflect from nearby stars. Other "warm" objects are detectable because of the infrared radiation they emit. But there is other matter in the universe—including, perhaps, 90 percent of our own galaxy, the Milky Way—that gives off no light at all and which has never been identified.

Such "dark matter" can only be detected by the effect of its gravitational pull on other objects. Astronomers have found evidence of this throughout the universe, and the further they search, the more they seem to find.

The mass of a spiral galaxy like the Milky Way can be measured by studying the movements of stars within it. Using this method, astronomers have calculated that the mass of the galaxy is between five and 10 times the mass of the visible stars, gas and dust. Moreover, most of this dark matter seems to exist outside the visible limits of the Milky Way in a surrounding dark halo.

Farther out in the universe, where galaxies gather in clusters, the problem is even worse. The mass of clusters is measured from the motions of the galaxies within it. Such calculations have shown that the total mass of any cluster is around 300 times the mass of its visible galaxies.

What could the dark matter be? One possibility is that the matter in the halos that surround galaxies is made up of mini-stars called brown dwarfs that are too small to shine by nuclear fusion. Another theory proposes that the dark halo is made up of a dense collection of black holes. Even so, it is unlikely that these so-called Massive Compact Halo Objects (or MACHOs for short) can account for all the unseen matter detected in distant galaxy clusters.

"OTHER" MATTER

According to the Big Bang theory, there is too little ordinary matter in the universe to explain the dark-matter effect in galaxy clusters. One theory is that there is "other" matter, consisting of subatomic particles, as yet undetected, created at the instant of the Big Bang. These Weakly Interactive Massive Particles (WIMPs) could pass through all our present detectors, and only make their presence felt through the effects of their gravity on visible matter. Whatever is out there, it is now clear that it makes up most of the universe—and that the visible galaxies are no more than drops in the vast, dark ocean of the cosmos.

WHAT IF?
...WE COULD FIND DARK MATTER?

Searches for dark matter take two directions: some concentrate on dense dark objects such as black holes, while others look for new forms of matter that are undetectable with current methods. Astronomers have confirmed that there are at least some massive objects in the halo of our galaxy. Particle detectors, meanwhile, have shown that neutrino particles, which were once thought to be massless, could contribute up to 10 percent of the "missing mass". But most of the dark matter remains obstinately hidden, although telescopic technology could one day change this.

HARD EVIDENCE

HOT GAS

ASTRONOMERS USING X-RAY TELESCOPES HAVE BEEN DISCOVERING SOME OF THE UNSEEN DARK MATTER IN THE UNIVERSE, MUCH OF IT IN THE FORM OF HOT GAS THAT IS INVISIBLE IN ORDINARY LIGHT. SUPERIMPOSED ON A NORMAL PHOTOGRAPH (RIGHT), AN X-RAY IMAGE OF THE NGC 2300 CLUSTER SHOWS A HUGE GAS CLOUD (SHOWN IN PURPLE, AND MOST LIKELY TO BE A FORM OF HYDROGEN) THAT WOULD BE INVISIBLE TO AN OPTICAL TELESCOPE. THIS PREVIOUSLY HIDDEN GAS COULD HAVE TWICE THE MASS OF THE VISIBLE CLUSTER, BUT THE DARK MATTER MYSTERY IS FAR FROM SOLVED. THOUGH MANY CLUSTERS CONTAIN SIMILAR CLOUDS, THERE IS STILL NOT ENOUGH OF THEM TO ACCOUNT FOR ALL OF THE "MISSING" MATTER.

ASTRAL CLUE

IN THE 1970s, THE U.S. ASTRONOMER VERA RUBIN MEASURED THE SPEEDS OF STARS IN THE NEARBY ANDROMEDA GALAXY. SHE FOUND THAT THESE STARS ALL MOVE IN UNISON, AS THOUGH THEY WERE ON A WHEEL. FROM THIS RUBIN CONCLUDED THAT THE GRAVITATIONAL PULL OF SOME UNSEEN MATTER MUST BE KEEPING THE STARS AT THE EDGE FROM FLYING OFF. RUBIN AND HER COLLEAGUE, KENT FORD, HAVE SINCE MEASURED HUNDREDS OF GALAXIES AND THE ANSWER IS ALWAYS THE SAME — GALAXIES CONTAIN FAR MORE MATTER THAN WE CAN SEE.

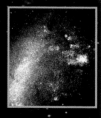

THE TRUTH IS OUT THERE

WIMPS
Some dark matter may consist of WIMPs (Weakly Interacting Massive Particles)—a theoretical group of subatomic particles whose reluctance to interact with other matter would make them extremely hard to detect. So far, WIMPs have proved elusive, but scientists such as French physicist Bernard Sadoulet (left) are continuing their search.

BLACK HOLES
It is possible that the universe is littered with many small black holes. If such bodies were distributed around our own galaxy, each with a mass no more than that of the Earth, they would be virtually undetectable. So far, the only black holes that have been identified are giant ones, as massive as stars—or even billions of stars (left). A black hole is thought to lie at the center of the Milky Way.

MACHOS
Anything in a galaxy that is composed of ordinary matter but does not emit light is referred to as a MACHO—a Massive Compact Halo Object. Such objects include black holes and brown dwarfs, as well as stray planets and the burnt-out shells of stars.

BROWN DWARFS
Stars that never grow massive enough to generate nuclear-fusion reactions at their core are known as brown dwarfs. With a mass of up to one-tenth that of the Sun, brown dwarfs are not strictly "dark;" they are warm enough to emit a detectable infrared glow. There is a chance that they could account for some of the "missing" matter, but as yet very few have been found.

EXPANDING UNIVERSE

The 1920s were an exciting time for astronomers. They had only just discovered that the universe was much larger than the Milky Way, with distant galaxies scattered as far as their telescopes could reach, but observations revealed that those far-off star cities were all moving away from the Earth. And the farther off they seemed to be, the faster they were moving. The universe was expanding like a balloon. But just how fast it was expanding would prove a difficult question to answer.

THE AGE OF THE UNIVERSE

	Hubble Constant[1]	Estimated Age of the Universe[2]
Hubble's original estimate	500	1.3–1.8 billion years (at less than the age of the Earth, this result is impossible)
Most recent measurement	70	9–13 billion years
Lowest recent measurement	50	13–18 billion years

[1] Hubble noticed that distant galaxies travel faster than nearer ones. The Hubble constant is a measure of speed in kilometers per second, over distance from the Earth in megaparsecs. One parsec is about 3.26 light-years. A megaparsec is a million parsecs.

[2] The range in age depends on the amount of mass in the universe. Only a fraction of that mass is visible or otherwise detectable — at least with present-day observational equipment.

LIGHTS ON THE SKY'S HORIZON

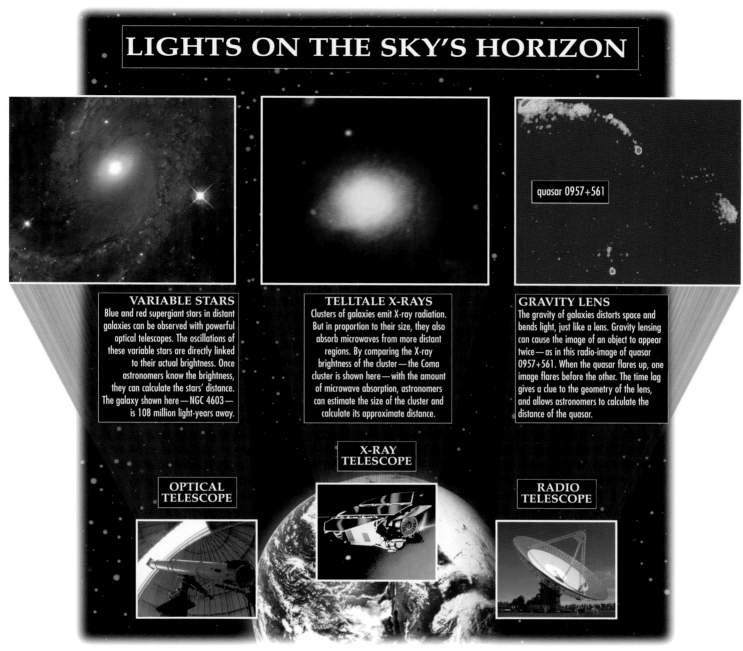

VARIABLE STARS
Blue and red supergiant stars in distant galaxies can be observed with powerful optical telescopes. The oscillations of these variable stars are directly linked to their actual brightness. Once astronomers know the brightness, they can calculate the stars' distance. The galaxy shown here—NGC 4603—is 108 million light-years away.

TELLTALE X-RAYS
Clusters of galaxies emit X-ray radiation. But in proportion to their size, they also absorb microwaves from more distant regions. By comparing the X-ray brightness of the cluster—the Coma cluster is shown here—with the amount of microwave absorption, astronomers can estimate the size of the cluster and calculate its approximate distance.

GRAVITY LENS
The gravity of galaxies distorts space and bends light, just like a lens. Gravity lensing can cause the image of an object to appear twice—as in this radio-image of quasar 0957+561. When the quasar flares up, one image flares before the other. The time lag gives a clue to the geometry of the lens, and allows astronomers to calculate the distance of the quasar.

quasar 0957+561

X-RAY TELESCOPE

OPTICAL TELESCOPE

RADIO TELESCOPE

INSIDE OUT

When American astronomer Edwin Hubble turned his telescope toward far-off galaxies beyond the Milky Way in 1929, he already knew that they were moving away from the Earth. A few years before, astronomers had measured a redshift in the light from these distant objects—the optical equivalent of the fall in pitch in the sound of a receding train. But Hubble now made an even more striking discovery.

The redshift was present in the light of almost every galaxy he could observe, but the shift was not constant. Instead, it increased with a galaxy's distance—which meant that the farther off the object, the faster it moved away.

The galaxies were not just receding from the Milky Way. They were receding from each other, too. The only possible explanation was that the universe was expanding.

But how fast was it expanding? The answer would give important clues to the age of the universe. Hubble sought to find what was later named the Hubble constant—a number that would spell out the link between a galaxy's distance and its velocity of recession.

IN THE DISTANCE

Then velocity was easy to measure: The redshift amounted to a galactic speedometer. But it was much harder to determine the distance of a far-off galaxy. Hubble's original discovery was based on his analysis of the universe's most convenient "standard candle": the light given out over a cycle of the variable stars known as Cepheids.

The rate at which a Cepheid pulses is directly related to the star's real brightness. So by timing the variation of a Cepheid anywhere in the universe, the star's brightness can be calculated, making it easy to estimate its distance from Earth.

The Cepheid method worked with the nearby galaxies that Hubble selected. But even then problems emerged. Dust clouds obscured Cepheid starlight and gave incorrect readings. And most galaxies are so distant that individual stars cannot be picked out. Hubble's first estimate was wildly wrong.

In the units used by today's astronomers, his calculations came to 310 miles (500 km) per second per megaparsec. Since a parsec is a distance of 3.26 light-years, that is equivalent to a recession speed of around 100 miles (160 km) per second for every million light-years of distance. Hubble's value put a strict limit on the size and age of the universe. If it were over 2 billion years old, galaxies would be moving faster than the speed of light—an impossibility.

Since then, astronomers have used completely different methods to find galactic distances and pin down the elusive constant. They have tracked far-distant supernova explosions, measured X-ray phenomena and calculated the link between a galaxy's spin and size.

COSMIC HISTORY

Our universe is expanding rapidly, and a huge weight of evidence points to the idea that this expansion began some 13 billion years ago, in an enormous explosion called the Big Bang. This explosion was the origin of all the matter in the universe, and the fabric of time and space itself. The Big Bang theory is the triumph of modern cosmology, and with a few tweaks (such as a required sudden rush of expansion in the first fraction of a second), it successfully explains how the modern universe could have formed from an initial massive burst of energy. It outlines the origin of the simple elements hydrogen and helium in the process called nucleosynthesis, and the beginnings of large-scale structure in the universe. Working from the present-day back, meanwhile, astronomers have recently begun to form ideas about the first generation of stars, vital to the formation of heavy elements and the universe we know today. As to the future of the universe, cosmologists are still trying to discover the ultimate fate of the cosmos—will it collapse under its own gravity, returning to a "Big Crunch?" Or will it continue to expand forever, eventually dying a cold death as all the stars go out and matter itself decays back to the most basic components?

Part of the giant elliptical galaxy NGC 1316, which is about 3,500 times wider than our solar system. This image reveals the dust lanes and star clusters of this giant galaxy — evidence of its formation in a merger of two gas-rich galaxies.

THE BIG BANG

The universe was born in an enormous explosion, called the Big Bang, about 13 billion years ago, and its fallout created not only mass and energy but also space and time. From a tiny, fantastically hot "seed," the universe swelled and cooled, resulting in forces and matter. For hundreds of thousands of years, this matter consisted of a seething mass of superheated subatomic particles, buffeted by high-energy radiation. Today's universe is cold and quiet by comparison, but at its edge astronomers can still detect the faint glow of its fiery birth—and with it, the beginning of time.

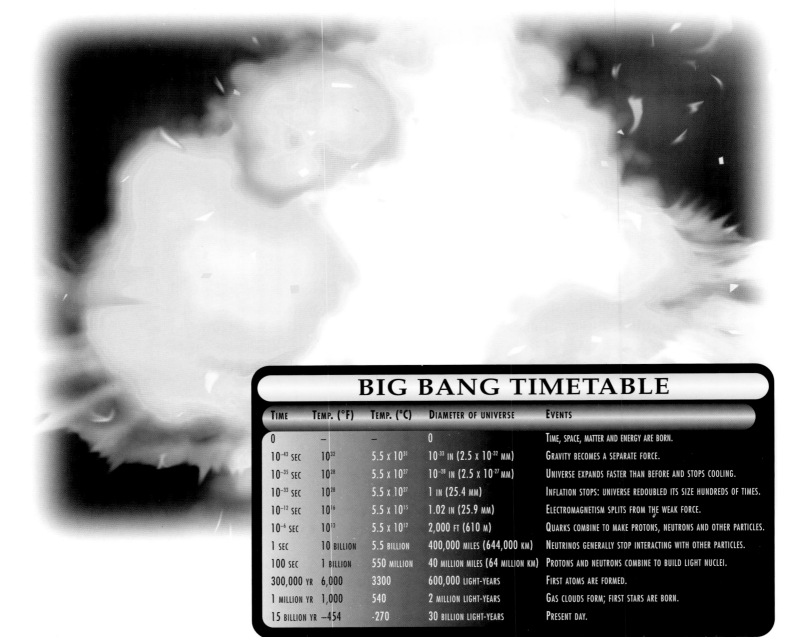

BIG BANG TIMETABLE

Time	Temp. (°F)	Temp. (°C)	Diameter of universe	Events
0	—	—	0	Time, space, matter and energy are born.
10^{-43} sec	10^{32}	5.5×10^{31}	10^{-33} in (2.5×10^{-32} mm)	Gravity becomes a separate force.
10^{-35} sec	10^{28}	5.5×10^{27}	10^{-28} in (2.5×10^{-27} mm)	Universe expands faster than before and stops cooling.
10^{-33} sec	10^{28}	5.5×10^{27}	1 in (25.4 mm)	Inflation stops: universe redoubled its size hundreds of times.
10^{-12} sec	10^{16}	5.5×10^{15}	1.02 in (25.9 mm)	Electromagnetism splits from the weak force.
10^{-6} sec	10^{13}	5.5×10^{12}	2,000 ft (610 m)	Quarks combine to make protons, neutrons and other particles.
1 sec	10 billion	5.5 billion	400,000 miles (644,000 km)	Neutrinos generally stop interacting with other particles.
100 sec	1 billion	550 million	40 million miles (64 million km)	Protons and neutrons combine to build light nuclei.
300,000 yr	6,000	3300	600,000 light-years	First atoms are formed.
1 million yr	1,000	540	2 million light-years	Gas clouds form; first stars are born.
15 billion yr	−454	-270	30 billion light-years	Present day.

TIMELINE FOR THE BIG BANG

0 SECONDS
TIME ZERO
Birth of the universe, and the appearance of space, time, matter and energy. The universe is a cauldron of high-energy, short-lived particles, and photons of radiation. There are equal amounts of matter and antimatter. Everything in the universe today was packed into a volume smaller than an atom.

10^{-35} SECONDS
INFLATION
In an instant, the universe swells to an object whose size is measured in inches. Particles and antiparticles annihilate, turning into radiation, but a tiny proportion of matter is left over — the matter we see today.

10^{-6} SECONDS
QUARKS COMBINE
Quarks are now moving too slowly to be able to stay out of each other's grasp. Some lump together in threes to form protons and neutrons, which are found in the heart of atoms today. A tiny proportion might survive singly, and may one day be found in cosmic rays.

100 SECONDS
ATOMIC NUCLEI BUILT
The temperature of the universe has fallen to a billion degrees. Neutrons and protons slow down and bind together, building up the light nuclei. These include helium (two protons and two neutrons) and deuterium (one proton, one neutron).

300,000 YEARS
FOG CLEARS
The temperature falls to that of the surface of the Sun today. The first atoms are born when electrons start to orbit protons and other nuclei. Suddenly the universe becomes transparent, as light can travel more easily through the uncharged atoms than it could through the "soup" of charged particles.

1 MILLION YEARS
BIRTH OF GALAXIES
There are slight variations in the density of the gas. At thicker points, the gas starts to form lumps that are pulled together by their own gravitational attraction. These clouds, or "protogalaxies," will develop into galaxies. Already the very first stars have formed and begun to shine.

13 BILLION YEARS
UNIVERSE TODAY
The universe has thinned out to the point where, on average, there is only one atom in every 10 cubic ft (0.3 m³). But nearly all this matter is gathered together into the galaxies in the form of stars, patches of interstellar gas and dust, and planets. The galaxies are gathered into clusters tens of millions of light years across, and the clusters are still rushing apart from each other. Away from the warmth of the stars, the universe is cold — just a few degrees above absolute zero.

IN THE BEGINNING

Scientists cannot explain with any certainty why the Big Bang happened, so it is pointless to speculate about what came "before" it. Time—along with space, matter and energy—was created in the Big Bang, so there was no "before." Similarly, scientists cannot tell what happened during the very first moments of creation. At that point the temperatures and pressures were so high that the laws of physics as we know them did not apply. But we do know for certain that as things expand, they also cool. So as the universe expanded outward from the initial explosion, the temperature and pressure began to drop.

We can start to piece together the story of the universe from a mere 10^{-43} seconds after the beginning. Around this time, the universe divided into energy and matter. For a while, energy turned into matter, and matter back into energy in a seething turmoil of collision and annihilation. But as the universe expanded and the temperature fell, the type of matter in it changed. Scientists believe that at first there were many types of matter particles, but that these were short-lived and soon disappeared. It also seems that in the immediate aftermath of the Big Bang, there was only one kind of force acting between particles.

THE FOUR FORCES

Within just a millionth of a second, the single force "broke up" into the four fundamental forces we know today: Gravitation, which holds galaxies, stars and planets together; electromagnetism, which binds atoms together; the strong nuclear force, which holds the nuclei of atoms together; and the weak nuclear force, which is involved in the process of radioactivity.

WHAT'S IN A NAME

IN THE 1950S, BRITISH ASTRONOMER SIR FRED HOYLE CLAIMED THAT THE UNIVERSE HAS ALWAYS EXISTED AND WOULD EXIST MUCH THE SAME AS IT IS TODAY. TO RIDICULE THE IDEA THAT IT HAD BEEN CREATED IN A CATASTROPHIC EXPLOSION, HE CALLED IT THE "BIG BANG" THEORY. ALTHOUGH HE WAS BEING SARCASTIC, THE NAME STUCK.

The particles we know as quarks—thought to be the basic building blocks of all the matter in the universe today—originally existed singly. Then, after a millionth of a second, they joined together to make protons, neutrons and the other particles found in atoms.

After about 100 seconds, some protons and neutrons were moving slowly enough to join together and build up the first atomic nuclei. But it was not for about another 300,000 years, when the universe had cooled to the temperature of white heat, that electrons fell into place, orbiting the nuclei and forming the first atoms. It was still so hot that only the lightest atoms—hydrogen, helium and lithium—could form. This hot gas of light elements expanded, thinned and cooled, and as it did so, the stars, galaxies and planets condensed out of it. The universe is still cooling. From an unimaginably high level to start with, the temperature in space is now down to –454°F (-270°C). Outlook: It's getting colder out there!

WHAT IF?
...EVERYTHING COLLAPSES BACK INTO A BIG CRUNCH?

Scientists studying the Big Bang would love to answer one question: Was it so powerful that the universe will keep expanding forever? Or is the gravitational pull of all the matter in the universe strong enough to slow down the expansion? If it is, then everything will start falling back in on itself again and the universe will end in a "Big Crunch." But to know how strong the gravitational pull is, we need to know how much matter there is in the universe.

Scientists suspect that there is at least 10 times as much matter as we can see. They believe the universe is full of "dark matter," undiscovered particles such as WIMPs (Weakly Interacting Massive Particles) that are almost impossible to detect. The search is on to find such particles, and evidence for their existence may lie in cosmic rays.

So far, about 10 percent of the predicted dark matter believed to exist has been found—it turned up when particle physicists proved that the extremely widespread neutrinos, once thought to be massless, had a tiny mass after all. Another important factor in predicting the fate of the universe is its current size—how far does it stretch beyond the limits of our observable universe? This will determine how widely matter is scattered in the universe. However, there is yet another wildcard in the equations—the recently discovered and still mysterious "dark energy" force that seems to be driving the universe apart with increasing speed. If dark energy is as strong as astronomers currently think, it could prevent a "Big Crunch" from ever becoming reality.

EARLY UNIVERSE

After the Big Bang, the universe was an astonishingly hot ball of gamma photons, interacting to produce short-lived particles that destroyed themselves in bursts of radiation. But within minutes, the universe had cooled enough for regular matter to form.

After 300,000 years, atoms had generated themselves from the primal debris. The radiation that marked the birth of the universe began to spread through the newly empty space. Gravity pulled matter into clumps—and the stars began to shine.

UNIVERSAL BEGINNINGS

10^{-43} SECONDS	BIG BANG (10^{-43} SECONDS REPRESENTS THE QUANTUM UNIT OF TIME—NO BRIEFER INSTANTS ARE POSSIBLE)
10^{-37} SECONDS	THE UNIVERSE GOES THROUGH A RAPID INFLATION PERIOD
10^{-34} SECONDS	TINY FLUCTUATIONS IN THE INFLATING UNIVERSE CREATE THE SEEDS OF FUTURE GALAXIES AND GALAXY CLUSTERS
10^{-32} SECONDS	RAPID INFLATION ENDS AND THE UNIVERSE BEGINS A LONG PERIOD OF SMOOTH EXPANSION
10^{-5} SECONDS	FREE QUARKS FORM PROTONS AND NEUTRONS
100 SECONDS	THE LIGHT ELEMENTS HYDROGEN, HELIUM AND LITHIUM BEGIN TO FORM
300,000 YEARS	ELECTRONS AND PROTONS COMBINE TO FORM COMPLETE HYDROGEN ATOMS; UNIVERSE BECOMES TRANSPARENT
1 MILLION YEARS	FIRST STARS ARE POSSIBLE
600 MILLION YEARS	FIRST GALAXIES FORM

COSMIC OATMEAL

Twelve billion years ago, the newborn universe was a place of ferocious temperatures and high-energy gamma photons—a hot soup that boiled with activity. Colliding gamma photons, obeying the laws of quantum physics, generated matter in paired particles. It was far too hot for protons and neutrons. Instead, the universe seethed with fundamental particles known as quarks. For every quark of regular matter, an anti-matter particle—an anti-quark—was generated to match. But at the colossal temperatures and densities of the early universe, the quarks and anti-quarks almost instantly collided again, annihilating each other in a blaze of gamma photons.

For reasons not yet completely understood, there was a mismatch in the production rate of quarks and anti-quarks—a tiny imbalance of around one part in 30 million. That minute surplus of regular quarks would go on to become the visible universe of galaxies, stars, planets and people. But about 30 microseconds after the Big Bang, the expanding universe had cooled to a point where the surviving quarks "condensed" into the protons, neutrons and electrons that make up the more familiar matter of later eras. As cooling continued, some of these particles were able to fuse together into what would become the nuclei of helium atoms. But the atom-building period was brief. In only a few minutes, the universe had cooled below the point at which nuclear fusion could occur. More complex atoms would be created later, inside stars. But before this could happen, the stars had to form. And for that to happen, the matter of the early universe had to clump together.

COOLING OFF

An important stage in the clumping occurred when matter and energy began to separate from each other. For thousands of years, the universe was an opaque soup—so hot and dense that photons and fragments of matter were constantly interacting. But around 300,000 years after the Big Bang, it had cooled enough to allow electrons to combine into the first atoms. The universe became transparent. The photons, no longer inextricably entangled with matter, were spread out through space.

Matter was expanding outward, too, but its expansion was not perfectly even. Where matter was densest, the gravitational pull was more powerful than in areas where the atoms were scattered more thinly. At first, the differentials were slight. But given time and gravity, they began to increase.

By cosmic standards, the process did not take long. Somewhere between 1 million and 10 million years after the Big Bang, the whorls and eddies of the expanding universe began to collapse under their own gravity. According to Russian physicist Yakov Zel'Dovich, chunks of matter weighing as much as entire clusters of galaxies began to collapse inwards, creating pancakes of matter that eventually contracted to form stars and galaxies. As they shrank, their core temperatures began to rise. Soon, they were hot enough to trigger nuclear fusion. The first stars were born, and with them the first galaxies.

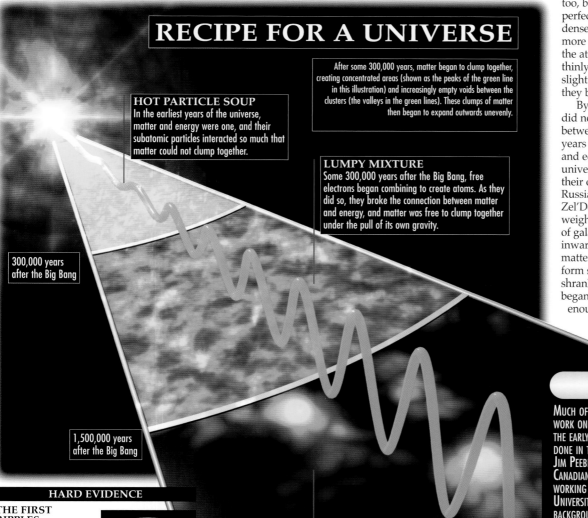

RECIPE FOR A UNIVERSE

After some 300,000 years, matter began to clump together, creating concentrated areas (shown as the peaks of the green line in this illustration) and increasingly empty voids between the clusters (the valleys in the green lines). These clumps of matter then began to expand outwards unevenly.

HOT PARTICLE SOUP
In the earliest years of the universe, matter and energy were one, and their subatomic particles interacted so much that matter could not clump together.

LUMPY MIXTURE
Some 300,000 years after the Big Bang, free electrons began combining to create atoms. As they did so, they broke the connection between matter and energy, and matter was free to clump together under the pull of its own gravity.

300,000 years after the Big Bang

1,500,000 years after the Big Bang

GALACTIC PANCAKES
Over time, the clumps of matter grew larger. Many scientists argue that today's galaxies come from clumps the size of galaxy clusters. These giant clumps collapsed into smaller clusters, which then collapsed into still smaller clusters, until they created galaxies and stars.

HARD EVIDENCE

THE FIRST RIPPLES
In 1990, NASA's COBE satellite made the first survey of cosmic background radiation across the whole sky. It confirmed what Earthbound experimenters had already discovered: that the radiation was uniform in every direction. This confirmed that the distant glow, equivalent to a temperature just 5.79°F above absolute zero, was a leftover from the origin of the universe. But COBE's detectors were able to pick up very slight variations in the background radiation—minute ripples showing that the early universe already had some kind of structure. In time, these ripples would evolve into galaxies and galaxy clusters.

SCOOPED

MUCH OF THE PIONEERING WORK ON THE STRUCTURE OF THE EARLY UNIVERSE WAS DONE IN THE 1960S BY JIM PEEBLES (RIGHT), A CANADIAN PHYSICIST WORKING AT PRINCETON UNIVERSITY. PEEBLES PREDICTED A GLOW OF BACKGROUND RADIATION CAUSED BY PHOTONS LEFT FROM THE BIG BANG, AND HAD BEGUN WORK ON APPARATUS TO DETECT THE GLOW. MEANWHILE, AT BELL LABS, SCIENTISTS ROBERT WILSON AND ARNO PENZIAS WERE PUZZLING OVER STRANGE STATIC THAT WAS INTERFERING WITH THEIR STUDIES OF RADIO TRANSMISSION. ALTHOUGH THEY DIDN'T KNOW WHAT THEY HAD FOUND UNTIL PEEBLES TOLD THEM, THEY HAD DETECTED COSMIC BACKGROUND RADIATION—AND WON THEMSELVES A NOBEL PRIZE.

INFLATION

Scientists have known for a century that the universe is expanding. Now, it is believed that for a fraction of a second, just after the Big Bang, that expansion was fantastically rapid. In this brief period of the universe's history, known as inflation, space was stretched out like the surface of a swiftly inflating tire. Inflation may have planted the cosmic seeds from which galaxies grew. And some scientists believe that inflation could preserve a record of humanity after the universe can no longer support life.

A HISTORY OF INFLATION

1927	BIG BANG MODEL OF THE UNIVERSE, TO WHICH INFLATION IS AN ADD-ON, PROPOSED BY GEORGES LEMAÎTRE
1929	ASTRONOMER EDWIN HUBBLE DISCOVERS EXPANSION OF THE UNIVERSE
1965	RUSSIAN PHYSICIST ERAST GLINER PROPOSES INFLATIONARY EPOCH IN THE VERY EARLY HISTORY OF THE UNIVERSE
1979	ALEXEI STAROBINSKY, ALSO RUSSIAN, POINTS OUT THAT RAPID EXPANSION IN THE EARLY UNIVERSE CAN ARISE WHEN QUANTUM PHYSICS IS APPLIED TO THE THEORY OF GRAVITY
1982	ALAN GUTH SHOWS HOW INFLATION THEORY SOLVES THE FLATNESS PROBLEMS OF BIG BANG COSMOLOGY
1983	ANDREI LINDE PROPOSES "CHAOTIC INFLATION," WHICH SAYS QUANTUM RANDOMNESS WOULD ALWAYS CREATE THE CONDITIONS FOR INFLATION SOMEWHERE IN THE UNIVERSE
1986	ANDREI LINDE PROPOSES THE CONCEPT OF "ETERNAL INFLATION," WHICH SAYS THAT SOME REGIONS OF THE UNIVERSE COULD STILL BE INFLATING TODAY

GROWING PAINS

The universe began a phase of rapid expansion— inflation—just one-hundred-million-billion-billion-billionth of a second after it was born. Space expanded enormously for an instant. Then inflation ended, almost as quickly as it had begun, and the universe reverted to the more sedate kind of expansion that astronomers observe today.

The best theory to describe the evolution of the universe is the Big Bang model, which was first suggested in 1927 by Belgian astrophysicist and priest Georges Lemaître (1894–1966). The theory says that around 12–15 billion years ago, the universe was born in a hot, dense fireball, that expanded, then cooled, and eventually become cool enough for galaxies, stars and planets to form.

According to the theory of relativity—proposed by Albert Einstein (1879–1955)—space can be curved, like the surface of a ball. A curved universe could either accelerate forever, or it could decelerate and collapse on itself. The Big Bang theory predicts the universe should become more curved the older it gets. But the universe appears to be "flat"—that is, its expansion is neither accelerating nor decelerating.

For the universe to seem as flat as it does today, it must have been almost perfectly flat initially. The Big Bang offers no explanation why, but inflation could provide the answer. Think of the universe as the curved surface of a ball—as the ball is inflated, its surface appears to get flatter. Flatness is just one of a problems to do with the Big Bang theory that inflation neatly resolves.

FUNDAMENTAL FORCES

In 1965, Russian physicist Erast Gliner published a theory that closely resembles inflation. In the 1970s, another Russian, Alexei Starobinsky developed an inflationary model by merging quantum physics with the theory of gravity. But because of Soviet restrictions, the Russians' went largely unnoticed in the West. Only when the idea was independently proposed by U.S. physicist Alan Guth in 1981 did inflation become well known. Shortly after Guth's announcement, a staggering consequence of the theory was realized: Inflation could explain how galaxies formed. Most explanations say that inflation happened when two fundamental forces—the strong and electroweak forces—split from the original unified force. Because of quantum theory, the behavior of subatomic particles can never be predicted exactly—there is always a random element. Some small regions of space would have been denser than their surroundings, and, although initially tiny, these regions would soon have grown very big as the universe inflated. Some regions would have become the size of galaxies, others the size of clusters of galaxies. The gravity of these large, higher-density regions would have attracted more matter, making them into denser objects still. Many astrophysicists now believe that these objects are what became the first galaxies and clusters.

SUPERNATURAL

IN 1981, U.S. PHYSICIST ALAN GUTH (RIGHT) COINED THE WORD "INFLATION" AS APPLIED TO THE EARLY UNIVERSE. GUTH IS NOW WORKING ON A VARIANT, "SUPERNATURAL INFLATION," IN WHICH RAPID EXPANSION TAKES PLACE AT LOWER ENERGIES. THIS MEANS THAT INFLATION WOULD HAVE HAPPENED MUCH LATER IN THE HISTORY OF THE UNIVERSE, WHEN THE HOT FIRES OF THE BIG BANG HAD COOLED CONSIDERABLY. SUPERNATURAL INFLATION SEEMS TO EXPLAIN THE STRUCTURE OF THE UNIVERSE NATURALLY.

HARD EVIDENCE

JUST HOT AIR?
Inflation theory seems to predict a universe that matches astronomers' observations. In 1990, the NASA Cosmic Background Explorer (COBE) satellite looked at the leftover radiation from the Big Bang, and found that its characteristics are consistent with the occurrence of inflation. In 1996, when astronomers at Cambridge University, England, used the Cambridge Anisotropy Telescope (CAT, above) to raise the accuracy of observations by a factor of 40, the microwave background was still in keeping with inflationary predictions

INFLATIONARY TIMESCALE

10^{-43} OF A SECOND AFTER THE BIG BANG (PLANCK ERA)
Russian cosmologist Andrei Linde suggests that inflation begins here as random quantum fluctuations would ensure that somewhere the conditions are always right for inflation to occur.

300,000 YEARS AFTER THE BIG BANG
The cosmic radiation background—the faint echo of the Big Bang—is released as the universe becomes transparent to radiation. Inflation produced fluctuations in the density of the universe from point to point, and these show up as tiny irregularities in the microwave background. These irregularities have now been detected by astronomers.

The universe that astronomers have been able to observe in the cosmic microwave background is consistent with inflationary theory.

10^{-35} OF A SECOND AFTER THE BIG BANG
Most theories say this is where inflation began. Rapid expansion of the universe occurred when the forces of particle physics broke away from one another and became distinct entities.

10^{-32} OF A SECOND AFTER THE BIG BANG
Inflation ends. The universe emerges from inflation as a hot firey ball.

NUCLEOSYNTHESIS

When the universe was young, only the lightest and simplest atoms existed—mainly hydrogen, with a fair proportion of helium and a sprinkling of lithium. From around 13 billion years ago to this day, all the elements from beryllium to uranium have come into existence by a process called nucleosynthesis. In the furnaces of stellar cores, a combination of colossal temperatures and pressures have fused light atoms together. And the cataclysms of the even more complex supernova explosions have forged elements that could have been assembled in no other way on Earth.

BURNING BIGGER

MAJOR STAGE	PRODUCTS	TEMP. (°F)	TEMP. (°C)	BURNING TIME (YEARS)	MIN. MASS (SOLAR MASSES)
HYDROGEN BURNING	HELIUM	36,000,000	20,000,000	7,000,000	0.1
HELIUM BURNING	CARBON, OXYGEN	360,000,000	200,000,000	500,000	1.0
CARBON BURNING	OXYGEN, NEON SODIUM, MAGNESIUM	1.5 BILLION	800,000,000	600	1.4
NEON BURNING	OXYGEN, MAGNESIUM	2.7 BILLION	1.5 BILLION	1	5
OXYGEN BURNING	MAGNESIUM TO SULFUR	3.6 BILLION	2 BILLION	6 MONTHS	10
SILICON BURNING	ELEMENTS UP TO IRON	5.4 BILLION	3 BILLION	1 DAY	20

FORGING ATOMS

When the universe began, the only element was hydrogen—the simplest and lightest of all, with just one proton at its nucleus. To make larger, more complex atomic nuclei, temperatures and pressures had to be great enough to force protons together against their naturally repulsive tendencies.

Minutes after the Big Bang, just such conditions prevailed. Some of the original hydrogen atoms were squeezed together to form helium—with two protons, and two neutrons, in its nucleus. A tiny proportion went on to further fusion reactions, and a small quantity of lithium and beryllium, the next lightest elements, were also created. By then, the expanding universe had cooled too much to allow any more nuclear fusion. The list of the elements it contained was a short one: hydrogen, helium, and a tiny proportion of slightly heavier atoms. Billions of years later, though, the universe includes every element from hydrogen— with its single proton—to uranium—with no fewer than 92 protons. Existing between two extremes, elements such as carbon, nitrogen and oxygen have made life possible. Altogether, elements heavier than helium amount to just two percent of the mass of the universe. But how did they come into being? The scientists of the mid-20th century found it easier to give a name to the process— nucleosynthesis—than to explain it. Atomic nuclei could only be forged in a furnace hot enough to match the temperature of the early universe. There was only one place where such a furnace existed: in the heart of a star.

TRIPLE-ALPHA REACTION

Most stars burn by converting hydrogen into helium in nuclear reactions. But it was hard to figure out a plausible route by which helium in turn could be fused into heavier elements. The toughest step was the jump from two-proton helium to six-proton carbon. Only in the 1950s did British astronomer Fred Hoyle, with the help of some colleagues, demonstrate the possibility of a so-called "triple-alpha" reaction that allowed three helium nuclei to form a carbon nucleus in one step.

From there on up to iron, new elements could be made in stars by the successive addition of yet more helium nuclei. At each stage of nucleosynthesis, the fusion reaction gave out energy— although as the size of the new nuclei increased, the energy surplus diminished.

Iron, though, represented a stable plateau. Further fusion required more energy than the fusion reaction itself could produce. Such element-building was impossible, even at the heart of a star—at least under normal circumstances. But when a star destroyed itself in the colossal explosion of a supernova, the rules changed. A huge flood of "spare" neutrons allowed heavier elements to be built. The energy from the explosion footed the bill for their creation. And although the star itself was destroyed in the process, those new, heavy elements were scattered throughout the universe. Thirteen billion years after the Big Bang, the universe had become a much more complex place.

BUILDING UP GRADUALLY

From the Big Bang to the present day, the universe has been building successively larger atoms through a process called nucleosynthesis. Once, there was nothing but hydrogen and helium. Now, the elements include those that make life here on Earth possible, as well as some that could make life somewhat precarious.

THE HARD WAY

DURING THE 1950s, SCIENTISTS MARGARET AND GEOFFREY BURBIDGE (RIGHT) MEASURED THE COMPOSITION OF STARS. THEY DISCOVERED THE PRESENCE OF MANY ELEMENTS HEAVIER THAN IRON. IN COLLABORATION WITH WILLY FOWLER AND FRED HOYLE, THEY REALIZED THAT THESE ELEMENTS COULD NOT BE MADE BY FUSING NUCLEI TOGETHER. INSTEAD, NEUTRONS WOULD HAVE TO BE ADDED TO AN IRON NUCLEUS ONE AT A TIME — A SLOW PROCESS THEY CALLED THE "S-PROCESS."

ELEMENT BUILDER
An expanding shell of gas marks the destruction of a star in a supernova explosion. Only massive stars erupt in this cataclysmic fashion, but the shell of debris that expands outward after the bang will include elements heavier than iron, which can only be made in such violent eruptions.

BIRTH OF
GALAXIES

Most of the matter in the universe is concentrated into vast bodies called galaxies. The one that we live in, the Milky Way, is only one among billions of others. How did these enormous bodies form? Using the Hubble Space Telescope and superfast computers, astronomers are starting to fit the puzzle together. It is now known that the first galaxies began to form 12 billion years ago. But they had to endure a dramatic and violent history before they became the galaxies that we see today.

GALAXY COUNTDOWN

TIME AFTER BIG BANG	STATE OF THE GALAXIES
TIME ZERO	RAPID INFLATION OF THE INFANT UNIVERSE SOWS THE SEEDS OF GALAXY FORMATION.
500,000 YEARS	THE FLUCTUATIONS CAUSED BY RAPID INFLATION LEAVE A "COSMIC FOOTPRINT" IN THE FORM OF TEMPERATURE VARIATIONS IN THE COSMIC MICROWAVE BACKGROUND RADIATION (CMBR).
1 BILLION YEARS	GRAVITATIONAL FLUCTUATIONS CAUSE CLOUDS OF GAS TO FORM MASSIVELY ENERGETIC STRUCTURES.
3 BILLION YEARS	PARTS OF THESE STRUCTURES COLLAPSE UNDER THEIR OWN GRAVITY AND IGNITE TO FORM STARS.
4–5 BILLION YEARS	GROUPS OF STARS CLUSTER INTO PRIMEVAL GALAXIES. SOME MERGE TO FORM ELLIPTICAL GALAXIES.
13 BILLION YEARS	EONS OF COLLISIONS AND MERGERS LEAVE THE GALAXIES AS WE SEE THEM TODAY.

GALACTIC BIRTH

Astronomers still know very little about the details of galaxy formation, but they know the basics. Billions of years ago, when most of the matter in the universe consisted of clouds of hydrogen and helium gas, fluctuations in the gravitational fields of these gas clouds caused parts of them to collapse into filaments. For years, the fluctuations remained purely theoretical. Then, in 1992, the Cosmic Background Explorer (COBE) satellite searched far back in time to the earliest days of the universe and found temperature variations that seemed to prove their existence. But what caused the fluctuations?

The most popular theory among astronomers is that of "Inflation." This states that in the first moments after the Big Bang, the fireball of energized matter that was to become the universe jumped in size by a factor of about 10 billion billion billion. As it did, tiny atom-sized fluctuations within it were inflated to cosmic proportions.

From that moment on, no one really knows what happened. The best theory says that the first galaxy-like structures appeared when the universe was about a billion years old, possibly as the gas filaments began to form dense "knots" of matter between 100,000 and a million times the mass of our Sun. Gradually, these knots of matter clustered together into larger structures, eventually

leading to the formation of the first disk-shaped spiral galaxies.

ELLIPTICAL GALAXIES

These larger structures eventually gave birth to other kinds of galaxies, including the so-called giant elliptical galaxies. Exactly how these egg-shaped collections of stars—which are much larger than spiral galaxies—came into being remained a mystery for many years. The probable answer came in 1996, when astronomers used the Hubble Space Telescope to study a small, distant region near the constellation of Ursa Major, called the Hubble Deep Field. The observations showed hundreds of galaxies in the process of merging with one another. Many of them had irregular shapes, which suggested that they had been disrupted by collisions or mergers with other galaxies.

Astronomers believe that the Hubble Telescope was looking in on the early stages of the formation of elliptical galaxies. It now seems likely that when two primitive spiral galaxies collide, their intricate structure is at first thrown into disarray. Then, gradually, gravity draws them closer together, and causes them to spin themselves into a single, smooth elliptical shape like clay on a potter's wheel.

WHAT IF?
...OTHER LIFE-FORMS HAVE SEEN GALAXIES BEING BORN?

Although it is fun to imagine what it would be like to stand on another world, watching the explosive formation of galaxies, the reality is less exciting. Scientists have concluded that there were no "other worlds" at the time the galaxies were formed.

In the early universe, the only elements were hydrogen and helium. It was not until later that the heavier elements needed to form rocky planets were forged in the cores of burning stars and scattered across the universe in supernova explosions.

Today we can only speculate on what the view was like. There would have been enormous areas of star formation, making the Orion Nebula look like a pinprick by comparison. The pink glow of hydrogen gas would mix with the brilliant glare of young stars. And hundreds of new stars would burst on the scene every year – with no creature alive to watch them.

GALACTIC COLLISIONS

COLLISIONS PLAY A CRUCIAL ROLE IN THE FORMATION OF GALAXIES. THE CHANCES OF ONE GALAXY COLLIDING WITH ANOTHER ARE HIGH, BECAUSE OF THEIR LARGE SIZE IN RELATION TO THE DISTANCE BETWEEN THEM. BUT WITHIN GALAXIES, INDIVIDUAL STARS TEND TO BE SPACED FAR APART. THIS MEANS THAT GALACTIC COLLISIONS ARE RELATIVELY PEACEFUL AFFAIRS— THE GALAXIES FUSE, RATHER THAN COLLIDE, AND THE STARS WITHIN THEM ARE SELDOM DESTROYED.

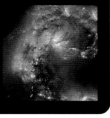

HARD EVIDENCE

NEW-BORN
The Hubble Deep Field analyzes a tiny region of the universe just a few billion years after the Big Bang. The region contains around 1,500 galaxies which, when seen from Earth, are packed into an area just one-thirtieth the diameter of a full moon. Some of these galaxies are the most distant ever seen — 4 billion times fainter than anything visible to the naked eye, and 10 times fainter than anything that can be seen through the most powerful Earth-based telescopes.

1 FILAMENTS
Soon after the Big Bang, the matter in the universe consists of dark matter and gas in long filaments. These illustrations are from a computer simulation of millions of gas and dark matter particles created for the movie Cosmic Voyage.

3 CLUSTERS
Galaxies from several filaments start to exert a gravitational pull on one another, and they begin to form clusters. At this stage, individual galaxies are still much smaller than we see them today, and have irregular shapes.

2 KNOTS
Where filaments cross, "knots" form. The mounting gravitational pressure causes stars to form within the denser parts of the knots, which become recognizable as galaxies. Between filaments, no galaxies are seen.

4 COLLISIONS
At the center of clusters, collisions take place between galaxies. As a result, some galaxies become larger and turn into the giant elliptical galaxies that will eventually dominate the cluster.

HOW GALAXIES FORM

HARD EVIDENCE

HOT SPOTS
In 1996, the Cosmic Anisotropy Telescope in Britain returned this colored temperature map of the universe just 100,000 years after the Big Bang. The blotches, each of which represents an area about the size of a full moon, represent fluctuations in the cosmic microwave background (CMB) radiation — white being hotter and black cooler. Scientists believe that these same fluctuations seeded the birth of galaxies.

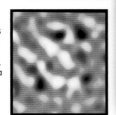

THE FIRST STARS

The early universe was a dark and empty place. Less than a million years after the Big Bang, there was nothing like the vast scattering of galaxies and galaxy clusters that now fill the sky as far as astronomers can see. Instead, there were only clouds of slowly cooling gas. Opaque to visible light, they glowed dimly with infrared radiation left over from the Big Bang. But in the swirling clouds, matter was clumping together and the first stars were forming. Massive but shortlived, they brought light back to the universe.

STARBIRTH CHRONOLOGY

TIME SINCE BIG BANG	
500,000 YEARS	GAS CLOUDS COOL TO OPACITY: DARK UNIVERSE
10–500 MILLION YEARS	FIRST STAR FORMATION: RADIATION FROM NEW STARS MAKES UNIVERSE TRANSPARENT
	FIRST SUPERNOVA EXPLOSIONS: UNIVERSE SEEDED WITH ITS FIRST HEAVY ELEMENTS
1 BILLION YEARS	MOST DISTANT KNOWN QUASARS FORM

EARLY LIGHT

Scarcely half a million years after the fireball explosion of the Big Bang, the expanding universe entered an age of darkness. As the hydrogen and helium that were its only elements cooled to around 5,000°F (2,760°C), they became opaque to light—but the darkness did not last for long.

The matter in the universe was not spread out perfectly evenly. There were swirls and eddies in the expanding cloud, and here and there these local concentrations of gas became dense enough for their own gravitational contraction to compress them still further. After a few million years, the temperature and pressure at the heart of these gas clumps reached levels that started nuclear fusion reactions. Hydrogen turned into helium, and vast quantities of energy were given off. These first stars lit up the universe, emitting enough radiation to heat the surrounding gas and turn space transparent again.

To produce so much radiation, most of these first stars must have been extremely massive—far larger than our own Sun. The more massive a star, the hotter and the faster it burns. Within only a few million years, the hydrogen fuel of these early giants had all been transformed by nuclear fusion into helium. In rapid succession, a chain of different fusion reactions created other, heavier elements. Finally, when no more nuclear reactions were possible, each of the stars died violently in the titanic blast of a supernova explosion.

ELEMENTAL LEGACY

These first giant stars died long before anyone was around to observe them. But astronomers are certain that they must have existed. And the best evidence lies in the most distant—and hence the oldest—objects that can be observed: quasars.

Some quasars are so far away that their light was emitted when the universe was only about a billion years old—less than a tenth of its current age. Massive black holes that devour matter at the heart of galaxies, they are only visible at such distances because of their immense power. But they are visible—which means that the gas surrounding them had been ionized into transparency by an earlier generation of stars.

Quasar light provides more information still about the first stars. In the course of its 10-billion-year journey to Earth, the light has passed through nine-tenths of the history of the universe, so it can tell astronomers a great deal about conditions in the distant past. Quasar light carries telltale traces of the elements that emitted or partially absorbed it along the way—and there are far more elements than the basic hydrogen and helium that came with the Big Bang.

The source of these new atoms could only have been the supernova explosions that marked the end of the first stars. In the last years of their lives, runaway fusion reactions forged hydrogen and helium into the oxygen, silicon and other elements that show up in the quasar light. The final supernova blast created heavier elements still, and scattered them widely across the raw hydrogen and helium of the interstellar medium.

The different atoms forged in these first stars would become part of each subsequent stellar generation. Given enough time, the new elements would form planets, too—and every living thing to exist anywhere in the universe.

BIRTH OF BRIGHTNESS

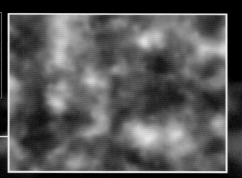

1 dark clouds
Half a million years after the Big Bang, the universe is filled with cooling gas—hydrogen and helium. Opaque to visible light, the gas glows dimly in infrared radiation left over from the Big Bang.

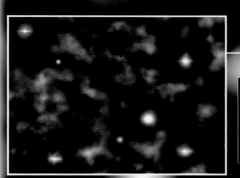

2 clumping
Some areas of the universe are denser than others. The gravitational pull of these clumps attracts yet more gas to them, and pressures and temperatures rise. The gas clumps begin to glow.

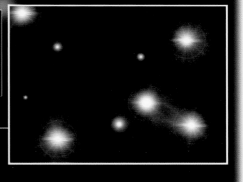

3 ignition
At the center of each gas clump, hydrogen begins to fuse into helium. Radiation from the new stars ionizes surrounding gas and turns it transparent—just as dawn mist clears in the morning sunlight.

The process of star formation possibly began only 10 million years after the Big Bang. After the stars formed, the first galaxies appeared.

COSMIC MAPPER

SCIENTISTS ARE LEARNING A GREAT DEAL MORE ABOUT THE EARLY UNIVERSE FROM THE WILKINSON MICROWAVE ANISOTROPY PROBE (WMAP) — SHOWN HERE UNDER CONSTRUCTION. LAUNCHED IN 2001, WMAP'S MISSION HAS BEEN TO CREATE A DETAILED MAP OF THE COSMIC MICROWAVE BACKGROUND RADIATION, WHICH SHOWS THE DENSITY OF THE EARLY UNIVERSE. AS A RESULT, IT HAS PUSHED BACK THE DATE OF THE EARLIEST STAR FORMATION TO JUST 200 MILLION YEARS AFTER THE BIG BANG.

DEATH OF THE UNIVERSE

All good things must come to an end—and our universe is no exception. If the universe continues to expand, the stars will gradually burn out and die, and the galaxies will fade. Matter as we know it will simply cease to exist. Giant black holes will prowl the wasteland, devouring the final traces of the universe's material. But not even black holes can last forever: They too will disappear, leaving a void. Alternatively, the universe may collapse violently back in on itself in a cataclysmic reversal of the Big Bang.

INTO THE FUTURE

YEARS AFTER BIG BANG	ERA	DESCRIPTION
1×10^{10}	STELLIFEROUS ERA	THE UNIVERSE AS IT IS TODAY, DOMINATED BY GALAXIES FULL OF STARS
1×10^{14}		THERE IS NO HYDROGEN AND HELIUM GAS LEFT IN THE UNIVERSE TO MAKE NEW STARS
1×10^{24}	DEGENERATE ERA	MOST OF THE UNIVERSE IS MADE OF DEGENERATE STELLAR CORPSES
1×10^{36}		PROTONS AND NEUTRONS DECAY; LAST REMNANTS OF NORMAL MATTER WIPED OUT
1×10^{54}	BLACK HOLE ERA	THE ONLY CONCENTRATIONS OF MASS LEFT IN THE UNIVERSE ARE BLACK HOLES
1×10^{65}		BLACK HOLES — CREATED WHEN MASSIVE STARS ENDED THEIR LIVES IN SUPERNOVA EXPLOSIONS — EVAPORATE AWAY
1×10^{100}		ALL THE BLACK HOLES IN THE UNIVERSE HAVE NOW DISAPPEARED
1×10^{110}	DARK ERA	THE UNIVERSE IS VIRTUALLY EMPTY
BEYOND	THE END	THERE IS NOTHING LEFT AT ALL

THE GAME IS UP

Eventually, the Sun will make our planet uninhabitable. The core of the Sun will have run out of hydrogen fuel, and will burn helium instead. The Sun will generate more heat and, as a result, our star will swell up to become a red giant. In 5 or 6 billion years, the temperature of the Earth will start to rise drastically. It will be the end for life on Earth, but only a step in the gradual evolution and death of the universe itself.

The path to destruction is not continuous. Our Milky Way galaxy is presently heading toward the Andromeda galaxy, at such a rate that in about 4 billion years, the two will crash together and merge into one giant galaxy. This merger of galaxies is likely to trigger a burst of fresh star formation before a new large elliptical galaxy settles down.

But no stars will endure for ever. Stars form from giant clouds of hydrogen and helium gas. As more stars are born, galactic gas reserves are eaten up and there is less material left to form subsequent generations.

In about 100,000 billion years, star formation will cease. Existing generations of stars will finish their lives and will sputter into darkness within about 10,000 billion years. The night sky seen by any observer in this far-future age would be blank and starless.

DEGENERATION GAP

Galaxies will still exist—but not as bright gatherings of stars. Instead, they will contain only black holes and other stellar corpses—white dwarfs and neutron stars—as well as objects known as brown dwarfs,which were never quite massive enough to become stars in the first place. Neutron stars and white dwarfs are made from collapsed, degenerate matter. They are prevented from collapsing under their own gravity by quantum mechanical forces, rather than the thermal pressure that supports normal stars.

This so-called degenerate era is expected to end somewhere around 10,000 trillion trillion trillion years—10^{40} in scientific notation—after the Big Bang. Gradually, the subatomic particles that make up even degenerate matter decay into radiation. The neutron stars and the dwarfs will vanish. Only black holes will remain.

But not even black holes are immortal. English physicist Stephen Hawking has shown that black holes gradually lose mass because of quantum effects. Hawking calls the process black hole evaporation, and predicts that it will eventually cause even the largest black holes to disappear, leaving empty space.

At any rate, that will be the outcome if our universe continues to expand. But although a continually expanding open universe is currently the favored theory, there is an alternative view of the universe's ultimate fate. The Big Crunch theory proposes that the universe will eventually stop expanding and fall back upon itself until it collapses into a point. Such an outcome—the precise opposite of the Big Bang—can only happen if there is enough matter in the universe for gravity to counteract expansion.

JOURNEY TO THE END OF TIME

7 Forever darkness? The ultimate fate of the universe will depend on quantum fluctuations of the vacuum itself. A so-called "phase transition" could even bring regeneration.

6 The dark era will begin 10^{100} years after the Big Bang. By then, the last black holes in the universe will have dissipated to nothing, and only a scattering of electrons and positrons, and a little radiation, will be left.

5 10^{50} years after the Big Bang, black holes still rule the universe. Slowly but surely, though, the weird effects of quantum mechanics cause their matter to evaporate.

4 The black hole era starts after about 10^{40} years, when only black holes remain. These bizarre singularities in space-time are so massive that not even light can escape them.

1 We are living in the stelliferous (star-bearing) era—some 10^{10} years after the Big Bang—when stars actively form, live and die.

2 Around 10^{14} years after the Big Bang, reserves of hydrogen and helium—the raw materials for star formation—will be exhausted. No more new stars will be able to form, and eventually the universe's last stars will burn out.

3 The degenerate era will begin about 10^{15} years after the Big Bang. Dead stars made of collapsed matter occasionally collide. Gradually, their matter decays into radiation and they vanish.

HARD EVIDENCE

OLD TIMER

Astronomers measure the motions of distant galaxies in an attempt to calculate the rate of cosmic expansion. They know how far apart the farthest galaxies are, so by working backward, they can figure how long it has been since these galaxies were on top of each other, as they would have been at the Big Bang. This calculation gives the age of the universe. The galaxy M 100 (right) is an accepted "starting point" in the calculation. Best estimates put the universe's age at 12–15 billion years.

MULTIVERSE

ENGLISH ASTROPHYSICIST MARTIN REES HAS SPECULATED THAT OUR UNIVERSE MAY BE ONLY ONE OF A FAMILY — OR EVEN AN INFINITY — OF UNIQUE UNIVERSES. IN REES' "MULTIVERSE" CONCEPT, EACH UNIVERSE HAS ITS OWN TIMESCALE. SO EVEN WHEN ONE UNIVERSE DIES, OTHERS MAY STILL BE IN EXISTENCE. AND OTHER UNIVERSES MAY COME INTO BEING IN THE FUTURE. REES (RIGHT) HAS ALSO ARGUED THAT OUR OWN UNIVERSE COULD END IN FIERY DESTRUCTION RATHER THAN DARKNESS — IF IT CONTAINS ENOUGH MATTER TO RESIST FURTHER EXPANSION. SUCH A UNIVERSE WOULD COLLAPSE ON ITSELF IN A BACKWARD RERUN OF THE BIG BANG THAT CREATED IT.

LIFE IN THE UNIVERSE

The existence of life elsewhere in the universe fascinates most people, not just astronomers. Is there anywhere else in the universe that conditions are even remotely favorable? Or is the Earth a unique environment—a habitat where, by astronomical coincidence, the conditions were "just right?" A small but influential group of astronomers have even suggested that life on Earth might have originated from the skies, and that the complex chemical building blocks it requires are carried between hospitable environments, deep-frozen, within comets. Considering just intelligent life, astronomer Frank Drake devised a famous equation to aid debate about the probability of finding extraterrestrials with whom we could communicate. Drake and many other serious astronomers have been involved in the Search for Extraterrestrial Intelligence (SETI) program, listening out for radio signals from the stars, and famously even sending their own message to E.T. With vast worldwide interest in the search, some people have seriously considered the implications of contact—how would the discovery that we are not alone be announced? Would it be safe to reply, and if so, who should have the responsibility? And what would any message say?

Scientists engaged in SETI (the Search for Extraterrestrial Intelligence) think that radio is the medium of communication most likely to be chosen by aliens in their efforts to contact us. Even if they receive a likely radio message, it will take a good deal of analysis to convince the public that an alien intelligence has been found.

PANSPERMIA THEORY

Life is a cosmic phenomenon, spread through the universe by the invisible currents of space. That is the basis of the panspermia theory, which claims that the spark of life responsible for existence reached Earth from elsewhere in the universe. Certainly, we know that life is tenacious enough to endure long space voyages. Some of our own world's bacteria thrive in the boiling water beside undersea volcanic vents, while others can grow in rock more than a mile under the surface. Some bugs have even survived a sojourn on the airless surface of the Moon.

COMET SAMPLERS

Mission	Space Agency	Launch Rocket	Launch Date	Rendezvous
Stardust	NASA	Delta-2	February 1999	Comet Wild-2
Rosetta	European Space Agency	Ariane	March 2004	Comet Churyumov-Gerasimenko
Deep Impact	NASA	Delta-2	January 2005	Comet Tempel-1

AGAINST THE ODDS

When the astronauts of Apollo 12 walked on the Moon, they were not alone. Though they did not know it at the time, another life-form was present. It was lurking on an earlier U.S. Moon probe, Surveyor 3, and was only later unmasked on Earth, after the moonwalkers took a piece of Surveyor back for study.

The life in question was a colony of *Streptococcus mitis* bacteria, probably sneezed onto the probe by one of the humans who had built it on Earth. What was extraordinary was that the hardy microbes had survived 31 months of lunar vacuum. Freeze-dried, they had entered a state of suspended animation.

The Surveyor story is the most dramatic demonstration yet of the potential for life beyond the "thin blue smear" of soil, water and atmosphere that we think of as home. But there is plenty of other evidence that life can survive in unimaginably harsh conditions.

In South Africa, inside the deepest mine in the world, researchers have found bacteria living inside solid rock almost two miles down. Thick layers of thermophilic microbes are found alongside volcanic ridges over a mile beneath the ocean's surface, despite temperatures of more than 750°F (400°C) and a complete absence of light. Pollen grains float 12 miles (19 km) above our heads. And samples taken from deep beneath the Antarctic ice cap have uncovered a variety of live but inactive bacteria, fungi, algae and plankton, all previously unknown to science.

MORE THAN COINCIDENCE?

The very first life on Earth must have been at least as tolerant of extreme conditions as today's microbes. The early Earth was an impact-battered, radioactive ball of hot rock with a thick, hot, carbon dioxide atmosphere, yet it seems that life was present as early as 3.8 billion years ago. A long period of violent cometary bombardment kept the surface sterile before that point, at the same time delivering some of the raw materials of our atmosphere and oceans. Life appeared very soon after the impacts stopped.

Some theorists believe this occurrence was more than simple coincidence. They argue that life did not evolve spontaneously. Instead, it was carried here from elsewhere in space.

This so-called panspermia hypothesis was suggested in 1905 by Swedish Nobel Prize-winner Svante Arrhenius, and more recently by British astronomer Sir Fred Hoyle and his Sri Lankan colleague Chandra Wickramasinghe. Skeptical of conventional theories of evolution, they argue that life exists throughout the universe. Analysis of the light spectra from interstellar dust clouds, they claim, shows that the clouds are composed of freeze-dried bacteria. According to Hoyle and Wickramasinghe, life is brought to planets by comets, which deliver water and living material through direct impacts or by scattering dust particles from their tails.

The theory is controversial, to say the least. But new space-based instruments have confirmed that organic chemicals, the raw materials of life, are widespread throughout space. And water, the other vital ingredient, has been detected in huge quantities on the moons Titan and Europa, within gas clouds and even frozen on the Moon. The conditions, it seems, are right. All that appears to be missing is the vital spark.

LIFE ON THE EDGE

OUTER SPACE
Streptococcal bacteria (like those at right)—the cause of a host of human infections—lived in the vacuum of the Moon's surface for 31 months after the accidental contamination of a space probe. The bugs survived.

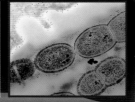

MILES HIGH
Pollen grains, the genetic material of plants, can drift for years in the stratosphere. Despite low atmospheric pressure, temperatures of around −100°F (−73°C) and ultraviolet radiation, pollen can still fertilize a plant.

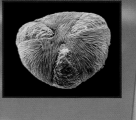

DEEP ICE
This protozoan was one of many species of microscopic life discovered by U.S. and Russian scientists in mile-deep, 400,000-year-old ice at Vostok Station, Antarctica. Many have been successfully revived from suspended animation.

HOT OCEAN
Volcanic vents in the deep ocean spew sulfur and water heated to 750°F (400°C). Yet around these "black smokers," a whole ecology of living things has evolved, from bacteria to giant tube worms.

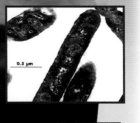

INSIDE ROCK
The aptly named "bug from hell," bacillus infernus, lives almost two miles deep in solid rock at a temperature of 167°F (75°C). The samples shown were found beneath the Taylorsville Basin in eastern Virginia.

0.5 µm

MARS METEORITE
In August 1996 NASA scientists astonished the world when they announced they had found tiny fossil bacteria in a meteorite from Mars. The three-billion-year-old rock was chipped off the Red Planet by an asteroid impact, displaying one possible method of panspermia. But many scientists doubt that the fossils are real.

THE DRAKE EQUATION

Most equations in science express knowledge in the unambiguous language of mathematics. The Drake equation spells out our ignorance. It is a formula for calculating the number of technological civilizations in our galaxy. Its terms include such million-dollar questions as: What are the chances of intelligence arising on a given planet? The equation multiplies "we don't know" by "we may never find out"—and is currently no closer to a solution than when the American astronomer Frank Drake suggested it in 1961. What it continues to do is fascinate many.

THE EQUATION EXPLAINED

$N = R^* \, f_p \, n_e \, f_l \, f_i \, f_c \, L$	MULTIPLY ALL THE TERMS TOGETHER TO OBTAIN THE ANSWER
N	THE NUMBER OF ACTIVE, HIGH-TECHNOLOGY ALIEN CIVILIZATIONS
R^*	THE ANNUAL RATE OF FORMATION OF STARS SIMILAR TO OUR SUN IN THE GALAXY
f_p	FRACTION OF THOSE STARS WITH PLANETS
n_e	NUMBER OF THOSE PLANETS CAPABLE OF SUPPORTING LIFE
f_l	FRACTION OF LIFE-CAPABLE PLANETS WHERE LIFE ARISES
f_i	FRACTION OF LIFE-BEARING PLANETS WHERE INTELLIGENCE EVOLVES
f_c	FRACTION OF INTELLIGENT RACES THAT DEVELOP TECHNOLOGY
L	LIFETIME OF TECHNOLOGICAL CIVILIZATIONS

ALIEN MATH

The conference held at Virginia's Green Bank Radio Observatory in 1961 had an unusual subject: the possibilities of extraterrestrial intelligence. The conference would lead to the beginnings of the SETI program—the Search for Extraterrestrial Intelligence. And one of the first things on its agenda was a very fundamental question. How many alien civilizations might be out there?

Radio astronomer Frank Drake realized that the problem could be broken down into a series of sub-questions. For example: How many stars have planets? On how

many planets does life evolve? How long does a technological civilization last? If astronomers could make good estimates of these factors, simple multiplication would give the chances of any given star developing the kind of intelligence that could communicate across interstellar space. Throw in the rate at which stars are formed, and the formula would yield the likely number of civilizations that SETI researchers might hope to find.

When the conference ended, delegates were no closer to answering Drake's questions. But they had formalized his idea into the equation that bears his name.

The math is elementary: $N = R^* \times f_p \times n_e \times f_l \times f_i \times f_c \times L$. N is the total of communicating interstellar civilizations. The other terms range from R^* (rate at which Sun-like stars form annually) and f_p

(fraction of stars with planets) to $=f_i$ (fraction that evolve intelligence) and L (lifetime of a high-tech civilization). Between them, they amount to an obstacle race that intelligence must win.

STILL LOOKING

FRANK DRAKE WAS BORN IN 1930 AND BEGAN HIS CAREER IN RADIO ASTRONOMY IN 1958. TWO YEARS LATER, DRAKE STARTED PROJECT OZMA—THE FIRST ORGANIZED ATTEMPT TO DETECT INTELLIGENT SIGNALS FROM THE STARS.

A SIEVE FOR INTELLIGENCE

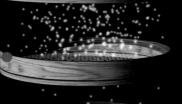

R* RATE OF STAR FORMATION

From observation, most astronomers agree that between 5 and 20 stars are formed in the galaxy each year. Not all of them will be capable of supporting life, though. Some will simply burn out too quickly, and others will not have a large enough "habitable zone" in the space around them. Even so, the numbers for R* are the most reliable in the whole equation.

OPTIMIST VALUE: 10 PESSIMIST VALUE: 1 DRAKE VALUE: 10

ne NUMBER OF HABITABLE PLANETS IN A SYSTEM

Life as we know it needs liquid water and warmth. So if our solar system is typical, then a star with planets will probably have just one, perhaps two, in an orbit with these requirements.

OPTIMIST VALUE: 1 PESSIMIST VALUE: 0.5 DRAKE VALUE: 2

fi FRACTION OF PLANETS WHERE INTELLIGENCE EVOLVES

Multicelled life took three billion years to emerge on Earth. Much later, human intelligence seems to have sprung from a fluke of evolution linked to climate changes in Africa. At best, intelligent life seems less than likely and may be extremely improbable.

OPTIMIST VALUE: 10% PESSIMIST VALUE: 0.01% DRAKE VALUE: 10%

L LIFETIME OF TECHNOLOGICAL CIVILIZATION

This is the most speculative term in the whole Drake equation. When the equation was first suggested in 1961, at the height of the Cold War and in the shadow of a nuclear holocaust, researchers grimly proposed 10 years as a top limit. Now, 50 years seems a fair minimum. Of course, it is possible that a high-tech civilization could last for a very long time indeed.

OPTIMIST VALUE: 10,000 YEARS PESSIMIST VALUE: 50 YEARS DRAKE VALUE: 10 YEARS

fp FRACTION OF STARS WITH PLANETS

Astronomers have detected a substantial number of extrasolar planets by measuring the gravitational wobble they induce in their parent stars. Current theory also suggests that planets are a likely by-product of star formation. Up to 90 percent of stars may have some kind of planetary system in orbit around them.

OPTIMIST VALUE: 90% PESSIMIST VALUE: 50% DRAKE VALUE: 50%

fl FRACTION OF PLANETS WHERE LIFE EVOLVES

Primitive, single-celled life arose on Earth more than 3.5 billion years ago, almost as soon as the new planet had cooled. It is risky to generalize from a sample of just one, but even so, it is a fair assumption that life's appearance is highly probable—perhaps a 90 percent chance.

Optimist value: 90% Pessimist value: 50% Drake Value: 100%

fc FRACTION OF INTELLIGENT RACES WITH COMMUNICATIONS TECHNOLOGY

For most of human history, people hunted and gathered without the trappings of civilization. And most civilizations were content with very modest technology. The scientific revolution 400 years ago was a unique event, not an inevitable stage in a march of progress. Elsewhere in the galaxy, it may never happen at all.

OPTIMIST VALUE: 10% PESSIMIST VALUE: 0.01% DRAKE VALUE: 10%

N POSSIBLE NUMBER OF HIGH-TECH ALIEN CIVILIZATIONS

If the optimistic assumptions are correct, then there should be about 84 technological civilizations currently active in the galaxy. The pessimistic figures work out at an insignificant 0.000000015. The Drake figures, used at the 1961 conference that promulgated the equation, yield an answer of exactly one. That may well turn out to be the best guesstimate: After all, we are here.

SETI

Back in the 1950s, astronomers realized that their newly developed radio telescopes should be able to receive signals from intelligent beings in outer space—always assuming that such beings existed and had radio technology similar to our own. Frank Drake at the National Radio Astronomy Observatory in West Virginia made the first search in 1960: He listened to two likely stars and heard nothing. Since then, thousands of stars have been scanned at literally billions of wavelengths in the Search for Extraterrestrial Intelligence (SETI). And we are still looking, with interest showing no sign of wavering.

INTERNATIONAL SEARCHES

1960	Project Ozma: Green Bank, West Virginia	Searched for signals from two stars
1972	Several sites in U.S.S.R. and Mars 7 spacecraft	Searched for stray radio signals
1972–6	Ozma II	Searched for signals from 674 stars
1973–4	Special Astrophysical Observatory, U.S.S.R.	Searched for pulses of light from 21 "peculiar" objects
1977	Ohio State University Radio Observatory	"Wow!" signal observed
1978–80	Pioneer Venus (U.S.), Venera (U.S.S.R.) probes	Searched for gamma-ray bursts from alien starships
1981	Project Signal: Westerbork, Netherlands	Searched for radio pulses from the center of the galaxy
1983	U.S. National Radio Astronomy Observatory	Searched signals from pulsars for messages
1992–3	NASA High-Resolution Microwave Survey	Searched from Puerto Rico and Goldstone, California
1995–2004	Project Phoenix: Australia; West Virginia	Observing 1,000 targeted stars at millions of frequencies

LISTENING FOR LIFE

Scientists engaged in SETI (the Search for Extraterrestrial Intelligence) have long thought that radio is the medium of communication most likely to be chosen by intelligent aliens in their efforts to contact us. If light waves were used, in the form of laser beacons, they might be masked by the light coming from the extraterrestrials' own star. Transmitting radio waves across space also requires less energy.

However, a major problem is choosing the right frequency. For example, if you tune your radio at home to the wrong frequency, you don't pick up the show you want to hear. Similarly, if you tune to the wrong frequency when you listen for signals from space, you will miss a message completely. Scientists assume that aliens will send a signal close to an important natural frequency, such as that of the radio waves given out by the vast clouds of dark hydrogen that make up much of our galaxy.

NASA launched a major effort, which they named HRMS (High-Resolution Microwave Search) in 1992. Aimed at 25 stars, it probed many different frequencies—until Congress ended the project's funding after just one year.

The search was taken up again by a private initiative, Project Phoenix, operated by the SETI Institute. The most ambitious search program in the world, it worked steadily through a list of about 800 promising stars that are all within 200 light-years of the Earth, with systems similar to Earth's. Fast computers analyzed incoming data immediately. If a likely signal showed up, then a second, smaller telescope looks at the same source. By comparing the data from the two telescopes, astronomers could verify that the signal was coming from deep space and not from a source on Earth or one of our spacecraft.

In addition, thousands of hours of radio signals were packaged out over the Internet for processing by home PCs in the SETI@home project. Only once SETI researchers have confirmed that a possible message comes all the way from the stars, do they begin to study it seriously. It will take a good deal of analysis to convince them that alien intelligence has been found.

FUTURE SEARCHES

When Project Phoenix began in 1995, its primary telescope was the 210-ft (64-m) Parkes radio telescope in New South Wales, Australia. Then the equipment for processing signals was shipped to Green Bank, West Virginia, where it was linked to a 140-ft (43-m) telescope. For extra sensitivity, future searches will also involve the giant 250-ft (76-m) Lovell Telescope at Jodrell Bank in England. The project came to an end in 2004 with no evidence of extraterrestrial life being found.

LITTLE GREEN MEN

In 1967, radio astronomers in Cambridge, England, found a highly artificial-looking signal: a pattern of ultra-short pulses that repeated itself every 1.03 sec. The unknown source was briefly labeled LGM, for "Little Green Men." But then astronomers came up with the real explanation. Instead of finding aliens, they had made the first observation of a pulsar — a distant, fast-spinning neutron star.

First observation of pulses from CP 1919

METHODS OF CONTACT

IS ANYBODY OUT THERE?
The 180-ft (55-m) radio telescope at the Green Bank National Radio Observatory in West Virginia was tracking signals from deep space since 1965 and is capable of following four different frequencies at once.

GOLDEN EAR
Green Bank's 140-ft (43-m) dish often worked together with other U.S. and European radio telescopes. Two or more receivers, separated by hundreds or thousands of miles, can pinpoint distant signals far more accurately than a single telescope working alone.

STARSONG ON SCREEN
After their powerful computer processed the raw data from the skies, SETI astronomers scanned incoming signals for any sign of alien intelligence.

ENCOUNTER GROUP

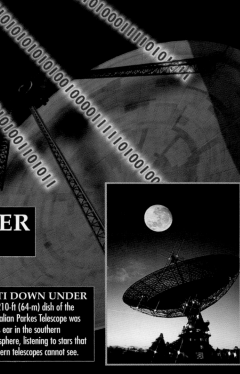

SETI DOWN UNDER
The 210-ft (64-m) dish of the Australian Parkes Telescope was SETI's ear in the southern hemisphere, listening to stars that northern telescopes cannot see.

FIRST CONTACT

Many of us believe that out among the stars there may exist an alien intelligence at least the equal of our own. Few of us are frightened by the idea. But if an authentic contact with an alien race turned the idea into reality, would it change the way we live? An advanced civilization could have much to teach us—if it wanted to do so. Could our culture survive the knowledge that we were not the only beings, as well as the smartest beings on the cosmic block? Or would the contact shock our world into panic, chaos and cultural collapse?

UNEXPLAINED SIGHTINGS

Alien contact may already be happening. Although most UFO sightings are easily accounted for, and most of the remainder are based on possibly unreliable eyewitnesses, a good number are backed by solid radar data and military reports. Files on these sightings from one 10-year period decades ago are still open.

Date	Witnesses	Location
October 15, 1948	Military: air visual and radar	Fusuoka, Japan
April 24, 1949	Military: visual	Arrey, New Mexico
March 20, 1950	Airline crew: air visual	Stuggart, Arkansas
March 13, 1951	Military and civilian: visual	Sacramento, California
April 14, 1952	Military: air visual	Memphis, Tennessee
June 24, 1953	Military: air visual	Iwo Jima
March 12, 1954	Military: air visual	Nouasseur, Morocco
February 1, 1955	Military: air visual	Cochise, New Mexico
February 19, 1956	Airline crew: air visual	Houston, Texas
November 30, 1957	U.S. Coast Guard: visual	New Orleans, Louisiana
April 14, 1958	Military: air visual	Philippines

HANDS ACROSS SPACE

WOULD YOU BELIEVE IT?

Even "incontrovertible" evidence of alien contact might not convince everyone. Despite sacks of Moon rock brought back to Earth and other solid scientific confirmation, four percent of the U.S. population believes that the Apollo Moon landings were a hoax. And thousands of people worldwide flatly refuse to accept that the death of Princess Diana really happened.

There is no reason why an alien life-form should have humanoid hands and fingers, as shown in this symbolic image. The real contact would be between minds, not limbs.

The Aztecs of Mexico were hit by an alien invasion in 1519, when Hernando Cortez arrived with about 500 musket-bearing Spanish soldiers, a dozen horses and a few cannons. Cortez had one thing in mind: conquest. His ruthlessness, his "alien" high technology and the smallpox virus that his men passed to the natives brought him total success. By 1521, the Aztec civilization had been all but destroyed.

Britain's Captain James Cook was the epitome of the humane, civilized 18th-century scientific explorer. In all his Pacific voyages, he made great efforts to respect the lives and customs of the people he visited. Cook punished his own men for assaulting natives, and he himself was killed as he tried to end a skirmish peacefully. Yet a few generations later, Hawaiian culture was in ruins, with many deaths caused by disease or alcohol introduced by Cook's men.

MEETING OF MINDS

There are only two ways for an alien civilization to make contact with us. We could receive a clear signal—by radio, most likely, or perhaps by laser—from a distant star. Or the outsiders could actually land on Earth, their ship detected by astronomers as it traveled toward us through the solar system.

So far, neither has happened. There have been occasional curious signals from outer space, but virtually all of them have been explained by natural phenomena, and none of them could really be described as an unambiguous signal from an intelligent being.

Similarly, although there have been many claims of physical contact with aliens, none have ever been backed by solid, incontrovertible evidence.

Certainly, no responsible government would announce that an alien message had been received without checking very carefully that it was not an error or a hoax. But no government on Earth could keep secret for long the existence of a broadcast received from space. The world has many radio telescopes and plenty of scientists from all nations who know how to use them.

If the aliens did arrive in person, filmed by news crews and shown on live TV as they touched down in Central Park in New York, for example, how many of us really would be astounded? After all, we have been conditioned by 50 years of science-fiction movies and TV series to accept the reality of alien visitors. According to recent opinion polls, more than 60 percent of Americans believe that aliens may well be coming soon. And in Britain, it is thought that more people believe in aliens than believe in God.

STRESS REACTION

A 1988 survey of mental health care professionals provided a warning note. Two-thirds of these psychiatric workers believed that the sudden discovery of an intelligence far greater than ours would produce an attack of global insecurity—and a reluctance to invest in the future. Some feared that much of humanity might see aliens as gods.

Maybe widespread insecurity would be justified, given the history of human civilization to date. Almost always, when an "advanced" human society has contacted a "primitive" one, the outcome has been disastrous and even deadly for the primitives—even when the advanced culture's intentions were good.

FALSE ALARM

WHEN BRITISH RADIO ASTRONOMERS DETECTED THE FIRST PULSAR — A SPINNING NEUTRON STAR THAT EMITS RAPID SEQUENCES OF REGULAR PULSES — THEY BRIEFLY THOUGHT THEY HAD FOUND AN ALIEN SIGNAL. LESS PLAUSIBLY, MANY HAD BELIEVED THAT THE "FACE ON MARS" (RIGHT) PHOTOGRAPHED BY THE VIKING PROBE IN 1976, WAS AN ALIEN ARTIFACT. PICTURES FROM A LATER MARS MISSION HAVE SHOWN THE FACE TO BE AN ILLUSION CAUSED BY LIGHT AND SHADOW.

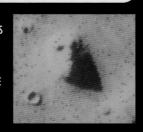

FIRST STEPS IN SPACE

America's first attempts to catch up with the Soviets' headline-grabbing Sputnik launch were rushed and ended in embarrassing failure on the launch pad. However, by early 1958 Jupiter and Vanguard rockets had successfully carried small science packages into orbit. The full story of Soviet "space shots" is still unclear, because the U.S.S.R. preferred to publicize only those craft that successfully left the atmosphere and for a time in the early 1960s that was only a small proportion of launches. Two explosions of military rockets in 1960 and 1963 caused huge loss of life, including many scientists, at the U.S.S.R.'s Baikonur space center but were kept secret until 1991. The U.S. suffered the loss of three astronauts in the Apollo 1 launchpad fire in 1967, and four cosmonauts were lost on missions in the 1960s and 1970s, but it is remarkable that the inherently dangerous and experimental nature of spaceflight in its early phase did not result in more disasters. Once the feasibility of single and two-person orbital flight had been proven, the next step (literally) was the "space walk," whereby an astronaut made a tethered excursion outside the spacecraft. This paved the way for many important scientific experiments, missions to launch and repair satellites, and construction of the International Space Station (ISS).

On May 15, 1963, the last of the Mercury astronauts, Gordon Cooper, was launched into orbit atop a Mercury Atlas 9 rocket. Cooper orbited the Earth 22 times and logged more time in space than all five of the previous Mercury astronauts combined.

SPUTNIK

Sputnik 1 did not look like the stuff that history is made of. It was a polished aluminum ball, just 22 in (60 cm) across. But on October 4, 1957, the ball was shot hundreds of miles into space on an adapted Soviet missile, never to return. For the first time ever, an artificial object had reached the 29,000-km/h (18,000-mph) speed required to escape the Earth's atmosphere and go into orbit around our planet. Sputnik, the so-called "Red Moon," amazed the world and panicked the U.S. into accelerating its own rocket program. It also marked the true beginning of the Space Age.

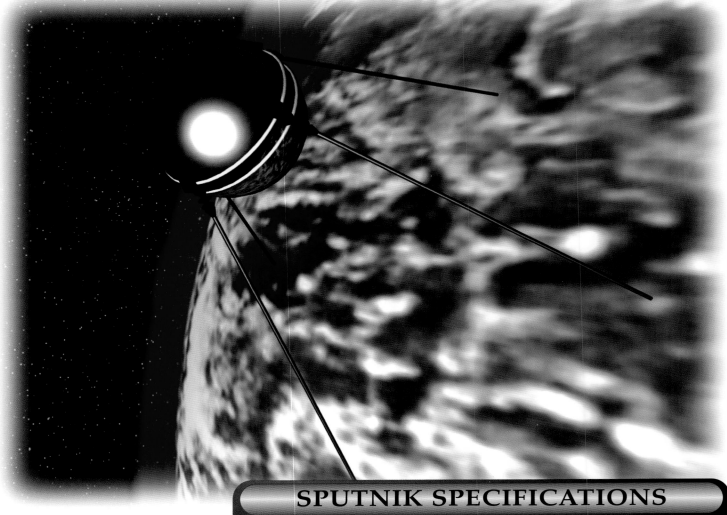

SPUTNIK SPECIFICATIONS

LAUNCH VEHICLE	R-7 SEMIORKA (NATO CODE NAME "SS-6 SAPWOOD")	ORBITAL INCLINATION	65°6'
		APOGEE	583.5 MILES (939 KM)
DIAMETER	22 INCHES (60CM)	PERIGEE	133 MILES (214 KM)
WEIGHT	183 LB (83 KG)	DATE OF LAUNCH	OCTOBER 4, 1957
ON-BOARD EQUIPMENT	2 RADIO TRANSMITTERS	DATE TRANSMISSIONS ENDED	OCTOBER 26, 1957
ORBITAL PERIOD	96.2 MIN	DATE OF REENTRY	JANUARY 4, 1958

BALL IN SPACE

For such an astonishing achievement, the Soviet Union announced the existence of Sputnik 1 in a surprisingly low-key manner. On October 5, 1957, the Earth's first artificial satellite barely made the front page of the government-controlled newspaper Pravda, where it was buried halfway down a side column with the anonymous headline "Tass Report." The satellite's existence was only mentioned in the story's third paragraph. It took the congratulations of the entire world to make the Kremlin realize its propaganda potential. To the Soviet government, Sputnik 1 was merely a sideshow to the all-important ballistic missile program that would maintain military parity with the U.S. during the Cold War.

The Soviet Union's space engineers felt very differently. The real passion of chief missile designer Sergei Pavlovich Korolev was not military superiority, but space exploration. Korolev spent the early 1950s designing and testing missiles with successively longer ranges until, in 1953, he created the A-Series R-7 rocket, which could carry a 5.4-ton (4.9-tonne) payload over a distance of 6,000 miles (9,650 km). It was not long before he suggested modifying the R-7 to place a satellite in orbit, although it it was several years before the Kremlin gave him the final go-ahead.

In July 1955, the Soviet government announced that it would launch an artificial Earth satellite—the day after U.S. President Dwight Eisenhower had made a similar promise. Development of Korolev's satellite went ahead in tandem with flight tests of the R-7. His design bureau built a one-ton probe filled with scientific equipment, but problems with the electronics caused it to be sidelined—although as Sputnik 3, it flew the following year.

SIMPLEST SPUTNIK

In August 1957, Korolev switched to a less advanced design. This consisted of a polished aluminum ball containing a radio, along with some simple scientific instruments: On-board pressure and temperature detectors that were supposed to send data back to the surface by modulating the radio signals. The package was launched in October using an R-7 fitted with additional boosters. It was never given an official name: The Soviet media simply referred to it as "the sputnik," meaning both "satellite" and "traveling companion."

The news electrified the world: Sputnik 1's distinctive "beep, beep" radio signals could be picked up worldwide, and people everywhere searched the night skies, hoping to catch a sight of the satellite. Its limited scientific payload did not work very well, but that hardly mattered. The "Red Moon" had risen and the sky would never seem the same again.

CHIEF DESIGNER

During his life, Sergei Pavlovich Korolev (1906–66) was known to the Soviet public only as "the Chief Designer." Korolev (right) survived a spell in one of Stalin's labor camps to give the Soviet Union many of its space firsts, including Sputnik, the first man and woman in space and the world's first view of the far side of the Moon.

SPUTNIK IN ORBIT

July 30, 1955 The U.S.S.R. announces it will launch an artificial satellite to coincide with International Geophysical Year.
August 21, 1957 After five failures, the R-7 ICBM (above) propels a dummy H-bomb 2,500 miles (4,000 km) across the Soviet Union.
September 21, 1957 The one-ton satellite originally planned to be first in orbit is delayed by technical problems, so chief designer Sergei Korolev and his staff manufacture a less ambitious replacement inside a month. It is known as Prostreishiy Sputnik or "simplest satellite".
September 30, 1957 An R-7 rocket modified for space is assembled in a Baïkonur hangar close to the launchpad.
October 2, 1957 The R-7 is rolled out for the mile-long journey to its launchpad.

Korolev and his designers walk in front of the rocket.
October 4, 1957 Sputnik 1 is launched into an elliptical orbit.
October 26, 1957 Sputnik 1 ceases its distinctive "beep, beep" radio transmissions.
January 4, 1958 Sputnik 1's orbit decays and the probe burns up in the Earth's atmosphere. By this time, another Soviet satellite has been launched, Sputnik 2, with the space dog Laika inside.

ANATOMY OF SPUTNIK

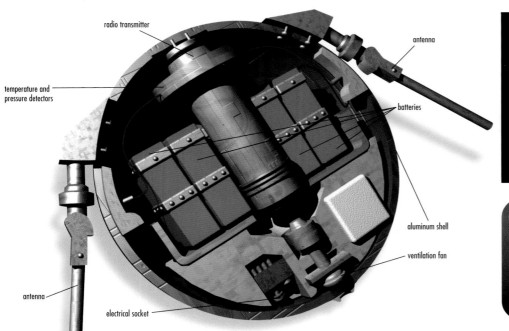

radio transmitter

antenna

temperature and pressure detectors

batteries

aluminum shell

ventilation fan

antenna

electrical socket

DESIGN BRIEF
The sole purpose of Sputnik 1 was to prove that an artificial object could be launched into orbit—and that the Soviet Union could do it first. It was therefore built to be as simple and reliable as possible and to broadcast radio signals on two wavelengths that were powerful enough to be tracked by amateurs worldwide for two to three weeks. In this way, the Soviet Union made sure that Sputnik could not be hushed up by Western governments.

RELAUNCH

On the 1997 anniversary of Sputnik 1's launch, a replica was deployed from the Mir Space Station by cosmonaut Pavel Vinogradov. U.S. astronaut Dave Wolf shared in the mission. The replica itself was built jointly by French and Russian teenagers—a symbol not of the old space race, but of a new era of cooperation.

ANIMALS IN SPACE

Since the beginning of the space age in the 1950s, animals of many species have journeyed beyond the Earth's atmosphere. Not all of them have returned alive. Scientists have learned much from their animal helpers, but there is plenty of opposition—from other scientists as well as animal rights activists—to sending animals into space. For some, it is a crime; to others, it is a valuable research resource that helps mankind learn more about the universe and the effects of spending time travelling in space.

ANIMAL FLIGHTS

DATE	ANIMAL	MISSION	STUDY
Nov 1957	Dog Laika	Sputnik 2	Survivability of space flight
Dec 1960	Rhesus Monkey Sam	Little Joe Project	Effects of high-g acceleration
Jan 1961	Chimpanzee Ham	Mercury Redstone 2	Survivability of manned space flight
June 1973	Minnows	Skylab 3	Disorientation in the space environment
Aug 1973	Spiders	Skylab 3	Ability of spiders to adapt to zero-g
Mar 1982	Moths and Flies	Shuttle Mission STS-3	Insect flight motion study
Sept 1992	Frogs	Shuttle Mission STS-47	Effects of weightlessness on development of eggs
Oct 1993	Rats	Shuttle Mission STS-58	Effects of weightlessness
May 1994	Newts and Goldfish	Shuttle Mission STS-65	Effects of microgravity on embryos

SPACE BEASTS

Early in November 1957, a dog named Laika ("Little Lemon") became the first living being from the Earth to venture into space and orbit the planet. Laika's one-way mission aboard the Russian spacecraft Sputnik 2 paved the way for manned spaceflight and marked the beginning of animal involvement in the space age.

A year later, two dogs, Belka ("Squirrel") and Strelka ("Little Arrow"), returned safely after a one-day flight on Sputnik 5. Strelka later gave birth to a litter of six puppies, one of which was given to President John F. Kennedy as a gift from the Soviet Union.

At the end of 1960, soon after the Sputnik mission, the U.S. instigated its Little Joe animal-flight program. A rhesus monkey named Sam was sent into space as part of a series of animal flights designed to investigate the effects of high-g acceleration and to test the equipment that would later be used in manned missions.

These early animal pioneers proved that there was no danger in space that humans could not face—with a lot of good engineering and a little luck. Later research animals have helped us to understand some of the long-term effects of weightlessness on bodies that have evolved to function in a powerful gravity field.

On short journeys, such effects are minor. But even a week or two in space is enough to affect heart muscles, depress immune systems and distort coordination and balance. A little longer and astronauts begin to suffer from osteoporosis, a weakening of the bones. This weakening is caused when their bodies recycle structural bone material, which is apparently no longer needed because of the absence of gravity.

Although some Russian cosmonauts have lived for many months on the Mir space station, they have needed considerable time to recover upon their return to Earth. Future missions to Mars, or the construction of space colonies, are likely to put the human body under considerable strain.

Spaceborne animals have helped to quantify at least some of the consequences of zero gravity (known as zero g). But such experiments have their opponents, too. Some scientists argue that the stress of weightlessness itself is enough to invalidate the results of some animal experiments, and that most animal anatomies are not close enough to our own for them to serve as testbeds. Also, creatures such as mice and rats are too short-lived for scientists to gain much long-term data from them. And animal well-being is taken seriously. The Bion program—a long-term collaboration between the U.S. and Russia—insists that animals involved in missions are retired soon after to live out the remainder of their natural lives in comfort.

LAIKA: SPACE PIONEER

OCTOBER 1957
THE RUSSIAN MONGREL LAIKA UNDERGOES A PROGRAM OF EXTENSIVE TRAINING TO ACCLIMATIZE HER TO CONFINED SPACES, HIGH ACCELERATION FORCES AND ENGINE NOISE THAT SHE WILL EXPERIENCE ON HER VOYAGE.

NOVEMBER 3, 1957
SPUTNIK 2 IS LAUNCHED INTO ORBIT (LEFT). THE TOP SECTION CONTAINS INSTRUMENTS TO MEASURE RADIATION, THE MIDDLE HOLDS THE RADIO CAPSULE AND BELOW IS THE COMPARTMENT CONTAINING LAIKA.

NOVEMBER 10, 1957
LAIKA DIES AFTER RUNNING OUT OF OXYGEN. SPUTNIK 2 CONTINUES TO ORBIT FOR MORE THAN SIX MONTHS. LAIKA AND THE CRAFT BURN UP ON REENTRY INTO THE ATMOSPHERE.

ORBITAL ZOO

AMPHIBIANS
Frogs and newts do not make heavy demands on the spacecraft's life-support systems. But they have helped teach scientists how zero gravity affects hearing and balance.

CHIMPANZEES
The flight of Ham the chimpanzee (seen to the right), aboard Mercury-Redstone 2 in January 1961, paved the way for Alan Shepard's historic Mercury mission four months later.

MONKEYS
The U.S. and Russia have launched 11 unpiloted biosatellites in their joint Bion Program; six of which have carried Rhesus monkeys. The program aims to increase our understanding of the biological effects of zero gravity.

RODENTS
Long periods in zero gravity often cause osteoporosis, a bone-weakening ailment that also occurs in old age. Mice and rats in orbiting labs have helped doctors to better understand the disease.

EXPLORER 1

During the late 1950s, the United States and the Soviet Union carried their rivalry into Earth orbit. The Soviets took an early lead by successfully launching two Sputnik satellites. The U.S., uneasy at the thought of Soviet space hardware tracking over North America, redoubled its efforts and responded with Explorer 1 early in 1958. But the first American satellite did more than save face for the U.S. in the Cold War. Once in orbit, the onboard instruments discovered belts of radiation in the Earth's magnetosphere.

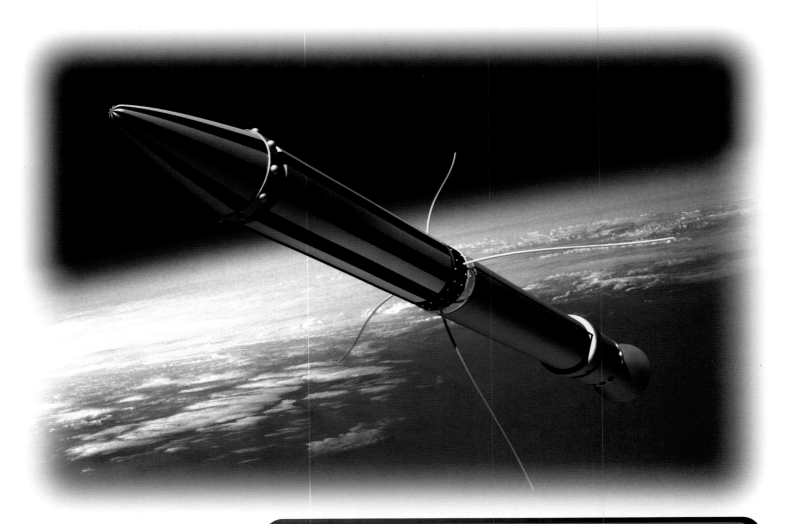

EXPLORER 1 SPECIFICATIONS

DIMENSIONS	80 IN (203 CM) LONG, 6 INCHES (15CM) IN DIAMETER
WEIGHT	30.66 LB (13.9 KG)
LAUNCH DATE/TIME	JANUARY 31, 1958, 10:47 P.M. EST
LAUNCH SITE	CAPE CANAVERAL, FLORIDA
LAUNCH VEHICLE	JUPITER-C
ORBITAL INFORMATION	PERIGEE: 1,575 MILES (2534 KM) APOGEE: 224 MILES (360 KM) INCLINATION: 33.24 DEGREES PERIOD: 114.9 MINUTES

INTO ORBIT

After the Soviet Union launched Sputnik 1, the world's first artificial satellite, opinion was divided in the U.S. as to the significance of the event. Did this little metal ball, spinning and beeping its way around the globe, really present a threat to the western world? President Eisenhower, in public, was on the side of the skeptics. But privately, after a U-2 spy plane was shot down over the Soviet Union, he saw the potential of satellite technology as a safe way of peeking over the Iron Curtain.

Certainly Eisenhower's military advisers saw Sputnik as a potential threat to American security, and their fears were voiced on Capitol Hill by Senator Stuart Symington. "Unless our defense policies are promptly changed, the Soviets will move from superiority to supremacy," Symington warned. The U.S. military wanted more resources for a reconnaissance satellite program.

Meanwhile, the Soviets surged ahead once more. On November 3, 1957, Sputnik 2 was launched carrying Laika the dog—the first living being in space. Sputnik 2 raised the stakes. It was suddenly clear that the Soviet space effort was looking far beyond the obvious military advantages of being able to send missiles into orbit: They wanted to put a man into space—an achievement with extraordinary propaganda value in a war of ideas between competing superpowers. Smaller nations might well be tempted to line up behind the winner of the space race.

The first U.S. satellite launch attempt failed on December 6 of that same year, when a Vanguard rocket exploded two seconds into its flight. But this left the field clear for rocket pioneer Wernher von Braun. On January 31, 1958, a four-stage Jupiter-C launched from Cape Canaveral with an upgraded Redstone rocket as the first stage. Inside was Explorer 1, which was launched into an orbit measuring 224 by 1,575 miles (360 by 2,534 km).

Two hours later, Eisenhower told the American people, "The United States has successfully placed a scientific satellite in orbit around the Earth. This is part of our participation in the International Geophysical Year." The International Geophysical Year (IGY) was a global venture, bringing together scientists from 66 countries to investigate Earth's climate and atmosphere.

Explorer 1 made a sensational contribution to the IGY, thanks to the on-board Geiger tube radiation detector that discovered belts of intense radiation girdling the Earth. The instrument was designed by James Van Allen, one of the architects of the IGY. Fittingly, the radiation belts still bear his name.

MEDIA FRENZY

EXPLORER 1 AROUSED INTENSE MEDIA INTEREST. AS VAN ALLEN HIMSELF RECALLED OF ONE PRESS CONFERENCE, "ALTHOUGH IT WAS 1:30 IN THE MORNING, THERE WAS STILL A HUGE CROWD OF REPORTERS WAITING AROUND." BUT THE STORY WAS MORE ABOUT HOW THE U.S. HAD CAUGHT UP WITH THE SOVIETS THAN ABOUT THE SATELLITE'S REMARKABLE SCIENTIFIC ACHIEVEMENTS.

WIRED

THE EXPLORER SERIES CONTINUES TO THIS DAY. EXPLORER 75, THE "WIDE-FIELD INFRARED EXPLORER," OR WIRE (RIGHT), WAS LAUNCHED ON MARCH 4, 1999, AND CARRIED AN INFRARED IMAGING TELESCOPE. UNFORTUNATELY, AN ACCIDENT SHORTLY AFTER LAUNCH MEANT THAT THE SPACECRAFT QUICKLY GREW TOO WARM. THE TELESCOPE COULD NOT BE USED AND THE MISSION WAS DECLARED A LOSS.

MISSION DIARY: EXPLORER 1

1957
WORK STEPS UP ON THE DEVELOPMENT OF EXPLORER 1 (RIGHT) AT THE U.S. ARMY RESEARCH FACILITY KNOWN AS THE JET PROPULSION LABORATORY IN PASADENA, CALIFORNIA.
NOVEMBER 3, 1957
THE SOVIET UNION LAUNCHES SPUTNIK 2 WITH LAIKA ON BOARD.
DECEMBER 6, 1957
UNSUCCESSFUL LAUNCH OF FIRST THE U.S. SATELLITE.

JANUARY 29, 1958
SCHEDULED LAUNCH OF EXPLORER 1 IS ABORTED DUE TO HIGH WINDS IN THE UPPER ATMOSPHERE.
JANUARY 30, 1958
LAUNCH POSTPONED A SECOND TIME. THE SATELLITE AND ITS LAUNCHER REMAIN ON THE LAUNCHPAD (RIGHT).
JANUARY 31, 1958, 10:47 P.M. EST
EXPLORER 1 LIFTS OFF FROM CAPE CANAVERAL (FAR RIGHT).

10:55:05 P.M.
EXPLORER 1 REACHES EARTH ORBIT.
FEBRUARY 1, 1958, 1:00 A.M.
PRESIDENT EISENHOWER ANNOUNCES "THE UNITED STATES HAS SUCCESSFULLY PLACED A SCIENTIFIC EARTH SATELLITE IN ORBIT AROUND THE EARTH."
MARCH 31, 1970, 5:47 A.M. EST
EXPLORER 1 BURNS UP DURING ITS REENTRY INTO EARTH'S ATMOSPHERE.

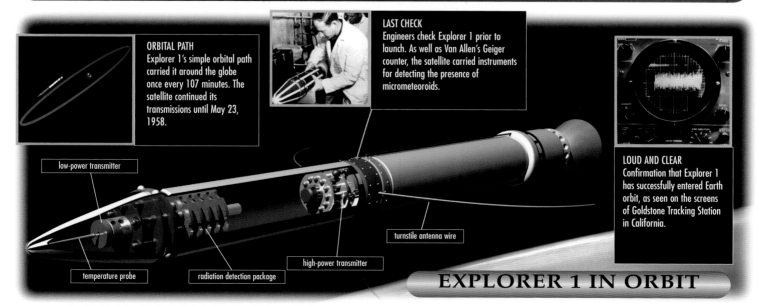

ORBITAL PATH
Explorer 1's simple orbital path carried it around the globe once every 107 minutes. The satellite continued its transmissions until May 23, 1958.

LAST CHECK
Engineers check Explorer 1 prior to launch. As well as Van Allen's Geiger counter, the satellite carried instruments for detecting the presence of micrometeoroids.

low-power transmitter

temperature probe

radiation detection package

high-power transmitter

turnstile antenna wire

LOUD AND CLEAR
Confirmation that Explorer 1 has successfully entered Earth orbit, as seen on the screens of Goldstone Tracking Station in California.

EXPLORER 1 IN ORBIT

MERCURY CRAFT

T he late 1950s saw the start of the race between the U.S. and the Soviet Union to launch a human being into orbit. In the interests of speed, both nations opted for systems based on a simple, recoverable nose cone that could be launched by an existing intercontinental ballistic missile. In the end, the Soviets won—with Vostok 1 in April, 1961. But America's Mercury capsule, which made its manned debut a month later, was a far more sophisticated craft and flew a total of six manned missions between 1961 and 1963.

MERCURY FLIGHT LOG

MERCURY SPACECRAFT MANNED FLIGHTS 1961–3

Name	Mission	Launcher	Launch date	Duration	Crew	Flight
Freedom 7	MR-3	Redstone	May 5, 1961	15 min	Shepard	Sub-orbital
Liberty Bell 7	MR-4	Redstone	July 21, 1961	16 min	Grissom	Sub-orbital
Friendship 7	MA-6	Atlas	February 20, 1962	4 hr, 55 min	Glenn	Three orbits
Aurora 7	MA-7	Atlas	May 24, 1962	4 hr, 56 min	Carpenter	Three orbits
Sigma 7	MA-8	Atlas	October 3, 1962	9 hr, 13 min	Schirra	Six orbits
Faith 7	MA-9	Atlas	May 15, 1963	34 hr, 20 min	Cooper	22.5 orbits

MAN IN A CAN

Enclose the driver's seat of a small compact as far as the pedals, put on six layers of clothes, then enter feet-first through the sunroof and you have an idea of what it was like to squeeze into a Mercury capsule. Those who flew it said that you didn't climb into a Mercury, you put it on! To add to the discomfort, the forces on astronauts at launch reached 7 g and during reentry up to 11 g—11 times their Earth weight.

Mercury's builders could not be sure how astronauts would react in space, so the craft was designed not to rely on them. The chief means of control was the onboard automatic stabilization and control system, which was monitored from the ground by a rate stabilization and control system. In emergencies, the astronaut could take over some of these functions—known as manual proportional control—and there was also a fully manual system.

Even so, an astronaut had only limited control over the capsule. He could align it from side to side or up and down, and roll it using 18 hydrogen peroxide-powered thruster nozzles. But if anything major went wrong, there was little that he could do about it.

WINDOW ON THE WORLD

The display console included a revolving globe to show the astronaut his position as he orbited the Earth at 17,500 mph (28,160km/h). There was also a periscope system with a screen that displayed a black-and-white image of what lay immediately below. For the first Mercury astronaut, Alan Shepard, this was his only means of viewing the outside world. However, windows were fitted to all the subsequent capsules in the Mercury program.

At the base of the capsule was a pack of three solid-propellant retrorockets that could be manually fired as the astronaut aligned the craft at the correct angle for reentry. The pack was then discarded to expose an ablative—designed-to-melt—heatshield. This absorbed the searing 3,000°F (1,600°C) heat of reentry, which occurred 25 miles (40 km) up, at a speed of 15,000 miles per hour (24,000 km/h).

Because the Mercury spacecrafts had a blunt shape and reentered base-down at a slight angle, they could generate enough lift to permit some aerodynamic control. By using the manual controls the astronaut could vary his flight path and hence the craft's point of splashdown in the ocean.

At an altitude of 10,000 ft (3,048 m) and a speed of 400 miles per hour (644 km/h), a 63-ft (19-m)-diameter chute was deployed to slow the craft to about 20 miles per hour (32 km/h) at sea level. Just before splashdown, an airbag inflated under the heatshield to cushion the impact.

WHERE ARE THEY NOW?
...THE MERCURY CAPSULES

Anyone looking at one of the surviving Mercury capsules will readily appreciate the courage of the astronauts who flew them.

Although the Soviet Union had already launched a successful manned spacecraft, the physical and psychological effects of spaceflight were still largely unknown when the manned Mercury flights began. The Mercury successes proved that manned spaceflight was not as dangerous to the body as many believed.

The biggest fears were that weightlessness would result in severe disorientation and that the stress of the g-forces during reentry would cause injury. There were also concerns that space travelers would be psychologically affected. These fears were largely dispelled by the success of Mercury. Even so, with space technology in its infancy, the risks were still enormous. The launch vehicles were no more than lightly modified guided missiles. And the capsules were equally crude by modern standards: The tiny conical section in which the astronaut traveled was just 6 ft 10 in (2 m) long by 6 ft 2½ in (1.9 m) at its widest point.

Of the six manned Mercury capsules, five have been preserved and are on public display, apart from Gus Grissom's Liberty Bell 7 capsule, which unfortunately sank after splashdown.

LUCKY 7

ALAN SHEPARD NAMED HIS SPACECRAFT *FREEDOM* AND ADDED THE NUMBER 7 BECAUSE IT WAS THE CRAFT'S FACTORY PRODUCTION NUMBER. GUS GRISSOM, WHO FLEW THE NEXT MISSION, NAMED HIS CRAFT *LIBERTY BELL*. HE, TOO, ADDED THE NUMBER 7, PARTLY BECAUSE SHEPARD HAD, BUT ALSO BECAUSE HE THOUGHT IT WOULD BE A GOOD WAY TO COMMEMORATE THE 7 ASTRONAUTS IN THE MERCURY PROGRAM. THE OTHER ASTRONAUTS FOLLOWED SUIT: *FRIENDSHIP 7* (JOHN GLENN), *AURORA 7* (SCOTT CARPENTER), *SIGMA 7* (WALTER SCHIRRA) AND *FAITH 7* (GORDON COOPER). GROUNDED ASTRONAUT DEKE SLAYTON WAS GOING TO NAME HIS CAPSULE *DELTA 7*.

MERCURY CAPSULE

heatshield

pressurized inner capsule

titanium/nickel alloy outer shell

retrorocket pack

ceramic fiber insulation

control stick

reentry parachutes

control thrusters

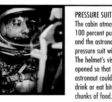

PRESSURE SUIT
The cabin atmosphere was 100 percent pure oxygen, and the astronaut wore a pressure suit with a helmet. The helmet's visor could be opened so that the astronaut could take a drink or eat bite-sized chunks of food.

ESCAPE system
The orange-painted nose-mounted launch escape rocket (right) was designed to fire and pull the Mercury capsule to safety in case the launch vehicle malfunctioned either during or immediately after launch.

Alan Shepard's capsule, is on display at the National Air and Space Museum.

CONTROLS
Aside from limited manual takeover in an emergency, the astronaut had very little control of the craft. Most of the displays were for monitoring.

periscope

antennae and infrared horizon sensors

escape rocket nozzles

aerodynamic spike

VOSTOK MISSIONS

T he Soviet Union stunned the world in 1957 with the launch of Sputnik 1, the Earth's first artificial satellite. By 1961, they were ready to extend their lead in the space race. Under the brilliant leadership of Sergei Korolev, Soviet engineers built the Vostok craft, designed to take a person into space. And on April 12, 1961, it did just that—Yuri Gagarin orbited the Earth in 108 minutes. Five missions later, Valentina Tereshkova became the first woman in orbit. The pioneering age of spaceflight had truly begun.

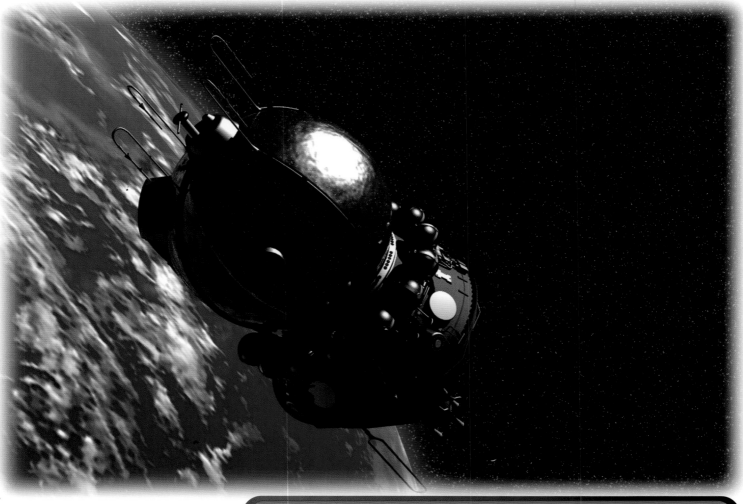

VOSTOK MISSION FACTS

CRAFT	COSMONAUT	DATE	ORBITS	DURATION
V1	YURI GAGARIN	APRIL 12, 1961	1	1 HR 48 MIN
V2	GHERMAN TITOV	AUGUST 6, 1961	17	1 DAY 1 HR 18MIN
V3	ANDRIAN NIKOLAYEV	AUGUST 11, 1962	64	3 DAYS 22 HR 22 MIN
V4	PAVEL POPOVICH	AUGUST 12, 1962	48	2 DAYS 22 HR 57 MIN
V5	VALERY BYKOVSKY	JUNE 14, 1963	81	4 DAYS 23 HR 6 MIN
V6	VALENTINA TERESHKOVA	JUNE 16, 1963	48	2 DAYS 22 HR 50 MIN

STARS OF THE EAST

Fifteen minutes into Yuri Gagarin's historic flight aboard Vostok 1, a monitoring post off Alaska detected what sounded like a conversation between the Baikonur cosmodrome in Soviet Kazakhstan and a spacecraft in Earth orbit. For once, the usually secretive Soviets were happy to be overheard. Months earlier, U.S. President John F. Kennedy had declared: "If the Soviet Union were first in outer space, that would be the most serious defeat the United States has suffered in many, many years." Now, his words would come back to haunt him.

If Vostok 1 was a political victory for the Kremlin, it was a personal triumph for Sergei Korolev and his team at Baikonur. Korolev had survived Stalinist purges, the Nazi invasion of Russia, and many other setbacks in his drive to build a workable spacecraft. As a new decade dawned, it was only a matter of time before one carried a cosmonaut into space. But who would it be?

The two leading contenders were Gagarin and Gherman Titov. Korolev chose the smiling Gagarin—the model of a communist hero. But Titov's Vostok 2 mission was another great leap forward—17 orbits and a full day in space. The American response came in February 1962, with John Glenn's three orbits aboard Friendship 7. Yet within months,

the Soviets surged ahead again when Vostoks 3 and 4, launched 24 hours apart, passed within three miles (five km) of each other in the first space rendezvous.

Vostoks 5 and 6 were also paired in June 1963, giving Korolev the chance to show that docking two spacecraft in orbit was within his reach. But the Soviets' biggest success was in the propaganda war. In Vostok 6 was a woman— Valentina Tereshkova.

MISSION DIARY: VOSTOK 1–6

JULY 1958
SERGEI KOROLEV OUTLINES THE ADVANTAGES OF VOSTOK MISSIONS IN LETTER TO SOVIET LEADERS.
NOVEMBER 1958
VOSTOK PROGRAM APPROVED.
MARCH 1960
TWENTY COSMONAUTS (INCLUDING GHERMAN TITOV, ABOVE) BEGIN INTENSIVE TRAINING FOR VOSTOK FLIGHTS.
AUGUST 19, 1960
TEST OF VOSTOK LAUNCH VEHICLE WITH TWO DOGS, BELKA AND STRELKA, ABOARD. IT IS SUCCESSFULLY RECOVERED.
MARCH 9, 1961
SUCCESSFUL RECOVERY OF A VOSTOK CRAFT WITH A DOG, CHERNUSHKA, ABOARD.
MARCH 25, 1961
FINAL TEST LAUNCH. CANINE PASSENGER ZVEZDOCHKA (RIGHT) RECOVERED SAFELY.
APRIL 12, 1961
FIRST HUMAN SPACEFLIGHT. YURI GAGARIN ORBITS EARTH ABOARD

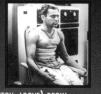

VOSTOK 1.
AUGUST 6, 1961
VOSTOK 2 COSMONAUT TITOV (RIGHT) COMPLETES A FULL DAY IN SPACE.
FEBRUARY 20, 1962
U.S. PUTS A MAN IN ORBIT—JOHN GLENN, ABOARD FRIENDSHIP 7.
AUGUST 11, 1962
JOINT MISSION OF VOSTOKS 3 AND 4. COSMONAUTS ANDRIAN NIKOLAYEV AND PAVEL POPOVICH PASS WITHIN JUST OVER THREE MILES (FIVE KM) OF EACH OTHER IN ORBIT.
AUGUST 12
POPOVICH (RIGHT) IN VOSTOK 4 IS BROUGHT BACK A DAY EARLY AFTER GROUND CONTROL MISINTERPRETS SOME OF HIS COMMENTS AS BEING CODE WORDS FOR A PROBLEM.
JUNE 14–16, 1963
JOINT MISSION OF VOSTOKS 5 AND 6. VOSTOK 5 FAILS TO REACH THE CORRECT ORBIT FOR RENDEZVOUS AND ITS MISSION IS CUT SHORT. VOSTOK 6 MAKES HISTORY, AS VALENTINA TERESHKOVA BECOMES THE FIRST WOMAN IN SPACE.

SIGN OF HONOR

ONE OF THE HIGHLIGHTS OF A COSMONAUT'S CAREER IS THE CEREMONIAL SIGNING OF YURI GAGARIN'S DIARY. THIS TRADITION WAS INITIATED AS A TRIBUTE TO THE "FIRST COSMONAUT" AFTER HE WAS KILLED IN A PLANE CRASH IN 1968. HERE, MIR 18 COSMONAUT VLADIMIR DEZHUROV SIGNS, WATCHED BY GUEST NASA ASTRONAUT NORMAN THAGARD (SEATED LEFT). THE TWO MEN HAD RECENTLY RETURNED FROM MIR ABOARD THE SHUTTLE ATLANTIS, AFTER THE FIRST MIR–SHUTTLE DOCKING IN 1995.

BAD NEWS

IT WAS 3:30 A.M. IN FLORIDA WHEN MOSCOW RADIO BROADCAST THE NEWS THAT GAGARIN HAD CIRCLED THE EARTH. WHEN TELEPHONED BY REPORTERS FOR A COMMENT, A SHOCKED AND ANGRY COLONEL JOHN "SHORTY" POWERS, PRESS OFFICER FOR NASA's MERCURY PROGRAM, CAM UP WITH THE UNFORTUNATE RESPONSE: "WE'RE ALL ASLEEP DOWN HERE!"

MISSION PROFILE

1 LIFTOFF
Vostok blasted off from the Baikonur cosmodrome in Soviet Kazakhstan atop a modified R-7 intercontinental ballistic missile containing no fewer than 32 thrust chambers. Once in orbit, the shields protecting the two-module spacecraft were discarded.

2 ORBIT
Gagarin sat upright in a modified pilot's ejection seat in the spherical crew module. This was supplied with power and a pressurized oxygen/nitrogen mixture by the equipment module. The orbit lasted 89 minutes.

3 REENTRY
Retro-rocket fired to brake the craft, then explosive bolts released the equipment module. The crew module plunged into the atmosphere, protected from the heat of air friction by an ablative shield, which was designed to burn off during reentry. At an altitude of four and a half miles (7 km) above the Soviet Union, Gagarin ejected.

GEMINI
1 & 2

Without the Gemini program, there would have been no Apollo. It was NASA's 12 Gemini missions that bridged the gap between single-person and multi-crew spacecraft and grappled with the technical problems of sending astronauts to the Moon. But before the twin-seat Gemini capsule could undertake crewed missions, its technology had to be rigorously tested. Geminis 1 and 2 verified that the new spacecraft was safe enough to send two people into orbit—and get them back again.

GEMINI DATA

	GEMINI 1	GEMINI 2
CREW	NONE	NONE
LAUNCH VEHICLE	TITAN 2	TITAN 2
LAUNCH WEIGHT	3.51 TONS (3.18 TONNES)	3.43 TONS (3.11 TONNES)
LAUNCH DATE	APRIL 8, 1964	JANUARY 19, 1965
LAUNCH COMPLEX	PAD 19, CAPE KENNEDY	PAD 19, CAPE KENNEDY
MISSION	THREE PLANNED ORBITS (BUT LASTED FOR 64)	18-MINUTE SUB-ORBITAL FLIGHT
TEST GOALS	LAUNCHER, LAUNCHER/SPACECRAFT COMPATIBILITY	ALL SYSTEMS, HEAT SHIELD, RECOVERY
HIGHEST ALTITUDE	200 MILES (321 KM)	107 MILES (172 KM)
RECOVERY DATE	NOT RECOVERED; BURNED UP APRIL 12, 1964	JANUARY 19, 1964, IN SOUTH ATLANTIC

MACHINE BEFORE MAN

The first two Gemini flights thundered off the launchpad in April 1964 and January 1965 without crew. In their place were instruments to record temperature, vibration, g force and other factors—and help make sure future launches were safe for astronauts.

Gemini 1, sitting atop its equally new two-stage Titan 2 launcher, reached space safely and was tracked as it orbited the Earth. Four days and 64 orbits after leaving Cape Kennedy, it burned up as planned over the South

Atlantic Ocean. Now NASA knew that their new spacecraft could fly. Gemini 2's job was to determine whether it could return astronauts in one piece.

Gemini 2's flight was planned as a short, sub-orbital mission—a ballistic hop, similar to Alan Shepard's Freedom 7 flight, that would test all systems from launch to splashdown. After four weather-related delays and one false start, Gemini 2 was finally launched successfully on its 18-minute flight. The first and second stages of the Titan launcher separated without a hitch, and soon the capsule was firing its retro-rockets to begin the

return to Earth. Gemini 2 was programmed to shoot through the atmosphere at much higher speeds than later flights to test its heat shield. It survived and splashed into the ocean, suspended from its single parachute.

The way was now clear for

more complex crewed missions. Two months after Gemini 2, astronauts Gus Grissom and John Young entered Earth orbit aboard Gemini 3 to practice the spaceflight techniques that would one day be used to land men on the Moon.

SAVING THE DAY

GEMINI 2 (BELOW) WAS ORIGINALLY SCHEDULED FOR A DECEMBER 9, 1964, LAUNCH. THE COUNTDOWN RAN SMOOTHLY AND AT 11:41 THE TITAN LAUNCHER'S FIRST STAGE ENGINES BURST INTO LIFE — ONLY TO SHUT DOWN THREE SECONDS LATER. THE AUTOMATIC FAULT DETECTION SYSTEM HAD LOCATED A GLITCH IN ONE OF THE THRUSTER STEERING CHAMBERS AND SHUT DOWN THE ENGINES FASTER THAN ANY HUMAN COULD HAVE. GEMINI 2 WAS SAVED FOR ANOTHER DAY.

MISSION DIARY: GEMINI 1 & 2

GEMINI 1
MAY 21, 1963
GEMINI'S BRAND-NEW TITAN LAUNCHER IS COMPLETED.
JULY 5, 1963
TESTING OF GEMINI 1 BEGINS.
OCTOBER 4, 1963
GEMINI 1 IS DELIVERED TO CAPE KENNEDY IN FLORIDA.
MARCH 3, 1964
GEMINI 1 IS PLACED ON LAUNCHPAD.
APRIL 8, 1964
GEMINI 1 IS LAUNCHED (ABOVE).

APRIL 12, 1964
AFTER A TOTAL OF 64 ORBITS, GEMINI 1 BURNS UP ON REENTRY.
GEMINI 2
AUG-SEP 1964
HURRICANES DELAY GEMINI 2'S LAUNCH. ITS LAUNCHER IS REMOVED FROM THE LAUNCHPAD.
SEPTEMBER 21, 1964
THE GEMINI 2 CAPSULE ARRIVES AT CAPE KENNEDY. THE LAUNCH IS RESCHEDULED FOR LATE FALL.
OCTOBER 18, 1964
GEMINI 2 IS DISPATCHED TO THE LAUNCHPAD.

NOVEMBER 28, 1964
FINAL TESTS ON THE SPACECRAFT AND LAUNCHER ARE COMPLETED.
DECEMBER 9, 1964
SECONDS AFTER THE TITAN'S LAUNCHER'S ENGINES IGNITE, THE LAUNCH IS AUTOMATICALLY HALTED.
JANUARY 19, 1965
ON ITS SECOND ATTEMPT, GEMINI 2 LAUNCHES (LEFT). DURING ITS 2,000-MILE (3,218 KM) JOURNEY, AN ONBOARD CAMERA BELOW ITS THRUSTERS TAKES THE PICTURE OF EARTH (ABOVE).

TWIN TEST MISSIONS

2 First stage separates 2½ minutes into the flight and splashes down in the Atlantic.

3 Second stage ignites to boost Gemini into space.

4 Capsule separates from second stage and uses thrusters to blast clear.

DOWN TIME
During the six months that elapsed between the Gemini 1 and Gemini 2 test missions, Gemini-3 astronauts John Young (far left) and Gus Grissom were kept hard at work training for their mission in flight simulators.

1 Liftoff from launchpad 19, Cape Kennedy.

GEMINI 1
Completes 64 orbits of Earth before burning up in the atmosphere.

5 Discarded second stage burns up in the atmosphere.

GEMINI OFF-THE-PAD EJECTION

ESCAPE PLAN
Unlike the Mercury or Apollo craft, the Gemini capsule had no escape rockets to lift the capsule clear of the launcher in an emergency. Instead, the crew had ejection seats.

GEMINI 2
Completes sub-orbital hop, then descends at high speed through the atmosphere before splashing down in the South Atlantic Ocean.

TEST TUBES
Gemini was conceived (above) as NASA's first two-person spacecraft. But on the first two Gemini missions, the crew was replaced with ballast and sensors to monitor physical conditions aboard the capsule in preparation for the manned flights.

VOSKHOD 1

October 13, 1964: Newspapers worldwide reported the flight of Voskhod 1, the first "space passenger ship." Only one-man spaceflights had taken place before Voskhod ("Sunrise") carried its three cosmonauts. But "space passenger ship" was not an accurate description. The Soviet Union had to upstage the forthcoming U.S. Gemini flights at almost any cost, and the three brave men were squeezed into a stripped-down single-seat Vostok capsule. They risked their lives for a mission whose sole purpose was propaganda.

VOSKHOD 1 STATISTICS

MISSION	VOSKHOD 1 (CODE-NAME RUBY), 13TH CREWED SPACEFLIGHT
CREW	VLADIMIR KOMAROV (COMMANDER; RIGHT, CENTER)
	KONSTANTIN FEOKTISTOV (ENGINEER; NEAR RIGHT)
	BORIS YEGOROV (DOCTOR; FAR RIGHT)
LAUNCH	OCTOBER 12, 1964, 7:30 A.M. GMT ABOARD AN A-2 ROCKET
LAUNCH SITE	BAIKONUR LAUNCH COMPLEX 1
SPACECRAFT DIMENSIONS	16.4 FT (5 M) LONG , 7.9 FT (2.4 M) IN DIAMETER
MASS	11,731 LB (5,321 KG)
MAXIMUM ALTITUDE	208 MILES (335 KM)
MISSION DURATION	1 DAY 17 MINUTES
NUMBER OF ORBITS	16
RECOVERY	OCTOBER 13, 1964, 7:47 A.M. GMT

CLOSE QUARTERS

The Soviet Vostok craft had put the first men into space and firmly established the Soviet lead in the space race. When Vostok flights ended in 1963, the Soviets hoped to follow it with a larger spacecraft called Soyuz, capable of carrying two or more cosmonauts. But the development of Soyuz had fallen behind schedule. Its first flight was not expected until 1965 at the very earliest.

Meanwhile, in the U.S., the Gemini program—which would place a two-man crew in orbit—was forging ahead. Soviet leader Nikita Khrushchev was appalled by the idea of an American "first." He ordered his space officials to ensure that three cosmonauts would fly in space before the first Gemini liftoff.

Because Soyuz was nowhere near ready, Soviet space engineers had no choice but to modify the obsolete, single-seater Vostok. Without its ejection seat and reserve parachute system, there was room for three cosmonauts with two days' supplies to squeeze in sideways—but without spacesuits. The "new" spacecraft, which was in reality a dangerously overloaded Vostok shuttle, was called Voskhod.

On October 12, 1964, Voskhod 1 headed toward space from the same launch pad used by Yuri Gagarin on his historic flight three years earlier. Mission commander Komarov sat in the right-hand seat in front of the capsule's controls. The mission engineer, Konstantin Feoktistov, was in the left-hand seat and sitting between the two men, raised a few inches above them, was Boris Yegorov, the mission's doctor.

DAY TRIPPERS

Since three cosmonauts were aboard what was really no more than a one-man spacecraft, the experiments carried out during the flight of Voskhod 1 were very basic. Yegorov carried out some simple medical examinations on his two colleagues. Komarov tested the spacecraft's control system and new ion thrusters, while Feoktistov used a special horizon sensor to test orbital navigation techniques. The three cosmonauts weren't alone in the crowded capsule— fruit flies and plants were carried to examine the effects of zero g on these life-forms. As Voskhod 1 passed over the Soviet Union, a

THREE MEN IN A CAN

The hurriedly improvised Voskhod spacecraft was not built for comfort or safety. The three crewmembers had to squeeze into a space designed for one. And in order to fit in, the crew did not wear spacesuits and had no ejection seats. If anything had gone wrong, they would have had no means of escape.

communication antenna

command antenna

modified Vostok capsule, with three seats instead of one

external oxygen tanks

KONSTANTIN FEOKTISTOV
Technical scientist Feoktistov gained invaluable experience during his only spaceflight. He went on to help design both spacecraft and space stations.

VLADIMIR KOMAROV
Flying his first space mission on Voskhod 1, Komarov was the only trained cosmonaut in the crew. He was killed in 1967 when Soyuz 1's parachutes failed to open for landing.

BORIS YEGOROV
The 27-year-old doctor was the youngest person aboard Voskhod 1. Yegorov returned to medicine and a successful career. He died of a heart attack in September 1994.

television camera on board beamed pictures of the crew into Russian homes, and the cosmonauts used a hand-held camera to take snapshots of Earth's surface 208 miles (335 km) below them.

After a day in orbit, the spacecraft was positioned for its return home. The inexperienced Yegorov was frightened by the blaze created as Voskhod began to plunge through the atmosphere: He thought the craft had caught fire. Deceleration increased to a

crushing eight g. But at 16,000 ft (4,900 m), Voskhod's parachutes opened, and just before touchdown, small retro-rockets reduced the landing speed so effectively that the crew didn't even feel the touchdown. They only knew that they had landed because they could hear wheat stubble rustling against the hull of the capsule.

The cosmonauts had only been in space a day, but in that time Khrushchev had been ousted from

power. When they returned to Moscow it was a new Soviet leader—Leonid Brezhnev—who welcomed them.

Although officially the mission's purpose was to test a new spacecraft and carry out experiments, in reality, Voskhod 1 was not much more than a propaganda mission. Its sole purpose was to beat Gemini into space, and allow the Soviet Union to maintain a psychological advantage over the Americans.

MISSION DIARY: VOSKHOD 1

MAY 1963 SPACE ENGINEERS BEGIN WORK ON SUCCESSOR CRAFT TO THE SINGLE-SEAT VOSTOK.
SEPTEMBER 1963 RAPID DEVELOPMENT OF THE VOSKHOD SPACECRAFT BEGINS (RIGHT).
MARCH 1964 A GROUP OF COSMONAUTS BEGIN THEIR TRAINING FOR THE VOSKHOD 1 MISSION.
JUNE 1964 YEGOROV, A DOCTOR, AND FEOKTISTOV, AN ENGINEER, JOIN THE CREW AS "SPECIALIST COSMONAUTS" JUST FOUR MONTHS BEFORE LAUNCH.
OCTOBER 6, 1964 LESS THAN A WEEK BEFORE THE ACTUAL FLIGHT, THE UNMANNED COSMOS 47 MISSION TESTS A VOSKHOD CRAFT.

OCTOBER 12, 1964 VOSKHOD 1 IS LAUNCHED (RIGHT) FROM BAIKONUR COSMODROME. NIKITA KHRUSHCHEV SPEAKS TO THE CREW WHILE ON VACATION. THIS WILL BE KHRUSHCHEV'S LAST PUBLIC STATEMENT: HE IS REMOVED FROM POWER DURING THE FLIGHT. CREWMEMBERS YEGOROV AND FEOKTISTOV SUFFER FROM SPACESICKNESS.
OCTOBER 13, 1964 THE VOSKHOD 1 SPACECRAFT REENTERS THE ATMOSPHERE AND PARACHUTES BACK TO THE SURFACE, RETURNING THE CREW SAFELY TO EARTH.

THE FIRST SPACEWALK

On March 18, 1965, Voskhod 2 cosmonaut Alexei Leonov crawled into an 8-ft (2.4 m) airlock tunnel far above the Earth. He floated out of the other end into open space, to hurtle around the planet as continents and clouds passed below. The spacewalk was the last Soviet space spectacular, carried out in haste to upstage the U.S. Gemini missions. Leonov's orbital adventure was risky and he was lucky to get back into his spacecraft alive. But survive he did—to go down in history as the first human to walk in space.

VOSKHOD 2 MISSION

SPACECRAFT	VOSKHOD 2, THE WORLD'S 14TH CREWED SPACEFLIGHT AND THE 8TH FROM THE SOVIET UNION	AIRLOCK DIMENSIONS	4 FT X 8 FT 4 IN (1.2 x 2.5M)
		AIRLOCK MASS	551 LB (250 KG)
LAUNCH	MARCH 18, 1965, FROM THE BAIKONUR COSMODROME	SPACEWALK DURATION	24 MINUTES OUTSIDE CAPSULE, WITH 12 MINUTES SPENT OUTSIDE AIRLOCK IN OPEN SPACE
CREW	PAVEL BELYAYEV AND ALEXEI LEONOV	MISSION DURATION	1 DAY 2 HR 2 MIN
MAXIMUM ALTITUDE	310 MILES (499 KM)	LANDING	MARCH 19, 1965,
SPEED	17,400 MPH (28,000 KM/H)		IN NORTHERN RUSSIA

RISKY VENTURE

Cold War officials in the Soviet Union made cosmonaut Alexei Leonov's first historic steps in space sound like a walk in the park. A government news agency reported that Leonov "felt well" during his swim in space and on his return to the Voskhod capsule. Leonov apparently enjoyed good control over his movements thanks to a 50-ft (15-m) tether. To the U.S. government and the world at large, the first spacewalk was presented as an easy triumph for Soviet engineering.

In reality, Leonov had been doing anything but enjoying the view during his 24-minute space adventure on March 18, 1965. He nearly suffered heat stroke as he somersaulted around space, and spent several fraught minutes struggling to reenter Voskhod 2. Leonov has since revealed that he carried a suicide pill in case commander Pavel Belyayev was forced to leave him in orbit.

The politics of the Cold War made it vital to paint Leonov's maneuver as a total success. With the Gemini program, the U.S. threatened to seize the lead in the space race, and the Soviets were determined to meet or beat Gemini's goals, one of which was the first spacewalk. At short notice and with Soyuz still under development, Soviet engineers had to work with what they had. In the end, Leonov exited a modified Vostok capsule based on the design that took Yuri Gagarin to another first—first person in orbit—in 1961. Voskhod 2 was fitted with a Volga inflatable airlock to maintain cabin pressures and prepare Leonov for his spacewalk.

HUMAN SATELLITE

Leonov entered the airlock tunnel through Voskhod's hatch 300 miles (500 km) above the Pacific Ocean. There was a short wait while the airlock pressure was lowered to the space vacuum—if the pressures had not been equalized Leonov would have shot out like a cork from a bottle. As the airlock opened, Leonov floated headfirst into space.

The conditions inside Leonov's spacesuit recreated a little Earth atmosphere, with steady temperature and the correct levels of breathing gases. But without the luxury of gravity, Leonov found it hard to control the cord that tied him to Voskhod. After a poorly

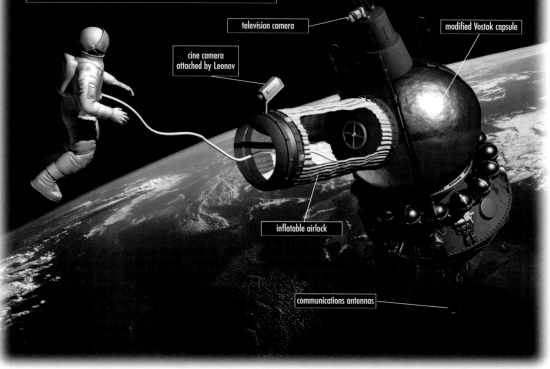

THE WALK OF LEONOV'S LIFE

Leonov's spacesuit protected him against the temperature extremes in space, from 300°F (150°C) on the sunward side to −220°F (−140°C) in the shade. Leonov exited through the fully extended Volga airlock, which was designed, built and tested in just nine months.

communications antennas

television camera

cine camera attached by Leonov

modified Vostok capsule

inflatable airlock

communications antennas

MISSION DIARY: THE LONG MARCH

APRIL 1964
BELYAYEV AND LEONOV (RIGHT) ARE SELECTED AS THE CREW FOR THE VOSKHOD 2 MISSION AND BEGIN TRAINING.
JUNE 1964
ENGINEERS BEGIN THE DESIGN OF AN AIRLOCK FOR VOSKHOD 2.
FEBRUARY 1965
COSMOS 57 IS LAUNCHED TO TEST VOSKHOD 2 BUT DISINTEGRATES IN ORBIT.
MARCH 18, 1965, 2:00 A.M. EST

VOSKHOD 2 IS LAUNCHED FROM THE BAIKONUR COSMODROME IN KAZAKHSTAN.
MARCH 18, 2:30 A.M.
THE INFLATABLE AIRLOCK IS EXTENDED FROM THE SIDE OF VOSKHOD 2.
MARCH 18, 2:45 A.M.
LEONOV ENTERS THE AIRLOCK FROM HIS SEAT IN VOSKHOD 2.
MARCH 18, 3:30 A.M.
AFTER THE AIRLOCK HAS BEEN PRESSURIZED, THE OUTER HATCH IS OPENED AND LEONOV FLOATS INTO OPEN SPACE.
MARCH 18, 3:42 A.M.
LEONOV BEGINS TO REENTER THE AIRLOCK (RIGHT) WITH DIFFICULTY.

MARCH 18, 3:49 A.M.
LEONOV IS SAFELY BACK INSIDE VOSKHOD 2.
MARCH 19, 1965
VOSKHOD 2 RETURNS TO EARTH BUT OVERSHOOTS THE LANDING AREA, ENDING UP IN A REMOTE SNOW-COVERED FOREST IN NORTHERN RUSSIA. THE CREW HAS A LENGTHY, COLD WAIT BEFORE THEY ARE RESCUED.

timed pull, Leonov crashed into the spacecraft, rocking his comrade.

Leonov spent 12 minutes floating freely in space before he was instructed to reenter the airlock. But with his spacesuit inflated like a balloon, Leonov could not bend his legs enough to climb back into the airlock. After several attempts, Leonov was forced to bleed some of the suit's air to make it less rigid. In doing so, he risked a dangerous attack of the bends. With his pulse

racing, Leonov finally squeezed himself back into the airlock and closed the outer hatch. He was close to suffering heat stroke and reported that he was "up to the knees" in sweat.

More trouble awaited on Earth. A malfunction in Voskhod's systems forced Belyayev to make a manually controlled descent. The spacecraft overshot its designated landing site by over 700 miles (1,100 km), to land in a remote, snowy forest in

northern Russia. The cosmonauts shivered for over two hours before a rescue helicopter arrived.

Whatever the difficulties, Leonov had made a landmark achievement—and most importantly, beaten U.S. astronaut Ed White to the first spacewalk by three months. Although the U.S. regained supremacy with the Apollo Moon landing and Neil Armstrong's giant leap, the first steps belong to Leonov.

GEMINI
8–12

When the Gemini program began in 1965, no one knew if humans could survive in space long enough to get to the Moon and back. No one had done an in-orbit rendezvous or a docking between two vehicles. And no one had made an EVA—a spacewalk.

But to achieve a lunar landing, these feats would have to be routine. Early Gemini missions started to tackle the issue, but the last five got results. Geminis 8 through 12 saw the first dockings and first successful spacewalk—crucial steps in reaching the Moon.

GEMINI MISSIONS 8–12

	Gemini 8	Gemini 9	Gemini 10	Gemini 11	Gemini 12
Crew	Neil Armstrong, Dave Scott	Tom Stafford, Gene Cernan	John Young, Michael Collins	Pete Conrad, Dick Gordon	Jim Lovell, Buzz Aldrin
Launch	11:41:02 A.M. EST, Mar. 16, 1966	8:39:33 A.M. EST, June 3, 1966	5:20:26 P.M. EST, July 18, 1966	9:42:26 A.M. EST, Sept. 12, 1966	3:46:33 P.M. EST, Nov. 11, 1966
Mission Highlight	First docking of two vehicles in space.	Cernan performed an EVA.	Docked with Agena rocket; Collins made a spacewalk.	Set world altitude record; performed a full orbit of Earth.	Aldrin made the most successful spacewalk of the Gemini program.

WHAT'S UP, DOCK?

Neil Armstrong and Dave Scott were blasted into space aboard Gemini 8 on March 16, 1966. Their assignment was a space first—to dock with an Agena rocket circling the Earth. But the mission nearly became one of the worst disasters in U.S. space history.

Armstrong soon caught up with the target rocket and performed a flawless docking. But after flying around the world for 30 minutes attached to the rocket, the spacecraft began rolling and yawing simultaneously. Suspecting it was a problem with the Agena, Armstrong hurriedly undocked. The spacecraft, though, spun even faster. The Sun and Earth flashed dizzyingly past the window. If the problem wasn't fixed soon, Armstrong and Scott would lose consciousness and Gemini would break apart. The fault was in the reaction control system, but Armstrong had no way of knowing. Still, he was resourceful and cool-headed. Switching off the thrusters, he used the reentry control system to gain control of the craft. Mission control instructed him to perform a deorbit burn. Without the main system, the flight would have to be aborted. So just 10 hours and 41 minutes after launch, Gemini 8 splashed into the Pacific.

Gemini 9 fared little better. This time the Agena failed on launch. An alternative docking target was launched. As Tom Stafford and Gene Cernan closed in, they saw that it, too, was faulty. The maneuver was abandoned. Cernan made his spacewalk as planned, connected to Gemini by nothing more than a 30-ft (9 m) umbilical cord. But with little training, he floundered around, quickly becoming exhausted, and the spacewalk was cut short.

SUCCESS AT LAST

The first spacecraft to make a completely successful docking was Gemini 10. Michael Collins and John Young circled the Earth for 39 hours attached to their Agena vehicle. A second difficult spacewalk was made by Collins. Gemini 11 also docked successfully with its Agena. Dick Gordon climbed out of the capsule and attempted the third spacewalk. But like all his predecessors, he kept

floating away from the capsule. He was struggling so much that he overloaded the cooling system in his suit and his heart rate reached 180 beats per minute. So the spacewalk was cut short again. After a not-very-restful sleep period, the tired astronauts opened the hatch a second time. Gordon stood up to take some photographs of the Earth and its clouds. No one was in a hurry. Before he realized it, Conrad had fallen asleep. Waking up with a start, he yelled to Gordon, "Hey, Dick, would you believe I fell asleep?" For a reply he received a "Huh? What?" To his amazement, Gordon had fallen asleep, too, with his head sticking out of the capsule into outer space, as the Gemini hurtled around the Earth at 17,000 miles an hour (27,500 km/h).

Gemini 12 was the final mission in the program, and it suffered from a faulty radar. So while Jim Lovell flew the spacecraft, Buzz Aldrin dug out a set of rendezvous charts and manually calculated the maneuvers needed to dock with the Agena. It was an impressive display of skill, and Aldrin was later to make the Gemini program's most successful spacewalk. Admittedly, NASA had trained the astronauts well and provided them with plenty of handrails and tethers in space, but Aldrin demonstrated real ability. Few were surprised when he and the cool-headed Armstrong were chosen for the first Moon landing. Gemini had not only given NASA the chance to test its technical expertise, but it had helped the agency try out its astronauts, too.

IN COMMAND
Command Pilot John Young photographed from Gemini 10. In Young's capable hands, this mission was the first to complete an entirely successful docking with the Agena vehicle.

HOOKING UP
The Agena Target Docking vehicle, photographed from Gemini 8 on March 16, 1966, is 2 ft (0.6 m) away from the spacecraft's nose (bottom left of image on the right). The Agena's instrument panel can be seen at the center of this picture.

TUCKING IN
Technicians prepare to close the hatches on astronauts Tom Stafford (left) and Gene Cernan (right) before Gemini 9's liftoff. Backup astronauts Jim Lovell and Buzz Aldrin taped a humorous message (top center) to the spacecraft.

SPACE STEPS
Buzz Aldrin during his EVA (extravehicular activity), the most successful spacewalk of the Gemini program, as snapped by the onboard Gemini 12 camera.

MISSION DIARY: GEMINI 8–12

FEBRUARY 28, 1966
ELLIOT SEE AND CHARLIE BASSETT, THE TWO ASTRONAUTS ASSIGNED TO GEMINI 9, ARE KILLED WHEN THEIR T-38 JET CRASHES.
MARCH 16, 1966, 11:41:02 A.M. EST
GEMINI 8 IS LAUNCHED FROM CAPE CANAVERAL (RIGHT).
MARCH 17, 1966
GEMINI 8 DOCKS WITH AN AGENA TARGET VEHICLE 185 MILES (298 KM) ABOVE THE EARTH, BUT A THRUSTER ON THE GEMINI CAPSULE MALFUNCTIONS AND THE SPACECRAFT LOSES CONTROL. AFTER REGAINING CONTROL, ARMSTRONG AND SCOTT BRING THE MISSION TO A PREMATURE END JUST 10 HOURS 41 MINUTES AFTER LAUNCH.
JUNE 3, 1966, 8:39:33 A.M.
GEMINI 9 IS LAUNCHED.

JUNE 5, 1966
CERNAN MAKES AN EVA (LEFT).
JUNE 6, 1966
GEMINI 9 SPLASHES DOWN.
JULY 18, 1966, 5:20:26 P.M. GEMINI 10 IS LAUNCHED.
JULY 21, 1966 GEMINI 10 SPLASHES DOWN.
SEPTEMBER 12, 1966, 9:42:26 A.M. GEMINI 11 IS LAUNCHED. THE SPACECRAFT DOCKS WITH THE AGENA.
SEPTEMBER 15, 1966 GEMINI 11 SPLASHES DOWN.
NOVEMBER 11, 1966, 3:46:33 P.M. GEMINI 12 IS LAUNCHED.
NOVEMBER 15, 1966 GEMINI 12 SPLASHES DOWN.

Friendship 7

THE PIONEERS

The first space travelers were dogs and chimpanzees. The very first living creature in orbit was the U.S.S.R.'s Laika, a husky cross found straying on a Moscow street. She survived four days aboard Sputnik 2, only the second craft to enter orbit, before running out of oxygen. The first human in space was cosmonaut Yuri Gagarin, who made just one orbit of the earth in April 1961. American efforts to catch up began more cautiously, with Alan Shepard making a sub-orbital flight in May 1961 before John Glenn became the first U.S. astronaut in orbit in February 1962. The so-called "Mercury 7" astronauts all flew in space solo before the more ambitious two-crew Gemini programme began, followed by the three-man Apollo missions that culminated in the Moon landings and Neil Armstrong's first steps on the surface of another world.

The Space Shuttle fleet was retired in 2011. Although the Space Shuttle may have seemed to be a mature, rather than a pioneering space vehicle, it required more piloting skills than earlier spacecraft. U.S. astronauts have traditionally come from military test pilot backgrounds, until recently ruling out female commanders. Eileen Collins became the first woman to command a US space mission in 1999 and was chosen to pilot the first Shuttle to fly following the 2003 Columbia disaster, confirming that the "Right Stuff" is not just a male attribute.

John Glenn clambers aboard Friendship 7 on February 20, 1962. Previous launches had been postponed due to technical problems and bad weather, but this time Glenn finally reached space, becoming the first American to orbit the earth.

YURI GAGARIN

My God, he's got two daughters, how did he decide to do that? He must be crazy!" On April 12, 1961, these were the words with which Zoya Gagarin greeted the news that her brother Yuri had become the first man in space. Elsewhere, the reaction was more positive. Idolized by the world press, Yuri Gagarin became an icon of Soviet achievement. Gagarin died in 1968 after his personal life and career had become troubled, but he still remains respected as one of the great pioneers of space exploration.

LIFE LINES: YURI GAGARIN

FULL NAME	YURI ALEXEYEVICH GAGARIN
DATE OF BIRTH	MARCH 9, 1934
PLACE OF BIRTH	KLUSHINO, RUSSIA
EDUCATION	PRIMARY AND SECONDARY SCHOOLS IN KLUSHINO AND GZHATSK; APPRENTICE AT MOSCOW'S LYUBERTSY STEEL PLANT 1950–1; STUDENT OF TRACTOR CONSTRUCTION AT THE SARATOV TECHNICAL SCHOOL 1951–5
FAMILY	MARRIED VALYA (VALENTINA) GORYACHEVA 1957; TWO DAUGHTERS
CAREER	TRAINEE ORENBURG PILOT'S SCHOOL 1955–7; FIGHTER PILOT, BASED NEAR MURMANSK 1957–9; COSMONAUT 1961; DEPUTY DIRECTOR OF THE COSMONAUT TRAINING CENTER AT STAR CITY 1963–7; TEST PILOT 1968
DATE OF DEATH	MARCH 27, 1968

> ## *Gagarin's flight will stir people's imaginations as long as the Earth exists.*
> SOVIET WRITER KONSTANTIN PAUSTOVKSI

Gagarin was the first man in space (above) on April 12, 1961. His capsule, the Vostok (center), was designed by Sergei Korolev and his team. After his record flight, he was treated as a hero, awarded medals (right) and feted by Soviet leader Nikita Khrushchev (top right).

Gagarin and his family became icons of Soviet progress (above center) and his untimely death sent millions into mourning. His state funeral (above) was one of the biggest ever seen in Moscow.

PEOPLE'S HERO

On October 4, 1957, the Soviet Union launched the world's first artificial satellite. Two years later the Soviets decided to replicate their triumph— but this time the satellite would carry a human being. From a list of 2,200 eager applicants for the honor of becoming the first cosmonaut, a shortlist of just 20 men was selected for further training. Among these men was a 25-year-old fighter pilot called Yuri Gagarin.

Born on March 9, 1934, Yuri Gagarin was not an obvious choice of cosmonaut. A farmworker's son from Smolensk, he had survived the German occupation of World War II and had trained as a foundry apprentice before joining tractor school in 1951. On graduation he had progressed to the Soviet air force, where he proved himself an enthusiastic MiG pilot with a taste for heavy g-forces.

Gagarin was shorter than average—he needed to sit on a cushion to get a clear view over the nose of his MiG—and had open, cheerful features. He married young and by the age of 25 he was already a father, living with his new family in standard Soviet military housing. Gagarin was unassuming, uncomplaining and optimistic. In short, he was a textbook example of a Soviet citizen.

Gagarin's flying experience had little to do with his inclusion on the shortlist. He had spent 252 hours and 21 minutes in the air. Of these, only 75 hours had been as a solo pilot. Other candidates had been airborne for some 1,500 hours. Instead, the selectors were swayed by his solid background, determination and, most prosaically, by his size—the Vostok capsule in which the successful cosmonaut would travel had very little legroom.

ROCKET RIDE TO FAME

By the end of 1960, the 20-man squad had been whittled down to six. And by the following April there were two favorites: Gagarin and an equally short pilot named Gherman Titov. After an examination of each man's abilities and his ideological soundness— Titov sported a suspiciously bourgeois hairstyle—the decision was reached on April 7, 1961. Five days later, Gagarin hurtled into space and completed a 108-minute orbit of the Earth.

On his return he was showered with honors. A publicist's dream, he smiled photogenically, talked simply but expressively, and charmed heads of state around the world. Such was his popularity that a special department was created to handle his fan mail.

Fame took its toll, however. On October 3, 1961, he incurred severe head injuries by jumping from a second-floor window in a Crimean resort. Officially, he had hurt himself rescuing his daughter from the Black Sea. In fact, his wife had found him with another woman.

Gagarin continued to work on the space program, but his advisory capacities were nullified by rapid leaps in technology. And in 1967, when he criticized the disastrous launch of a Soyuz spacecraft—he had been back-up to the man who died aboard it—he was relieved of duties. He returned to the air force, and died in a plane crash in 1968. Ironically, he had been flying with an instructor. He left behind him a widow and two daughters.

CAREER TIMELINE

1934 BORN IN THE VILLAGE OF KLUSHINO LOCATED 100 MILES (160 KM) WEST OF MOSCOW.

1951 AFTER A YEAR'S APPRENTICESHIP AT MOSCOW'S LYUBERTSY STEEL PLANT, ENROLLS IN THE SARATOV TECHNICAL SCHOOL TO STUDY TRACTOR CONSTRUCTION.

1955 ON GRADUATION JOINS THE ORENBURG PILOT'S SCHOOL, MAKING HIS FIRST MIG SOLO FLIGHT ON MARCH 26, 1957.

1957 MARRIES VALYA GORYACHEVA. THE FOLLOWING MONTH GRADUATES FROM ORENBURG AND IS POSTED TO NIKEL AIRBASE NEAR MURMANSK.

1960 ALONG WITH 19 OTHER WOULD-BE COSMONAUTS, GAGARIN IS TRANSFERRED TO THE STAR CITY SPACE BASE, 30 MILES (48 KM) NORTHEAST OF MOSCOW.

APRIL 12, 1961 CHOSEN AS THE WORLD'S FIRST COSMONAUT ONLY FIVE DAYS PREVIOUSLY, GAGARIN BECOMES THE FIRST MAN IN SPACE. HIS COLLEAGUE, GHERMAN TITOV, MAKES THE SECOND SOVIET SPACEFLIGHT A FEW MONTHS LATER.

APRIL 14, 1961 A RAPTUROUS RECEPTION FROM KHRUSHCHEV INAUGURATES SEVERAL YEARS AS A NATIONAL HERO.

1963 TO KEEP GAGARIN OUT OF TROUBLE, HE IS APPOINTED DEPUTY DIRECTOR OF THE COSMONAUT TRAINING CENTER AT STAR CITY.

1967 CRITICIZES AUTHORITIES WHEN A SOYUZ SPACECRAFT CRASHES, KILLING ITS OCCUPANT, AND IS DISMISSED FROM THE SPACE TEAM.

1968 NOT HAVING FLOWN FOR FIVE MONTHS, GAGARIN TAKES OFF WITH AN INSTRUCTOR IN A MIG-15. THE PLANE CRASHES IN POOR WEATHER. GAGARIN IS IDENTIFIED BY A BIRTHMARK ON A SCRAP OF FLESH FROM THE BACK OF HIS NECK, AND THEN GIVEN A HERO'S FUNERAL.

GUS GRISSOM

Raised in small-town Indiana, Virgil "Gus" Grissom was a man of few words. One of NASA's "Original Seven" pioneering astronauts, his flying record spoke for itself. In July 1961, he made the second Mercury flight, a 15-minute sub-orbital trip. Grissom then commanded the first crewed Gemini mission, and his performance on that flight marked him out as a future key player in the Apollo missions to the Moon. Appointed commander of the first Apollo mission, Grissom died in 1967 along with his crew in a tragic training accident, just a few short weeks before the Apollo mission was to launch.

LIFE LINES

FULL NAME	VIRGIL IVAN "GUS" GRISSOM
DATE OF BIRTH	APRIL 3, 1926
PLACE OF BIRTH	MITCHELL, INDIANA
EDUCATION	MITCHELL HIGH SCHOOL CLASS OF 1944; BS, MECHANICAL ENGINEERING, PURDUE UNIVERSITY, 1950
FAMILY	MARRIED BETTY MOORE, JULY 1945; TWO SONS, SCOTT AND MARK
CAREER	FIGHTER PILOT, KOREAN WAR, 1951–2; U.S.A.F. TEST PILOT, WRIGHT-PATTERSON AIR FORCE BASE, OHIO, 1957–9; SELECTED FOR ASTRONAUT TRAINING, 1959; SECOND AMERICAN IN SPACE, ABOARD MERCURY FLIGHT LIBERTY BELL 7, JULY 1961; COMMANDER, FIRST MANNED GEMINI MISSION, MARCH 1965; COMMANDER, APOLLO 1, 1967
DATE OF DEATH	JANUARY 27, 1967, IN APOLLO 1 FIRE

FRONTIER MARTYR

At the end of World War II, Gus Grissom was discharged from the U.S. Air Force. At the age of 20, he found himself without qualifications and unemployed. He had married high-school sweetheart Betty Moore in the summer, while on leave, and money was tight. But Grissom had a burning ambition to be a fighter pilot. He earned a degree in engineering at Purdue University in Indiana, funded by his job in a diner, Betty's income, and a small government grant. By 1952, Grissom had achieved his ambition, and had flown 100 missions in the Korean War.

By 1959, Grissom was a respected test pilot, qualified to instruct. But then came the telegram from Washington, labeled "Top Secret," that would change everything. NASA, the new government agency in charge of advanced aviation and space projects, was looking for recruits. After two months of exhaustive physical and psychological testing, Grissom and six others made the final cut and were quickly dubbed the "Mercury Seven."

When the Soviet Union launched Yuri Gagarin into Earth orbit in April 1961, U.S. pride was on the line. Grissom served as backup with John Glenn for Alan Shepard's sub-orbital flight on May 5, 1961. Eleven weeks later, Grissom become the second American in space. After a 15-minute excursion beyond the atmosphere, his Liberty Bell 7 capsule splashed down in the Atlantic. Grissom's life was suddenly imperiled when a hatch unexpectedly blew and water flooded in, but he managed to swim to safety as the capsule sank.

RETURN TO SPACE

When Alan Shepard was grounded and John Glenn left the space program, Grissom was penciled in to pilot the next generation spacecraft, the twin-seated Gemini. He commanded its first crewed outing, with John Young as his co-pilot. With the loss of Liberty Bell 7 still on his mind, Grissom named the Gemini craft Molly Brown, after the "unsinkable" survivor of the Titanic. Grissom became the first human to fly in space twice.

In March 1966, NASA confirmed Grissom's status as "first among equals" in the astronaut corps, by giving him command of the first Apollo mission. He began training with Gemini pilot Ed White and rookie Roger Chaffee for an Earth-orbit test of the craft that was designed to take Americans to the Moon. On January 27, 1967, with the launch just weeks away, fire broke out during a command module test at the Kennedy Space Center. Sealed into the mock capsule by a hatch that was difficult to open from the inside, Grissom, White and Chaffee were dead within seconds. At Grissom's funeral at Arlington National Cemetery, his casket was borne by the six surviving members of the Mercury Seven.

The conquest of space is worth the risk of life.
GUS GRISSOM

Gus Grissom (right) was one of the first seven American astronauts (below) selected for the Mercury project. His second flight was with the first Gemini mission, which launched March 25, 1965 (left). He lost his life January 27, 1967, with the crew of Apollo 1 (mission patch, below left) when fire broke out in the training capsule (after the accident, below right).

CAREER TIMELINE

1926 BORN IN MITCHELL, INDIANA.
1944–5 SERVES IN THE U.S. AIR FORCE, BUT IS DISCHARGED AT THE END OF WORLD WAR II BEFORE RECEIVING ANY FLIGHT TRAINING.
1946–50 STUDIES FOR A DEGREE IN MECHANICAL ENGINEERING AT PURDUE UNIVERSITY, INDIANA, AND REENLISTS IN THE U.S.A.F. AFTER GRADUATION.
1951 GRISSOM WINS HIS AIR FORCE PILOT WINGS (ABOVE). FLIES **100** COMBAT MISSIONS IN THE KOREAN WAR WITH THE 334TH FIGHTER-INTERCEPTOR SQUADRON. AWARDED DISTINGUISHED FLYING CROSS AND AIR MEDAL WITH CLUSTER.
1952–5 FLIGHT INSTRUCTOR TO AIR FORCE CADETS.

1957 RECEIVES TEST PILOT CREDENTIALS AFTER FURTHER TRAINING AT WRIGHT-PATTERSON AIR FORCE BASE, OHIO.
1959 GRISSOM IS SUMMONED TO WASHINGTON AND INVITED TO APPLY FOR ASTRONAUT TRAINING.
APRIL 9, 1959 AFTER INTENSIVE TESTING, GRISSOM BECOMES ONE OF THE FINAL SEVEN MERCURY ASTRONAUTS.
MAY 5, 1961 ALAN SHEPARD TAKES THE FIRST MERCURY MISSION, A **15**-MINUTE SUB-ORBITAL FLIGHT.
JULY 21, 1961 GRISSOM IS LAUNCHED ATOP A REDSTONE ROCKET FOR THE SECOND AND FINAL SUB-ORBITAL MERCURY FLIGHT. THE MISSION GOES ACCORDING TO PLAN UNTIL SPLASHDOWN IN THE ATLANTIC OCEAN. GRISSOM HAS TO SWIM FOR SAFETY AFTER A CAPSULE HATCH BLOWS OPEN.
MARCH 1965 GRISSOM COMMANDS THE FIRST CREWED FLIGHT

OF NASA'S 2-MAN GEMINI CAPSULE.
MARCH 1966 NAMED COMMANDER OF THE FIRST APOLLO MISSION.
JANUARY 27, 1967 GRISSOM AND CREWMATES ED WHITE AND ROGER CHAFFEE ARE KILLED IN A CAPSULE FIRE DURING TRAINING AT CAPE KENNEDY.
JANUARY 30, 1967 GRISSOM IS BURIED AT ARLINGTON NATIONAL CEMETERY, ARLINGTON, VIRGINIA (SHOWN ABOVE).

JOHN GLENN

In 1962, wartime fighter pilot John Glenn became the first American to orbit the Earth. His dramatic mission made him an international hero, but his new-found fame put a stop to his career as an astronaut. President Kennedy grounded him, believing that if Glenn died, the public would turn against the U.S. space program. But Glenn always believed that one day he would travel into space again, and 36 years later his belief was vindicated. In 1998, at age 77, he became the oldest man in space.

LIFE LINES

Full Name	John Herschel Glenn, Jr.	**Family**	Married Anna Margaret Castor, 1943; two children, John David and Carolyn Ann, and two grandchildren
Date of Birth	July 18, 1921		
Place of Birth	Cambridge, Ohio		
Education	Primary and secondary schools in New Concord, Ohio; Muskingum College, New Concord. Bachelor of Science in Engineering, plus nine honorary doctoral degrees	**Career**	U.S. Marines pilot and instructor 1943–56; test pilot 1956–9; NASA astronaut and spacecraft engineer 1959–64; business executive 1965–74; elected U.S. Senator 1974–98; payload specialist, Shuttle mission STS-95 October 1998

SPACE SENATOR

By the winter of 1961, the United States was losing the Space Race—the bitterly contested battle for space supremacy being fought between the U.S. and the Soviet Union. That spring, Soviet cosmonaut Yuri Gagarin had become the first person to orbit the Earth. Several months later, after a triumphant 17-orbit space flight by Soviet cosmonaut Gherman Titov, the score was: Soviet Union 18 crewed orbits, U.S. none.

These Soviet successes sent NASA scrambling to catch up, and on February 20, 1962, millions of people watched the television coverage of a 95-ft (29-m) Mercury-Atlas launch vehicle shooting into the sky and out of sight. The rocket's Mercury space capsule, Friendship 7, circled the Earth three times before reentering the atmosphere and landing in the Atlantic Ocean near Grand Turk Island, West Indies.

The occupant of the tiny capsule was Lieutenant-Colonel John H. Glenn, Jr., a U.S. Marine Corps pilot who had joined the NASA Space Task Group in 1959. Glenn, born in Cambridge, Ohio, on July 18, 1921, saw action as a fighter pilot in both World War II and the Korean War and went on to became a test pilot.

Scheduled for no further space flights after his historic Mercury mission, Glenn left NASA in 1964 and spent most of the next decade as a businessman. In 1974, he was elected to represent Ohio in the Senate. On Capitol Hill, Glenn took a strong interest in environmental issues and his technical expertise was often called upon when he served on committees, including the Senate Armed Forces Committee. He was elected to the Senate a record fourth consecutive time in 1992.

A 36-YEAR WAIT

For years, Senator Glenn lobbied for his own return to space and in

> *Too often people set their lives by the calendar. It takes the fun out of life.*
> JOHN GLENN

Friendship 7 (top) lifts off with John Glenn on board. He returned to Earth a national hero, which helped him launch a career as a senator (top left). The Shuttle **Discovery** (top center) blasts off in October 1998. On board, Glenn takes a picture of Earth (center). Before takeoff, his wife Annie snaps a photo of Glenn (above).

U.S. President Bill Clinton samples some of Glenn's space food (left). Glenn and his wife Annie (above) pose after his historic second spaceflight.

1998 his persistence finally paid off. NASA administrator Dan Goldin called Glenn "the most tenacious man alive" when he signed up the 77-year-old for the Shuttle mission STS-95 that fall.

On board the Shuttle Discovery, Glenn found that NASA technology had come a long way since his last flight in the the 1960s. During takeoff, he experienced less than half the gravitational force that he had on Friendship 7, and he also

had far more room in which to move around.

As the oldest astronaut ever, Glenn once again served as an orbiting guinea pig. Weightlessness affects the human body much as old age does, for example, with a loss of bone mass. Glenn, now going through both at once, wore an electrode cap while asleep to monitor his brainwaves, and had blood samples taken by fellow astronauts. The data collected was

used in an ongoing study by the National Institutes of Health into the effects of aging.

But in one way, at least, 36 years haven't aged the hero. A day into the flight, Shuttle commander Curtis Brown observed, "Let the record show that John has a smile on his face and it goes from one ear to the other one, and we haven't been able to remove it yet." Glenn and the other crewmembers landed safely eight days later.

CAREER TIMELINE

1942 RECEIVES DEGREE IN ENGINEERING FROM MUSKINGUM COLLEGE, NEW CONCORD, OHIO.
1942 ENTERS NAVAL AVIATION CADET PROGRAM.
1943 ENLISTS IN THE MARINE CORPS.
1943–5 DURING WW2, GLENN FLIES 59 COMBAT MISSIONS IN F-4U FIGHTER PLANES.
1948–50 ADVANCED FLIGHT INSTRUCTOR IN CORPUS CHRISTI, TEXAS.
1950–3 IN THE KOREAN WAR, GLENN FLIES A FURTHER 90 COMBAT MISSIONS. GLENN HAS SIX DISTINGUISHED FLYING CROSSES AND THE AIR MEDAL WITH 18 CLUSTERS FOR HIS

SERVICE IN TWO WARS.
1957 FLIES AN F-8U CRUSADER FROM LOS ANGELES TO NEW YORK IN A RECORD TIME OF 3 HOURS 23 MINUTES. THIS IS THE FIRST TRANSCONTINENTAL FLIGHT TO AVERAGE ABOVE THE SPEED OF SOUND.
1956–9 HELPS DESIGN FIGHTER PLANES AT U.S. NAVY BUREAU OF AERONAUTICS.
1959 CHOSEN WITH SIX OTHERS (CARPENTER, COOPER, GRISSOM, SCHIRRA, SHEPARD AND SLAYTON) AS A MERCURY ASTRONAUT.
FEBRUARY 20, 1962 GLENN FLIES ON MERCURY 6, MAKING

THE FIRST AMERICAN ORBITAL FLIGHT AND BECOMING THE FIFTH PERSON IN SPACE. HE MAKES THREE ORBITS.
1964 RESIGNS FROM SPACE PROGRAM.
1974 BECOMES U.S. SENATOR FOR OHIO.
OCTOBER 29, 1998 RETURNS TO SPACE ON BOARD DISCOVERY AS A PAYLOAD SPECIALIST.
NOVEMBER 7, 1998 RETURNS TO EARTH ON DISCOVERY (ABOVE) AFTER A MISSION LASTING NEARLY NINE DAYS.

VALENTINA TERESHKOVA

On June 19, 1963, in the wilds of the Soviet republic of Kazakhstan, herdsmen on horseback found a young Russian woman calmly waiting. Despite her curious appearance—she wore a white helmet and bright orange overalls—the herdsmen hospitably offered bread, cheese and fermented mare's milk. She was eating heartily when a recovery helicopter arrived. Valentina Tereshkova had just spent almost three days in orbit: The first woman in space. Tereshkova heralded another Soviet new frontier.

LIFE LINES

FULL NAME	VALENTINA VLADIMIROVNA TERESHKOVA	**FAMILY**	MARRIED FELLOW COSMONAUT ANDRIAN NIKOLAYEV 1963 (DIVORCED 1982); ONE DAUGHTER, YELENA ANDRIANOVA
DATE OF BIRTH	MARCH 6, 1937		
PLACE OF BIRTH	MASLENNIKOVO, YAROSLAVL, FORMER U.S.S.R.		
EDUCATION	GRADUATED SPINNING TECHNOLOGIST 1961; GRADUATE ZHUKOVSKY AIR FORCE ENGINEERING ACADEMY 1969; CANDIDATE OF TECHNICAL SCIENCES 1976	**CAREER**	TEXTILE WORKER 1955–62; JOINED THE COMMUNIST PARTY 1962; COSMONAUT 1963; MEMBER OF OF SUPREME SOVIET 1966; MEMBER OF THE SOVIET CENTRAL COMMITTEE 1974; ELECTED TO CONGRESS OF PEOPLE'S DEPUTIES 1989

STAR WOMAN

Born on March 6, 1937, in the village of Maslennikovo in the Yaroslavl Region, Valentina Tereshkova had a hard childhood. Her father, a tractor driver on a local collective, was killed during World War II. His widow brought up three children on her own. The family moved to the nearby city of Yaroslavl where Valentina had to quit school at the age of 16 to supplement the family income, first with a job in a tire factory and then, from 1955, as a skilled loom operator in the Krasnyi Perekop Cotton Mill.

She might have spent her life as a factory worker—had it not been for Yuri Gagarin. In 1961 he became the first man in space and inspired thousands of young Soviet citizens to apply for the chance of cosmonaut training.

Valentina Tereshkova was one of these citizens.

She never expected to succeed. True, she was fit, strong and a keen parachutist, but a diploma in cotton-spinning was not exactly a qualification for space. Luckily for her, qualifications mattered little to Soviet leader Nikita Khruschev. He had beaten the Americans by putting the first man in space. Now, he wanted to beat them again.

COSMONAUT CRASH COURSE

The Soviet Vostok capsule did not have to be flown; ground control attended to that. Vostok was really no more than an endurance test, and a woman could endure it at least as well as any man. The only part of the trip that required experience was the parachute descent after reentry. And Valentina Tereshkova had made more than 100 jumps. Even better, she was also a sound communist.

In February 1962, she was invited to join four other women at the Cosmonaut Training Center. Tereshkova's progress was impressive. Within a year she had a grasp of navigation, geophysics and spacecraft construction, had passed rigorous physical tests and could even fly a jet.

She lifted off aboard Vostok 6 at noon on June 16, 1963, and orbited the Earth 48 times in tandem with another capsule, Vostok 5, carrying Valeri Bykovsky. The two cosmonauts came within three miles (five km) of each other and regularly beamed TV pictures to the planet below. Tereshkova returned to Earth after two days, 22 hours and 50 minutes. Bykovsky followed her 2½ hours later. As Khruschev had intended, her flight stung American pride. Not only was she the first woman in space—she had been out there longer than all the U.S. astronauts put together.

CAREER TIMELINE

MARCH 6, 1937 BORN IN THE RUSSIAN VILLAGE OF MASLENNIKOVO.

1953 LEAVES SCHOOL AND BEGINS WORK AT A TIRE FACTORY, BUT CONTINUES TO STUDY BY CORRESPONDENCE COURSE. TWO YEARS LATER SHE BECOMES A LOOM OPERATOR AT A COTTON MILL.

MAY 21, 1959 MAKES FIRST PARACHUTE JUMP AT YAROSLAVL AVIATION CLUB. LATER FORMS THE TEXTILE MILL WORKERS PARACHUTE CLUB.

1961 GRADUATES AS A COTTON-SPINNING TECHNOLOGIST, BECOMES SECRETARY OF THE LOCAL KOMSOMOL (YOUNG COMMUNIST LEAGUE).

FEBRUARY 16, 1962 SELECTED AS ONE OF FIVE TRAINEE FEMALE COSMONAUTS (RIGHT).

JUNE 16, 1963 BECOMES THE FIRST WOMAN IN SPACE ON BOARD VOSTOK 6.

NOVEMBER 3, 1963 MARRIES FELLOW COSMONAUT ANDRIAN NIKOLAYEV AND SEVEN MONTHS LATER, ON JUNE 8, 1964, GIVES BIRTH TO A DAUGHTER, YELENA ANDRIANOVA.

1964 ENTERS ZHUKOVSKY MILITARY AIR ACADEMY TO COMPLETE HER EDUCATION.

OCTOBER 1969 BECOMES A STAFF MEMBER AT THE YURI GAGARIN TRAINING SCHOOL FOR COSMONAUTS. THE FEMALE COSMONAUT DETACHMENT IS DISBANDED.

1974 ELECTED TO THE PRESIDIUM OF THE SUPREME SOVIET AND BECOMES A GOVERNMENT REPRESENTATIVE, APPEARING AT NUMEROUS INTERNATIONAL EVENTS.

1982 AFTER A PROLONGED SEPARATION SHE IS FINALLY DIVORCED FROM ANDRIAN NIKOLAYEV.

1989 ELECTED TO CONGRESS OF PEOPLE'S DEPUTIES.

1990 AFTER THE COLLAPSE OF COMMUNISM TERESHKOVA FADES FROM PUBLIC LIFE.

I have invaded their little playground.
VALENTINA TERESHKOVA ON BECOMING A COSMONAUT

After her flight, Tereshkova became an international celebrity. She was given numerous awards including a gold medallion from the British Interplanetary Society in 1964 (above left). Just a few months later, she gave birth to a baby girl (below), an event of some interest to scientists investigating the physiological effects of space travel on women.

After months of training (above left), Valentina Tereshkova became the first woman in space in 1963. Even years after her historic flight, Tereshkova was given VIP treatment. On a visit to England, for example, she became one of the first women to sit at the controls of the supersonic Concorde airliner (top).

ON JANUARY 24, 1969, TERESHKOVA WAS NEARLY KILLED AFTER A GOVERNMENT RECEPTION. AS THE LIMOUSINES LEFT THE KREMLIN, AN ARMY OFFICER OPENED FIRE ON THE VEHICLES, HOPING TO ASSASSINATE GENERAL SECRETARY LEONID BREZHNEV (BELOW). TERESHKOVA'S CAR, CONTAINING HERSELF AND TWO OTHER COSMONAUTS, WAS RIDDLED BY BULLETS. THE LIMOUSINE DRIVER WAS KILLED.

JAMES LOVELL

uring his career as an astronaut, Jim Lovell scored some spectacular firsts. His Gemini 7 flight saw the first rendezvous between two spacecraft in Earth orbit. As Command Module pilot on the crew of Apollo 8, Lovell shared with Frank Borman and Bill Anders the distinction of being the first humans to leave Earth for another world. But Lovell holds one record he never wanted. As Commander of the aborted Apollo 13 lunar mission, Lovell became the only astronaut to travel to the Moon twice without landing on it.

LIFE LINES

FULL NAME	JAMES ARTHUR LOVELL JR.	**FAMILY**	MARRIED MARILYN GERLACH, 1952. CHILDREN: BARBARA, 1953; JAMES, 1955; SUSAN, 1958; JEFFREY, 1966
DATE OF BIRTH	MARCH 25, 1928		
PLACE OF BIRTH	CLEVELAND, OHIO		
EDUCATION	UNIVERSITY OF WISCONSIN 1946–8; U.S. NAVAL ACADEMY, BACHELOR OF SCIENCE 1952; TEST PILOT SCHOOL, PATUXENT RIVER, MARYLAND, 1958; AVIATION SAFETY SCHOOL, UNIVERSITY OF SOUTHERN CALIFORNIA 1961; ADVANCED MANAGEMENT PROGRAM, HARVARD BUSINESS SCHOOL 1971	**CAREER**	SELECTED FOR ASTRONAUT TRAINING 1962; GEMINI 4 BACKUP CREW, JUNE 1965; GEMINI 7 CREW, DECEMBER 1965; GEMINI 9 BACKUP CREW, JUNE 1966; GEMINI 12 CREW, NOVEMBER 1966; APOLLO 8 COMMAND MODULE PILOT, DECEMBER 1968; APOLLO 11 BACKUP COMMANDER, JULY 1969; APOLLO 13 COMMANDER, APRIL 1970

Lovell was one of NASA's most experienced astronauts. He flew the record-breaking Gemini 7 mission (near left) and the final Gemini, Gemini 12 (below, center). Ironically, he is remembered for Apollo 13 (launch, far left), his only failure. With Fred Haise and Jack Swigert (bottom center), Lovell regained control of the craft (left) and returned to Earth (right). Later, he read about his ordeal in the papers (below, right) and was greeted as a hero by President Nixon (bottom right).

> *Apollo 13 is a significant addition to the knowledge of what human beings are capable of.*
> JAMES LOVELL

MOON OR BUST

As a student in 1940s Milwaukee, Jim Lovell was obsessed with space. Inspired by the Moon voyages in the novels of Jules Verne, he experimented with model rockets propelled by gunpowder. Lovell attended the University of Wisconsin and then graduated from the U.S. Naval Academy at Annapolis in 1952. After four years at the Naval Test Pilot School in Maryland, he found himself on the shortlist for the U.S. space program.

NASA was recruiting test pilots to support and succeed the original seven Mercury astronauts. In 1962, Lovell was selected for the second astronaut group, or the "New Nine." His first spaceflight came in December 1965, alongside Frank Borman in Gemini 7. The two astronauts endured two weeks aboard a craft dubbed "a flying men's room" due to its unsanitary conditions. The flight set a new spaceflight duration record, but its real achievement came 11 days into the mission. Gemini 6, piloted by Walter Schirra and Tom Stafford, matched orbit with Gemini 7 and approached within 2 ft (0.6 m). The crews waved at each other across the vacuum of space.

When astronauts Elliot See and Charlie Bassett were killed in a jet crash, Lovell inherited the last Gemini flight with rookie Buzz Aldrin. Their Gemini 12 mission in November 1966 was most notable for Aldrin's successful 5.5-hour EVAs solving problems that had dogged previous spacewalkers. By the end of 1968, NASA was under pressure to send a crew to circumnavigate the Moon before the Soviets. Lovell and Bill Anders, with Frank Borman commanding, got the job.

SO NEAR, SO FAR

Apollo 8 was launched atop the first Saturn V rocket to carry passengers. Lovell, Anders and Borman braked into lunar orbit on Christmas Eve. As millions watched on television, the astronauts read passages from Genesis while the stark moonscape rolled below. Looking back at the home planet, Lovell said, "the Earth from here is a grand oasis in the big vastness of space." On Christmas Day, after 10 Moon orbits, Apollo 8 headed home.

Jim Lovell would leave his "grand oasis" once again on April 11, 1970. Lovell had been Neil Armstrong's backup for the first lunar landing. Now he had his own mission, with rookies Fred Haise and Jack Swigert for company. But after an oxygen tank in the Service Module exploded, Apollo 13's primary mission objective became survival. Using the Lunar Module Aquarius as a lifeboat, Lovell and his crew swung around the Moon on a "free return" path. After a cold trip home, the exhausted astronauts splashed down to a hero's welcome. Lovell has claimed he wouldn't change a thing about his career, even the events of April 1970. "Apollo 13 was a test pilot's mission," he said. He came through the test with distinction.

CAREER TIMELINE

1958–62 SPENDS FOUR YEARS AS A TEST PILOT AT THE NAVAL AIR TEST CENTER, PATUXENT RIVER, MARYLAND. SERVES AS DEVELOPMENT PROGRAM MANAGER FOR THE F4H PHANTOM JET FIGHTER.

1962 AFTER A YEAR AT THE AVIATION SAFETY SCHOOL, LOVELL IS SELECTED FOR ASTRONAUT TRAINING AS A MEMBER OF THE "NEW NINE."

JUNE 1965 FIRST CREW ASSIGNMENT, TEAMING UP WITH FRANK BORMAN TO BACK UP GEMINI 4 ASTRONAUTS ED WHITE AND JIM MCDIVITT.

DECEMBER 1965 LOVELL AND BORMAN (ABOVE RIGHT) ORBIT EARTH FOR 14 DAYS ON GEMINI 7. THE MISSION SEES THE FIRST-EVER SPACECRAFT RENDEZVOUS, AS WALTER SCHIRRA AND TOM STAFFORD CLOSE TO WITHIN 2 FT (0.6 M) ABOARD

GEMINI 7.

JUNE 1966 ANOTHER BACKUP ASSIGNMENT, THIS TIME PAIRED WITH BUZZ ALDRIN, ON GEMINI 9.

NOVEMBER 1966 SECOND SPACEFLIGHT, LASTING JUST FOUR DAYS, WITH BUZZ ALDRIN ON GEMINI 12. LOVELL'S FIRST COMMAND.

DECEMBER 1968 LOVELL'S THIRD FLIGHT MAKES HISTORY. FIRST CREWED LAUNCH OF THE SATURN V ROCKET SENDS APOLLO 8 ON COURSE FOR A RENDEZVOUS WITH THE MOON. LOVELL SPENDS CHRISTMAS IN LUNAR ORBIT TOGETHER WITH FRANK BORMAN AND

BILL ANDERS.

JULY 1969 AS BACKUP TO NEIL ARMSTRONG, COMMANDER OF THE FIRST MOON LANDING, LOVELL TRAINS TO LEAD HIS OWN MISSION TO THE LUNAR SURFACE.

APRIL 1970 APOLLO 13 LIFTS OFF FROM FLORIDA, BOUND FOR THE FRA MAURO HIGHLANDS OF THE MOON. AN OXYGEN TANK EXPLOSION 200,000 MILES (322,000 KM) INTO THE FLIGHT FORCES THE CREW TO ABANDON THE LANDING. THEY USE THE MOON'S GRAVITY TO SWING THEIR STRICKEN SHIP BACK TOWARD THE EARTH.

1973 RETIRES FROM NAVY AS A CAPTAIN.

1994 PUBLISHES A BOOK ABOUT THE APOLLO 13 DRAMA, LOST MOON. THE FOLLOWING YEAR, IT BECOMES THE HOLLYWOOD MOVIE, APOLLO 13.

NEIL ARMSTRONG

A short hop off the bottom rung of his lunar lander's ladder, and Neil Armstrong was firmly on the Moon's surface—the first human ever to stand upon another world. "That's one small step for man, one giant leap for mankind," Armstrong radioed to Mission Control. The words were his own, not the product of NASA's public relations office. Armstrong messed up his delivery a little—he had meant to say "a man." But the line typified an astronaut who said less so that he could think more.

LIFE LINES

Full Name	Neil Alden Armstrong
Date of Birth	August 5, 1930
Place of Birth	Anglaize County, Ohio
Education	Student at Purdue University 1947–8, 1952–5; BS in aeronautical engineering 1955; MS in aerospace engineering, University of Southern California 1970; several honorary doctorates
Family	Marries Janet Shearon; two children
Career	U.S. Navy pilot 1948–52; test pilot for the National Advisory Committee on Aeronautics, later part of NASA 1955–62; NASA astronaut and aeronautics administrator 1962–71; professor of aeronautical engineering, University of Cincinnati 1971–9; currently chairman of AIL Systems
Date of Death	August 25, 2012

LUNAR LANDER

Even among a team of astronauts selected for their courage, fast reactions and coolness under pressure, the first man to set foot on the Moon stood out. It seemed Neil Armstrong had no sense of fear.

Once, Armstrong and co-pilot Edwin "Buzz" Aldrin were practicing the Moon landing in the Lunar Module simulator. The lander began to spin out of control. As it hurtled toward the virtual Moon surface, Armstrong never punched the abort button. They crashed.

Aldrin thought Armstrong had frozen. Aware of NASA's fact-tallying mentality, he worried that the "crash" would be a strike against the two of them. Later, Armstrong said his decision was deliberate. He wanted to test the reactions of ground control—and, equally, test himself.

From childhood, Armstrong set high standards for himself, and reached them. Like many boys growing up in the 1940s, he built model airplanes. But he tested his in a homemade wind tunnel. Like many teenagers, he got his first learner's permit at 16, but his was for an airplane, not the family car.

SUCCESS IN SPACE

Armstrong flew fighter planes in the Korean War, and later the X-15 rocket plane, before NASA selected him for astronaut training in 1962. He was in space less than four years later.

That first mission was a dramatic success. Before mission control had even given them the go-ahead, Armstrong and his co-pilot performed the first-ever space docking. Half an hour later, they managed to stop their now out-of-control capsule from shaking them to pieces.

After the mission, Armstrong rejoined the astronaut duty roster. His name, along with that of Aldrin and Michael Collins, came up next on the list for the Apollo 11 mission—originally scheduled to be the second landing trip, with Armstrong due to be the third man on the Moon. But when NASA realized that the lunar module would not be ready in time, the plans were moved back. Apollo 10 thoroughly rehearsed every part of the complex Moon mission except the landing itself.

Its smooth success cleared the way for Apollo 11. On July 20, 1969, Armstrong fulfilled U.S. President John F. Kennedy's eight-year-old,

$26 billion pledge to put a man on the Moon. Modestly, the astronaut insisted that the thousands of Apollo support personnel be credited, too: "It's their success more than ours."

Two years later, Armstrong left NASA to become a professor of aerospace engineering, and in the late '70s he went into business. Armstrong died on August 25, 2012.

EYEWITNESS

ARMSTRONG DESCRIBED THE SURFACE OF THE MOON AS "FINE AND POWDERY." HE CONTINUED, "I CAN KICK IT UP LOOSELY WITH MY TOE... IT DOES ADHERE IN FINE LAYERS, LIKE POWDERED CHARCOAL, TO THE SOLE AND SIDES OF MY BOOTS. I ONLY GO IN [TO THE SURFACE] A SMALL FRACTION OF AN INCH, MAYBE AN EIGHTH OF AN INCH, BUT I CAN SEE THE FOOTPRINTS OF MY BOOTS AND THE TREADS IN THE FINE, SANDY PARTICLES."

CAREER TIMELINE

1948–52 U.S. NAVY PILOT. FLIES 78 MISSIONS DURING THE KOREAN WAR. EJECTS TO SAFETY WHEN PLANE STRIKES A TRAP WIRE STRETCHED OVER A VALLEY. RECEIVES THREE MEDALS FOR BRAVERY.
1955 RECEIVES BACHELOR'S DEGREE IN AERONAUTICAL ENGINEERING, PURDUE UNIVERSITY.
1955 MADE TEST PILOT, NATIONAL ADVISORY COUNCIL OF AERONAUTICS, EDWARDS AIR FORCE BASE, CALIFORNIA.
1956 MARRIES JANET SHEARON.
MARCH 16, 1966 GEMINI 8 LAUNCHES.

ARMSTRONG MAKES FIRST-EVER DOCKING IN SPACE, STABILIZING THE CRAFT AFTER FAULTY THRUSTER PUTS CAPSULE IN DANGER.
SEPTEMBER 12–15, 1967 SERVES AS BACKUP PILOT FOR GEMINI 11 (ON EARTH).
1968 BAILS OUT OF LUNAR LANDING TRAINING VEHICLE SECONDS BEFORE IT CRASHES.
JULY 16, 1969 LAUNCH OF APOLLO 11 MISSION, WHICH TAKES ARMSTRONG, MICHAEL COLLINS AND BUZZ ALDRIN TO

THE MOON.
JULY 20, 1969 BECOMES FIRST PERSON TO WALK ON THE MOON AFTER LANDING LUNAR MODULE WITH ALDRIN.
JULY 24, 1969 APOLLO 11 RETURNS TO EARTH. CREW IS KEPT IN A MOBILE QUARANTINE FACILITY UNTIL 21 DAYS AFTER LUNAR LIFTOFF.
1971–9 PROFESSOR AT UNIVERSITY OF CINCINNATI.
1986 SERVES ON PRESIDENTIAL COMMISSION ON SPACE SHUTTLE CHALLENGER ACCIDENT.

It suddenly struck me that that tiny pea, pretty and blue, was the Earth.
NEIL ARMSTRONG

The Saturn 5 rocket blasted Apollo 11 into space on the morning of July 16, 1969 (far left). Four days later, the lunar module Eagle (left) carried Neil Armstrong (top left) and Buzz Aldrin down to the Moon's surface, where they planted the American flag (center). The command module Columbia returned safely to Earth on July 24 (below).

The Apollo 11 crew were put into quarantine (above) when they returned to Earth. Their ticker-tape parade through New York was the biggest in history (right).

BUZZ ALDRIN

On July 20, 1969, minutes after Neil Armstrong had stepped out on to the lunar surface, Buzz Aldrin became the second human to walk on the Moon. It was the high point of an impressive career. In the preceding years, Aldrin had not only

demonstrated his ability as an astronaut, but had also been instrumental in helping the NASA ground crew solve the technical problems involved in sending people to the Moon. He was both intelligent and practical—just what was needed on the Moon.

LIFE LINES

FULL NAME	BUZZ ALDRIN (ORIGINALLY EDWIN EUGENE ALDRIN JR.; CHANGED TO BUZZ IN 1988)	**FAMILY**	MARRIED TO LOIS DRIGGS CANON (THIRD WIFE); 3 CHILDREN FROM PREVIOUS MARRIAGE
DATE OF BIRTH	JANUARY 20, 1930	**CAREER**	ACTIVE SERVICE IN KOREA, 1951–3; AERIAL GUNNER INSTRUCTOR, NELLIS AIR FORCE BASE, NEVADA, 1953; AIDE TO FACULTY DEAN AT THE AIR FORCE ACADEMY, 1953–6; PILOT IN 36TH FIGHTER DAY WING IN GERMANY, 1956; TRAINEE ASTRONAUT, 1963; COMMANDER OF THE TEST PILOTS SCHOOL, EDWARDS AIR FORCE BASE, 1971–2
PLACE OF BIRTH	MONTCLAIR, NEW JERSEY		
EDUCATION	GRADUATED FROM MONTCLAIR HIGH SCHOOL, 1947; WEST POINT MILITARY ACADEMY, 1948–51; MASSACHUSETTS INSTITUTE OF TECHNOLOGY, 1959–63		

WHAT'S THE BUZZ?

Like nearly all his Apollo colleagues, Buzz Aldrin was a fighter pilot before he became an astronaut. He flew 66 missions in the Korean War and shot down two MiG-15s. But he was not one of the test pilots—the elite group from which the vast majority of early astronauts were drawn. He chose a more academic route into space. In 1959, instead of going to the Edwards Air Force Test Pilot School as he had previously planned, Aldrin went to Massachusetts Institute of Technology. His doctoral thesis, titled "Guidance for Manned Orbital Rendezvous" and written in 1963, contributed directly to the Apollo program. Following this, Aldrin applied to NASA, and in October 1963 was taken on as a trainee astronaut.

He waited for three years before his first mission, but on November 11, 1966, he finally entered orbit aboard Gemini 12. He and his Commander Jim Lovell were going to put into practice what Aldrin had spent so long studying—a docking in space. Previous Gemini missions had proved it was possible, but it needed to be perfected if NASA was to send men to the Moon.

Lovell was in the pilot's seat as they approached the target, an Agena rocket stage. But then disaster struck. The radar malfunctioned, meaning that the spacecraft's computer was deprived of the vital data it needed to calculate the trajectories. Undaunted, Aldrin made the necessary calculations on the spot. Lovell guided the spacecraft to a successful docking based on Aldrin's figures. Aldrin then took the controls and put all his theorizing into practice to carry out a flawless docking.

> The significance [of Apollo 11] was the reaction of the people watching it...It changed lives.
> BUZZ ALDRIN

The most important week in Aldrin's life began on July 16, 1969, as he prepared for the Moon (far right). The historic event itself (above left) was followed by three weeks in quarantine, which included a meeting with President Nixon (bottom right). Then the crew got a hero's welcome around the world (New York ticker-tape parade, top right.)

A LONG JOURNEY HOME

After Gemini 12, Aldrin's next spaceflight was to make him the second human on the Moon. With Neil Armstrong he spent over two hours walking on the lunar surface, collecting rocks and performing simple experiments. It was an incredible achievement, but for Aldrin, the hardest part was coming home. He, Armstrong and Command Module pilot Michael Collins went on a goodwill world tour on their return. But it wasn't long before life returned to normal, and Aldrin soon suffered a bout of depression. After walking on the Moon, he found it difficult to adjust to an ordinary existence.

Aldrin worked for a time as commander of the Test Pilot School at Edwards Air Force Base before retiring from the Air Force in 1972. He wrote several books, including a frank autobiography that detailed his experience with depression following his time in space. Today, though, he has managed to put his life in order. He travels the world to lecture and promote his own vision of the future of space exploration. In doing so, Aldrin continues to inspire new generations of space travelers—even those too young to remember the Moon landings.

CAREER TIMELINE

1951 GRADUATES WITH A BACHELOR OF SCIENCE DEGREE FROM THE WEST POINT MILITARY ACADEMY, NEW YORK. ASSIGNED TO 51ST FIGHTER WING IN KOREA FLYING F-86S.
1953 POSTED TO NELLIS AIR FORCE BASE, NEVADA, AS AN AERIAL GUNNER INSTRUCTOR; BECOMES AIDE TO A FACULTY DEAN AT THE U.S.A.F. ACADEMY, COLORADO SPRINGS, COLORADO.
1956 F-100 PILOT BASED AT BITBURG, GERMANY.
1959 GOES TO MASSACHUSETTS INSTITUTE OF TECHNOLOGY (MIT) TO STUDY ASTRONAUTICS.
1963 GAINS HIS DOCTORATE WITH A THESIS CALLED GUIDANCE FOR MANNED ORBITAL RENDEZVOUS.
OCTOBER 1963 JOINS NASA ASTRONAUT TEAM.
AUGUST 1965 CAPCOM (SPEAKING TO THE ASTRONAUTS FROM MISSION CONTROL) FOR GEMINI 5.
JULY 1966 CAPCOM FOR GEMINI 10.
NOVEMBER 11, 1966 LAUNCHED INTO SPACE WITH ASTRONAUT JIM LOVELL ABOARD GEMINI 12.
NOVEMBER 15, 1966 SPLASHES DOWN IN GEMINI 12.
JULY 16, 1969 LIFTS OFF ABOARD APOLLO 11 WITH NEIL ARMSTRONG AND MICHAEL COLLINS.
JULY 20, 1969 BECOMES THE SECOND MAN TO WALK ON THE MOON (RIGHT).
JULY 24, 1969 RETURNS TO EARTH ABOARD APOLLO 11 COMMAND MODULE.
1971 BECOMES COMMANDER OF THE TEST PILOTS SCHOOL AT EDWARDS AIR FORCE BASE, CALIFORNIA.
1972 RETIRES FROM THE AIR FORCE AND GOES INTO BUSINESS.
1973 WRITES HIS AUTOBIOGRAPHY, RETURN TO EARTH.
1989 WRITES MEN FROM EARTH, DESCRIBING HIS APOLLO MISSION AND HIS VISION OF AMERICA'S FUTURE IN SPACE, WITH MALCOLM MCCONELL.
1996 ENCOUNTER WITH TIBER, A SCIENCE FICTION NOVEL WRITTEN WITH JOHN BARNES, IS PUBLISHED.

EILEEN COLLINS

When the Space Shuttle Columbia launched on July 23, 1999, it was the first time that a woman had sat in the Commander's seat. Air Force Lieutenant Colonel Eileen Collins was on her third space flight and in command of a crucial mission that would deploy the multi-billion-dollar Chandra X-Ray Observatory into orbit. On the return flight she would make history again—as the first woman to guide the Shuttle to touchdown. It remains a great moment—for NASA, for Eileen Collins, and for women around the world who dream of space travel just as Collins did.

LIFE LINES

FULL NAME	EILEEN COLLINS
DATE OF BIRTH	NOVEMBER 19, 1956
PLACE OF BIRTH	ELMIRA, NEW YORK
EDUCATION	GRADUATED FROM ELMIRA FREE ACADEMY, 1974; ASSOCIATE DEGREE IN MATH AND SCIENCE, CORNING COMMUNITY COLLEGE, 1976; BA IN MATH AND ECONOMICS, SYRACUSE UNIVERSITY, 1978; MS IN OPERATIONS RESEARCH, STANFORD UNIVERSITY, 1986; MA IN SPACE SYSTEM MANAGEMENT, WEBSTER UNIVERSITY, 1989
FAMILY	DAUGHTER OF JIM AND ROSE COLLINS; MARRIED TO PAT YOUNGS; ONE DAUGHTER
CAREER	T-38 INSTRUCTOR, VANCE AIR FORCE BASE, OKLAHOMA, 1979–82; C-141 AIRCRAFT COMMANDER AND INSTRUCTOR, TRAVIS AIR FORCE BASE, CALIFORNIA, 1983–5; ASSISTANT PROFESSOR IN MATH AND T-41 INSTRUCTOR PILOT, U.S.A.F. ACADEMY, COLORADO, 1986–9; JOINED NASA 1990; STS-63, PILOT; STS-84, PILOT; STS-93, COMMANDER

GIRL POWER

Eileen Collins was born on November 19, 1956, just as the space race was entering its most exciting phase. In 1969, she watched with millions as Neil Armstrong and Buzz Aldrin walked on the Moon. But the figures who inspired her most were the early women aviators. Their pioneering example showed that women had as much of a role to play in aviation as men—despite what America's aerospace establishment thought.

After attending Corning Community College, Collins won a scholarship to Syracuse University, where she earned a degree in mathematics and economics. During her time at Syracuse, she also managed to obtain her pilot's license. With the necessary qualifications to join the U.S. Air Force and, armed with a letter of recommendation from her flying instructor, she was accepted on the pilot training program at Vance Air Force Base in Oklahoma in 1978.

So successful was Collins that she stayed on at Vance after her graduation in 1979 to be an instructor. As her career blossomed in the following years, she conceived her boldest ambition yet: She would become an astronaut.

Collins began to build up the experience and qualifications that would make her a good astronaut candidate. It paid off. In 1989, she was selected for the Test Pilot School at Edwards Air Force Base, California. This was her chance: Edwards is the traditional selection center for trainee astronauts. It was not long before Collins' talents were recognized and she started her career with NASA in 1991.

CAREER TIMELINE

November 19, 1956 Born in Elmira, New York.
1979 Graduates from Air Force Undergraduate Pilot Training, Vance Air Force Base, Oklahoma.
1979–82 T-38 jet instructor pilot at Vance Air Force Base.
1983–5 C-141 aircraft commander and instructor pilot at Travis Air Force Base, California.
1986–9 Assistant math professor and T-41 instructor pilot at the Air Force Academy in Colorado.
1990 Graduates from Air Force Test Pilot School, Edwards Air Force Base, California. Selected by NASA to join the astronaut training program.
July 1990 Returns to Vance for astronaut training.
July 1991 Begins work at Kennedy Space Center as part of the Orbiter engineering support team.
February 2–11, 1995 After four years of ground duties, Collins finally goes to space as pilot of STS-63. She and the crew engage in the first Shuttle rendezvous with the Mir space station.
May 15–24, 1997 Returns to space as Pilot of STS-84. This time she actually boards Mir as part of a 9-day mission.
March 5, 1998 Meets President Clinton and Hillary Clinton, who announces

Collins as Commander of Shuttle mission STS-93.
July 22–27, 1999 Becomes the first female Commander of a Shuttle mission, STS-93 (above). She oversees the launch of the Chandra Observatory, and was the first woman to land the Shuttle.

FLYING INTO HISTORY

Collins first did her share of ground jobs, working as a Shuttle engineer and in mission control as CapCom—the person with voice contact with Shuttle crews.

In 1995, she finally got the job she wanted. Assigned to the crew of STS-63, she was to be the Shuttle's first woman pilot. On February 2, 1995, Collins began her first space flight on board Discovery. STS-63 was scheduled to perform the first Shuttle rendezvous with the Mir space station. The crew had to contend with a leaky Reaction Control System (RCS) thruster that was threatening to prevent the maneuver. In the end, Discovery came within 37 ft (11 m) of Mir. Both the Americans and Russians were delighted. The mission paved the way for the first Shuttle-Mir docking, STS-71.

Two years later, Collins was back in space. As pilot on board STS-84, she got to see the inside of Mir when the Shuttle docked with the space station. Then, as commander of STS-93—her most famous mission—Collins would break new ground for women, just like the early aviators she so admired.

Eileen Collins (left, as Commander of the historic STS-93 Shuttle mission) flew a number of aircraft before the Shuttle, including the massive C-141 Starlifter (below). She visited Mir with STS-84 in 1997 (mission patch, below left) and deployed the Chandra X-Ray Observatory (bottom) when she commanded STS-93.

> When I was a child, I dreamed about space—I admired pilots, astronauts, and I've admired explorers of all kinds. It was only a dream that I would someday be one of them.
>
> Eileen Collins

HEROES

When she was growing up, Collins was inspired by women pilots of the past. Ultimately, her fascination led her to become an astronaut. "I began reading voraciously about famous pilots," she says, "from Amelia Earhart to Women Air Force Service Pilots (WASPs) who played an important role in World War II." There were over a thousand WASPs, such as Jane Straughan, serving in the U.S.A.F. during the War. They did not fly combat missions, but their work was far from safe. WASP duties included towing targets for live air-to-air gunnery and live anti-aircraft artillery practice. Thirty-eight were killed in active duty.

ROCKETS AND LAUNCHERS

The first practical payload-carrying rockets were the A4 or V-2 rockets designed by Wernher von Braun and used by Nazi Germany in 1944–5. After World War II, V-2s and German scientists fell into Allied hands and V-2 production continued in the U.S. and U.S.S.R., where the rockets were used for upper atmosphere science as well as military missile research. Intermediate-range missiles such as the U.S. Redstone followed, and these proved adaptable to carrying manned capsules such as Mercury. Using converted missiles for manned flight purposes was a calculated risk, as they had a worrying tendency to blow up upon launch. Fortunately this never occurred with astronauts aboard. The U.S.S.R.'s first rockets were hardly more successful, particularly the modified SS-6 "Sapwood" missiles lifting early Sputnik and Venera missions, many of which failed to reach orbit. By the mid-1960s purpose-built civilian space launchers such as the Saturn series were replacing military designs, and were followed by the Titan, Delta, and Europe's Ariane series. In addition to the U.S., Russia and Europe, India, China, and Japan have flown rockets of their own designs and are likely to be joined by further nations, particularly in Asia.

An Atlas-Agena rocket is launched on September 12, 1966, as part of the Gemini 11 mission. American astronauts Pete Conrad and Richard Gordon would maneuver their craft to rendezvous with the Agena rocket in orbit, as preparation for the planned Apollo moon shots.

FROM V-2 TO EXPLORER 1

When the world's first ballistic missiles—Adolf Hitler's V-2 rockets—began raining down on London in September 1944, it heralded the violent birth of the space age. But little could the V-2's designer, the brilliant Wernher von Braun, have imagined that just 14 years later he would have his finger on the ignition button of the rocket carrying America's first satellite, Explorer 1, into orbit around the Earth.

EARLY US ROCKETS

ROCKET	STAGES	LENGTH (FT/M)	MASS (LB/KG)	LIFTOFF THRUST (LBF/KN)
V-2 (A-4)	ONE	40/12	28,230/128,804	59,547/265
BUMPER	TWO	54/16	28,930/13,122	59,547/265
VANGUARD	THREE	65/20	22,123/10,034	27,833/124
REDSTONE	ONE	60/18	62,700/28,440	82,600/367
JUNO (JUPITER C)	FOUR	65/20	64,066/29,059	82,969/369

SCIENCE WEAPONS

America gained 103 unusual new citizens on April 14, 1955, in a ceremony at Huntsville High School in Alabama. Ten years earlier at the end of World War II, many of these men had been Adolf Hitler's top weapons scientists. Their leader, Wernher von Braun, was the brilliant engineer who had designed the V-2, the Nazis' long-range missile that terrorized London in the final months of the war.

At the end of the war, von Braun and 125 of his staff gave themselves up to the U.S. Army. They were shipped back to America and put to work designing a long-range missile that could deliver a nuclear warhead. The first fruits of this research came in 1953 with the Redstone missile. But space exploration was never far from the scientists' minds: In 1954, von Braun put forward his first practical proposal for launching a satellite. The following January,

the idea was submitted to the U.S. Department of Defense as a joint Army-Navy endeavor called Project Orbiter.

Six months later, President Dwight D. Eisenhower announced that the U.S. would launch an artificial satellite into orbit before December 1958. But Project Orbiter was rejected in favor of Project Vanguard, which was based on the Navy's Viking research rocket.

But von Braun's Army engineers continued with

unauthorized tests of their own. So when Vanguard 3 exploded on the launchpad in December 1957—after two successful Soviet satellite launches—von Braun's team was able to produce a new rocket. In less than two months, these German designers and engineers rescued U.S. pride by launching Explorer 1.

ROCKETS INTO SPACE

October 3, 1942 First successful launch of the V-2 by the Nazis.
February 24, 1949 U.S. Army launches Bumper 5, which becomes the first artificial object in space.
August 20, 1953 A prototype Redstone missile is launched.
June 25, 1954 Wernher von Braun proposes a Redstone-based rocket for launching satellites.

July 29, 1955 President Dwight D. Eisenhower announces that the U.S. will send a satellite into orbit before the end of 1958.
September 20, 1956 First launch of U.S. Army Jupiter C rocket.
December 8, 1956 The first test rocket in the official U.S. satellite program, a single-stage Viking, attains an altitude of 126 miles (203 km).

August 8, 1957 The nose cone of a Jupiter C rocket is recovered 1,333 miles (2,145 km) from the launchpad, after reaching a height of 260 miles (418 km). It is the first object ever retrieved from space.
October 4, 1957 The Soviet Union launches Sputnik 1, the first satellite into orbit.
November 3, 1957 The Soviet Union

launches Sputnik 2.
December 6, 1957 The first Vanguard rocket with three live stages explodes on the launchpad.
January 31, 1958 A Juno rocket (above) successfully launches Explorer 1 into space.

FAMILY TREE

BUMPER
This was the first rocket to reach space. Launched from White Sands Proving Ground, New Mexico, in 1949, it broke a world record by reaching a speed of 5,510 mph (8,867 km/h). Bumper was a hybrid rocket that used a German V-2 captured at the end of World War II to boost a U.S.-built WAC Corporal upper stage to a maximum altitude of 244 miles (393 km).

VANGUARD
This was the rocket that was intended to launch the first U.S. satellite. It had liquid propellant engines in the first and second stages and a solid propellant third stage. Vanguard was derived from the Navy's Viking and Aerobee research rockets.

PROJECT ORBITER
First the U.S. and then the Soviet Union announced intentions to launch a scientific satellite into orbit as part of the 1957–8 International Geophysical Year, a worldwide effort to study the Earth. The Army proposed Project Orbiter to launch the U.S. satellite, using a modified Redstone missile, which in turn had been derived from the German V-2. The government eventually vetoed this plan in favor of the politically more acceptable Vanguard, which was descended from research rockets.

JUNO
America at last managed to put the satellite Explorer 1 into orbit using Juno, a renamed Jupiter C rocket. Designed by the von Braun team and built by the Army, the Jupiter C was a modified Redstone ballistic missile with a top stage designed for reentry. The rocket had a liquid-propellant main-stage engine, while the upper stages used solid propellant.

HARD EVIDENCE

EXPLORER 1
Explorer 1, the first U.S. probe into orbit, occupied the fourth stage of the Juno rocket and was built by the Army Ballistic Missile Agency and the Jet Propulsion Laboratory. Instruments on board Explorer 1, designed by scientist James van Allen, revealed the Earth's radiation belts, which were named Van Allen Belts in his honor. Explorer weighed 10.5 lb (4.75 kg) and measured just six in (15 cm) across and less than 40 in (1 m) long. After circling the Earth more than 58,000 times, it reentered the atmosphere in March 1970 and burned up.

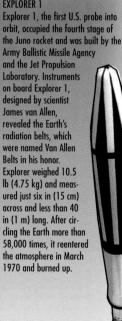

MERCURY REDSTONE

At the end of the 1950s, the U.S. and the Soviet Union were in the grip of the Cold War. Space was a new frontier where East and West could compete for prestige and find another use for some of their vast arsenals of missiles. The Soviet Union struck first, when a modified R-7 intercontinental missile put Sputnik 1 into orbit in 1957. An upgraded Redstone missile allowed the U.S. to catch up. Further modifications created the Redstone-Mercury rocket that would loft America's first astronaut into space.

MERCURY REDSTONE ROCKET

NOVEMBER 21, 1960	MERCURY-MR1 LAUNCH FAILURE, ENGINE CUTS OUT 1 SECOND AFTER IGNITION
DECEMBER 19, 1960	SUCCESSFUL LAUNCH OF MERCURY-MR1A
JANUARY 31, 1961	SUCCESSFUL LAUNCH OF MERCURY-MR2; CARRIED HAM, A CHIMPANZEE
MARCH 24, 1961	SUCCESSFUL LAUNCH OF MERCURY-MR BOILERPLATE; CARRIED MERCURY TEST CAPSULE
MAY 5, 1961	ALAN SHEPARD BECOMES AMERICA'S FIRST ASTRONAUT, RIDING ON MERCURY MR-3
JULY 21, 1961	ASTRONAUT GUS GRISSOM IS LAUNCHED ON MERCURY MR-4; LAST MANNED FLIGHT OF MERCURY-REDSTONE ROCKET
OCTOBER 30, 1964	MERCURY-REDSTONE ROCKET IS RETIRED FROM MILITARY SERVICE

MAN LIFTER

The story of the Mercury-Redstone rocket began at the end of World War II, when German rocket pioneer Wernher von Braun and his colleagues surrendered to the advancing U.S. Army in 1945. Von Braun had developed Germany's V-2 rocket, the world's first true ballistic missile. Post-war, his technological know-how combined with American skills led to creation of the Redstone, the first operational U.S. missile, by 1953.

The Redstone was designed to throw a 6,000-lb (2,700-kg) nuclear warhead 200 miles (320 km). With a small upper stage in place of a bomb, the rocket would be powerful enough to put a small satellite into orbit—which had been von Braun's ambition for decades. But in 1956, the U.S. government vetoed von Braun's request for a satellite launch. Instead, the first U.S. satellite would be lofted by the specially designed Vanguard rocket, a Navy project with civilian funding that President Eisenhower hoped would "demilitarize" the nascent space program.

On October 4, 1957, though, the Soviets won the satellite race when Sputnik 1 reached orbit on a modified R-7 missile. A month later, the half-ton Sputnik II took a live dog into space aboard the same booster. In December, Vanguard failed spectacularly in a launchpad explosion. Shaken into action, American Secretary of Defense Neil McElroy gave von Braun the go-ahead that the rocket scientist had sought for more than a year. With a new upper stage, the trusty Redstone metamorphosed into the Jupiter-C rocket, which in February 1958 launched Explorer I—America's first satellite.

THE NEXT ROUND

Now, both nations raced for the next goal: a man in orbit. The newly formed National Aeronautics and Space Administration (NASA) turned again to the Redstone rocket to use as a launch vehicle for project Mercury—the project designed to place the American agency's first astronauts into orbit. But before the Redstone could qualify as a manned launch vehicle, approximately 800 engineering changes were needed.

The modifications for manned spaceflight began in 1959. Included in the redesign was the more reliable Rocketdyne engine, which mixed liquid oxygen and kerosene to provide 78,000 lb of thrust (347

kN) at launch. To prolong the burn time of the engine, the Redstone's fuel tank was extended by 6 ft (1.8 m) to achieve the increased speed and altitude necessary to carry an astronaut into space. By 1960, the Redstone rocket had metamorphosed once more—into the Mercury-Redstone launch vehicle rocket.

The first Mercury-Redstone launch attempt took place in November 1960. But the rocket lifted only an inch or two above the pad before the engine shut down. Faulty circuitry on the ground was the culprit. Luckily, success followed with further launches. During the next few months, three Mercury-Redstones took to the

skies, one of them carrying a full-size dummy Mercury capsule.

To the chagrin of America's rocketeers, the Soviets beat them once more: Their sturdy R-7 put cosmonaut Yuri Gagarin into orbit on April 12, 1961. But Mercury-Redstone was not far behind. After passing its final tests, the rocket stood ready to launch its first

human cargo into space. On the morning of May 5, 1961, Mercury astronaut Alan Shepherd soared 116 miles (187 km) skyward, remaining weightless for 4 minutes and 45 seconds. The sub-orbital hop was trivial by the standards of later missions, but the flight of Mercury-Redstone 3 had carried the first American into space.

ROCKET SCIENCE
Technicians check out the Rocketdyne A-6 engine used on Mercury 3 and Mercury 4. The liquid-fueled motor burned a mixture of alcohol and liquid oxygen to yield 78,000 lb of thrust (347 kN) for a burn time of 155 seconds.

MODIFIED MISSILE

Just like its wartime V-2 ancestor, the Redstone burned alcohol with liquid oxygen. The Redstone-Mercury version had an upgraded motor that provided more thrust and a longer burn time—not enough to put an astronaut into orbit, but sufficient to lift the Mercury capsule briefly to a height of 116 miles (187 km).

emergency escape rocket

Mercury capsule

instrument compartment

alcohol fuel

liquid oxygen

fins and rudders

Rocketdyne A-6 motor

OLD RELIABLE
A Redstone rocket makes a successful test launch. The Redstone relied on just one well-tried engine to supply the thrust needed to launch the Explorer 1 satellite and—in Mercury-Redstone configuration—carry the first two Mercury astronauts on their sub-orbital flights in May and July 1961.

HERO'S RETURN

AFTER A FLIGHT THAT LASTED JUST OVER 15 MINUTES, ALAN SHEPARD (RIGHT) WAS HAULED ABOARD A HELICOPTER FROM THE RECOVERY VESSEL U.S.S. *LAKE CHAMPLAIN* IN THE ATLANTIC OCEAN 300 MILES (482 KM) EAST OF CAPE CANAVERAL, WHERE THE HISTORIC MISSION BEGAN.

SOVIET
N-1

There was more than one horse in the race to land a man on the Moon during the 1960s. The Soviet Union had plans to blast two cosmonauts into lunar orbit, one of whom would touch down on the surface. But the project faced seemingly impossible hurdles.

Starting too late, in an atmosphere of political infighting, it lacked support from the military who ran the Soviet space program. Even worse, the N-1 rocket—the U.S.S.R.'s answer to NASA's mighty Saturn 5—failed on all four of its launch attempts.

N-1 LAUNCHER STATS

PAYLOAD (INTO 125-MILE/200-KM EARTH ORBIT)	99 TONS (90 TONNES)			EACH OF 170 TONS-FORCE (1,512 KN)
TOTAL WEIGHT (AT LAUNCH)	3,086 TONS (2,800 TONNES)	2ND STAGE (BLOCK B)	8 x NK-43 ENGINES,	
PROPELLANT MASS (OXYGEN)	1,906 TONS (1,729 TONNES)			EACH OF 198 TONS-FORCE (1,760 KN)
PROPELLANT MASS (KEROSENE)	750 TONS (680 TONNES)	3RD STAGE (BLOCK V)	4 x NK-3 ENGINES,	
TOTAL HEIGHT	345 FT (105 M)			EACH OF 45 TONS-FORCE (400 KN)
BASE WIDTH	55 FT (16 M)			
1ST STAGE (BLOCK A)	30 x NK-33 ENGINES,			

CATALOG OF DISASTER

The N-1 rocket was developed by the Soviet Union during the 1960s and early 1970s as a launch vehicle to carry two men to the Moon. The plan was similar to the Apollo program, in that it employed the concept of Lunar Orbit Rendezvous. This involved firing a pair of spacecraft with a two-person crew toward the Moon on a giant rocket (the N-1). The two craft would separate, leaving a lunar module (code-named LK) to land on the surface. Part of the LK would then lift off to rejoin its sister craft (code-named LOK) in lunar orbit and the crew would fire the LOK's main engine to head home.

The N-1 rocket, however, was very different from the Apollo program's Saturn 5 launch vehicle. Soviet chief designer Sergei Korolev, under pressure from his masters in Moscow, was aware that his design team simply didn't have the time to perfect the super-efficient cryogenic liquid hydrogen rocket engines being developed by NASA. To stay in the race, he had to rely on the tried-and-tested liquid oxygen/kerosene engines that had blasted previous Soviet rockets into space.

Korolev knew that the pound-for-pound performance of these engines was considerably less than that of the American rockets. To compensate, the first stage of the N-1 rocket had no less than 30 engines—compared with just five in Saturn 5. This presented major construction difficulties that Korolev hoped to get around by designing the propellant tanks as huge spheres and then building the walls of the rocket around them.

TOO HEAVY BY FAR

Unfortunately, Korolev's design solution made for a heavier, even less efficient rocket. The N-1 was so big that it had to be built panel by panel at the launchpad using parts shipped in by rail. And, as it turned out, all four test launches failed while the first stage was firing due to component failures.

Above the N-1's problematic first stage were conventional second and third stages, similar to those on the Saturn 5. Beyond these were were two "extra" stages—specially designed to burn in Earth orbit—that would give the LOK/LK craft its final kick toward the Moon. The last stage, called "Block D" was originally developed in the mid-1960s under the code name

N-1 ON THE LAUNCHPAD

Taller than a Saturn 5, with an even higher gantry, the N-1 rocket was a monumental feat of engineering.

escape tower

crew capsule

stage 5

stage 3

stage 4

stage 2

stage 1

STAGE 1
Substituting quantity for what it lacked in technology, the N-1's first stage contained no fewer than 30 engines. But the stresses at launch proved too much for the components that linked them together.

N-1 LAUNCHES

1 February 21, 1969
After 66 seconds, an engine oxidizer line fractures and a fire starts. All engines immediately shut down and the N-1 crashes.

2 July 3, 1969
Debris inside an engine causes it to explode seconds after liftoff. A fire starts, all engines shut down and the rocket falls back onto the launchpad.

3 June 27, 1971
The rocket spins faster and faster as it climbs. After 48 seconds, the top stages start to break up. Following this, the engines shut down.

4 November 23, 1973
After 90 seconds, the six central engines shut down as planned. But the shock severs internal pipework, a fire starts and the rocket explodes.

ENGINES
Although they were designed in the 1960s, the N-1's rocket engines are so advanced that they have been adopted by the consortium building the Kistler K-1 reusable launch vehicle.

"Sputnik." It is still used today on the Proton rocket.

At the very top of the N-1 was an escape tower to carry the crew capsule away from a launchpad disaster. The tower is known to have fired during three of the four launch failures, carrying real, but unoccupied, crew capsules to safety. Rumors persist, however, of a manned escape tower failure.

Despite the problems, development of the N-1 continued as various engine design bureaus sought to incorporate more powerful liquid hydrogen/oxygen engines into the original design concept. Pairs of these rockets, designated N-1M, were intended

HARD EVIDENCE

BIG BLAST
The second N-1 launch failure ended with the rocket falling back onto launchpad 110R, completely destroying it and showering the neighboring pad, where another N-1 rocket was being readied for launch, with debris. Rebuilding the 110R took two years. The blast damage and scars (right) were clearly visible on contemporary U.S. spy satellite photos.

to launch large lunar landers that could be assembled in Earth orbit.

The N-1 program was finally canceled in 1974, by which time two more rockets had been prepared for launch. Its successor—the brainchild of chief designer Korolev's old rival, Valentin Glushko—was a rocket

called Vulkan, later to become the Energia. Today, reminders of the once-mighty N-1 litter the plains of Baikonur Cosmodrome. Ever short of funds, the resourceful Russians have put the old hardware to good use—as water tanks, a bandstand and even a children's play area in the nearby town of Leninsk.

SATURN SERIES

The 364 ft (111 m) -tall monster that carried men to the Moon was the last and largest variant of an entire family of Saturn designs. German rocket designer Wernher von Braun and his team of engineers configured their Saturn launcher in a variety of different ways, to serve all of America's potential needs in space. In the end, only three members of the Saturn series ever exchanged the drawing board for the launchpad—the Saturn 1, the upgraded and crew-rated Saturn 1B and the Moon-bound Saturn 5.

THE SATURN STORY

DECEMBER 30, 1957	WERNHER VON BRAUN PRODUCES A "PROPOSAL FOR A NATIONAL INTEGRATED MISSILE AND SPACE VEHICLE DEVELOPMENT PLAN," WHICH PROPOSES DEVELOPMENT OF THE SATURN 1
JULY 29, 1958	SATURN 1 PROJECT CONTRACT ISSUED BY ARPA
NOVEMBER 2, 1959	TRANSFER OF SATURN 1 PROJECT FROM THE U.S. ARMY TO NASA ANNOUNCED
OCTOBER 27, 1961	FIRST SATURN 1 FLIGHT
JANUARY 5, 1962	NASA ANNOUNCES DEVELOPMENT OF THE SATURN 5 LAUNCH VEHICLE FOR APOLLO
OCTOBER 30, 1963	MANNED SATURN 1 FLIGHTS CANCELED, TO BE REPLACED BY SATURN 1B FLIGHTS
FEBRUARY 26, 1966	FIRST SATURN 1B FLIGHT
NOVEMBER 9, 1967	FIRST SATURN 5 FLIGHT (APOLLO 4)
OCTOBER 11, 1968	FIRST MANNED SATURN 1B FLIGHT (APOLLO 7)
DECEMBER 21, 1968	FIRST MANNED SATURN 5 FLIGHT (APOLLO 8)
JULY 16, 1969	SATURN 5 LIFTS OFF WITH CREW OF APOLLO 11
MAY 14, 1973	FINAL SATURN 5 LAUNCH CARRIES SKYLAB INTO ORBIT IN PLACE OF ITS THIRD STAGE

GROWING FAMILY

The Saturn launchers were the first rockets designed solely to transport men into space. Earlier designs, such as the Redstone, the Atlas and the Russian R-7, were ballistic missiles modified to carry crew capsules in place of warheads. The Saturns' peaceful origin is perhaps surprising, given that when designer Wernher von Braun and his team began work on the rockets in 1958, they were still employed by the military.

After the U.S. Army plucked the rocket builders out of defeated Nazi Germany in 1945, they worked at the Army Ballistic Missile Agency (ABMA), based in Huntsville, Alabama. But von Braun had always dreamed of the peaceful exploration of space. He proposed a 1.5-million-lb thrust (66,700 kN) booster, 10 times more powerful than the existing Jupiter, to be used for the purpose of space exploration. In the aftermath of Russia's surprise launch of Sputnik 1, the Pentagon responded very positively to von Braun's proposal. The ABMA began work on a first-stage Saturn booster while also studying possible upper-stage designs.

CLUSTERS, QUICK!

To save time and money, the kerosene and liquid oxygen first stage was built by clustering together eight Rocketdyne H-1 engines—previously used one at a time in the Thor and Jupiter missiles. This raised concerns about whether so many boosters could work together reliably: Skeptics dubbed the Saturn 1 "Cluster's Last Stand." In response, the infant civilian space agency NASA contracted Rocketdyne to build a new engine—the F-1—with enough thrust to match all eight H-1s.

PRESSED FOR TIME

In November 1959, NASA inherited the Saturn program, along with the ABMA itself, from the Army. During the next 18 months, combination tests of H-1 engines showed cluster fears to be misplaced, and work proceeded on a liquid hydrogen and oxygen upper stage for the Saturn.

The first two-stage Saturn 1 flew from Cape Canaveral on a suborbital test flight on October 27, 1961. Initially, von Braun believed that it would be sufficient to achieve his dream of men on the Moon—the plan was to launch up to 15 Saturn 1s, to assemble a moonship in Earth orbit. But President Kennedy's pledge to place a man on the Moon by the end of the decade put a strict deadline on the project that the Saturn 1 plan was simply unable to meet.

To reach the Moon in a single launch, a much more powerful multi-stage rocket would be needed. Von Braun's answer was the three-stage Saturn 5, so-called because it had no less than five mighty F-1 engines clustered together to form the first stage.

As work proceeded on the Saturn 5, the Saturn 1 was upgraded with improved first-stage engines, increased automation with a computerized Instrumentation Unit, and a liquid hydrogen and oxygen upper stage that also served as the third stage for Saturn 5.

This upgraded model, known as the Saturn 1B, had double the payload capacity of its predecessor, enabling it to be used for flight tests of Apollo hardware. The first uncrewed Saturn 1B flew in February 1966.

The first Saturn 5 followed in November 1967. Just under a year later, a crewed Saturn 1B successfully flew as Apollo 7, followed in December by a crewed Saturn 5 that sent Apollo 8 around the Moon.

For the next four years, Saturn 5s carried men to the lunar surface, and in 1973 the final Saturn 5 hoisted the Skylab space station into low Earth orbit. Meanwhile, Saturn 1Bs carried three separate crews up to Skylab and, in 1975, lifted the Apollo Command Module that docked with a Russian Soyuz spacecraft in orbit. It was a perfect flight record.

WAR AND PEACE

THE SATURN LAUNCHERS WERE DIRECT DESCENDANTS OF THE V2 "VENGEANCE WEAPON" ROCKET (RIGHT) UNLEASHED BY THE NAZIS DURING WORLD WAR II. THE SAME TEAM OF GERMAN ENGINEERS WORKED ON BOTH PROJECTS. SATURN 5 PROGRAM MANAGER ARTHUR RUDOLPH LATER FLED THE U.S. BECAUSE HE WAS BEING INVESTIGATED AS A SUSPECTED WAR CRIMINAL BY FEDERAL AUTHORITIES.

FIVE SATURNS

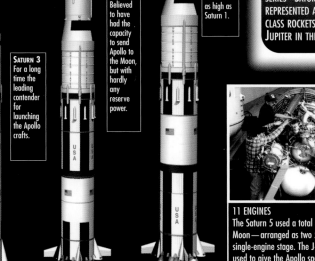

As NASA raced to put men on the Moon, the design for the rocket that would launch them on their way grew larger and larger. In the end, only two of the family were built—the smallest and the largest.

SATURN 1 Built as a launch vehicle. Its height was 180 ft (55 m) in total.

SATURN 2 Initially considered for a lunar landing, but the landing craft had to be assembled in Earth orbit.

SATURN 3 For a long time the leading contender for launching the Apollo crafts.

SATURN 4 Believed to have had the capacity to send Apollo to the Moon, but with hardly any reserve power.

SATURN 5 Worked for 13 flawless launches. At 363 ft (111 m), it was more than twice as high as Saturn 1.

MOVING ON

SATURN 1 WAS ORIGINALLY NAMED "JUNO 5" TO FOLLOW ON FROM THE JUNO 2 JUPITER-CLASS ROCKET. BUT VON BRAUN (RIGHT) RENAMED THE NEW LAUNCHER SERIES "SATURN" BECAUSE IT REPRESENTED A MAJOR STEP FORWARD FROM PREVIOUS JUPITER-CLASS ROCKETS AND SATURN IS THE NEXT PLANET OUT FROM JUPITER IN THE SOLAR SYSTEM.

3 STAGES
As the Moon race gathered momentum, it became clear that nothing less than a 3-stage Saturn (shown below, in assembly) would do the job.

11 ENGINES
The Saturn 5 used a total of 11 engines to reach the Moon—arranged as two 5-engine stages and one single-engine stage. The J-2 engine (above) was used to give the Apollo spacecraft its final boost into a translunar trajectory.

SATURN 5

Saturn 5, the launcher that lifted the Apollo crews to the Moon, was the mightiest rocket the United States has ever built. Taller than the Statue of Liberty, heavier than a Navy destroyer and containing almost three million working parts, this massively powerful machine never failed once in its short lifetime. The giant Saturn 5 first flew in 1967, and its final mission—to launch the Skylab space station—came just six years later. Only 15 Saturn 5s were built and, because of budget cuts, two of these never left the ground.

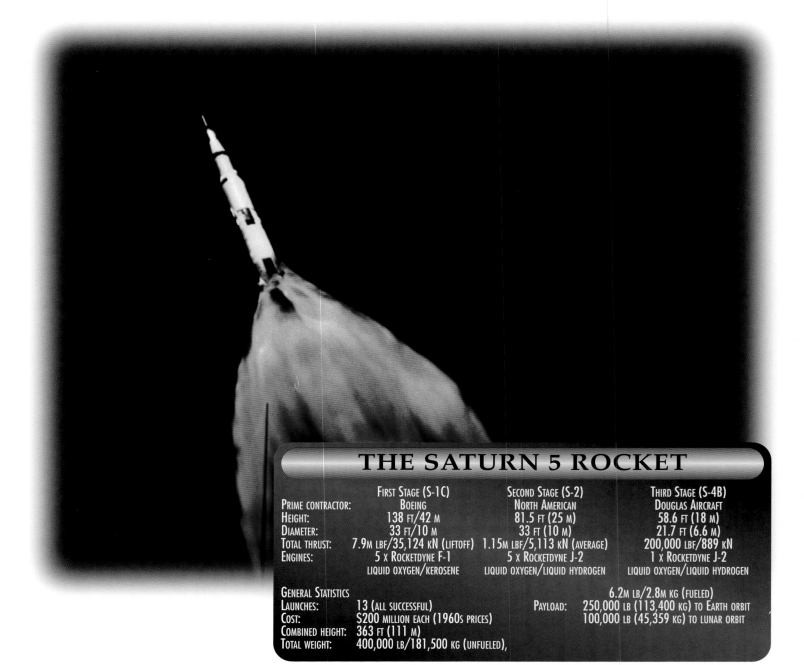

THE SATURN 5 ROCKET

	First Stage (S-1C)	Second Stage (S-2)	Third Stage (S-4B)
Prime contractor:	Boeing	North American	Douglas Aircraft
Height:	138 ft/42 m	81.5 ft (25 m)	58.6 ft (18 m)
Diameter:	33 ft/10 m	33 ft (10 m)	21.7 ft (6.6 m)
Total thrust:	7.9m lbf/35,124 kN (liftoff)	1.15m lbf/5,113 kN (average)	200,000 lbf/889 kN
Engines:	5 x Rocketdyne F-1	5 x Rocketdyne J-2	1 x Rocketdyne J-2
	liquid oxygen/kerosene	liquid oxygen/liquid hydrogen	liquid oxygen/liquid hydrogen

General Statistics			
			6.2m lb/2.8m kg (fueled)
Launches:	13 (all successful)	Payload:	250,000 lb (113,400 kg) to Earth orbit
Cost:	$200 million each (1960s prices)		100,000 lb (45,359 kg) to lunar orbit
Combined height:	363 ft (111 m)		
Total weight:	400,000 lb/181,500 kg (unfueled),		

MOON ROCKETS

On July 16, 1969, Neil Armstrong, Buzz Aldrin and Michael Collins lifted off from Kennedy Space Center (KSC), Florida, at the start of the first mission to land men on the Moon. The rocket that carried them into space was a Saturn 5, a three-stage vehicle over 360 ft (110 m) high, 33 ft (10 m) in diameter at its widest and weighing over 3,000 tons (3,306 tonnes). At liftoff, its 5 Rocketdyne F-1 rocket engines generated a total thrust of 7.65 million lb (34,000 kN). Later versions, then the most powerful engines built, produced up to 7.9 million lb thrust (35,000 kN).

The three stages of the Saturn 5 were themselves all rockets of the Saturn family—the first stage was a Saturn 1C, the second a Saturn 2, and the third a Saturn 4B. During a launch, the engines of the first stage burned for two minutes 50 seconds, taking the vehicle to an altitude of about 38 miles (61 km). Then explosive bolts were fired to separate it from the two upper stages, and it fell into the Atlantic Ocean about 375 miles (600 km) downrange from KSC.

If there had been an emergency during liftoff—such as a launch pad explosion—or any life-threatening problem during the first three minutes of the flight, an escape rocket on top of the Saturn 5 would have fired to haul the command/service module and its crew clear of the vehicle. Later in their mission, the crew could have separated their command module from the Saturn 5 without the assistance of the escape rocket.

After first-stage separation, the five Rocketdyne J-2 second-stage engines were ignited. These burned for another 6½ minutes until at an altitude of 115 miles (185 km), more explosive bolts fired and the second stage, too, fell back into the ocean far below.

THIRD STAGE

The single J-2 engine of the third stage burned for about 2½ minutes to put the spacecraft into Earth orbit. After one orbit, Apollo was redirected toward the Moon by a second, five-minute firing of the same engine.

Finally, the third stage separated from the rest of the spacecraft, leaving the thrusters to steer the module safely out of harm's way. What little remained of the once-mighty rocket was left to crash down onto the surface of the Moon.

The Saturn 5 rockets carried each of the Apollo lunar mission spacecraft. Each launch (as shown below) took place at John F. Kennedy Space Center (known as KSC) in Florida. The three launch stages took around 20 minutes in total.

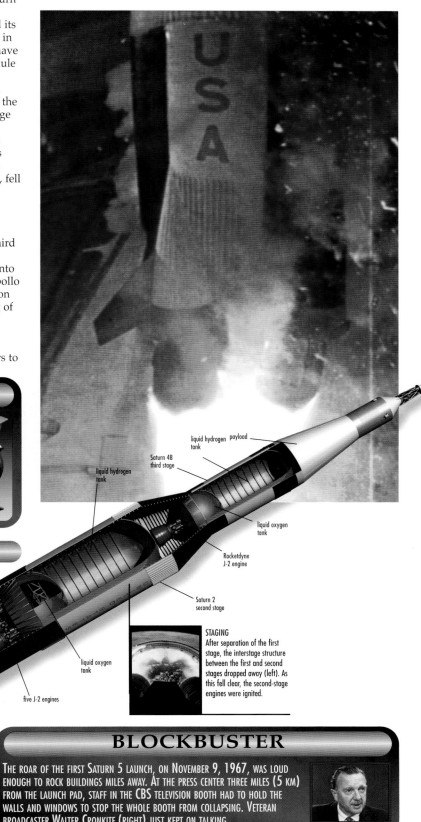

CAMERA CAPSULE

ROCKET ENGINEERS WERE CONCERNED ABOUT THE RELIABILITY OF SATURN 5 STAGE SEPARATIONS, SO EARLY ROCKETS CARRIED MOVIE CAMERA CAPSULES TO FILM THESE CRITICAL MOMENTS OF THE FLIGHT. THE CAMERAS WERE EJECTED INTO THE OCEAN, WHERE THEY WERE RECOVERED BY DIVERS WHO REACHED THE SCENE BY PARACHUTE.

lens — "parabolloon" for tanking

quartz window

camera

stabilizing fin

SATURN 5

liquid hydrogen tank — payload

Saturn 4B third stage

liquid hydrogen tank

liquid oxygen tank

Rocketdyne J-2 engine

Saturn 2 second stage

ENGINE NOZZLES
The nozzle of each F-1 engine in the first stage of the Saturn 5 was big enough to hold a small car. The first stage burned up to 15 tons (13.5 tonnes) of fuel per second, and some of the fuel lines were big enough for a man to crawl through.

five F-1 engines

liquid oxygen tank

RP-1 (kerosene) tank

Saturn 1C first stage

liquid oxygen tank

five J-2 engines

STAGING
After separation of the first stage, the interstage structure between the first and second stages dropped away (left). As this fell clear, the second-stage engines were ignited.

BLOCKBUSTER

THE ROAR OF THE FIRST SATURN 5 LAUNCH, ON NOVEMBER 9, 1967, WAS LOUD ENOUGH TO ROCK BUILDINGS MILES AWAY. AT THE PRESS CENTER THREE MILES (5 KM) FROM THE LAUNCH PAD, STAFF IN THE **CBS** TELEVISION BOOTH HAD TO HOLD THE WALLS AND WINDOWS TO STOP THE WHOLE BOOTH FROM COLLAPSING. VETERAN BROADCASTER WALTER CRONKITE (RIGHT) JUST KEPT ON TALKING.

SOYUZ SERIES

The orbiting workhorse of the Soviet and Russian space programs was first proposed in 1962 as a two-man capsule for space rendezvous and docking that could also be used on a Moon mission. But as with the disaster that killed three Apollo astronauts in January 1967, catastrophe forced the redesign of the craft. The Soyuz ("Union") capsule that emerged proved phenomenally successful, flying more than 100 missions. In modified form, it will be used well into this century—over 40 years after its first flight.

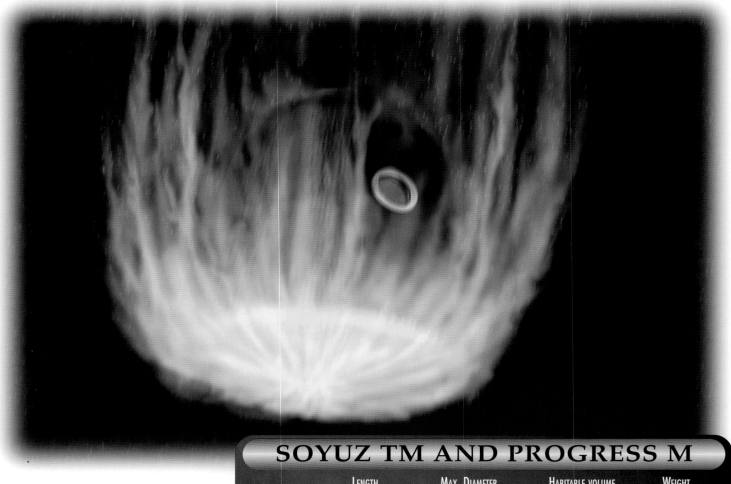

SOYUZ TM AND PROGRESS M

	Length	Max. Diameter	Habitable volume	Weight
Soyuz TM Spacecraft	24.6 ft (7.5 m)	8.9 ft (2.7 m)	318 cubic ft (9 m³)	15,984 lb (7,250 kg)
Descent Module	7.2 ft (2.2 m)	7.2 ft (2.2 m)	141 cubic ft (4 m³)	6,614 lb (3,000 kg)
Orbital Module	9.8 ft (3.0 m)	7.5 ft (2.3 m)	177 cubic ft (5 m³)	2,866 lb (1,300 kg)
Service Module	7.5 ft (2.3 m)	8.9 ft (2.7 m)	N/A	6,504 lb (2,950 kg)

	Length	Max. Diameter	Overall Mass	Payload
Progress M Spacecraft	23.6 ft (7.2 m)	8.9 ft (2.7 m)	16,424 lb (7,450 kg)	5,600 lb (2,540 kg)
Cargo Module	9.8 ft (3 m)	7.5 ft (2.3 m)	5,555 lb (2,519 lb)	2,954 lb (1,340 kg)
Refueling Module	7.2 ft (2.2 m)	7.2 ft (2.2 m)	4,365 lb (1,980 lb)	2,646 lb (1,200 kg)
Service Module	6.8 ft (2.1 m)	8.9 ft (2.7 m)	6,504 lb (2,950 lb)	N/A

SPACE CARRIER

Soyuz is the most successful series of spacecraft yet built, but its early days were dogged by disaster. The first Soyuz flight, in April 1967, ended in tragedy: Its pilot, Vladimir Komarov, was killed when the craft crashed after reentry. It took 18 months for the program to recover, with a successful orbital near-docking of Soyuz 2 and Soyuz 3.

Then in June 1971, another catastrophe struck. Three cosmonauts were sent aloft in Soyuz 11 and transferred to a new 20-ton space station, Salyut. This new Soviet "first" drew tremendous publicity, but when Soyuz 11 returned to Earth, on June 30, its occupants were found dead in their capsule. A valve had been jolted open during reentry, releasing all the capsule's air, and the crew had suffocated.

But the Soviets continued developing Soyuz and produced a thoroughly reliable design. Their faith in the craft was publicly demonstrated in 1975, when a Soyuz docked successfully in orbit with a U.S. Apollo spacecraft. This Apollo-Soyuz linkup led nowhere, because the Apollo program was almost over. But Soyuz soldiered on. After 34 missions, it was updated to the T (for "transport") version and ferried crews to and from the Salyut space stations. These space station missions were supported with supplies sent up in Soyuz's uncrewed version, Progress. And in a third incarnation, the TM series, some two dozen Soyuz missions enabled cosmonauts to build the first giant space station, Mir.

SOYUZ TM

The latest crew-carrying version of Soyuz, the TM, is a three-part vehicle consisting of a descent module, an orbital module and a service module. The bell-shaped descent module, about 7 ft (2.1 m) long and 7 ft (2.1 m) in diameter, is where the crew of three stays during launch, orbital maneuvers and reentry, and contains the spacecraft's main control systems. It sits between the orbital and service modules, and is the only part of the spacecraft that returns to Earth at the end of a mission—the orbital and service modules are jettisoned during reentry and are left to burn up in the atmosphere. The descent module carries the cosmonauts back through the atmosphere, using parachutes to slow descent and retrorockets to ensure a safe and soft landing for the crew.

The near-spherical orbital module, positioned in front of the descent module, carries life-support and rendezvous and docking systems. Its habitable internal volume is about 177 cubic ft (5 m³)—about 25 percent more than that of the descent module. When Soyuz is coasting in orbit, the module serves as the cosmonauts' working, recreation and sleeping quarters, and when the craft is docked to the Mir space station or the International Space Station, it functions as an airlock.

The service module, to the rear of the descent module, is over 7 ft (2.1 m) long with a diameter of nearly 9 ft (2.7 m). It contains the orbital flight systems, including propulsion and maneuvering engines, and a pair of wing-like solar panels with a span of about 35 ft (10.6 m). The panels are stowed away during the mission's launch phase and unfurl when the craft is in orbit. They have a total area of about 108 square ft (10 m²) and generate 600 watts of electricity for the craft, which also carries batteries.

HARD EVIDENCE

SOFT LANDING
When Yuri Gagarin returned to Earth after making the first human space-flight, he ejected from his Vostok capsule after reentry and parachuted to the ground. With Soyuz, which holds two or three cosmonauts, ejection is impossible, so it descends by parachute (left). Just before landing, rocket engines cut in to slow its fall, allowing it to land gently at a mere two mph (three km/h). On several occasions these rockets have failed, making touch-down bumpy but survivable.

SOYUZ SPACECRAFT

The Soyuz spacecraft, built by the RSC Energia company, is about 25 ft (7.6 m) long and carries a crew of three. The latest version, the Soyuz TM, first flew in 1986.

PROGRESS
Progress (right)—consisting of a service module, refueling module and cargo module—is the uncrewed cargo version of Soyuz. It ferries supplies to Mir and the International Space Station.

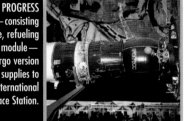

- rendezvous system antenna
- orbital module
- thrusters
- descent module
- optical sighting system
- solar panel
- service module
- propulsion system

LIFTOFF
A Soyuz 11A511U rocket carrying Soyuz spacecraft TM-29 blasts off from Baikonur Cosmodrome, Kazakhstan, in February 1999, carrying its three cosmonauts to the Mir space station.

DOCKED
The Salyut-7 space station docks with the Soyuz T-14 spacecraft—the Soyuz is at the right-hand end of the Salyut. This picture was taken in 1985 by the crew of Soyuz T-13.

ARIANE

Many countries around the world have developed the capability to launch machines and people into space, mostly in the interest of national security. But space is also big business. The space launch industry spends approximately $20 billion a year putting satellites into orbit, and one company, Arianespace, has led that market for over a decade. Arianespace has developed a series of rockets that have become some of the most successful launchers on the planet, the Ariane 4 and Ariane 5—still operational today.

ARIANE 4 AND ARIANE 5

	Ariane 42P	Ariane 42L	Ariane 44P	Ariane 44L	Ariane 5
Length	191.6 ft (58.4 m)	191.6 ft (58.4 m)	191.6 ft (58.4 m)	191.6 ft (58.4 m)	191.6 ft (58.4 m)
Max diameter	12.5 ft (3.8 m)	12.5 ft (3.8 m)	12.5 ft (3.8 m)	12.5 ft (3.8 m)	37.7 ft* (11.5 m)
Weight	373 tons (338 tonnes)	441 tons (400 tonnes)	394 tons (357 tonnes)	520 tons (471 tonnes)	785 tons (712 tonnes)
Liftoff thrust	445 tons (3,964 kN)	455 tons (4,047 kN)	587 tons (5,223 kN)	606 tons (5,388 kN)	1,404 tons (12,492 kN)
GTO payload	6,523 lb (2,958 kg)	7,691 lb (3,488 kg)	7,625 lb (3,458 kg)	10,800 lb (4,898 kg)	15,000 lb (6,803 kg)
Cost	$70 million	$80 million	$90 million	$105 million	$120 million
Propulsion	N2O4/UDMH	N2O4/UDMH	N2O4/UDMH	N2O4/UDMH	LOX/LH2
	plus 2 solids	plus 2 liquids	plus 4 solids	plus 4 liquids	plus 2 solids

*INCLUDING SOLID BOOSTERS

SPACE BUSINESS

Almost since its inception, Arianespace has been the most successful space launch company in the world, consistently cornering 50 percent or more of the commercial launch market. Arianespace is actually the European Space Agency's (ESA) launch services operator, and funding for all ESA projects, including the development of the Ariane 5 launcher, comes from the 12-nation consortium that makes up the ESA.

Responding to the needs of a European market, the ESA began development of a European space launcher in the late 1970s. France's space agency, the Centre National d'Etudes Spatiales (CNES), quickly led the development effort and the Ariane 1, a modification of the French-designed Diamant rocket, made its debut in 1979.

Over the years, ESA, CNES, and Arianespace have all made tremendous advances in their technology and technical abilities. Their latest effort, the Ariane 5, demonstrates the high degree of skill and knowledge ESA's engineers have developed. A multibillion-dollar program, the Ariane 5 took more than 10 years to go from the drawing board to the launch pad. The vehicle was completely new in design, having a cryogenic main stage with only one engine and twin solid-fueled boosters. Despite the totally new design, Arianespace expects the Ariane 5 to end up being cheaper, safer, and easier to operate than its predecessors.

HIGH FIVE

The 177-ft (54-m) high Ariane 5 launcher consists of a single-engined main stage, a single-engined upper stage, and two strap-on, solid-fueled boosters. These solid booster rockets provide over 90 percent of the Ariane 5's thrust at liftoff, and after burning for just over two minutes, they separate from the main stage and fall into the Atlantic Ocean. The propellant in the solid boosters is a mix of 68 percent ammonium perchlorate (oxidizer), 18 percent aluminum (fuel) and 14 percent polybutadiene (binder). The boosters hold about 262 tons (237 tonnes) of propellant each.

The main stage, a cryogenic rocket, is 100 ft (30.4 m) long and holds some 146 tons (132 tonnes) of liquid oxygen and 28 tons (25 tonnes) of liquid hydrogen to feed its main Vulcain engine. The Vulcain ignites on the launch pad and burns for about eight minutes after the boosters have separated, and then it too falls into the ocean, leaving the upper stage to deliver the payload to orbit.

The upper stage is powered by a single Aestus engine, fueled by MMH with nitrous oxide as the oxidizer, and the fuel and oxidizer are forced into the engine by pressurized helium. It can be shut down and reignited to deliver multiple payloads to different orbits, and has a total burn time of 1,100 seconds.

LUXURY LAUNCH

ARIANE ROCKETS ARE LAUNCHED FROM THE EUROPEAN SPACE AGENCY (ESA) CENTER NEAR KOUROU ON THE NORTHEASTERN COAST OF FRENCH GUIANA. THE ESA OWNS THE CENTER (RIGHT) AND ALL FACILITIES THERE, WHICH ARE OPERATED ON ITS BEHALF BY ARIANESPACE. THESE FACILITIES WERE DEVELOPED WITH COMMERCIAL CLIENTS IN MIND — THE CITY OF KOUROU NOW OFFERS FINE HOTELS, ENTERTAINMENT AND TRAVEL FACILITIES.

ARIANE 5

The all-new Ariane 5 can lift over one-and-a-half times the maximum payload of the most powerful version of the Ariane 4. It can launch multiple payloads, with the satellites mounted on top of each other in the rocket's payload bay. After launch, the upper stage motor carries each satellite to orbit.

PAYLOADS
The European satellites Maqsat-H and TeamSat are prepared for launch on Ariane 502 (above). Ariane 5 can carry two or more satellites on each flight. Payloads are mated to the rocket in the Final Assembly Building near Kourou's pad ALA-3.

satellite payload

EAP solid-fuel booster

payload bay

EPS upper stage with reignitable Aestus engine

vehicle equipment bay

EAP solid-fuel booster

cryogenic main stage with single Vulcain main engine

ARIANE 4
The AR 44P (shown above) is a version of the Ariane 4, one of the world's most successful launchers. After failures in the early years of its development, it racked up over 50 successful launches in a row.

Ariane 1   Ariane 2   Ariane 3   Ariane 4   Ariane 5

SPACE FAMILY ARIANE
The Ariane family first developed as a series of upgrades and expansions from Ariane 1 to Ariane 4. Ariane 1 was a redesign of the Diamant B launch vehicle, 2 and 3 had stretched engines and strap-on boosters, and 4 was a much more powerful model with triple the payload capacity. The Ariane 5 is an entirely new design from the ground up.

CHINESE LAUNCHERS

The world's most populous nation has long moved on from an emerging economy and entered the space age. China sent its first satellite into orbit in April 1970—in the words of premier Zhou Enlai, "…through our own unaided efforts." Briefly, between 1956 and 1960, China relied on help from the Soviet Union. But, since then, it has been on its own. Over the last four decades, its space program has survived several political crises and a number of disasters, and emerged as a commercial and scientific force on the international stage, their launchers now lifting Chinese exploration missions into space.

THE LONG MARCH (CZ)-B3

LENGTH	172 FT (52.4 M)	DIAMETER	11 FT (3.3 M)
CAPABILITY	5,000 LB (2,267 KG) TO GEOSTATIONARY ORBIT	WEIGHT AT LIFTOFF	417 TONS (378 TONNES)

	STRAP-ONS	1ST STAGE	2ND STAGE	3RD STAGE
LENGTH	52.5 FT (16 M)	76 FT (23 M)	34 FT (10.3 M)	29 FT (8.8 M)
WEIGHT	45 TONS (41 TONNES)	197 TONS (178 TONNES)	44 TONS (40 TONNES)	22.7 TONS (20.5 TONNES)
ENGINES	YF-20B	4 x YF-20B	YF-25/23	2 x YF-75
FUEL	LIQUID	LIQUID	LIQUID	LIQUID
THRUST	292 TONS (2,596 KN)	366 TONS (3,254 KN)	93 TONS (827 KN)	17.6 TONS (157 KN)
BURN TIME	128 SECONDS	155 SECONDS	135 SECONDS	47 SECONDS

THE LONG MARCH CZ-3B

THE FAMILY
From mid-1998, China was offering a range of launch vehicles to the international market from the CZ (Chang Zheng, or Long March) line. From left, with first launch date: CZ-D (1995), CZ-2C (1997), CZ-2E (1990), CZ-2EA (unlaunched), CZ-3 (1984), CZ-2B (1996), CZ-3C (unknown).

VENERABLE ANCESTOR
The DF-2, launched in 1966, was China's first intermediate range ballistic missile. It now rests outside the People's Army Museum in Beijing.

propellant

STAGE 3

propellant

two YF-75 engines

propellant

STAGE 2

propellant

YF-25/23 engine

STAGE 1

propellant

STRAP-ON BOOSTERS

propellant

YF-20B engine

satellite

The CZ-3B was capable of putting 110,000 lb (5,000 kg) of payload into low Earth orbit. In May 1998, it launched a Zhongwei 1 satellite, and in July, a Sinosat satellite.

four YF-20B engines

COMRADES

TSIEN HSUE-SHEN IS THE ACKNOWLEDGED FATHER OF CHINESE ROCKETRY. IRONICALLY, HE GAINED THIS POSITION AS A RESULT OF BEING EXPELLED FROM THE U.S. LIKE MOST CHINESE ROCKET SCIENTISTS, TSIEN WENT TO THE U.S. BEFORE THE COMMUNISTS SEIZED POWER, IN 1949. DURING THE MCCARTHY ANTI-COMMUNIST WITCHHUNT OF THE 1950'S, THE U.S. EXPELLED TSIEN WITH 93 OTHER CHINESE SCIENTISTS. HE RETURNED HOME AND USED HIS U.S. TRAINING TO FOUND CHINA'S SPACE PROGRAM.

MORE PADS
China's space industry continues to grow. This new launch pad is under construction at the Xichang mission center, as part of China's long-term plan to develop its commercial satellite facilities.

ONWARD & UPWARD

By 1960, the two greatest communist nations—China and the Soviet Union—had abandoned their past cooperation. If the Chinese wanted a satellite, they had to build their own rocket. They did: Chang Zheng (Long March), named for an epic communist fighting retreat during the Chinese civil war in the 1930s.

Long March had two lower stages, using liquid fuels. But these were not enough to lift a satellite into orbit. Work started on a 13-ft (4-m) solid-fuel third stage, and somehow, despite Mao Zedong's Cultural Revolution, managed to survive the late 1960s.

Finally, on April 24, 1970, the 82-ton (74-tonne) Long March 1 streaked off. Thirteen minutes later, China's first satellite, Dong Fang Hong (The East is Red), was in orbit, broadcasting the anthem after which it was named.

Two new launchers followed. One, Feng Bao, orbited the first of a series of scientific satellites, and three other secret ones, possibly used for surveillance. The other, an updated Long March, delivered the first of nine recoverable satellites into orbit.

These satellites, known as FSW, for Fanhui Shi Weixing, or Recoverable Experimental Satellite, were a technical leap forward. They had a service module with a retro-rocket and a recoverable capsule. The launch vehicle, Long March 2, was more powerful than anything used before, with four engines that could swivel to steer the rocket. Special computer systems were designed from scratch to meet the launcher's new demands.

LONG MARCH TO SUCCESS

After one explosion on takeoff in 1974, Long March launched the first FSW in November 1975. Forty-seven orbits later, it returned to Earth, placing China in the same league as the U.S. and U.S.S.R., the only two nations so far to have recovered a satellite from orbit.

Now China set its sights higher. It planned to place communications satellites 22,500 miles (36,210 km) above fixed points on Earth, in geostationary orbits. With one of these, it could communicate across the nation; with three, across the world. But to reach that orbit a more powerful rocket with sophisticated maneuvering was needed.

At first, the satellite program suffered setbacks. In 1978, a third-stage motor exploded, killing several people. And when Long March 3 blasted off on January 29, 1984, the third stage failed, leaving the satellite stranded in a low orbit. Four months later, all went well. China had its first comsat, servicing 200 phone lines and 15 channels.

Now Long March was available in versions of varying power to anyone ready to pay. There were few takers until 1986, when three U.S. rockets blew up, as did Europe's Ariane. Suddenly, Long March was starting to look much more attractive and several telecommunications companies in Hong Kong, Pakistan and Sweden all commissioned Long March launches for their satellites.

Then came several disasters: Of 15 commercial launches in 1990–7, seven failed. But after stringent checks, Long March has reestablished its reputation, leading to long-term contracts with two U.S. corporations, Motorola and Hughes. To date, there have been 178 successful Long March launches out of 188 launches in total.

COMMERCIAL LAUNCH VEHICLES

No one could ever call the U.S. space program profitable—the Apollo program cost about $25 billion, and the International Space Station (ISS) could cost NASA up to four times that amount. But now, a new generation of privately developed, relatively low-cost launch vehicles has begun to enter service, launching communication satellites for profit. While they aren't the most powerful rockets ever built, these commercial launch vehicles get the job done and continue to develop in size, power and reliability.

COMMERCIAL LAUNCHERS

NAME	HEIGHT	WEIGHT (FUELED)	STAGES	FUEL TYPE	COST/FLIGHT (IN $)	LOW-EARTH ORBIT PAYLOAD WEIGHT
ATHENA-1	49.2 FT (15 M)	146,264 LB (66,344 KG)	2	SOLID	$17.5 MILLION	1,760 LB (800 LB)
ATHENA-2	85.3 FT (26 M)	265,000 LB (120,200 KG)	3	SOLID	$23 MILLION	4,400 LB (2,000 KG)
TAURUS	89 FT (27 M)	161,000 LB (73,000 KG)	4	SOLID	$22 MILLION	3,000 LB (1,360 KG)
CONESTOGA	50 FT (15 M)	192,000 LB (87,089 KG)	4	SOLID	$19.8 MILLION	1,960 LB (889 KG)

BOOSTER BARGAINS

Today, the lightweight launch vehicle industry is booming, thanks to the growing demand for communications satellites (comsats). Modern global communications networks are based on constellations of 20 to 30 satellites in low Earth orbits (LEOs), and the telecom companies that operate these networks pay private firms generously to put the satellites into orbit.

What keeps the commercial launch vehicle industry in business is a slight advantage that low-orbit satellites have over the geostationary satellites that were launched in the 1970s and 1980s.

Geostationary satellites orbit the Earth at the same rate as the Earth spins, so they appear stationary in the sky. These satellites travel in very high orbits—22,400 miles (36,000 km) above Earth—and so they require large launchers. At that distance, it takes a signal about a quarter of a second to travel from the ground to the satellite and back, a time lag large enough to create significant transmission problems. Low Earth orbit satellites, only about 600 miles (968 km) above Earth, benefit from much smaller time lags.

Small comsats and their launchers are relatively cheap because they are mass produced from off-the-shelf parts, and if something goes wrong—if a satellite burns out, or a rocket explodes on launch—it is easy to send up another. In contrast, large geostationary communication satellites and their correspondingly large launch vehicles tend to be expensive, and it takes a great deal of time and money to replace a failure.

SIMPLE SOLID FUELS

Production-line economics also explain why most commercial launch vehicles burn relatively low-performance solid fuels, instead of higher-thrust liquid fuels. Solid fuels are easy to handle and need no complex gas tanks, valves or pumps. And solid-fuel rocket engines are cheaper, lighter and more reliable than their liquid-fuel counterparts because they have fewer moving parts. Rocket makers can also save money by using solid-fuel engines reclaimed from decommissioned missiles.

One example of a successful commercial launch vehicle is Lockheed Martin's Athena rocket, originally called the Lockheed Martin Launch Vehicle (LMLV). Although there were problems with some of the early launches, two versions of the Athena have sent up two satellites—Lewis and ROCSAT-1—and the Lunar Prospector space probe, which used a Star kick motor to travel from low Earth orbit to the Moon. Additionally, India and Japan both run thriving launch vehicles.

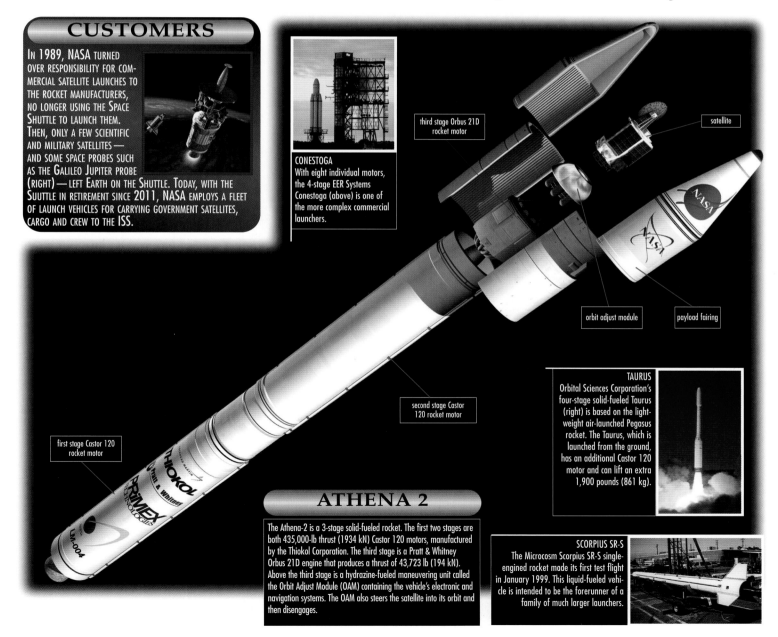

CUSTOMERS

In 1989, NASA turned over responsibility for commercial satellite launches to the rocket manufacturers, no longer using the Space Shuttle to launch them. Then, only a few scientific and military satellites — and some space probes such as the Galileo Jupiter probe (right) — left Earth on the Shuttle. Today, with the Shuttle in retirement since 2011, NASA employs a fleet of launch vehicles for carrying government satellites, cargo and crew to the ISS.

third stage Orbus 21D rocket motor

satellite

CONESTOGA
With eight individual motors, the 4-stage EER Systems Conestoga (above) is one of the more complex commercial launchers.

orbit adjust module

payload fairing

second stage Castor 120 rocket motor

first stage Castor 120 rocket motor

TAURUS
Orbital Sciences Corporation's four-stage solid-fueled Taurus (right) is based on the lightweight air-launched Pegasus rocket. The Taurus, which is launched from the ground, has an additional Castor 120 motor and can lift an extra 1,900 pounds (861 kg).

ATHENA 2
The Athena-2 is a 3-stage solid-fueled rocket. The first two stages are both 435,000-lb thrust (1934 kN) Castor 120 motors, manufactured by the Thiokol Corporation. The third stage is a Pratt & Whitney Orbus 21D engine that produces a thrust of 43,723 lb (194 kN). Above the third stage is a hydrazine-fueled maneuvering unit called the Orbit Adjust Module (OAM) containing the vehicle's electronic and navigation systems. The OAM also steers the satellite into its orbit and then disengages.

SCORPIUS SR-S
The Microcosm Scorpius SR-S single-engined rocket made its first test flight in January 1999. This liquid-fueled vehicle is intended to be the forerunner of a family of much larger launchers.

SPACESHIPONE

On December 17, 2003, exactly 100 years after the first powered flight by the Wright Brothers, Brian Binnie became the first person to fly supersonically in a craft developed by a small company without government funding, and in doing so reach the edges of space. The small single-engined

SpaceShipOne is immediately recognisable as a design from the stable of prolific designer Burt Rutan's Scaled Composites Inc, as is its carrier plane or mothership, known as White Knight. Together they formed "Tier One," which took the first steps toward commercial space tourism.

SPACESHIPONE SPECIFICATIONS

CREW:	1
POWERPLANT:	ONE 16,535 LB THRUST (74 kN) SpaceDev HYBRID SOLID ROCKET ENGINE
MAX SPEED:	MACH 3.09 (2,185 MPH/3,518 KM/H)
MAX ALTITUDE:	367,442FT (111,996 M)

SPAN:	16 FT 4 IN (4.97 M)
LENGTH:	16 FT 5 IN (5.00 M)
HEIGHT:	UNKNOWN
WEIGHT:	LOADED 7,937 LB (3,600 KG)

RIDING ON A WHITE KNIGHT

Although there has been commercial involvement in the US space program from the beginning, the construction of spacecraft has been the domain of large aerospace companies, funded by NASA or the military. The X-Prize was created as a means of fostering innovation by independent private firms and creating the market for commercial spaceflight.

On September 30, 2004, White Knight launched SpaceShipOne on the first qualifying flight for the X-Prize. It was not without drama for the pilot, Mike Melvill and the tens of thousands watching from the Mojave Airport. At the top of its climb, the spacecraft oscillated and began a series of rolls at nearly Mach 3, causing Melvill to cut the engine 11 seconds early and reach a lower than planned altitude. After landing he said: "Did I plan the roll? I'd like to say I did but I didn't. You're extremely busy at that point. Probably I stepped on something too quickly and caused the roll but it's nice to do a roll at the top of the climb."

Following this, on October 4, well within the stipulated two-week window, Brian Binnie took SpaceShipOne to 368,000ft (112,000 m) in a flawless flight, easily capturing the $10 million prize. Afterwards Binnie said: "It's a fantastic feeling. There is a freedom there and a sense of wonder that—I tell you what—you all need to experience."

The awarding of the X-Prize was by no means the end of the story. Together with Richard Branson's new company Virgin Galactic, Scaled Composites plans to develop a seven-seat "SpaceShipTwo" to offer commercial space flights.

The X-Prize has been established as the focus of an annual event in New Mexico to encourage the runners up in the original X-Prize to continue developing their craft.

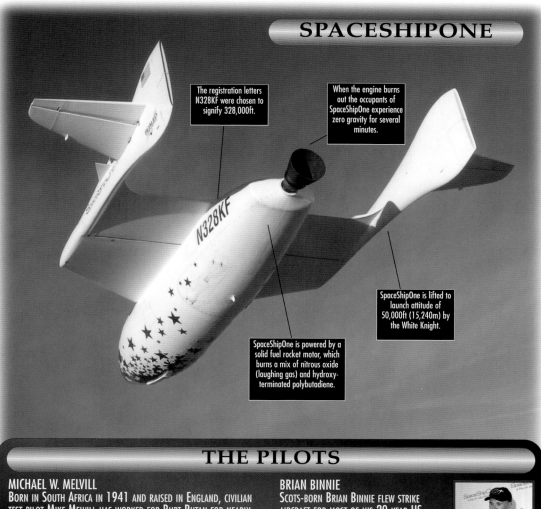

SPACESHIPONE

The registration letters N328KF were chosen to signify 328,000ft.

When the engine burns out the occupants of SpaceShipOne experience zero gravity for several minutes.

SpaceShipOne is lifted to launch attitude of 50,000ft (15,240m) by the White Knight.

SpaceShipOne is powered by a solid fuel rocket motor, which burns a mix of nitrous oxide (laughing gas) and hydroxy-terminated polybutadiene.

THE PILOTS

MICHAEL W. MELVILL
BORN IN SOUTH AFRICA IN 1941 AND RAISED IN ENGLAND, CIVILIAN TEST PILOT MIKE MELVILL HAS WORKED FOR BURT RUTAN FOR NEARLY 30 YEARS AND HAS FLOWN 140 FIXED- AND ROTARY-WING AIRCRAFT TYPES, ACCUMULATING OVER 7,050 FLIGHT HOURS. HE HOLDS NINE US AND WORLD SPEED AND ALTITUDE RECORDS, ALL ACHIEVED IN RUTAN AIRCRAFT.

BRIAN BINNIE
SCOTS-BORN BRIAN BINNIE FLEW STRIKE AIRCRAFT FOR MOST OF HIS 20-YEAR US NAVY CAREER, AND HAS OVER 4,600 HOURS EXPERIENCE IN 59 DIFFERENT TYPES OF AIRCRAFT. A GRADUATE OF THE US NAVY'S TEST PILOT SCHOOL, HE HAS FLOWN EVALUATIONS ON MANY NEW SYSTEMS AND WEAPONS FOR THE A-6, A-7 AND F/A-18 AIRCRAFT.

MISSION DIARY

MAY 1996
X-PRIZE OFFERED

APRIL 18, 2003:
SCALED COMPOSITES UNVEILED THEIR COMMERCIAL MANNED SPACE PROGRAMME, WHICH HAD BEEN UNDERWAY AT ITS MOJAVE FACILITY FOR TWO YEARS.

MAY 20, 2003:
FIRST (UNMANNED) CAPTIVE FLIGHT OF SPACESHIPONE, DURATION 1 HOUR, 48 MINUTES

JULY 29, 2003:

FIRST RELEASE AND GLIDE FLIGHT. PILOT MIKE MELVILL, TOTAL DURATION 2 HOURS, 6 MINUTES
17 DECEMBER, 2003: FIRST POWERED LAUNCH, REACHING MACH 1.2 AND 67,900 FT (20,700 M). PILOT BRIAN BINNIE, DURATION 18 MINUTES, 10 SECONDS

JUNE 21, 2004:
FIRST FLIGHT OVER 62 MILES (100 KM). PILOT MIKE MELVILL. TOP SPEED MACH 2.9, DURATION 24 MINUTES, 5 SECONDS

SEPTEMBER 29, 2004:
MIKE MELVILL MAKES THE FIRST QUALIFYING FLIGHT FOR THE X-PRIZE, REACHING 337,000 FT (102,900 M) AND A MAXIMUM SPEED OF MACH 2.92 DURING A 24-MINUTE FLIGHT
OCTOBER 4, 2004: THE TIER ONE TEAM WINS THE ANSARI

X-PRIZE BY TWICE EXCEEDING 100 KM IN TWO WEEKS. BRIAN BINNIE REACHED 69.5 MILES (112 KM) AT MACH 3.09 ON A 23 MINUTE AND 56 SECOND FLIGHT

PSLV

The Indian PSLV (Polar Satellite Launch Vehicle) is the first expendable launch system from the Indian Space Research Organisation (ISRO) that is capable of launching satellites into heliostationary orbits as well as geostationary transfer orbit. Despite the maiden flight failing to launch its payload, the PSLV has been highly successful for the ISRO, with twenty-three out of its twenty-five launches being completely successful. The PSLV system is also known for launching the Indian Mars Orbiter Mission (MOM) and unmanned lunar probe, Chandrayaan-1, making India a country with a presence in space to watch with interest.

PSLV LAUNCH RECORD

PSLV HISTORY	FLIGHTS LAUNCHED	SUCCESSES
1993–96	3	2 (MAIDEN LAUNCH FAILED)
1997–99	2	1 (1 PARTIAL FAILURE)
2000–02	2	2
2003–05	2	2
2006–08	5	5
2009–11	6	6
2012–PRESENT	5	5

INDIA'S SUCCESS STORY

The PSLV system was first developed in the 1990s, with its first launch in September 1993. With an initially successful performance of the engines, problems with the attitude controls during the second and third launch stages meant that the maiden launch was a failure. Since then, every PSLV has launched successfully, with only one other flight—the fourth to launch in September 1997—resulting in a partial failure when the Indian Remote Sensing (IRS) 1D satellite was launched into a lower orbit than planned. With mounting successes, India launched its own space missions using the PSLV.

The latest PSLV launch on November 5, 2013, sent the Mars Orbiter Mission (MOM) on India's first interplanetary mission. After a successful launch, MOM orbited the Earth seven times before being propelled onto the correct interplanetary trajectory towards Mars, meaning that it is on course to orbit Mars on September 24, 2014. This current schedule means that MOM will enter Mars orbit two days after MAVEN, the NASA Mars orbiter. MOM will study the chemical composition, geology and surface of Mars in detail, as well as analyzing the Martian atmosphere. If everything goes to plan, the PSLV will make India the fourth space agency to reach Mars, joining NASA, the ESA and Russia. The project is estimated to cost approximately $73 million.

For the launch of MOM, the PSLV-XL was used, the extra solid-fuel rocket boosters ensuring that MOM was successfully launched into its elliptical orbit around Earth before the rocket's propulsion system sent the probe off on its trajectory towards Mars.

In addition to launching MOM, PSLV launched Chandrayaan-1, India's first lunar probe. Chandrayaan-1 was launched on October 22, 2008, entered lunar orbit on November 8, and landed on the surface of the moon on November 14, 2008. The orbiter took readings and photos, while the probe searched for evidence of lunar water and surface deposits. Equipped with near infrared (NIR) and X-ray sensors, Chandrayaan-1 was able to make a 3-D atlas of the Moon, as well as map the terrain for chemical and mineral deposits. It found evidence of many minerals found on Earth, as well as potentially useful energy sources such as Radon. Information on the evolutionary history of the Moon and impacts and craters caused by collisions was also sent back to Earth for further analysis.

MAKING HISTORY

The first flight from PSLV was a failure. Flight D1 (carrying the satellite IRS 1E) was launched on September 20, 1993, but was not successfully placed into orbit. The second stage of the launch failed when the attitude control command exceeded its maximum value and failed. The satellite crashed into the Bay of Bengal in the Indian Ocean. However, this first launch failure is PSLV's only complete failure to date. Currently numbering of twenty-five launches and twenty-three successes, the PSLV launch system is also known for its record-breaking launch of ten satellites at once in April 2008. With such an excellent record for safe launches, it is no wonder that more than half of the launches have been on behalf of foreign satellites with some being on a private basis. In addition, the PSLV system launches its own Indian Remote Sensing (IRS) satellites.

THE CHAIRMAN
Koppillil Radhakrishnan has been the chairman of the ISRO since 2009. Also a scientist, Radhakrishnan began his career at the ISRO as an Avionics engineer in 1971. Under him, all PSLV launches have been successful and the company looks to expand even farther into space.

CHANDRAYAAN-1
The Chandrayaan-1 spacecraft (shown above) was India's first lunar probe. National pride was enhanced by the fact that the craft had been researched and developed almost entirely in India, as well as being launched by the Indian PSLV system. Such success means that the ISRO are currently designing a second lunar mission scheduled for 2016. Chandrayaan-2 will include a lunar orbiter and a rover.

PSLV SYSTEM

FALCON

The most recent Falcon rocket family launch took place on January 6, 2014, utilizing the latest breakthroughs in technology, including its updated Merlin 1D engines. Such updates have meant that payloads have increased to a massive 29,000 lb (13,150 kg). This is over 9,000 lb (4,000 kg) heavier than previous Falcon launch capabilities, also outperforming similar vehicles such as the Space Shuttle, Ariane and Delta rockets. The Falcon 9 was the first commercial launch vehicle to put supplies in orbit for rendezvous with the International Space Station (ISS) and is the first rocket family to be developed exclusively in the 21st century.

PAYLOAD CAPACITY

Launch vehicle	Falcon Heavy	Space Shuttle	Delta IV Heavy	Ariane 5	H-IIB
Maximum payload	116,850 LB (53,000 KG)	53,800 LB (24,000 KG)	49,700 LB (22,560 KG)	44,000 LB (20,000 KG)	36,300 LB (16,500 KG)

THE FALCON FAMILY

Owned, designed and operated by Space Exploration Technologies (SpaceX), the Falcon rocket family consists of a series of launch vehicles that first flew in September 2008 with the Falcon 1. Previously planned to launch in 2006, its maiden flight failed only seconds after initial launch. With the second launch also failing, redevelopments to the coolant system meant a delay until 2008. The Falcon 1 marked a first as it was the first liquid-fuelled launch vehicle developed privately. While plans were on the table for a Falcon 5 version, these never got further than design stages as SpaceX began developing the Falcon 9 rocket in 2005 as an Evolved Expendable Launch Vehicle (EELV). Since then, Falcons gone from strength to strength.

The first version of Falcon 9 flew five successful orbital missions. Falcon 9v1.1 is the second version of Falcon 9 and is the rocket currently in service. The first Falcon 9 made its maiden voyage on June 4, 2010, after several delays where the rocket failed to launch. In total, Falcon 9 rockets have made eight launches to date, all of which have been successful in delivering their payloads. These flights have included NASA demonstrations and launches as well as private launches of satellites.

Version 1.1 made its second flight as part of the NASA Commercial Orbit Transportation Services (COTS) contract. This demonstration flight was a success, deploying an operational SpaceX Dragon spacecraft, which entered Earth's orbit, orbited the planet twice, then made a controlled reentry in the Pacific Ocean. With the successful recovery of the Dragon spacecraft, SpaceX became the first private company to launch, orbit and recover their craft, with only government agencies doing this beforehand.

Falcon 9 rockets stand out from similar launch vehicles in that they were actively designed to carry humans into space. While this has not yet been done, SpaceX is working hard to fulfill their goal of launching humans into space.

The Falcon 9 is a two-stage rocket, which uses nine Merlin 1D engines in the first stage of launch. The thrust provided here means that the rockets are—in theory at least—able to complete their missions even if the second stage engine then shuts down. Made to be reliable and safe as well as cost-effective, the Falcon family continues to grow.

FALCON HEAVY

With the onset of more private companies competing for spacecraft and launch system contracts comes competition to do the job more reliably, for less money. Currently under development, the Falcon Heavy has the ability to launch an incredible 116,850 lb (53,000 kg) into lower earth orbit and up to 42,000 lb (19,000 kg) into geostationary orbit in a single payload for a cheaper than average launch price per pound lifted. The design follows the Falcon 9 rocket, but it also has an additional two Falcon 9 rockets, each equipped with nine Merlin 1D engines. This gives the rocket an initial thrust of nearly 4 million lb (17,600 kN). SpaceX also boast that all this power can be delivered for one-third of the cost of other heavy-lift launchers such as the Delta IV Heavy. Originally planned for initial launch in 2013, Falcon Heavy is now scheduled to launch in 2015. If the current success of Falcon rockets is any judge, the Falcon Heavy could change how the ISS is equipped.

MERLIN 1D
Also produced by SpaceX, the Merlin engine is shown on the left being rigorously test-fired.

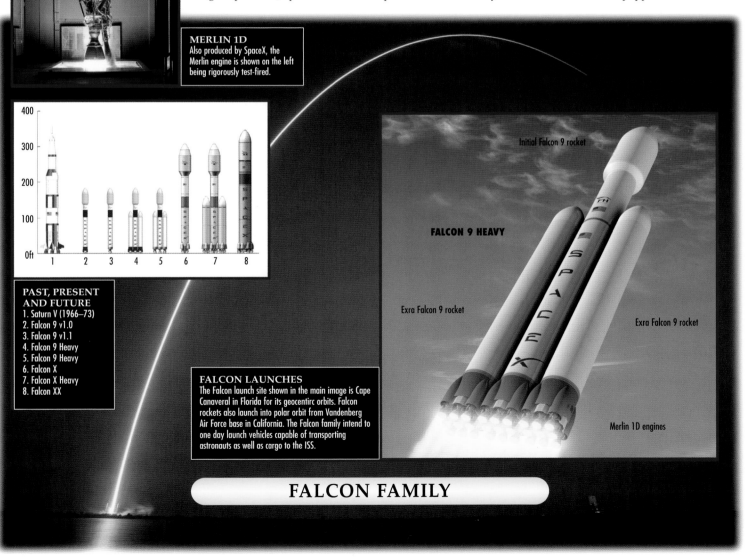

PAST, PRESENT AND FUTURE
1. Saturn V (1966–73)
2. Falcon 9 v1.0
3. Falcon 9 v1.1
4. Falcon 9 Heavy
5. Falcon 9 Heavy
6. Falcon X
7. Falcon X Heavy
8. Falcon XX

FALCON LAUNCHES
The Falcon launch site shown in the main image is Cape Canaveral in Florida for its geocentirc orbits. Falcon rockets also launch into polar orbit from Vandenberg Air Force base in California. The Falcon family intend to one day launch vehicles capable of transporting astronauts as well as cargo to the ISS.

Initial Falcon 9 rocket

FALCON 9 HEAVY

Exra Falcon 9 rocket

Exra Falcon 9 rocket

Merlin 1D engines

FALCON FAMILY

H-IIB

H-IIB is an expendable launch system designed and ran by the Japan Aerospace Exploration Agency (JAXA), which was formed in 2003, and Mitsubishi Heavy Industries (MHI). H-IIB has evolved from the earlier H-II and H-IIA launch systems. The ground-based launch system was designed to lift the H-II launch vehicle family. These built upon the H-IIA design which aimed to do launch rockets in a safer and more cost-effective way. H-IIB is capable of carrying a payload of 17,600 lb (8,000 kg) into geostationary transfer orbit. Since the first H-IIB launch in September 2009, there have been three other launches to date, all of which have been successful.

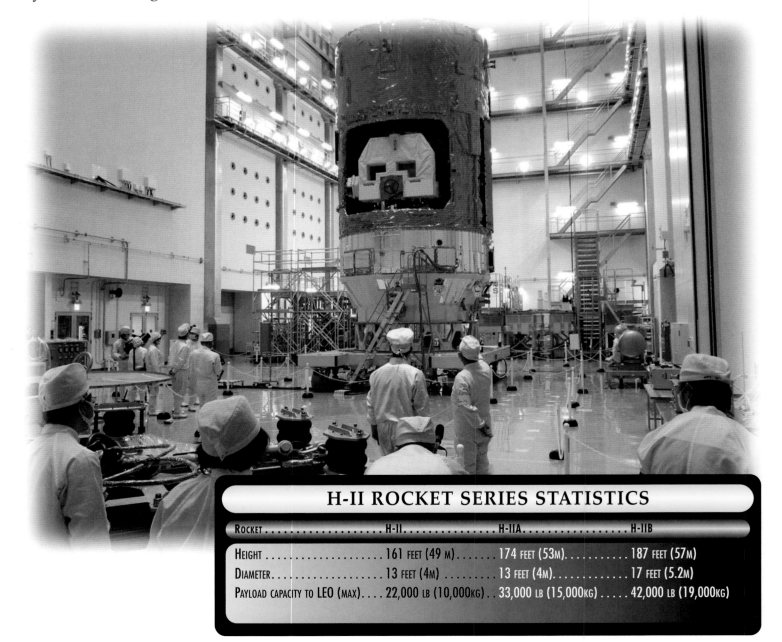

H-II ROCKET SERIES STATISTICS

Rocket	H-II	H-IIA	H-IIB
Height	161 feet (49 m)	174 feet (53m)	187 feet (57m)
Diameter	13 feet (4m)	13 feet (4m)	17 feet (5.2m)
Payload capacity to LEO (max)	22,000 lb (10,000kg)	33,000 lb (15,000kg)	42,000 lb (19,000kg)

SUPPLYING SPACE

The H-IIB launch system has allowed Japan to move forward as a contending country in space. Its successful launch of the Kounotori 4 spacecraft carried essential supplies as well as experimental research supplies to the International Space Station (ISS). The system also has the capability to launch more than one satellite at once—meaning that it could become a serious contender for private industry use. To date, all of its launches have been successful since the initial launch carrying payload to the ISS in 2009. The rocket is primarily used to carry H-II Transfer Vehicles (HTV) and was at one point the only spacecraft able to send interchangeable International Standard Payload Racks (ISPRs) to the ISS after the retirement of the Space Shuttle in 2011. These resupply vehicles can carry up to 16,750 lb (7,600 kg) of cargo. After they have successfully deposited their cargo, they are refilled with waste and destroyed on reentry. There are currently as least four planned HTV missions, all of which intend to use the H-IIB rocket launch system.

All H-IIB rockets are launched from the Tanegashima Space Center , situated on Tanegashima Island in Japan. The latest flight saw the launch of Kounotori 4, which is the fourth H-II Transfer Vehicle to launch resupplies to the ISS and its six astronauts. Kounotori 4 was launched on August 3, 2013, and successfully docked with the ISS six days later. Measuring approximately 13 feet (4 m) across by 33 feet (10 m) long, it carried 5.9 tons (5.4 tonnes) of cargo, including pressurized and unpressurized cargo. This consisted of samples, scientific equipment, refrigeration and storage—including cryogenic storage—data recorders and spare parts. Kounotori 4 is the latest HTV, which used reaction control system (RCS) thrusters manufactured by Aerojet, capable of giving small, controlled amounts of thrust during reentry in a combination of directions. Subsequent Kounotori craft will use IHI Aerospace thrusters amde by a Japanese company. Kounotori 4 was also the first time for a HTV to reenter Earth's atmosphere with waste cargo. The craft undocked from the ISS on September 4, 2013, and made a successful reentry on September 7, having achieved its mission aims. Continued missions are expected to lead to manned spacecraft in the future.

With every H-II rocket building on the technology of the one before it, Japan's aims to send future missions into space seem ever more likely. Indeed, Japan has successfully sent a lunar explorer, SELENE—known as "Kaguya," after the Japanese moon princess—to the moon in September 2007. A manned mission to the Moon is still in the pipeline.

POWER AND SPEED

Working on a two-stage rocket launch, the H-IIB is larger than the previous model. The extra space allows for larger quantities of propellant, meaning a more powerful launch despite the increase in size and weight. The larger launch capability of H-IIB compared to H-IIA rockets means that it will be possible for simultaneous launches of more than one satellite, meaning a significant reduction in cost per launch. The last two H-IIB launches have both successfully launched several satellites at once, carrying both Japanese and foreign payloads. In addition, JAXA intend to use elements of H-IIA rockets combined with their own developments in technology to run more cost-effective launches. This, combined with the reliability of its launches, makes H-IIB a viable contender for both government agencies and private industry.

LAUNCHING H-IIB

H-II LAUNCH
This dramatic image of a H-IIB launch from the Tanegashima Space Center in Japan, the largest in the country.

SUCCESSFUL DELIVERY
The crew of the ISS (above) enter a H-II vehicle after it successfully docked at the space station's Harmony node carrying supplies.

HTV "KOUNOTORI" 4
The craft's name means "white stork" in Japanese, representing the eagerly anticipated delivery of equipment to the ISS.

ANTARES

The Antares rocket family was first developed to send resupply crafts to the International Space Station (ISS) on behalf of NASA. The medium-class rockets add to Orbital Sciences Corporation's existing small-class rockets and aim to provide a low cost and highly reliable launch system. They are also capable of launching single or multiple payloads of up to 13,000 lb (6,000 kg) into low earth orbit (LEO), with smaller amounts to heliocentric orbit and interplanetary trajectories. The maiden launch on April 21, 2013 was successful, despite being initially planned for 2012, then being postponed on both April 17 and 20, 2013. Since its maiden flight, the Antares family has successfully launched each of its three rockets.

CURRENT AND FUTURE LAUNCHES

CURRENT LAUNCHES	PLANNED LAUNCHES
APRIL 21, 2013	MAY 2014
SEPTEMBER 18, 2013	OCTOBER 2014
JANUARY 9, 2014	2015 ONWARDS

LAUNCHING FUTURE LEGENDS

The Antares rockets work on a two-stage launch system. They are also capable of launching single or multiple medium-class payloads reliably and cost-effectively. Used initially to resupply the ISS, the maiden flight—Antares A-ONE—in April 2013 was used to send a Cygnus Mass Simulator (CMS) into orbit as a test flight for the Cygnus spacecrafts that Antares would carry in future flights. The Mass Simulator weighed over 8,000 lb (3,600 kg), with a height of 199 inches (5 m). It successfully separated from the rocket and reached orbit. For the Cygnus spacecraft—which was also developed by Orbital—launches, Orbital and NASA worked together as part of NASA's Commercial Orbital Transportation Services (COTS program) and will be one of the systems used to resupply the ISS in the wake of the Space Shuttle's retirement in 2011.

Following its test flight, Antares was the first rocket to launch the Cygnus spacecraft. NASA awarded the American Orbital company the contract in 2008 and the first Cygnus mission was launched by an Antares rocket on September 18, 2013. This demonstration mission successfully rendezvoused and docked with the ISS in late September 2013. The third Antares launch—and the second Antares rocket to carry a Cygnus spacecraft—launched successfully on 9 January 2014. It carried supplies to the ISS, including physics equipment and medicinal research, as well as an ant colony to observe how the insects behave in space. While it cannot return equipment or experiments safely back to Earth, the Cygnus craft can be filled with waste and obsolete equipment for disposal during destructive reentry.

Orbital Sciences Corporation also run small-class rocket launchers, which Antares was based on. These small-class rocket families are Pegasus, Taurus, and Minotaur. All successfully and deliver commercial, government and defense payloads between them. Orbital are also working on an air launch transportation vehicle called Stratolaunch. This system aims to send payloads of up to 15,000 lbs (6,800 kg) into low Earth orbit (LEO). The first test flight is planned for 2016. Air-launch systems negate several of the problems that can occur with ground launches, especially unexpected poor weather.

All Antares launches of the Cygnus craft have taken place at Wallops Flight Facility in East Virginia, which was founded in 1945. The Flight Facility works primarily in unison with NASA to launch scientific and exploratory missions. The facility now also runs commercial launches.

STAR POWER

Initially named Taurus II, the rocket family was renamed Antares on December 12, 2011, after the star, which in turn took its name from the original Greek *anti-Ares*, or "anti-Mars," because its red glow made people liken the star to the planet Mars. Antares is classed as a red supergiant, meaning it is in a group of stars with the largest volumes of any star in the universe. Antares itself has a massive radius over 800 times greater than the Sun and is even larger than the Red Planet. It is part of the Milky Way and one of four stars that make up the "Royal Stars of Persia" group. This group is made up of Aldebaran, Regulus, Antares and Fomalhaut. Antares is also unique because it has a companion star called Antares B. Antares B often appears to look green, making the contrast with its bigger red companion even more marked.

ANTARES

ANTARES AT WALLOPS
The Wallops Flight Facility in Virginia runs NASA educational programs and lectures, as well as allowing model rockets to be launched once a month.

ANTARES STAR
The red supergiant Antares in the Milky Way has a radius measuring over a staggering 880 times that of the Sun.

CYGNUS
The Cygnus spacecraft (above) can be seen on its approach to the ISS, stocked with essential supplies and equipment.

SATELLITES

On October 5, 1957, to U.S. and world surprise, the Soviet Union launched Sputnik I ("fellow traveler"), the first manmade object into orbit. Sputnik I was nothing more than a bleeping radio transmitter, but many practical applications have since been found for artificial satellites. Today well over 2,000 are in Earth orbit. Satellites relay telephone calls, data, and television programmes, observe changes in the environment, and provide accurate location data to GPS receivers, which have a wide range of civil and military applications. Purely military uses include monitoring ballistic missile launches, listening to enemy communications and electronic emissions, as well as imaging sites of military interest. The type of orbit is important. A geostationary orbit (in which the satellite remains over one point on Earth) allows communications to be relayed over most of the planet. Spy satellites and most other Earth-observing craft need to make moving orbits, passing over their targets for a short period each day. The modern world would barely function without satellites, and new launches will need to be made far into the foreseeable future.

Three Shuttle crewmembers capture the 4.5 ton (4 tonne) INTELSAT VI communications satellite by hand, prior to installing a new engine before repositioning the craft in the correct orbit.

LAUNCHING SATELLITES

A satellite's journey into space usually involves several phases, each with its own hazards. First, the launching rocket places its payload in low Earth orbit. Then a rocket burn sends the satellite out along an elliptical transfer orbit. Finally, another rocket motor, strapped to the satellite or built into it, puts the craft permanently into its planned orbit. Such maneuvers are all routine for rocket engineers. But a single failure at any point can turn an expensive piece of technology into a piece of space junk.

ORBITAL MILESTONES

FIRST SATELLITE LAUNCH INTO ORBIT	OCTOBER 4, 1957 (SPUTNIK-1)
FIRST US SATELLITE LAUNCH INTO ORBIT	FEBRUARY 1, 1958 (EXPLORER-1)
FIRST LAUNCH INTO POLAR ORBIT	FEBRUARY 28, 1959 (DISCOVERER-1)
FIRST LAUNCH OF SEVERAL SATELLITES AT ONCE	JUNE 22, 1960 (TRANSIT-2A, SUNRAY)
FIRST LANDING OF A SATELLITE FROM ORBIT	AUGUST 18, 1960 (DISCOVERER-14)
FIRST COMMERCIAL COMMUNICATIONS SATELLITE LAUNCH	JULY 10, 1962 (TELSTAR-1)
FIRST LAUNCH INTO GEOSTATIONARY ORBIT	AUGUST 19, 1964 (SYNCOM-3)
FIRST SHUTTLE RETRIEVAL OF A SATELLITE	NOVEMBER 16, 1984 (PALAPA B-2 & WESTAR-6)

KICK START

The first part of a satellite's journey to its working orbit usually begins with a rocket launch that leaves the spacecraft at least 80 miles (129 km) above the Earth and moving at around 17,000 miles per hour (27,500 km/h)—orbital velocity. At this height, no orbit is stable: The Earth's atmosphere is still thick enough for its drag to bring the satellite down within a few days or weeks. Most spacecraft are designed to work from a higher altitude, from a few hundred miles for most observational satellites to the 22,700-mile (36,500 km) geostationary orbit

that is now the home of much communications equipment.

To get the satellite to its planned orbit, at least two more rocket burns are necessary. Both must be made in strict accordance with the laws of orbital mechanics. The first takes place at the satellite's perigee—where it is closest to the Earth's surface and moving at its fastest. The extra speed sends the craft on a transfer orbit that joins its original low orbit with its planned final orbit. This is usually performed by the perigee kick motor (PKM), which may be part of the launching rocket or the satellite itself.

The next burn takes place when the satellite reaches the apogee of its transfer orbit—its highest point above the Earth. The apogee kick motor (AKM), usually mounted on board the satellite, increases the spacecraft's speed once more, and converts the long ellipse of the transfer orbit into the near-perfect circle usually required for its permanent, final orbit.

GIVEN A BOOST

Without the help of the AKM to boost speed, the satellite would simply fall back to the low point in its orbit where it fired the PKM. The extra thrust

gives the orbit a new and much higher perigee, leaving the satellite where its designers intended. On-board thrusters may make a few minor course and attitude adjustments.

Next, the electricity-producing solar panels are unveiled, antennas unfold, instruments extend and communications dishes open up and snap into place—although some of this apparatus may have deployed earlier during the transfer orbit to enable mission control to talk to the satellite or to run the satellite's electrical systems. With the satellite operational in its final orbit, the launch vehicle is destroyed—unless the satellite has been carried into space by a reusable craft, which returns to Earth on completion of a mission.

HARD EVIDENCE

MOTORING
A satellite reaches low Earth orbit (LEO) after a rocket or Shuttle launch. Then, a perigee kick motor fires to send the satellite into a transfer orbit. Finally, an apogee kick motor (example below) fires to project the satellite into its final orbit. Some perigee and apogee rocket firings are achieved by the upper stage of the launch rocket—for example, the Russian Proton's Block DM or the U.S. Atlas rocket's Centaur.

4 ADJUSTMENT
Compressed springs free the satellite from the rocket stage. A small motor burns to send it to its precise orbit.

3 JETTISON
With no more air resistance to overcome, streamlined shrouds around the satellite are jettisoned.

2 SECOND STAGE
Explosive bolts separate the second stage, which accelerates to orbital velocity — about five miles (eight km) per second.

1 LAUNCH
The first stage, often with extra boosters, drives the rocket and its cargo through most of the atmosphere.

INTO ORBIT

The journey from launchpad to final orbit involves several rocket firings, each with a precise purpose. Usually, the spacecraft will travel from low Earth orbit to a higher station by means of a transfer orbit. The journey depends on accurate timing: A small error can leave the satellite hopelessly lost.

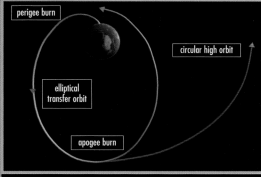

perigee burn

circular high orbit

elliptical transfer orbit

apogee burn

Placed by its booster in an initial low Earth orbit, a satellite first makes a perigee burn at the lowest point. The burn sends the satellite climbing into an elliptical transfer orbit. At the apogee — the highest point — a second burn pushes the satellite into a much higher, possibly geostationary, orbit.

UNMANNED SPUTNIKS

The Soviet Union amazed the world in 1957 when it launched the world's first artificial satellite, Sputnik 1. But this was just the first in a series of unmanned missions that ranged from scientific research to test flights for crewed space capsules and Venus-probe rocket stages. Together with three satellites that launched dogs into space, the success or failure of every mission was hidden behind the word "sputnik"—the name given to them by the Soviets to conceal their true purpose from the rest of the world.

UNMANNED LAUNCHES

Nickname	Real Name	Launch Date	Launch Vehicle	Reentry Date	Purpose
Sputnik 1	Object PS-1	October 4, 1957	8K71 (A-class)	January 4, 1958	Publicity
Sputnik 3	Object D-1	May 15, 1958	8A91 (A-class)	April 6, 1960	Scientific research
Sputnik 4	Object KS-1	May 15, 1960	8K72 (A-1 class)	October 15, 1965	Vostok capsule test
Sputnik 7	1VA No.1	February 4, 1961	8K78 (A-2-e class)	February 26, 1961	Venus probe launch
Sputnik 8	1VA No.2	February 12, 1961	8K78 (A-2-e class)	February 25, 1961	Venus probe launch

SPUTNIK 1
Launched from the Baikonur Cosmodrome, Soviet Union, on October 4, 1957, Sputnik 1 (replica shown right) was the first human-made object to go into orbit around the Earth. The shiny sphere was carried into space by a modified R-7 booster. The satellite's orbit decayed after three months in space, at which point it burned up in the Earth's atmosphere.

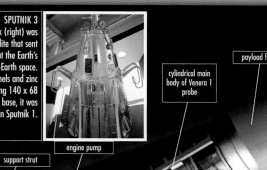

SPUTNIK 3
The third Sputnik (right) was a geophysical satellite that sent back information about the Earth's atmosphere and near-Earth space. Powered by solar panels and zinc batteries, and measuring 140 x 68 in (3.5 x 1.7 m) at the base, it was much larger than Sputnik 1.

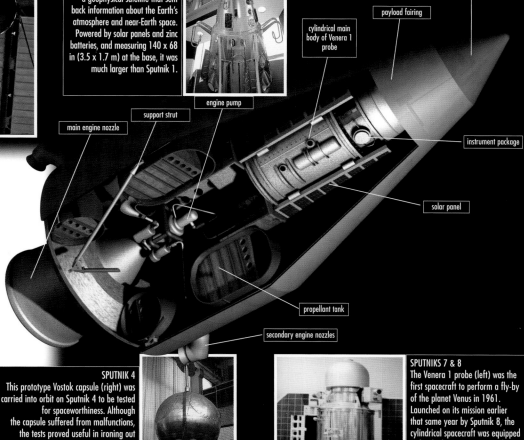

nose cone

payload fairing

cylindrical main body of Venera 1 probe

instrument package

engine pump

support strut

main engine nozzle

solar panel

propellant tank

secondary engine nozzles

SPUTNIK 4
This prototype Vostok capsule (right) was carried into orbit on Sputnik 4 to be tested for spaceworthiness. Although the capsule suffered from malfunctions, the tests proved useful in ironing out design flaws, meaning that subsequent Sputnik missions were successful.

SPUTNIKS 7 & 8
The Venera 1 probe (left) was the first spacecraft to perform a fly-by of the planet Venus in 1961. Launched on its mission earlier that same year by Sputnik 8, the cylindrical spacecraft was equipped with a high-gain antenna and a wide range of scientific instruments.

FIRST SHOTS

Sputnik 1, the world's first artificial satellite, was one of the smallest and simplest spacecraft ever built. The 2-ft (60-cm)-wide, 184-lb (83-kg) aluminum alloy ball contained batteries, radio transmitters and four long antennas, and transmitted a "beep...beep...beep" signal that could be received by amateur radio enthusiasts all over the world. But this simplicity of design was the secret to its success.

Sputnik 2, along with Sputniks 5 and 6, carried dogs into orbit to test the effects of space travel on animals. The next Sputnik without a living passenger was the 2,900-lb (1,315-kg) Sputnik 3. Larger and more sophisticated than Sputnik 1, it was originally intended to be the first Soviet satellite to reach space. Problems with its construction delayed the launch until May 1958—more than seven months after the first Sputnik.

A dozen instruments were fitted to Sputnik 3 to study the Earth's upper atmosphere, magnetic field and radiation belt, as well as any cosmic rays and micro-meteoroids that might be found there. Small solar panels were built around its cone-shaped main body to provide power. Sputnik 3 succeeded in transmitting data back to Earth until April 6, 1960, when its orbit decayed, causing it to burn up in the atmosphere.

The Soviet Union greeted the 1960s with the launch of Sputnik 4. This mission was the first test flight in space of the Vostok capsule—the spacecraft later used by Yuri Gagarin to become the first human in orbit. The engineers behind the new capsule called it Object KS-1 or "Spaceship-1." This first Vostok was a stripped-down, 7-ft 5-in (2.2-m)-wide test capsule; it had no heat shield, no parachutes and no ejection seat, and was intended to burn up in the atmosphere. On the outside of the ball-like capsule were a pair of small solar panels and some radio antennas. Strapped to the back of the Vostok was a service section containing thrusters and propellant tanks, more antennas, and heat control systems. The service section also housed Sun and Earth sensors for orientation of the capsule, and the main rocket engine used for reentry—but things went wrong when the time for reentry arrived. The capsule was facing the wrong direction when the rocket fired. Instead of descending, it shot into a higher orbit and didn't come down for five years.

Sputnik 7 and 8 were not actually satellites, but the upper stages of rocket launchers designed to send Venera space probes to Venus. Built by Sergei Korolev's Design Bureau OKB-1, these "Block L" rocket stages relied upon a sophisticated motor that burned kerosene and liquid oxygen propellants during launches.

Block L was the first rocket engine designed to be fired while in orbit around the Earth. In the weightlessness of space, propellants tend to float around inside their tanks, which makes it difficult to pump them into the engine. On Sputniks 7 and 8, small rockets were fired to force the propellants toward the bottom of their tanks and into the engine pumps. Due to a technical failure, Sputnik 7 failed to release its payload. But on February 12, 1961, Sputnik 8 did succeed in its mission—the upper rocket stage engine ignited in low orbit to successfully propel the Venera 1 probe toward its destination.

SPY IN THE SKY

On May 1, 1960, a U-2 spy plane (right) flown by CIA pilot Gary Powers was shot down by an surface-to-air missile over Baikonur Cosmodrome in the Soviet Union. At the time, Sputnik 4 was being prepared for liftoff. The spacecraft was eventually launched two weeks later, on May 15.

TELSTAR 1

One day in July 1962, scientists at a receiving station in France beamed with delight when they heard "The Star-Spangled Banner" and saw a picture of the American flag on a TV screen. They had just received the first-ever transatlantic TV relay, transmitted from the United States by the new Telstar satellite. Although the experimental satellite could only broadcast during a limited period each day, its pioneering transmissions paved the way for a revolution in international communications.

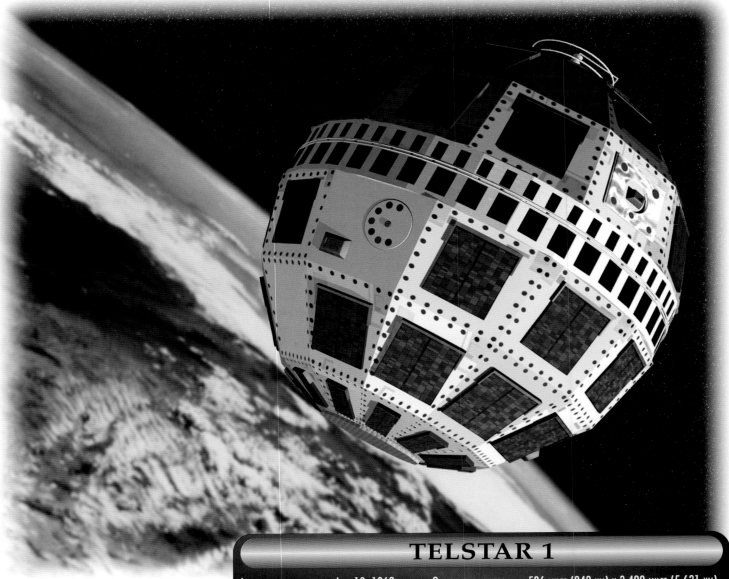

TELSTAR 1

LAUNCH DATE	JULY 10, 1962	ORBITAL PARAMETERS	586 MILES (943 KM) x 3,499 MILES (5,631 KM)
LAUNCH VEHICLE	DELTA BOOSTER	ORBITAL INCLINATION	44.8°
LAUNCH SITE	CAPE CANAVERAL	FREQUENCIES	UPLINK: 6,390 MHz
WEIGHT	171 LB (77.5 KG)		DOWNLINK: 4,170 MHz

MOVING PICTURES

As early as October 1945, science fiction writer Arthur C. Clarke had discussed the possibility of worldwide television and radio broadcasts using spacecraft as orbiting relays. In Clarke's model, space stations would travel in geostationary orbit, providing total coverage of the Earth for television and radio.

By 1962, the technology required to maintain stations in space was still on the drawing board, but John R. Pierce and his team at AT&T's Bell Laboratories were designing a simpler, less costly kind of relay—the artificial satellite Telstar. Pierce's strategy was ambitious. It called for "a system of 40 satellites in polar orbits, and 15 in equatorial orbits…and about 25 ground stations, so placed as to provide global coverage."

Truly worldwide broadcasts, though, would require worldwide cooperation. The reality of Cold War politics made this impossible, and the goal of the Telstar project was simplified: Put a satellite into low Earth orbit (LEO), and use it to transmit television pictures across the Atlantic.

AT&T paid NASA $3 million to launch Telstar 1 on July 10, 1962. The spacecraft was placed into a high, elliptical orbit, where it immediately encountered an unforeseen hazard: The day before launch, the United States had detonated Starfish, a powerful nuclear weapon that exploded high above the atmosphere. Radiation from the blast would take its toll on Telstar in the months to come. But in the hours after launch, the Telstar team stayed glued to their television sets, awaiting the first intercontinental telecast.

ATLANTIC LINKUP

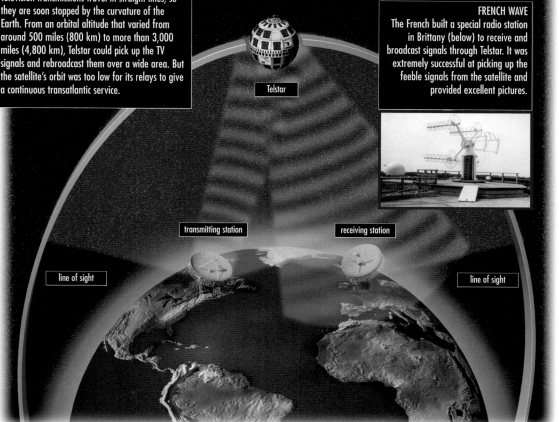

Television transmissions travel in straight lines, so they are soon stopped by the curvature of the Earth. From an orbital altitude that varied from around 500 miles (800 km) to more than 3,000 miles (4,800 km), Telstar could pick up the TV signals and rebroadcast them over a wide area. But the satellite's orbit was too low for its relays to give a continuous transatlantic service.

FRENCH WAVE
The French built a special radio station in Brittany (below) to receive and broadcast signals through Telstar. It was extremely successful at picking up the feeble signals from the satellite and provided excellent pictures.

Telstar

transmitting station

receiving station

line of sight

line of sight

WAVES ACROSS THE WORLD

In Andover, Maine, Bell Laboratories flew the American flag for its broadcast. In Pleumeur-Bodou in Brittany, France, technicians were poised to transmit recordings of an actor, a singer and a guitarist. And at Goonhilly Down in Cornwall, England, the control room was ready to receive the first images. But all three stations had to wait for Telstar to reach the right place. The satellite's low orbit meant that there was only a limited period during which it was above the horizon—and in the line of sight— for both European and U.S. transceiver stations. Transatlantic TV was only possible for 102 minutes each day.

At the appointed moment, France picked up Old Glory. Technical problems delayed British reception, and it was late in the night before the BBC received pictures of AT&T chairman Frederick Kappel reading a statement. They couldn't hear him because the sound had failed.

Despite technical glitches, Telstar 1 was an outstanding achievement, blazing a trail for the extraordinary growth in global telecommunication. Arthur C. Clarke is the author of many science fiction classics, but his "extraterrestrial relays" have become a reality.

MISSION DIARY: TELSTAR 1

1960 AT&T BEGINS RESEARCH AND DEVELOPMENT FOR A SATELLITE COMMUNICATIONS SYSTEM: TELSTAR (RIGHT).
1961 J.R. PIERCE OF BELL LABORATORIES, AN AT&T SUBSIDIARY, ESTIMATES COST OF TELSTAR PROJECT AT $500 MILLION.
JULY 24 CONCERNED ABOUT THE PROSPECT OF AN AT&T MONOPOLY IN TELECOMMUNICATIONS, PRESIDENT KENNEDY ANNOUNCES MEASURES TO GUARANTEE COMPETITION AND ADVOCATES INTERNATIONAL PARTNERSHIP IN THE FIELD.
JULY 9, 1962 THE U.S. MILITARY DETONATES A HUGE

THERMONUCLEAR TEST WEAPON, STARFISH, AT HIGH ALTITUDE WITHOUT ADVANCE WARNING.
JULY 10, 1962 TELSTAR 1 LAUNCHED INTO ELLIPTICAL EARTH ORBIT FROM CAPE CANAVERAL IN FLORIDA.
JULY 11, 1962 TELSTAR RELAYS TV PICTURES FROM A STATION IN ANDOVER, MAINE, TO A RECEIVER ON FRANCE'S EAST COAST. FRANCE RETURN PICTURES OF AN ACTOR, SINGER AND GUITARIST (ABOVE).
BRITAIN PICKS UP SIGNAL LATER, AT GOONHILLY RECEIVING STATION (FAR RIGHT).
AUGUST 31 U.S. GOVERNMENT PASSES COMMUNICATION

SATELLITE ACT. IT SETS UP A FEDERALLY FUNDED SATELLITE COMMUNICATIONS CORPORATION, COMSAT.
OCTOBER TELSTAR, ALREADY DAMAGED BY ATMOSPHERIC RADIATION FROM THE U.S. NUCLEAR TEST IN JULY, IS FURTHER COMPROMISED BY A MATCHING SOVIET NUCLEAR TEST. GROUND CONTROLLERS MANAGE TO CARRY OUT SOME REMOTE REPAIRS.
DECEMBER TELSTAR FINALLY CEASES TO OPERATE.
MAY 7, 1963 TELSTAR 2 LAUNCHED. COMMUNICATIONS RESUME SUCCESSFULLY.

DIRECT BROADCAST SATELLITES

Satellite technology has turned broadcasting into a massive global industry. Images beamed from space already reach hundreds of millions of people all over the planet, and from Alaska to Afghanistan, from Siberia to South Carolina, more viewers are signing up every day. New digital compression techniques mean that there are many more channels available to be viewed. The latest satellites can transmit more than 200 channels simultaneously, and high-definition television and videophone links are now being beamed, too, straight to people's homes using direct-to-home satellites.

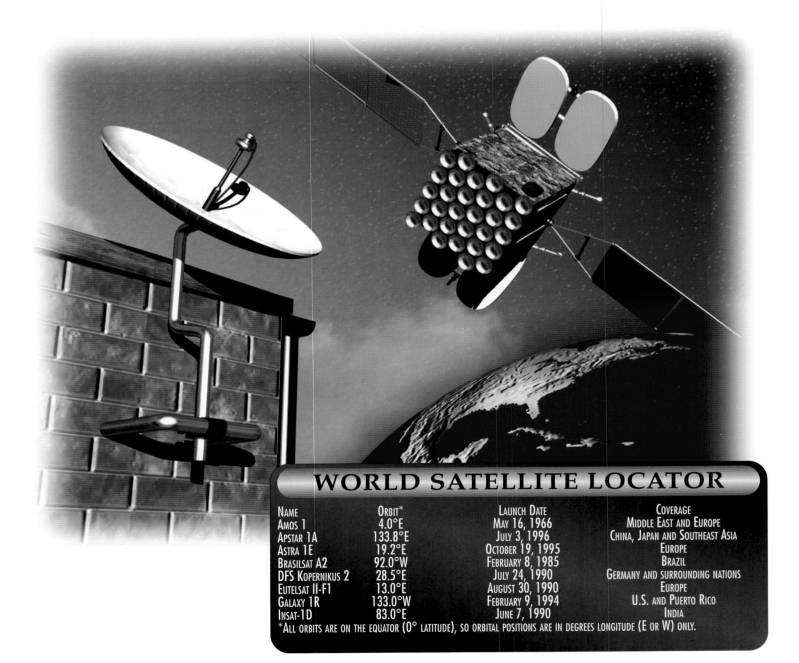

WORLD SATELLITE LOCATOR

NAME	ORBIT*	LAUNCH DATE	COVERAGE
AMOS 1	4.0°E	MAY 16, 1966	MIDDLE EAST AND EUROPE
APSTAR 1A	133.8°E	JULY 3, 1996	CHINA, JAPAN AND SOUTHEAST ASIA
ASTRA 1E	19.2°E	OCTOBER 19, 1995	EUROPE
BRASILSAT A2	92.0°W	FEBRUARY 8, 1985	BRAZIL
DFS KOPERNIKUS 2	28.5°E	JULY 24, 1990	GERMANY AND SURROUNDING NATIONS
EUTELSAT II-F1	13.0°E	AUGUST 30, 1990	EUROPE
GALAXY 1R	133.0°W	FEBRUARY 9, 1994	U.S. AND PUERTO RICO
INSAT-1D	83.0°E	JUNE 7, 1990	INDIA

*ALL ORBITS ARE ON THE EQUATOR (0° LATITUDE), SO ORBITAL POSITIONS ARE IN DEGREES LONGITUDE (E OR W) ONLY.

TV FROM ORBIT

Television signals have been beamed to Earth from satellites since 1962, when a satellite called Telstar began the era of worldwide TV. But until the 1990s, satellite signals were weak. To receive them, you needed a big dish antenna, up to 12 ft (3.5 m) across. Often, such equipment was owned by cable TV broadcasters, who used it to distribute programs nationwide, and most of the dishes had motorized controls that allowed them to move easily from one satellite to another.

Now, the giant dishes have gone the way of the dinosaurs. A new generation of Direct Broadcast Satellites (DBS) have been placed in orbit. These offer easily accessible direct-to-home (DTH) digital broadcasts, which can be received by dishes as small as 15 in (38 cm) across. The new satellites send out tightly focused, high-power digital signals. And they are capable of transmitting up to 200 TV channels at once—all with high-quality stereo sound.

A DBS receives the programs transmitted from TV companies' ground stations. Onboard devices called transponders relay the signals back to Earth at a different frequency. Dish antennae focus the signals into a narrow, powerful beam, just as reflectors focus a flashlight bulb.

STANDING STILL IN SPACE

A typical DBS satellite has 32 transponders working at any one time—plus a few spares, since there is no easy way to repair a satellite once it has been set in orbit. The beam from each transponder is carefully aimed to cover a particular area of the Earth far below. Together, the transponders create what satellite controllers call a "footprint"—an area where signals are reliably received.

A geostationary orbit takes precisely one day, so the satellite remains permanently above the same spot on the Earth. The receiving dishes down below need only be aimed once and then locked into place.

Because of the effects of lunar and solar gravity, even a perfectly placed geostationary satellite wavers a little off course. A wobble of 100 miles (160 km) or so will not affect reception on Earth, but from

time to time ground controllers must maneuver their satellites back into their proper positions. Such adjustments use up only tiny quantities of onboard fuel. Sooner or later, though, the fuel is expended—one reason why satellite lifetimes are limited to around 15 years, despite the reliability of the DBS components.

Since all geostationary satellites must orbit in the same plane, there is a limited number of orbital "slots" whose allocation is decided by international agreement. Each slot takes up about 2° of the 360° orbit—around 900 miles (1,500 km). Several satellites may be in each slot, spaced about 100 miles (160 km) apart.

When transponders on one satellite fail, another satellite can sometimes take over its faulty neighbor's workload so smoothly that television viewers are unaware that anything has gone wrong.

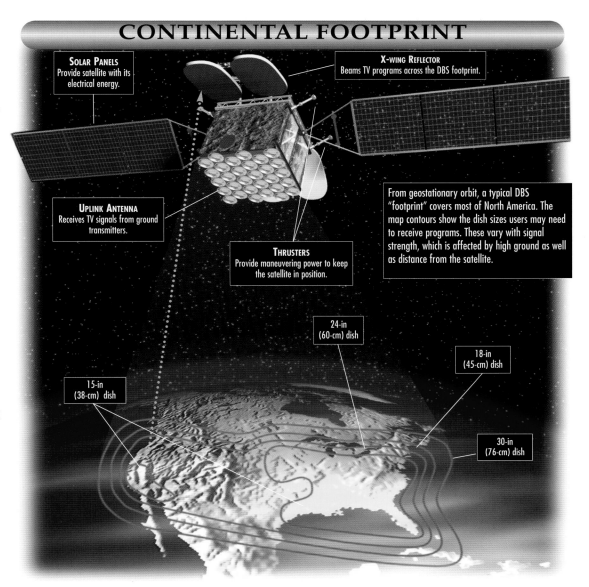

CONTINENTAL FOOTPRINT

SOLAR PANELS
Provide satellite with its electrical energy.

X-WING REFLECTOR
Beams TV programs across the DBS footprint.

UPLINK ANTENNA
Receives TV signals from ground transmitters.

THRUSTERS
Provide maneuvering power to keep the satellite in position.

From geostationary orbit, a typical DBS "footprint" covers most of North America. The map contours show the dish sizes users may need to receive programs. These vary with signal strength, which is affected by high ground as well as distance from the satellite.

24-in (60-cm) dish

18-in (45-cm) dish

15-in (38-cm) dish

30-in (76-cm) dish

HARD EVIDENCE

GEOSTATIONARY ORBIT

A satellite's speed depends on the height in which it is positioned above the Earth. At altitudes of around 300 miles (500 km), a satellite will complete one orbit every 95 minutes or so. At lunar distance, it will orbit the earth once a month—just as the Moon does. And at what is known as geosynchronous altitude, 22,240 miles (35,800 km) above the planet, it will complete an orbit in exactly 24 hours. For a geosynchronous orbit to also be geostationary, the satellite must be in the plane of the Earth's equator. In that case, as seen from Earth, the satellite will always be in the same position in the sky. Such orbits are essential for direct satellite broadcasts, since home users have a fixed target for their dish antennae.

24-hour orbital period

22,240 miles (35,800 km)

HARD EVIDENCE

THE SATELLITE REVOLUTION

Satellite television in the U.S. began in March 1978, when the Public Broadcasting Service (PBS) first used satellites to distribute programs to its local stations. By the early 1980s, direct-to-home (DTH) satellite receivers were commonplace, especially in rural areas where regular broadcast quality was poor and cable nonexistent. Satellite TV rapidly went global, with North America, Europe and Japan leading the way and virtually the whole world following as fast as it could. DBS satellites themselves have grown in size and complexity: The Galaxy model, built by the Hughes Corporation, weighs 3,800 lb (1,723 kg) and can transmit more than 200 separate TV channels.

EARLY WARNING SATELLITES

The chilling words "Missile launch alert!" quicken the hearts of military personnel around the world. They mean that some form of attack could be under way—and if it is, every second of early warning is invaluable. Missile early warning is the mission of the United States military's Defense Support Program (DSP). Providing worldwide coverage, the DSP uses a network of at least five satellites in geosynchronous orbit to monitor the Earth, watching for space and missile launches.

CURRENT DSP SATELLITES

PRIMARY MISSION	STRATEGIC AND TACTICAL MISSILE LAUNCH DETECTION	POWER GENERATION	SOLAR ARRAYS GENERATING 1,485 WATTS (SATELLITE USES 1,274 WATTS)
ORBITAL ALTITUDE	22,233 MILES (35,780 KM)		
HEIGHT	32.8 FT (10 M) ON ORBIT, 28 FT (8.5 M) AT LAUNCH	FIRST DEPLOYED	NOVEMBER 6, 1970
		UNIT COST	APPROXIMATELY $250 MILLION EACH
DIAMETER	22 FT (6.7 M) ON ORBIT, 13.7 FT (4.1 M) AT LAUNCH	SATELLITES IN PROGRAM	23
		CONTRACTOR TEAM	TRW AND AEROJET ELECTRONICS SYSTEMS
WEIGHT	5,250 LB (2,381 KG)		

TIMELY WARNINGS

The U.S. military's Defense Support Program (DSP) is a survivable and reliable satellite-based system that uses infrared sensors to detect missile and space launches and nuclear detonations. The early warning program began in 1966, but the first launch of a satellite didn't occur until November 6, 1970. Since then, DSP satellites have fed a constant stream of warning data, 24 hours a day, 365 days a year, to the Missile Warning Center at Cheyenne Mountain, Colorado, via ground stations as far away as Australia and Germany.

As the DSP program progressed, the satellite went through five major design changes, each one increasing its capabilities. Phase 1 satellites had 2,048 sensor elements—optimized to detect a single infrared wavelength—and a planned three-year life span. By the fifth design, DSPs had 6,000 sensors on two wavelengths and seven- to nine-year lifetimes. They were also hardened against laser jamming and nuclear attack, and they were capable of detecting any imminent physical threat from an attack satellite and maneuvering themselves out of harm's way.

The DSP proved its worth during *Operation Desert Storm*, in the Gulf War of 1991. Originally designed to detect strategic threats against the continental United States, the DSP satellites turned their attention to the Persian Gulf and detected Iraqi ballistic missiles being launched against the U.S.-led coalition forces.

SCUDBUSTERS

The DSP's superb operational performance during Operation Desert Storm demonstrated that the system, although designed to detect intercontinental missile launches, could also provide significant early warning against comparatively small tactical missiles. Every Scud missile launch made during the Gulf War was detected within seconds of liftoff. Warnings were relayed to civilian populations and coalition forces, including Patriot missile defense batteries, in Saudi Arabia and Israel.

Without a doubt, the Defense Support Program was also a key factor in America's winning the Cold War. Because of the DSP's global satellite coverage, no missile launch, no matter where it came from, could go unnoticed. No aggressor could launch an attack without being detected—and they knew it. The program continues to be one of the U.S. military's most successful programs ever.

WATCHING FROM ABOVE

A DSP satellite spins at about 6 rpm so that its detector systems can make continuous scans of the Earth below. Its magnetic plasma and synchronous orbit particle analyzers monitor electrical and radiation conditions in the atmosphere.

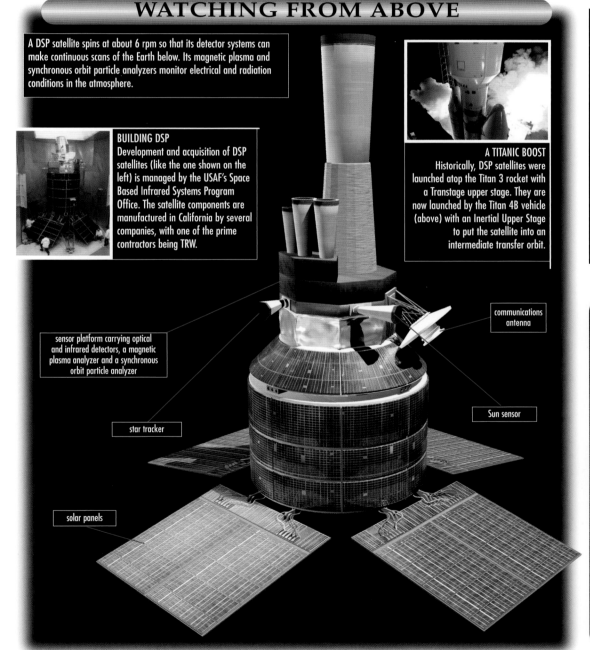

BUILDING DSP
Development and acquisition of DSP satellites (like the one shown on the left) is managed by the USAF's Space Based Infrared Systems Program Office. The satellite components are manufactured in California by several companies, with one of the prime contractors being TRW.

A TITANIC BOOST
Historically, DSP satellites were launched atop the Titan 3 rocket with a Transtage upper stage. They are now launched by the Titan 4B vehicle (above) with an Inertial Upper Stage to put the satellite into an intermediate transfer orbit.

sensor platform carrying optical and infrared detectors, a magnetic plasma analyzer and a synchronous orbit particle analyzer

communications antenna

star tracker

Sun sensor

solar panels

HARD EVIDENCE

WATCHING THE WORLD
The current DSP satellites use sensor arrays of 6,000 lead sulfide and mercury cadmium telluride elements to detect infrared radiation. These sensors detect  and track the exhaust heat generated by ballistic missiles (above right) and are sensitive enough to detect military jet aircraft operating on afterburners. Additionally, DSPs carry optical sensors that can detect nuclear detonations and large meteoroids entering the atmosphere. The main sensor barrel of a DSP satellite is tilted 7.5° to the side and the vehicle spins as it travels around its orbit, so the sensors sweep out a cone-like pattern to cover a wide area.

PAYLOAD

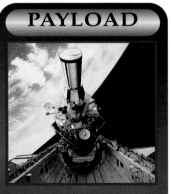

DSP SATELLITE NUMBER 16 (ABOVE) WAS THE FIRST UNCLASSIFIED DSP LAUNCH AND SO FAR THE FIRST AND ONLY LAUNCH OF A DSP SATELLITE BY THE SPACE SHUTTLE. THE SHUTTLE DISCOVERY DEPLOYED THE SATELLITE ON NOVEMBER 25, 1991, ON THE SECOND DAY OF THE STS-44 MISSION. THE SATELLITE WAS BOOSTED TO GEOSYNCHRONOUS ORBIT BY THE NASA-DEVELOPED INERTIAL UPPER STAGE AND WAS THE ONLY DSP PUBLICLY GIVEN A NAME — LIBERTY.

SPY
SATELLITES

Insurgent movements in Afghanistan, troop deployments in Iran, and the drug barons of Colombia are among the many targets being spied on by military satellites of the U.S., Russia and several other countries. These photoreconnaissance satellites usually fly at an altitude of 100 miles (160 km) or more above the ground and at speeds of over 17,000 miles per hour (27,000 km/h), but they produce highly detailed images that can reveal even such relatively small objects as individual people—and their abilities are constantly being improved. Both visible and infrared images can now be transmitted.

US SPACE SPIES

	ADVANCED KH-11/IMPROVED CRYSTAL	LACROSSE/VEGA
LAUNCH VEHICLE	SPACE SHUTTLE ATLANTIS, 1990	SPACE SHUTTLE COLUMBIA, 1988
BUILDER	LOCKHEED MARTIN	LOCKHEED MARTIN
SOLAR PANEL WINGSPAN	115 FT (35 M)	150 FT (45 M)
DIAMETER	14 FT (4.2 M)	14 FT (4.2 M)
WEIGHT	18 TONS (16 TONNES)	16 TONS (14.5 TONNES)
MISSION	HIGH-RESOLUTION DIGITAL IMAGES OF SPECIALLY IDENTIFIED TARGETS TRANSMITTED VIA DATA SATELLITES FOR IMMEDIATE USE AT THE NATIONAL RECONNAISSANCE OFFICE.	DAY AND NIGHT COVERAGE OF TROOP AND ARMOR MOVEMENTS, AND RADAR IMAGES TO PROVIDE TARGET IDENTIFICATION FOR KH-11 (CRYSTAL) SATELLITES.

SPIES IN THE SKY

Spying from above is nothing new—balloons were used to spy on enemy positions during many 19th-century wars, and aircraft have been used for reconnaissance since as early as World War I. The coming of space technology and the ability to get satellites into orbit—out of range of missiles—made the spy satellite a logical development in reconnaissance. The ideal orbit is one that takes the satellite over the poles of the Earth at a relatively low altitude of about 200 miles (320 km). At that height, 17 orbits—covering the whole of the Earth— can be flown in a single day.

The U.S. flew its first spy satellites under the name

Discoverer in 1959. These top-secret craft, code-named Corona by the CIA, first became operational in 1960 and took pictures on film. The film was then returned to Earth for analysis in a reentry capsule. The Soviet Union launched its first spy satellite in 1962. Code-named Zenit, this also returned a recoverable film capsule.

Hundreds of spy satellites have been launched since the early 1960s. In addition to the U.S. and Russian programs, spy satellite missions launched by other countries include those of China and Israel, and a joint European venture by France, Spain and Italy.

DIGITAL SYSTEMS

The smallest ground-based object that could be seen in the early satellite images was the size of a house. Today, the technology is improving so much that spy satellites could soon be reading the headlines on a newspaper.

Film capsules are being replaced by high-resolution, multispectral digital systems that take both visible-light and infrared pictures, and transmit these images

back to ground stations. Infrared photography produces images of heat patterns, so it can be used by night as well as day, and radar reconnaissance satellites can record images day or night through even the thickest cloud cover.

The digital images recorded by U.S. satellites are transmitted to the National Reconnaissance Office in Washington, D.C., via military communications satellites and NASA's Tracking and Data Relay Satellites, for analysis.

KH-11
The first of the U.S. KH-11 (Crystal) series of spy satellites was launched from the Space Shuttle in 1990. Since then, several others have been launched on Titan 4 rockets. The satellites in this series are equipped with digital multispectral imaging systems, as well as electronic intelligence sensors.

SHUTTLE SPY

A SPACE SHUTTLE MISSION LAUNCHED IN NOVEMBER 1991 DEPLOYED A MISSILE EARLY WARNING SATELLITE AND ALSO CARRIED OUT EXPERIMENTS CALLED "TERRA SCOUT" AND "MILITARY MAN IN SPACE." THESE INVOLVED THE FIRST AMERICAN SPACE SPY, THOMAS HENNAN (RIGHT), WHO TESTED THE EFFECTIVENESS OF HUMAN RECONNAISSANCE FROM SPACE USING HIGH-RESOLUTION SENSORS AND CAMERAS.

MISSILE GAP

ONE OF THE FIRST SPY SATELLITE IMAGES, TAKEN BY DISCOVERER 14 IN 1960 AS PART OF THE CORONA PROGRAM, SHOWED A MILITARY AIRFIELD IN NORTHEAST RUSSIA. THE PROGRAM SHOWED THAT, DESPITE THE CLAIMS OF SOVIET PREMIER NIKITA KRUSCHEV, THE SOVIET UNION DID NOT HAVE MORE INTERCONTINENTAL BALLISTIC MISSILES DEPLOYED THAN THE U.S. DID. CORONA IMAGES BROUGHT THE ESTIMATE OF THE NUMBER OF MISSILES THEN IN THE SOVIET UNION'S NUCLEAR ARMORY DOWN FROM HUNDREDS TO TENS.

HIGH RES

Russia operates Zenit, Yantar and Kometa satellites that return high-resolution images on film in recoverable capsules. Since the collapse of the Soviet Union, some of these images have been sold commercially. They show that the cameras could see details as small as three ft (one m) across.

EUROPEAN SPACE SPY
Europe's first military spy satellite, Helios 1, was launched in 1995 aboard an Ariane rocket. Helios was based on the successful Spot commercial remote-sensing satellites, one of which took this infrared image of Baghdad, the capital of Iraq.

KOSMOS/ZENIT
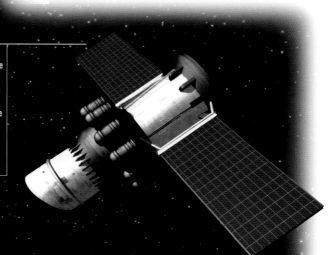
The Soviet Union attempted to conceal the launches of its Zenit spy satellites by making them part of its Kosmos program of scientific satellites. This Zenit satellite carries a number of flask-like recoverable film capsules that are periodically dropped back to Earth. Newer versions transmit digital images directly back to ground stations.

SCIENTIFIC SATELLITES

Every minute of every day, scientific satellites look both inward and outward, studying everything from deforestation and the hole in the Earth's ozone layer to exploding stars and supermassive black holes at the hearts of galaxies. Since the dawn of the Space Age, the world's space agencies have launched hundreds of scientific satellites into Earth orbit and sent scores more to study the other bodies of the solar system. Future probes will look deeper into our own planet—and into the farthest reaches of time and space.

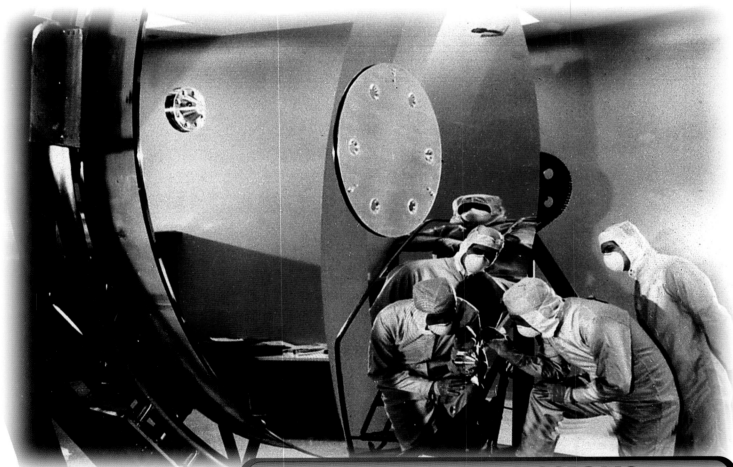

SATELLITE MISSIONS

Satellite	Mission
Landsat 7	Monitor crop resources, minerals and forests
TOPEX/ Poseidon	Monitor global ocean circulation and sea levels
SoHO	Study the structure and physics of the Sun
Imager	Produce 3-D images of Earth's magnetosphere
Hubble Space Telescope	Optical ultraviolet, infrared observations of the universe
Chandra X-Ray Observatory	Study hot, violent objects and events
Extreme Ultraviolet Explorer	Study white dwarfs and other objects
Mars Global Surveyor	Map the surface of Mars and study Martian climate
NEAR Shoemaker	Map the surface and chemical content of asteroid Eros
Galileo	Study Jupiter and its moons
Cassini	Rendezvous with Saturn

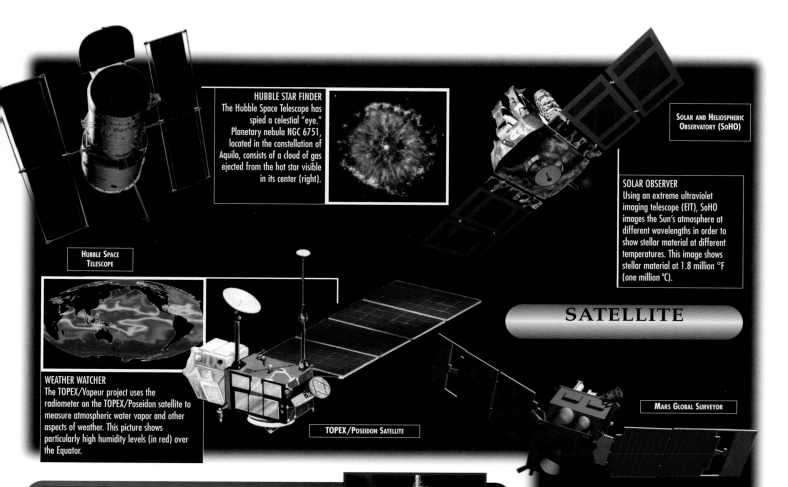

HUBBLE STAR FINDER
The Hubble Space Telescope has spied a celestial "eye." Planetary nebula NGC 6751, located in the constellation of Aquila, consists of a cloud of gas ejected from the hot star visible in its center (right).

HUBBLE SPACE TELESCOPE

SOLAR AND HELIOSPHERIC OBSERVATORY (SoHO)

SOLAR OBSERVER
Using an extreme ultraviolet imaging telescope (EIT), SoHO images the Sun's atmosphere at different wavelengths in order to show stellar material at different temperatures. This image shows stellar material at 1.8 million °F (one million °C).

SATELLITE

WEATHER WATCHER
The TOPEX/Vapeur project uses the radiometer on the TOPEX/Poseidon satellite to measure atmospheric water vapor and other aspects of weather. This picture shows particularly high humidity levels (in red) over the Equator.

TOPEX/POSEIDON SATELLITE

MARS GLOBAL SURVEYOR

MARTIAN SURVEYOR
Mars Global Surveyor took this photo of the Apollinaris Patera volcano in March 1999. This ancient volcano is thought to be as much as three miles high. The crater is about 50 miles (80 km) across.

TAKE TWO

AFTER THE SUCCESS OF SPUTNIK 1, ENGINEERS AND LAUNCH CREW WERE CALLED BACK FROM VACATION TO ASSEMBLE SPUTNIK 2 IN JUST ONE MONTH. LAUNCHED ON NOVEMBER 3, 1957, SPUTNIK 2 WAS THE FIRST TRUE SCIENTIFIC SATELLITE. ITS SENSORS WERE DESIGNED TO DETECT ULTRAVIOLET AND X-RAY ENERGY FROM THE SUN. SENSORS ALSO STUDIED THE EFFECTS OF SPACE ON THE PHYSICAL PROCESSES OF LAIKA THE DOG, SPUTNIK 2'S PASSENGER, WHO UNFORTUNATELY PERISHED IN ORBIT.

LAB PARTNERS

May 9, 2000, is a good example of a busy day around the solar system. From Earth orbit, Landsat 7 surveyed an out-of-control wildfire that was advancing on Los Alamos, New Mexico. Landsat 7's optical and infrared images helped firefighters assess the size and movement of the blaze and pinpoint hot spots. At the same time, the Tropical Rainfall Measuring Mission was peering through the clouds to measure the temperature of the ocean surface. Such measurements can help scientists understand and predict climate changes, such as the El Niño and La Niña events. Far from Earth, the NEAR Shoemaker spacecraft was orbiting less than 30 miles (50 km) above the surface of 433 Eros, a large asteroid. And

a half-billion miles away, the Galileo satellite was preparing for another encounter with Ganymede, the largest moon of Jupiter.

These and many other scientific satellites are extending our knowledge of Earth and of humanity's impact on our planet, as well as the interaction between the Sun, the Earth and the cosmos—from the Moon and planets to the very edge of the visible universe.

Satellites have conducted scientific missions since the very beginning of the Space Age. Explorer 1, the first American satellite, discovered the radiation belts that encircle Earth in 1958. Since then, the world's space agencies have launched hundreds of satellites designed to expand our understanding of physics, astronomy, meteorology,

oceanography and many other fields. Earth resources satellites locate mineral deposits, monitor deforestation and measure ozone depletion and global warming. City planners use satellite data to help draft new zoning laws, and satellite images have been used as evidence in lawsuits against industrial polluters.

Several craft are studying the interaction of the Sun's magnetic field and the solar wind—a steady flow of charged particles from the Sun's outer atmosphere—with Earth's magnetic field. Outbursts from the Sun can knock out power grids, disrupt radio communications and zap orbiting satellites, so understanding this interaction is especially important for our progressively more technological society.

Beyond Earth, probes have scanned the Moon and every planet except the dwarf planet Pluto (which NASA's New Horizons is due to reach in 2015), plus several asteroids and comets. They have discovered ancient river valleys on Mars, possible oceans beneath the icy crust of Jupiter's moon Europa and giant volcanoes on Io, another Jovian moon. Observatories in Earth orbit have discovered the "seeds" from which stars and galaxies grew, imaged powerful jets of hot gas squirting away from black holes, and found evidence of a "dark energy" that may be forcing the universe to expand ever faster.

These missions continue to push back the boundaries of the known universe, expand our knowledge of our own world, and increase our understanding of our place in the cosmos.

WEATHER SATELLITES

For as long as people have looked at clouds in the sky, there have been people who have tried to predict what tomorrow's weather will be. Forecasting the weather is still a tricky business, but accurate information about it is crucial to modern life—advance knowledge of dangerous winds, rain or snow can help save property, crops, and even lives. Fortunately, space science has provided meteorologists with a reliable and accurate tool for predicting the weather: the weather satellite.

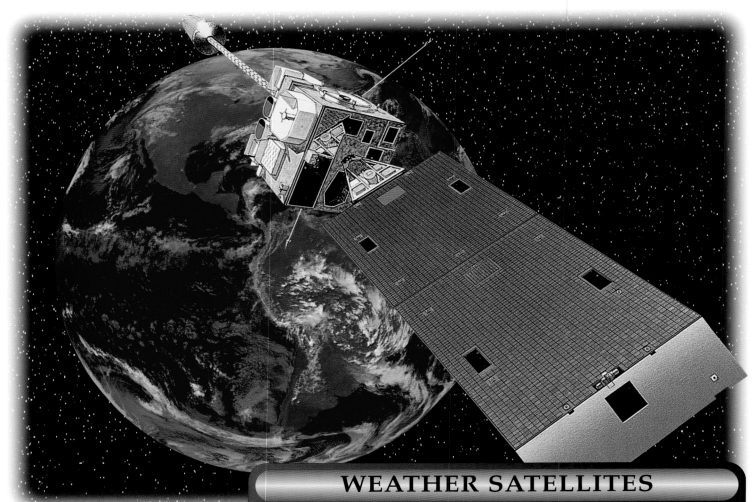

WEATHER SATELLITES

AUGUST 1959	LAUNCH OF EXPLORER 6; FIRST PICTURES OF CLOUDS FROM SPACE
APRIL 1, 1960	LAUNCH OF TIROS 1, WORLD'S FIRST WEATHER SATELLITE
AUGUST 28, 1964	LAUNCH OF NIMBUS 1, FIRST POLAR WEATHER SATELLITE

MAJOR WEATHER SATELLITE SYSTEMS
TIROS (U.S.) 1960–65
COSMOS (U.S.S.R.) 1962–68
NIMBUS (U.S.) 1964–78

ESSA (U.S.) 1966–69
METEOR (U.S.S.R./RUSSIA) 1969–PRESENT
NOAA (U.S.) 1970–PRESENT
GOES (U.S.) 1975–PRESENT
METEOSAT (EUROPE) 1977–PRESENT
GMS (JAPAN) 1977–PRESENT
BHASKARA (INDIA) 1979–81
INSAT (INDIA) 1982–PRESENT
FENG YUN (CHINA) 1988–PRESENT

EYE ON THE STORM

The introduction of weather satellites, combined with the use of other advanced equipment such as supercomputers, greatly improved the accuracy of weather forecasts. At any one time, there are no fewer than a dozen different operational weather satellites from half a dozen countries orbiting the Earth. The images and other data from these satellites provide weather forecasters with details of storm systems, weather fronts, cloud formations, winds, rainfall, fog, ice and snow.

The United States was the first country to test the idea of beaming pictures of clouds back from an orbiting satellite. In August 1959, Explorer 6 radioed the first experimental photos of cloud cover from space. Eight months later, the world's first operational weather satellite, the Television and Infrared Observation Satellite (TIROS), went into orbit. Altogether, 10 TIROS-class satellites were launched in the early 1960s, broadcasting almost 650,000 images.

Other countries around the world soon began launching meteorological satellites, with the Soviet Union launching its first in 1962. The European Space Agency's first came in 1977, and China launched its first in 1988.

More than 200 different weather satellites have now been launched into Earth orbit. These include over 60 sent aloft by the United States. Today, more than 120 countries around the world receive most or all of their weather pictures from U.S. satellites.

VERSATILITY

As weather satellite designers and engineers gained more experience of the new technology, the designs and functions of weather satellites became increasingly sophisticated. In addition to sending back photographs of clouds and weather systems, weather satellites began recording atmospheric and ocean temperatures at various altitudes and depths, and estimating rainfall.

Today's meteorological satellites can pinpoint weather formations with a high degree of accuracy. They can photograph clouds at night using infrared cameras, and take pictures in several different frequencies of light simultaneously. And to peer inside and through the clouds, some weather satellites use instruments that detect the microwave energy given off by the Earth and atmosphere. These instruments can scan cloud formations to detect hailstorms

and tornadoes, and can give as much as 25 minutes warning before a tornado strikes. In addition, they provide data about surface wind speeds over the oceans, ground moisture, rainfall, sea ice packs and snow cover.

Weather satellites also produce other forms of useful information

about the Earth—for instance, by mapping the world's ocean currents, or by capturing infrared images of the Earth's surface that scientists can use to study land usage and assess crop health. Some of them can even listen for distress signals from ships at sea and downed aircraft.

A NEW ERA

THE AGE OF SPACE-BASED WEATHER FORECASTING BEGAN ON APRIL 1, 1960 WITH THE LAUNCH OF THE TELEVISION AND INFRARED OBSERVATION SATELLITE (TIROS). HARRY WEXLER, DIRECTOR OF RESEARCH FOR THE U.S. GOVERNMENT WEATHER BUREAU, HAD SUGGESTED THAT CAMERAS IN SPACE WOULD BE ABLE TO SEE THE EARTH'S CLOUD PATTERNS, AND TIROS PROVED HIM RIGHT. THOUGH THE 270-LB (122-KG) SATELLITE OPERATED FOR ONLY 89 DAYS, IT RADIOED BACK 22,952 PHOTOGRAPHS OF CLOUD COVER FROM ITS 450-MILE (725-KM) -HIGH ORBIT, FOREVER CHANGING THE SCIENCE OF WEATHER FORECASTING.

HARD EVIDENCE

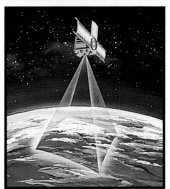

ORBITS

Weather satellites are launched into either polar orbits or geosynchronous orbits. Those in polar orbits usually fly at altitudes of about 450–900 miles (725–1,500 km), crossing over the north and south polar regions in each orbit. They take very detailed close-up pictures as the Earth rotates below, but only cross over any one spot on the Earth once per day. Geosynchronous satellites orbit at 22,500 miles (36,200 km) and stay in the same position over the Earth all the time. This allows them to take continuous pictures of the area below them and track the motions of weather fronts and storm systems as they occur.

WATCHING THE WEATHER

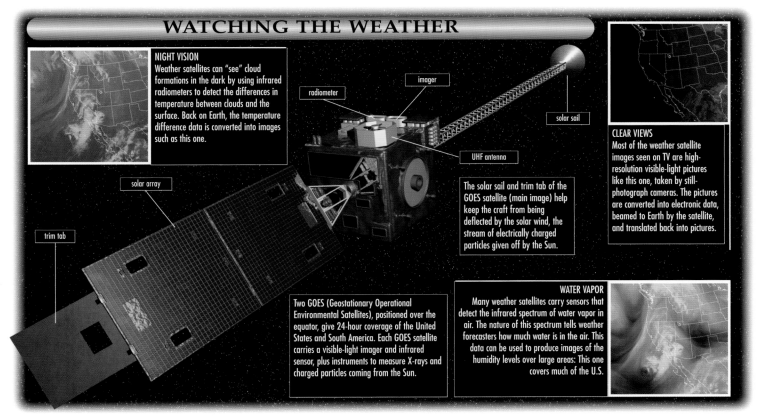

NIGHT VISION
Weather satellites can "see" cloud formations in the dark by using infrared radiometers to detect the differences in temperature between clouds and the surface. Back on Earth, the temperature difference data is converted into images such as this one.

radiometer

imager

solar sail

UHF antenna

solar array

trim tab

The solar sail and trim tab of the GOES satellite (main image) help keep the craft from being deflected by the solar wind, the stream of electrically charged particles given off by the Sun.

CLEAR VIEWS
Most of the weather satellite images seen on TV are high-resolution visible-light pictures like this one, taken by still-photograph cameras. The pictures are converted into electronic data, beamed to Earth by the satellite, and translated back into pictures.

Two GOES (Geostationary Operational Environmental Satellites), positioned over the equator, give 24-hour coverage of the United States and South America. Each GOES satellite carries a visible-light imager and infrared sensor, plus instruments to measure X-rays and charged particles coming from the Sun.

WATER VAPOR
Many weather satellites carry sensors that detect the infrared spectrum of water vapor in air. The nature of this spectrum tells weather forecasters how much water is in the air. This data can be used to produce images of the humidity levels over large areas: This one covers much of the U.S.

INFRARED SATELLITES

Throughout the universe, objects too cool to produce much visible light glow brightly at infrared wavelengths. They can be detected by infrared cameras, but the Earth's atmosphere absorbs most incoming infrared energy, so the best way to study them is from space. Astronomers have launched two major infrared observatories, plus an infrared camera aboard the Hubble Space Telescope. In the future, even better infrared space telescopes will provide detailed views of some of the coolest objects in the universe.

INFRARED SATELLITES

SATELLITE	TELESCOPE	LAUNCHED	CEASED OPERATION
IRAS	22 IN (56 CM)	JANUARY 1983	NOVEMBER 1983
ISO	24 IN (61 CM)	NOVEMBER 1995	MAY 1998
HST*	92 IN (233 CM)	APRIL 1990	STILL WORKING
SIRTF	33 IN (84 CM)	AUGUST 2003	STILL WORKING
ASTRO-F	28 IN (71 CM)	FEBRUARY 2006	NOVEMBER 2011
HERSCHEL	138 IN (3.5 M)	MAY 2009	APRIL 2013
JAMES WEBB	160–320 IN (4–8 M)	2018**	

*THE HUBBLE SPACE TELESCOPE IS PRIMARILY AN OPTICAL TELESCOPE, WITH ONE LARGE INFRARED CAMERA
**PLANNED LAUNCH DATE

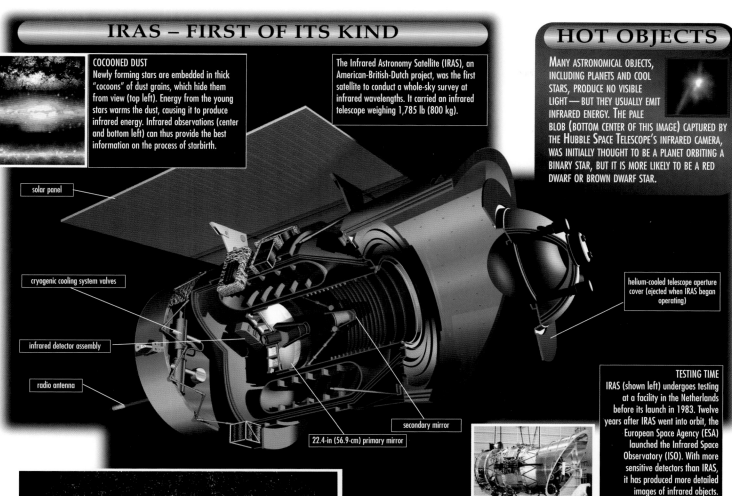

COCOONED DUST
Newly forming stars are embedded in thick "cocoons" of dust grains, which hide them from view (top left). Energy from the young stars warms the dust, causing it to produce infrared energy. Infrared observations (center and bottom left) can thus provide the best information on the process of starbirth.

The Infrared Astronomy Satellite (IRAS), an American-British-Dutch project, was the first satellite to conduct a whole-sky survey at infrared wavelengths. It carried an infrared telescope weighing 1,785 lb (800 kg).

HOT OBJECTS
MANY ASTRONOMICAL OBJECTS, INCLUDING PLANETS AND COOL STARS, PRODUCE NO VISIBLE LIGHT — BUT THEY USUALLY EMIT INFRARED ENERGY. THE PALE BLOB (BOTTOM CENTER OF THIS IMAGE) CAPTURED BY THE HUBBLE SPACE TELESCOPE'S INFRARED CAMERA, WAS INITIALLY THOUGHT TO BE A PLANET ORBITING A BINARY STAR, BUT IT IS MORE LIKELY TO BE A RED DWARF OR BROWN DWARF STAR.

solar panel

cryogenic cooling system valves

infrared detector assembly

radio antenna

helium-cooled telescope aperture cover (ejected when IRAS began operating)

secondary mirror

22.4-in (56.9-cm) primary mirror

TESTING TIME
IRAS (shown left) undergoes testing at a facility in the Netherlands before its launch in 1983. Twelve years after IRAS went into orbit, the European Space Agency (ESA) launched the Infrared Space Observatory (ISO). With more sensitive detectors than IRAS, it has produced more detailed images of infrared objects.

INFRARED SKY
This all-sky map shows all the infrared point sources discovered by IRAS. In total, IRAS detected about 350,000 of these, increasing the number of known sources six-fold.

PENETRATING THE FOG
The center of our Milky Way galaxy is packed with stars, gas and dust clouds, and possibly a black hole a million times the mass of our Sun. This region is invisible to our eyes because it is hidden behind thick clouds of dust. But because infrared energy emitted by objects within the region penetrates the dust, infrared satellites can get a good view of them. These satellites can also see into the cores of other galaxies that are obscured by their own dust clouds. These two pictures show the Milky Way as seen in visible light (top left), and the same view as seen by an infrared satellite (bottom left).

DISTANT PROSPECTS

When the Infrared Astronomy Satellite (IRAS) was launched in early 1983, astronomers had already charted about 6,000 objects that emit most of their energy at infrared wavelengths. By the end of the same year, IRAS had identified almost 350,000 sources of infrared energy—a leap forward in knowledge that was unparalleled since Galileo turned his first optical telescope toward the heavens four centuries earlier.

Infrared light is a form of electromagnetic energy, like radio waves and visible light. Its wavelengths are longer than those of visible light, so infrared light is invisible to human eyes. Instead, we feel infrared as heat. As a rule, though, objects that emit the most infrared light are actually cooler than those that emit more visible light.

The catalog of known infrared objects includes cocoons of dust grains that surround newly forming stars; brown dwarfs, which are too small to become stars but too big to be considered planets; and shells of gas and dust expelled by dying stars. In addition, infrared energy can penetrate the clouds of cold dust that cloak galaxies.

Infrared telescopes allow astronomers to see into the heart of our own Milky Way and other galaxies.

Water vapor in our atmosphere absorbs infrared energy, so astronomers (or their instruments) must climb above the atmosphere to get a clear, uninterrupted view of the infrared sky. To do this, they build telescopes on mountain peaks, carry them on airplanes, float them on research balloons—or launch them into space.

COOL VIEW

Although infrared is a form of heat energy, most infrared objects are relatively cool (compared with stars), with temperatures of just a few hundred degrees. Because of this, their infrared signals can be faint, and a warm telescope emits so much infrared energy that it drowns out the weaker signals from celestial sources.

To cool an infrared telescope's detectors, designers encase them in bottles of liquid helium, at a temperature just a few degrees above absolute zero. At such a super-cold temperature, the sensitive IRAS instruments could detect the minute warmth from a 20-watt lightbulb on Pluto.

X-RAY SATELLITES

I n 1962, as the U.S. was hitting its stride in the space race, NASA sent up a small suborbital rocket to detect X-rays in space. Once above the atmosphere, which absorbs X-rays and therefore clouds data, the detector instantly recorded an abundance of these high-energy, short-wavelength rays, and astronomers realized they had found a new "window" through which to observe the universe. Since then, dozens of satellites have analyzed X-rays from hundreds of stars and galaxies—and revealed a complex X-ray "zoo" that includes some of the weirdest objects ever seen in the universe.

X-RAY SATELLITE LAUNCHES

1962	AEROBEE SOUNDING ROCKET DETECTS FIRST COSMIC SOURCE OF X-RAYS
1970	FIRST X-RAY SATELLITE, UHURU
1974	ARIEL 5 X-RAY SATELLITE
1978	EINSTEIN OBSERVATORY (HEAO-2) LAUNCHED, WITH X-RAY TELESCOPE
1983	EUROPEAN X-RAY OBSERVATORY SATELLITE (EXOSAT)
1990	RÖNTGEN SATELLITE (ROSAT)
1991	YOHKOH ("SUNBEAM") X-RAY SOLAR OBSERVATION SATELLITE
1993	ARRAY OF LOW-ENERGY X-RAY IMAGING SENSORS (ALEXIS)
1995	ROSSI X-RAY TIMING EXPLORER (RXTE)
1996	SATELLITE FOR X-RAY ASTRONOMY (BEPPOSAX)
1999	CHANDRA AND XMM
2005	ASTRO-E2

X-RAY HUNTERS

By 1970, rocket-borne experiments had identified over 30 X-ray sources in our own galaxy, and several more beyond it. But the exact nature of these sources was hard to pin down, because scientists could not actually see them.

A new window on the universe opened with the first satellite devoted to X-ray astronomy. This was one of the Explorer series of satellites, Explorer 42, originally called Small Astronomical Satellite 1 (SAS-1) but later renamed Uhuru. Launched in 1970, it carried a simple X-ray detector and could measure the strength of X-rays and pinpoint the direction from which they were coming. Uhuru spent three years scanning the sky and recorded 160 X-ray sources. Its data revealed that most of the brightest sources were clustered along the plane of the galaxy, toward its center, and intriguingly, many X-ray sources were variable. One, named Centaurus X-3, pulsed on and off every 4.84 seconds on a 2.1-day cycle. What could the mysterious object be? What made the X-rays? And why the regular, rapid pulse?

Gradually, a theory emerged. A pulsing X-ray source could only be a neutron star—a small but super-dense object—that was sucking in gas from a neighboring star. This gas was being heated to millions of degrees and releasing vast amounts of X-ray energy. The rotation of the neutron star caused the pulsation of the X-rays. To study these extraordinary objects, astronomers needed details that Uhuru could not provide.

X-RAY IMAGING

The success of Uhuru encouraged the U.S., the U.S.S.R. and several European countries to launch many more satellites carrying X-ray detectors. But what astronomers really wanted was a telescope that could "see" X-rays, using carefully shaped mirrors placed almost parallel to the incoming rays to focus them onto detector instruments. This instrument would produce X-ray images instead of the visible-light images produced by ordinary telescopes.

A simple imaging X-ray telescope had been launched on a small rocket in 1965, and it produced crude images of hot spots in the Sun's upper atmosphere. Much better X-ray images of the Sun were produced by the first large focusing X-ray telescope, the NASA Apollo Telescope Mount (ATM) that was flown aboard the Skylab orbiting laboratory in the early 1970s.

The experience gained during the design, construction and use of the ATM was put to good use in the development of the first large mirror-based X-ray telescope. This satellite-based telescope, NASA's High Energy Astrophysical Observatory 2 (HEAO-2), was launched in 1978, and because that year was the centennial of physicist Albert Einstein's birth, HEAO-2 was renamed the Einstein Observatory. It offered a 1,000-fold increase in sensitivity compared with earlier instruments, and by 1979, its 7,000 images had revealed thousands of new X-ray sources, in our own galaxy and in others.

The Einstein Observatory vastly extended the new field of study and discovered many X-ray sources, some of which can also be seen with optical and radio telescopes. More than two decades later, X-ray satellites, including the Chandra and XMM orbiting X-ray telescopes, continue to add to our understanding of the galaxy and the history of its stars.

COSMIC RAYS

The first satellite to detect cosmic X-rays, rather than X-rays from the Sun, was actually a solar observation satellite (right). The Third Orbiting Solar Observatory (OSO-3) was launched into Earth orbit on March 8, 1967, and carried instruments for detecting gamma rays and X-rays. It traveled in a nearly circular orbit about 340 miles (550 km) above the Earth, and made its final data transmission on November 10, 1982.

ALEXIS X-RAY SATELLITE

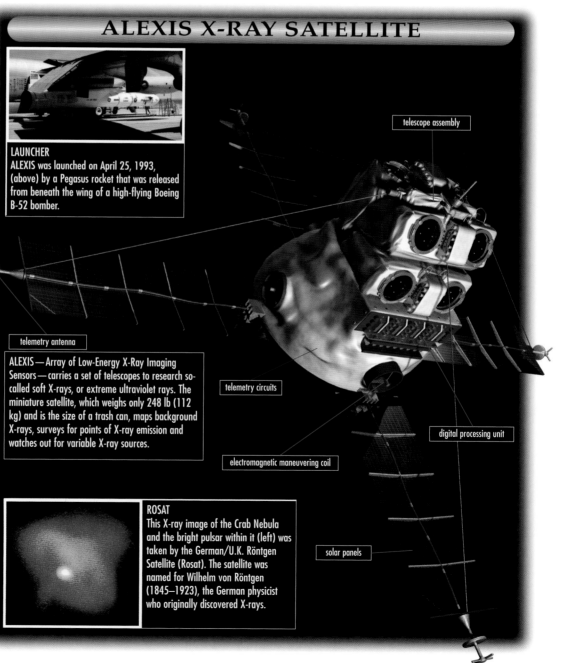

LAUNCHER
ALEXIS was launched on April 25, 1993, (above) by a Pegasus rocket that was released from beneath the wing of a high-flying Boeing B-52 bomber.

ALEXIS—Array of Low-Energy X-Ray Imaging Sensors—carries a set of telescopes to research so-called soft X-rays, or extreme ultraviolet rays. The miniature satellite, which weighs only 248 lb (112 kg) and is the size of a trash can, maps background X-rays, surveys for points of X-ray emission and watches out for variable X-ray sources.

ROSAT
This X-ray image of the Crab Nebula and the bright pulsar within it (left) was taken by the German/U.K. Röntgen Satellite (Rosat). The satellite was named for Wilhelm von Röntgen (1845–1923), the German physicist who originally discovered X-rays.

telescope assembly

telemetry antenna

telemetry circuits

electromagnetic maneuvering coil

digital processing unit

solar panels

REMOTE SENSING

Today, dozens of remote sensing satellites scrutinize the entirety of the Earth's surface. With instruments and cameras that see farther into the spectrum than the human eye, they chart previously hidden geological features, record the shifting pattern of global land use and uncover hidden archeological sites. They also play a pivotal role in response to natural disasters and pollution control. Remote sensing provides a health check for the entire biosphere, and gives us new insights into climatic change.

REMOTE SENSING SATELLITES

	Landsat 5	Landsat 7	SPOT 3	Radarsat	Terra
Operator	U.S.	U.S.	France	Canada	U.S.
Launch Site	Vandenburg	Vandenburg	Kourou	Vandenburg	Vandenburg
Launch Vehicle	Delta	Delta	Ariane 4	Delta	Atlas 2AS
Orbital Inclination	98.2°	98.2°	98.7°	98.6°	98.2°
Mass	4,266 lb (1,935 kg)	4,332 lb (1,964 kg)	4,195 lb (1,900 kg)	5,969 lb (2,700 kg)	10,679 lb (4,843 kg)
Instruments	MULTISPECTRAL SCANNER AND THEMATIC MAPPER	ENHANCED THEMATIC MAPPER	2 HIGH-RESOLUTION CAMERAS	SYNTHETIC APERTURE RADAR	MULTISPECTRA IMAGERS, RADIATION AND GAS DETECTORS

SCENES FROM SPACE

Remote sensing from space detects features invisible to ground-level observers, and has transformed our knowledge of the Earth. Mining companies use remote sensing imagery to guide excavations. Farmers can accurately estimate seasonal crop yields. Before-and-after pictures of communities hit by floods or hurricanes help disaster relief efforts. Authorities identify tankers illegally dumping fuel at sea. And fast-food companies assess suburb growth to locate new restaurants.

Satellite-mounted cameras permit the simultaneous observation of large areas of the Earth's surface. Along with this wide perspective, they also allow a deeper view—into electromagnetic (EM) wavelengths beyond the range of human vision. EM energy from the sun is variously scattered, reflected or absorbed by terrestrial materials. Different materials reflect solar energy in different ways, some of which our eyes detect as the various colors of visible light. But light comprises only a tiny fraction of the entire EM spectrum. For instance, vegetation reflects with more intensity in infrared than it does in visible light, and its exact reflectivity provides a guide to its state of health.

Besides reflected infrared radiation, everything with a temperature of above absolute zero gives out thermal infrared radiation. By measuring this radiation, researchers can learn a material's physical characteristics and temperature. Remote sensing cameras typically image several different visible and infrared EM bands at once. These correspond to the reflected or emitted energy of specific materials—loose sand, say, or cultivated soil, vegetation, water or different mineral types.

As well as these "passive" methods, satellites can also use "active" sensing. Satellite-mounted Synthetic Aperture Radar (SAR), for example, beams radio waves to the ground and records their reflection. SAR can penetrate cloud cover, vegetation or even layers of surface soil.

Remote sensing spacecraft were developed from early weather satellites, which had simple onboard infrared cameras to image cloud formations by night. The first dedicated remote sensing satellite was Landsat-1, equipped with a multispectral camera that transmitted digital data, launched in 1972. There have been Landsat satellites in orbit ever since. Landsat-7 was launched by NASA in April 1999. Its predecessor, Landsat-5, is still in service, although it is now operated by the commercial company Space Imaging EOSAT. The satellites are able to photograph almost the whole Earth every 16 days.

In turn, the Landsats have inspired various foreign equivalents, such as the French SPOT series, the Russian Meteor-Priroda, and counterparts from Europe, Canada, China and Japan. And along with the National Oceanographic and Atmospheric Administration, NASA operates remote sensing satellites to monitor the Earth's oceans and poles.

HIGH LIGHT

THE POTENTIAL OF REMOTE SENSING WAS DEMONSTRATED EARLY IN THE SPACE PROGRAM WITH OBSERVATIONS BY MERCURY ASTRONAUT GORDON COOPER IN 1963. DURING VISUAL OBSERVATIONS FROM THE TINY PORTHOLE OF HIS FAITH 7 SPACECRAFT, COOPER WAS ABLE TO SEE A TEST 44,000-WATT XENON LAMP BEAMED AT HIM FROM SOUTH AFRICA, AS WELL AS CITIES, OIL REFINERIES AND EVEN SMOKE FROM INDIVIDUAL HOUSES AROUND THE PLANET.

WHEAT FUTURES

IN A 1970S REMOTE SENSING EXPERIMENT, NASA AND THE DEPARTMENT OF AGRICULTURE USED DATA FROM A LANDSAT SPACECRAFT (RIGHT) TO ACCURATELY FORECAST THE FUTURE WHEAT PRODUCTION OF THE ENTIRE WORLD. TOTAL WHEAT PRODUCTION POTENTIAL WAS CALCULATED FROM LANDSAT IMAGES OF MUCH OF THE EARTH. THEN LOCAL WEATHER FORECASTS WERE USED TO FINE-TUNE ESTIMATES OF THE LIKELY YIELD IN EACH REGION.

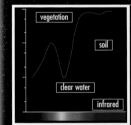

Different surfaces reflect light in distinctive patterns. Vegetation, of course, strongly reflects green light—but it reflects invisible infrared radiation even more. Water peaks at the short-wave, blue end of the spectrum, whereas bare soil reflects more energy as wavelengths increase.

ON ORBITAL WATCH

Landsat observation satellites ceaselessly transmit a grid of images from the entire surface of the Earth. Satellite coverage of the planet has been virtually continuous since the 1960s, allowing scientists to note the effects of environmental change over a long period.

FARMLAND
A radar image of crop fields in Manitoba, Canada, about 50 miles (80 km) south of Winnepeg. Images like this allow scientist to build a picture of seasonal changes in plant growth and the moisture content of soil.

CITYSCAPE
A false-color infrared image of Washington, D.C. in which the city's parks and other green areas show up as a startlingly conspicuous red— vegetation is a powerful reflector of infrared "light." The black indicates the Potomac river.

MOUNTAINS
A space radar image of the mountains of Tibet, about 56 miles (90 km) east of the capital city, Lhasa. In the bottom right-hand corner is the deep rift valley of the Lhasa river, the key waterway of the region.

OIL SPILL
An image of an offshore drilling field 93 miles (150 km) west of Bombay, India. The white dots are oil drilling platforms, while the many dark streaks show the oil spillage that has occurred around them.

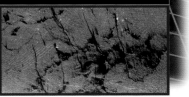

SATELLITES AND MOBILE PHONES

The cellular telephone system has freed phone users all over the world from the restrictions of hard-wired landlines and given them the ability to make calls on the move—plus a whole lot more, but the system has its limitations. To get a connection, you have to be within range of a base station. If your phone isn't compatible with the systems in other countries, you won't be able to use it abroad. These restrictions would vanish if the new generation of mobile phones could link directly to satellites. However, this poses some impressive technical challenges which have yet to be overcome.

AIRBORNE ALTERNATIVE

A Proteus HALE unmanned aircraft could circle for hours at 60,000 ft (18,000 m), with its large antenna relaying phone signals as effectively as an expensive satellite.

GOING GLOBAL

Iridium was to be the first of the new systems to become operational. Originally intended to use 77 satellites, this was amended to 66, with 11 in each of six separate orbits. The satellites would travel at a height of 485 miles (780 km) and take less than two hours to orbit the Earth. An Iridium satellite's signal coverage would cover an area on the ground about the size of the eastern U.S. This area is divided up into 48 overlapping zones. A separate spotbeam of signals would serve each zone, measuring nearly 100 miles (160 km) across.

Calls from Iridium phones would be routed by the satellite. A call from one Iridium phone to another could be sent directly if both phones are covered by the same satellite. If one was farther away, the call would be cross-linked to another Iridium satellite that can "see" the other phone. If the call is to a non-Iridium phone, the message would be routed to an Iridium ground station, either directly or via a number of other Iridium satellites. From the ground station it would enter the ordinary telephone system and then proceed to its destination.

Calls to Iridium phones from other networks would be routed in the opposite direction. During the course of a conversation, the satellite handling the call would of course move across the sky and perhaps go "out of sight" of either person talking. If that happened, the system was set up to automatically transfer the call signal to another Iridium satellite in the same orbit or in a neighboring one. The other systems were to work in a broadly similar way.

SATELLITE CONSTELLATIONS

The Ellipso system was to deploy its satellites in two "sub-constellations" with Ellipso-Borealis covering the north of the Earth and Ellipso-Concordia covering the tropical and southern latitudes. Ellipso-Borealis was to have five satellites in each of two orbits; Ellipso-Concordia would have had six satellites in one orbit and four in the other.

Creating a useful hand-held satellite receiver proved to be an immense technical challenge. Attaché-case sized units are possible, such as the Inmarsat unit, but mobile phone users have become accustomed to small, slim handsets and are not inclined to buy a large and bulky unit that does not offer many advantages over the existing ground-based cellphone system.

Thus Iridium and other satellite phone networks never quite came to be. It is likely that the concept will be revisited at some point in the future, however. In the meantime other technical innovations are entering the market. Landlines and satellites also could be joined by yet another new communications link: High Altitude Long Endurance (HALE).

HALE uses large airborne antenna to relay the signals of phones and ground stations. These antenna will be carried on HALE aircraft—airplanes or balloons—that will fly high over densely populated areas. Each aircraft will stay aloft for 18 hours or more and may operate under remote control. Relief aircraft will take over at refueling time, so HALE will provide continuous service. HALE is not a space-based system, but it is based on the same concepts.

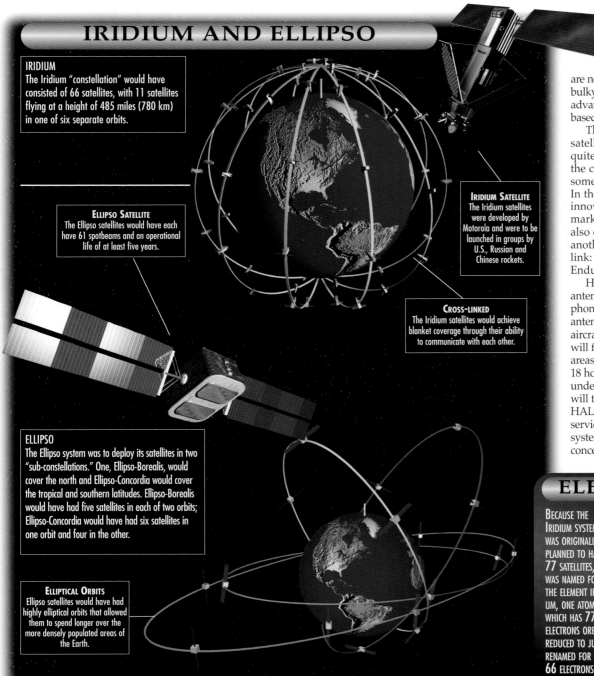

IRIDIUM AND ELLIPSO

IRIDIUM
The Iridium "constellation" would have consisted of 66 satellites, with 11 satellites flying at a height of 485 miles (780 km) in one of six separate orbits.

ELLIPSO SATELLITE
The Ellipso satellites would have each have 61 spotbeams and an operational life of at least five years.

IRIDIUM SATELLITE
The Iridium satellites were developed by Motorola and were to be launched in groups by U.S., Russian and Chinese rockets.

CROSS-LINKED
The Iridium satellites would achieve blanket coverage through their ability to communicate with each other.

ELLIPSO
The Ellipso system was to deploy its satellites in two "sub-constellations." One, Ellipso-Borealis, would cover the north and Ellipso-Concordia would cover the tropical and southern latitudes. Ellipso-Borealis would have had five satellites in each of two orbits; Ellipso-Concordia would have had six satellites in one orbit and four in the other.

ELLIPTICAL ORBITS
Ellipso satellites would have had highly elliptical orbits that allowed them to spend longer over the more densely populated areas of the Earth.

ELEMENTARY

BECAUSE THE IRIDIUM SYSTEM WAS ORIGINALLY PLANNED TO HAVE 77 SATELLITES, IT WAS NAMED FOR THE ELEMENT IRIDIUM, ONE ATOM OF WHICH HAS 77 ELECTRONS ORBITING ITS NUCLEUS. THE SYSTEM WAS REDUCED TO JUST 66 SATELLITES, BUT IT WAS NOT RENAMED FOR DYSPROSIUM — THE ELEMENT THAT HAS 66 ELECTRONS PER ATOM.

HUBBLE TELESCOPE

In 1990, the Hubble Space Telescope (HST) was carried into Earth orbit by the Space Shuttle Discovery. Its original 15-year mission was to take a closer look at our solar system, the Milky Way and other galaxies and to gaze back in time into the farthest reaches of the universe. Although there are larger telescopes based on Earth, the HST has the benefit of being above the atmosphere, enabling it to give us a much clearer view of the heavens—the pictures it has sent back have been truly stunning.

HUBBLE SPACE TELESCOPE

MASS	11.4 TONS (10.3 TONNES)		POINTING ACCURACY	0.007 ARC-SEC FOR 24 HR
LENGTH	43 FT (13 M)		MAGNITUDE RANGE	5 TO 29
DIAMETER	14 FT (4.2 M)		ORBIT	380 MILES (611 KM)
PRIMARY MIRROR	8 FT (2.4 M)		ORBITAL PERIOD	94 MIN
SECONDARY MIRROR	1 FT (30 CM)		PLANNED LIFETIME	15 YR
WAVELENGTH RANGE	110 NANOMETERS (UV) TO 1 MM (IR)		CURRENT LIFETIME	24 YR
ANGULAR RESOLUTION	0.1 ARC-SEC			

WINDOW ON THE UNIVERSE

No matter how big you build an Earth-based telescope, it has one great drawback: the atmosphere absorbs and deflects incoming light, thereby degrading the view. The solution—putting a telescope into orbit—only became feasible with the development of the Space Shuttle, due to the size and sensitivity of the equipment involved. Even so, plans for a Large Space Telescope or LST (named Hubble in 1983) were already well under way by the time of the launch of the first shuttle, Columbia, in 1981.

GROUND CONTROL

The Hubble is roughly the size of a railroad car and built to fit inside the Shuttle's cargo bay. It occupies a low Earth orbit (LEO), circling at an altitude of just 320 miles (515 km). Attached to its "eyepiece" are two cameras—one that looks in great detail at a small area of space, and one that focuses on much larger areas or objects. Other instruments analyze the infrared waveband and characteristics of light.

Data from Hubble is relayed to White Sands, New Mexico, then on to mission control at the Goddard Space Flight Center near Washington, D.C. Another link forwards the data to the Space Telescope Science Institute in Baltimore. The HST costs an estimated $8 a second to use. Excluding the cost of shuttle launches, at least $10 billion has been spent on the Hubble to date.

HUBBLE SPACE TELESCOPE

1977 Hubble Space Telescope project approved. Budget estimated at $450 million — 85 percent to come from NASA and the rest from the European Space Agency. Launch date is set for 1983.
1979 Construction of Hubble begins. Launch is rescheduled for 1986.
1986 Launch of Hubble is postponed by the Challenger disaster. By now costs have already soared to $1.6 billion — three times the original budget.
April 24, 1990 Hubble is finally launched in the cargo bay of Discovery.
April 24, 1990 Hubble is deployed in low Earth orbit (LEO).
May 20, 1990 The

space telescope's "first light" — Hubble is turned toward the star cluster NGC 3532, but the image is out of focus, rendering the HST only marginally better than Earth-based telescopes.
December 5–9, 1993 Astronauts from Endeavour make the longest U.S. spacewalk to date: 29 hr, 40 min.
December 18, 1993 Repairs proclaimed a success.
February 19, 1997 A second service mission adds two new instruments and effects running repairs.
1999 Service mission 3A installs new computer and replaces RSU (Rate Sensing Units)
2002 Service Mission 3B installs Advanced Camera (ACS) and replaces solar arrays
2004 Fourth service mission is cancelled
2005 Hubble placed on 2-gyro operating mode, extending lifetime
2014 Hubble is still running.

HOW BIG?
The Hubble can see out toward the farthest reaches of the universe, helping us to estimate how big it is, and also how old it is. Data from Hubble has helped scientists confirm that the universe will continue to expand instead of collapsing back in a "Big Crunch."

The HST was named after the astronomer Edwin Hubble (1889–1953), who discovered other galaxies and proved that they were expaning and speeding away from us. His work led to the development of the Big Bang theory.

LIFE SEARCH
The Hubble allows us to search for planets orbiting other stars, which no ground-based telescope can see. Where there are planets, there may also be life. Here, Hubble shows a new solar system beginning to form around the star Beta Pictoris.

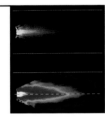

STAR DEATH
The Hubble telescope has brought us this spectacular picture of the Hourglass Nebula. The nebula is made up of the remnants of a dead star, puffed into space at the end of the star's life. By analyzing images like these, scientists gain new insights into the life cycle and evolution of stars.

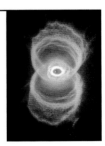

COMET WATCH
Although Hubble's pictures of other planets in the solar system cannot compare with those taken by fly-by space probes, it does allow for regular and long-term observation. A prime example of the Hubble's value came when it showed the comet Shoemaker-Levy 9 as it crashed into Jupiter (right).

$1.6 BILLION BLUNDER

The Hubble's main mirror was ground from a $1 million blank by the U.S. company Perkin Elmer, one of whose instruments was calibrated wrongly. The mistake should have been picked up by a pre-launch check, but Perkin Elmer was under pressure to deliver on time and on budget, so it was not spotted until the Hubble was in orbit. Dubbed "the $1.6 billion blunder" by the media, the fault was eventually corrected during a spacewalk by replacing one of the Hubble's instruments with a refocusing unit. The repair and servicing mission cost $800 million.

INSIDE HUBBLE

The Hubble Space Telescope (HST) is one of our single clearest windows on the universe, but it is neither the largest nor the farthest-seeing telescope ever built. What makes the billion dollar telescope so effective is its position—in near-circular orbit 330 miles (530 km) above the Earth. The images seen by terrestrial telescopes are smeared by atmospheric turbulence, dust and light, so that fine detail is lost. But up in the vacuum of space, the HST's 94½-in (2.4-m) primary mirror is capable of resolving an image 10 times better than even the best ground-based telescope.

HST SPECIFICATIONS

Instrument	Field of view (arc-seconds)	Projected pixel spacing on sky (arc-seconds)	Wavelength range (angstrom units)	Magnitude Limit
WF/PC	154 x 154	0.10	1,200–11,000	28.0
	35 x 35	0.0455	1,200–11,000	27.7
FOC	14 x 14	0.014	1,150–6,500	26.2
NICMOS	11 x 11	0.043	8,000–19,000	24.5
	19 x 19	0.075	8,000–25,000	25.0
	51 x 51	0.20	8,000–25,000	25.0
STIS	51 x 51	0.05	2,500–11,000	28.5
	25 x 25	0.024	1,650–3,100	26.5
	25 x 25	0.024	1,150–1,700	24.0

FAR SIGHTED

The Hubble Space Telescope is essentially a telescope like any other, albeit one with 400,000 different parts and 26,000 miles (40,000 km) of electrical wiring, all designed to function in the unforgiving environment of outer space. The HST is an aluminum cylinder, 43½ ft (13.25 m) long, fitted with a 94½-in (2.4-m) concave mirror at one end. This primary mirror reflects light back to a smaller, secondary mirror, which measures 12½ in (31.7 cm) in diameter. The secondary mirror redirects the reflected rays through a hole in the larger mirror into a rear bay, where separate cameras and instruments record and analyze the light. These currently include the Faint Object Camera (FOC), which is used to see extremely distant or dimly lit objects, and the Near Infrared Camera and Multi-Object Spectrometer (NICMOS). The latter is used to examine cool celestial objects and clouds that radiate infrared instead of visible light. Another piece of essential hardware is the Space Telescope Imaging Spectrograph (STIS)—this covers the ultraviolet, visible and near-infrared wavelengths and can simultaneously divide light into its component colors at 500 separate points in a single image.

SPACE SENSORS

STIS can provide an instant chemical "fingerprint" of a planet's atmosphere, a dust cloud or numerous stars within a galaxy. It gives information about the target's temperature, chemical composition and motion. To steer the Hubble toward its astronomical targets, the instrument bay also contains three Fine Guidance Sensors (FGS). A star catalog listing 15 million potential guide stars is used by the FGS as a reference. Another camera, known as the Wide Field/Planetary Camera (WF/PC), occupies a separate bay. It gathers light with a mirror mounted at 45°, which intercepts part of the secondary mirror's beam. The WF/PC has taken many of the Hubble's most famous pictures, such as the famous image of the M16 Eagle Nebula. Like the Space Telescope's other instruments the WF/PC doesn't use photographic film— instead, it uses Charge Coupled Devices (CCDs) arranged in a distinctive "L" shape. CCDs are light-sensitive computer chips that are also found in consumer digital and video cameras. One of the WF/PC's four CCDs can be switched into Planetary Camera mode for a detailed view of a narrower area, such as the observation of a dust cloud on Mars. The CCDs are a hundred million times more sensitive than the human eye, but very vulnerable to damage—the HST cannot be pointed too close to the Sun or they will be burned out. As an extra safeguard, the Hubble has an aperture door. Should the spacecraft ever go out of control, it will shut automatically.

HITCHES

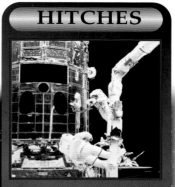

WHEN THE FIRST PICTURES CAME BACK FROM THE NEWLY-LAUNCHED HUBBLE IN MAY 1990, ASTRONOMERS NOTICED A DISTURBING HALO AROUND THE IMAGES THEY RECEIVED. IT TURNED OUT THAT THERE WAS AN OPTICAL FLAW IN THE HST'S PRIMARY MIRROR. IN 1993, A SHUTTLE SERVICING MISSION CORRECTED THE SPACE TELESCOPE'S MYOPIA. A SYSTEM OF CORRECTIVE MIRRORS KNOWN AS THE CORRECTIVE OPTICS SPACE TELESCOPE AXIAL REPLACEMENT (COSTAR) WAS FITTED TO REFOCUS THE LIGHT RECEIVED BY THE TELESCOPE. A REPLACEMENT WIDE FIELD/PLANETARY CAMERA (WF/PC) WAS ALSO INSTALLED.

HUBBLE TECHNOLOGY

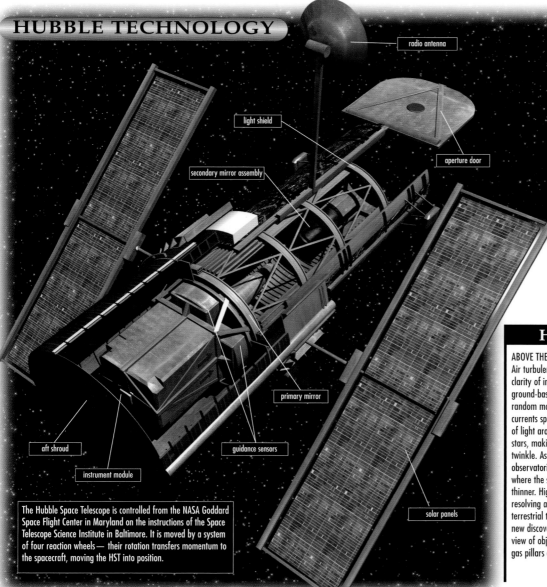

radio antenna

light shield

aperture door

secondary mirror assembly

primary mirror

aft shroud

guidance sensors

instrument module

solar panels

The Hubble Space Telescope is controlled from the NASA Goddard Space Flight Center in Maryland on the instructions of the Space Telescope Science Institute in Baltimore. It is moved by a system of four reaction wheels — their rotation transfers momentum to the spacecraft, moving the HST into position.

HARD EVIDENCE

ABOVE THE ATMOSPHERE
Air turbulence reduces the clarity of images received by ground-based telescopes. This random movement of air currents spreads a fuzzy patch of light around the center of stars, making them appear to twinkle. Astronomers favor observatories on mountain tops, where the skies are less polluted by artificial light and the air is thinner. High above the atmosphere, the Hubble is capable of resolving an image in space 10 times more clearly than the best terrestrial telescope. Although the HST has made few fundamental new discoveries, it has given astronomers a much more detailed view of objects that were already well-known, such as the famous gas pillars of the M16 Eagle Nebula (above).

Gaseous Pillars - M16   HST · WFPC2

SHUTTLES AND
STATIONS

Mankind has long dreamed of a permanent habitation in space. Science fiction writers, artists, and filmmakers depicted massive stations serving as communities or staging posts for missions to the stars. The massive wheel-like space stations of sci-fi publications and films such as *2001: a Space Odyssey* have not yet come to pass. The Soviet Soyuz and U.S. Skylab were followed by the long-lived Mir, but all eventually fell to earth when their working lives were over, and today the International Space Station (ISS) is the only permanently manned outpost in space. Of course, a space station needs a means of delivering and returning its residents and their provisions, as well as getting its components into orbit in the first place. Constructing and servicing a station was one rationale behind the Space Transportation System or Space Shuttle, first proposed at the end of the Apollo programme. Critics of NASA say that the Space Shuttle's only justification was to support the ISS, and the ISS only exists to give the Shuttle a mission, although since its retirement in 2011, commercial launches have been used to supply the ISS. While there is still some urgency to the development of the new Crew Exploration Vehicle, there has now been a gap of several years during which the U.S. has not had its own manned launch capability.

The launch of the Space Shuttle Atlantis on December 2, 1988. At launch the combined rockets develop a thrust of 7.82 million lb (34.8 mN). The Shuttle takes 8½ minutes to accelerate to speeds of 17,000 mph (27,300 km/h) from which it can go into orbit.

SALYUTS 1–5

The early Soviet space stations, launched in the 1970s, went from problems to solutions and tragedy to triumph. What started as a hasty modification of the Almaz military space station—to regain Soviet prestige after the Americans beat them to the Moon—developed into a world-leading mastery of space technology. During the Salyut program, ingenious designers had to struggle with unreliable launch systems and changing priorities, while brave cosmonauts faced the constant threat of death.

MISSIONS TO SALYUTS

Mission	Date	Result
Soyuz 10	April 1971	Failure. Unable to dock properly
Soyuz 11	June 1971	Failure. Crew killed on re-entry
Soyuz 14	July 1974	Success. Military mission to Salyut 3
Soyuz 15	August 1974	Failure. Nearly rams Salyut 3
Soyuz 17	January 1975	Success. First mission to Salyut 4
Soyuz 18–1	April 1975	Failure. Sub-orbital launch abort
Soyuz 18	May 1975	Success. Crew spends two months on Salyut 4
Soyuz 21	July 1976	Partial success. Crew makes emergency return from Salyut 5
Soyuz 23	October 76	Failure. Docking fails: splashdown return
Soyuz 24	February 77	Success. End of operations on Salyut 5

SPACE OUTPOSTS

In 1969, the Soviets lost the race to the Moon. But they had a functional spacecraft—the Soyuz moonship—and space-station hulls built for the Almaz military program. By combining these two technologies, they could build a space station and beat the Americans that way.

Salyut 1 was an Almaz with Soyuz systems bolted on. Two small sets of solar panels were fitted to provide electrical power, and a Soyuz service module was placed at the rear. The front docking port replaced the Almaz's return capsule and its self-defense gun (a Nudelman 23mm cannon). Then came two examples of the "standard" military Almaz, Salyuts 2 and 3. Salyut 4 was civilian, with improved systems, but Salyut 5 was another Almaz.

With each new Salyut, increasingly advanced technology was tested. Salyuts 3 and 5 were fitted with gyroscopes that controlled the stations' orientation. Similar systems have since been used for Mir and the International Space Station (ISS). Salyut 4 incorporated a computer that automatically kept the station pointed in the correct direction. And in November 1975, Soyuz 20 and Salyut 4 achieved the world's first uncrewed docking, proving the technology used by Progress ferries and the later Soviet stations.

SCIENCE ON SALYUT

The military origins of Salyut meant that much of the main compartment was taken up by a housing for a spy camera or telescope. Although Moscow was keen to publicize the economic advantages of photographing the

Earth, much of the Salyuts' photographic activity was a cover for military missions to evaluate the potential of crewed spy satellites. But some observations were very important: Salyuts 4 and 5 used an infrared spectrometer to measure the water content of the stratosphere, and were therefore able to discover some of the first signs of ozone depletion.

Biology was covered by Salyuts 1 and 4, which had miniature greenhouses where cosmonauts tried to grow plants. These stations also carried out many astronomical observations, mainly in wavelengths blocked by the atmosphere. Salyut 1's primary instrument was an ultraviolet telescope, while Salyut 4's was a solar telescope. The instrument was crippled by a broken sensor, but the Soyuz 17 crew learned to steer it by controlling its servo motors by ear.

During the operational lives of the first Salyut stations, great progress was also made in the medical evaluation and consequences of of long-duration flights: By 1977, 13 cosmonauts had each flown in space for more than two weeks at a time.

RED STARS IN ORBIT

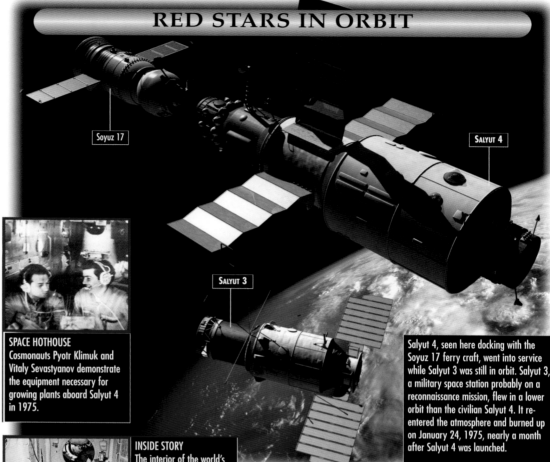

Soyuz 17

Salyut 4

Salyut 3

SPACE HOTHOUSE
Cosmonauts Pyotr Klimuk and Vitaly Sevastyanov demonstrate the equipment necessary for growing plants aboard Salyut 4 in 1975.

INSIDE STORY
The interior of the world's first successful space station, Salyut 1. This station was launched in April 1971, where it remained in orbit for 175 days.

Salyut 4, seen here docking with the Soyuz 17 ferry craft, went into service while Salyut 3 was still in orbit. Salyut 3, a military space station probably on a reconnaissance mission, flew in a lower orbit than the civilian Salyut 4. It re-entered the atmosphere and burned up on January 24, 1975, nearly a month after Salyut 4 was launched.

MISSION DIARY: SALYUTS 1–5

APRIL 19, 1971 SALYUT 1 IS LAUNCHED FROM BAIKONUR COSMODROME ON A PROTON ROCKET.
APRIL 23, 1971 THE SOYUZ 10 SPACECRAFT TAKES OFF CARRYING THE FIRST CREW (RIGHT) TO VISIT SALYUT 1. THE CREWS ARE UNABLE TO DOCK SUCCESSFULLY WITH THE SPACE STATION AND RETURN TO EARTH ON APRIL 25.
JUNE 7, 1971 THE CREW OF SOYUZ 11 — GEORGY DOBROVOLSKY, VIKTOR PATSAYEV AND VLADISLAV VOLKOV — (ABOVE) SUCCESSFULLY DOCK WITH SALYUT 1 AND STAY UNTIL JUNE 29. THE MISSION ENDS IN TRAGEDY WHEN ALL THREE DIE AFTER THEIR CAPSULE CABIN PRESSURE FAILS AT REENTRY.

JULY 29, 1972 A SOVIET ATTEMPT TO PUT ANOTHER SPACE STATION INTO ORBIT FAILS WHEN IT IS DESTROYED DURING THE LAUNCH.
APRIL 3, 1973 SALYUT 2 IS LAUNCHED SUCCESSFULLY FROM BAIKONUR, BUT IT BREAKS UP IN ORBIT.
MAY 11, 1973 ANOTHER SALYUT, CODENAMED COSMOS 557, IS LAUNCHED BUT GOES OUT OF CONTROL AND RE-ENTERS THE ATMOSPHERE ON MAY 22.
JUNE 25, 1974 SALYUT 3, A MILITARY SPACE STATION, IS LAUNCHED FROM BAIKONUR.
JULY 3, 1974 SOYUZ 14 IS LAUNCHED, CARRYING COSMONAUTS PAVEL POPOVICH AND YURI ARTYUKHIN TO SALYUT 3. THEY STAY ABOARD THE STATION UNTIL JULY 19.
DECEMBER 26, 1974 SALYUT 4 IS LAUNCHED.

JANUARY 11, 1975 ALEXEI GUBAREV AND GEORGY GRECHKO (RIGHT) TAKE OFF ON SOYUZ 17 FOR A FOUR-WEEK VISIT TO SALYUT 4.
JUNE 22, 1976 SALYUT 5, A MILITARY SPACE STATION, IS LAUNCHED SUCCESSFULLY FROM BAIKONUR.
JULY 6, 1976 SOYUZ 21 CARRIES BORIS VOLYNOV AND VITALY ZHOLOBOV TO SALYUT 5.
FEBRUARY 7, 1976 YURI GLAZKOV AND VIKTOR GORBATKO LIFT OFF ON SOYUZ 24, THE FINAL MISSION TO SALYUT 5.

SALYUTS 6 AND 7

The operation of the two space stations Salyuts 6 and 7 from 1977 to 1986 was a vital stage in the development of human spaceflight. The experience gained was crucial to later successful operations on the Mir space station and for future human missions into the solar system. Cosmonauts worked routinely aboard the stations, carrying out a wide range of experiments as well as acting as orbiting repairmen. Salyuts 6 and 7 clearly placed the Soviet Union ahead of the rest in the field of long-duration spaceflight.

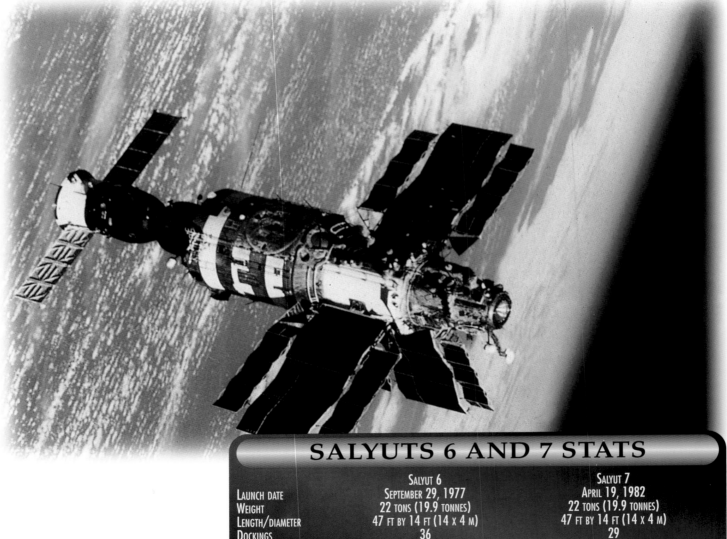

SALYUTS 6 AND 7 STATS

	Salyut 6	Salyut 7
LAUNCH DATE	SEPTEMBER 29, 1977	APRIL 19, 1982
WEIGHT	22 TONS (19.9 TONNES)	22 TONS (19.9 TONNES)
LENGTH/DIAMETER	47 FT BY 14 FT (14 x 4 M)	47 FT BY 14 FT (14 x 4 M)
DOCKINGS	36	29
CREW VISITS	16	10
SPACEWALKS	3	13
VISITING INTERNATIONAL CREW	9	2
LONGEST CREW STAY	185 DAYS (SOYUZ 35)	237 DAYS (SOYUZ T-10)
REENTRY	JULY 29, 1982	FEBRUARY 7, 1991
TIME IN ORBIT	1,764 DAYS	3,215 DAYS

THE LONG RUN

When Salyut 6 reached orbit in September 1977, it marked an important step toward the construction of a permanent orbiting space station. The improved Salyut station had two docking ports and could receive two spacecraft at once. This meant that refueling of the propulsion engine and crew changes could both take place in orbit.

Salyut 6 was planned to support long duration missions of between 90 and 180 days. But the Soyuz ferry spacecraft were only designed to stay in space for about 80 days. So the main crew would spend a long mission on the space station and other crews would arrive in a new Soyuz and depart in the main crew's Soyuz. These secondary crews would often include a guest cosmonaut from socialist countries such as Czechoslovakia, Cuba, Vietnam, East Germany, Mongolia and Poland.

Salyut 6 marked the first use of the uncrewed Progress cargo ferries. These brought supplies for the crew as well as fuel for the station. Progress was also used as a space tug to boost the station's orbit. Before releasing the cargo ship to burn up in the atmosphere the crews would stuff all their refuse, dirty clothes and redundant equipment into the ferry.

Over a period of four years, five long-stay crews visited the outpost, notching up mission durations of 96, 140, 175, 185 and 75 days. In addition, 11 short-stay crews visited. The crews carried out hundreds of experiments and occupied Salyut 6 for 676 days, far ahead of the 171 days' occupation of the U.S. Skylab station.

RECORD BREAKER

Salyut 7 entered orbit with several improvements, including larger and stronger docking ports, an improved computer, a refrigerator and even hot and cold running water. The first crew aboard Salyut 7 set a new world record by spending 211 days in orbit, and the third long-stay crew managed an even longer stay of 237 days.

Salyut 7 suffered many technical breakdowns during its life and its crews had to repeatedly carry out repairs both inside and outside the station. During its time in orbit, two large modules docked with Salyut 7, bringing supplies and providing a larger work area for

the crew. These modules were the forerunners of the type later used on the Mir station.

Salyut 7 crews had their fair share of frightening moments. During the Soyuz T-9 flight, the crew began to evacuate the station when they heard a loud crack. On investigation they discovered that a micrometeorite or piece of space debris had hit one of the station's windows leaving a tiny crater.

Although not quite as successful as Salyut 6, Salyut 7 met its objectives—and in the process established the Soviet Union as the then undisputed leader in long-duration crewed spaceflight.

MISSION DIARY: SALYUTS 6 AND 7

SEPTEMBER 29, 1977 SALYUT 6 IS LAUNCHED FROM BAIKONUR COSMODROME.
OCTOBER 9, 1977 THE FIRST CREW TO VISIT SALYUT 6, VALERY RYUMIN AND VLADIMIR KOVALENOK (ABOVE, LEFT TO RIGHT), FAIL TO DOCK WITH THE STATION.
JANUARY 23–4, 1978 SALYUT 6 IS REFUELED FOR THE FIRST TIME FROM THE DOCKED PROGRESS 1 CARGO SPACECRAFT.
MARCH 2, 1978 SOYUZ 28 FERRIES THE FIRST INTERNATIONAL CREW TO SALYUT 6.
APRIL 9, 1980 COSMONAUTS LEONID POPOV AND VALERY RYUMIN ARE LAUNCHED ABOARD SOYUZ 35. THEY SPEND A RECORD 185 DAYS IN ORBIT.
MARCH 1981 VICTOR SAVINYKH BECOMES THE 100TH TRAVELER IN SPACE ON A MISSION TO SALYUT 6.
APRIL 19, 1982 SALYUT 7 (BELOW LEFT, BEING

ASSEMBLED) IS LAUNCHED.
MAY 13–DECEMBER 10, 1982 SALYUT 7'S FIRST CREW SPEND 211 DAYS ABOARD THE SPACE STATION.
JUNE 24, 1982 FRENCH "SPATIONAUTE" JEAN-LOUP CHRETIEN SPENDS A WEEK ABOARD SALYUT 7.
FEBRUARY 1985 MISSION CONTROLLERS LOSE CONTACT SALYUT 7.
JUNE 1985 THE SOYUZ T-13 CREW BRINGS THE TUMBLING, FROZEN SALYUT 7 BACK TO LIFE (ABOVE).
MAY 6, 1986 SOYUZ T-15 CREW FLY FROM MIR TO SALYUT 7 TO COMPLETE EXPERIMENTS BEGUN BY THE SOYUZ T-14 CREW.
FEBRUARY 7, 1991 SALYUT 7 REENTERS EARTH'S ATMOSPHERE OVER SOUTH AMERICA.

SALYUT 7 IN ORBIT

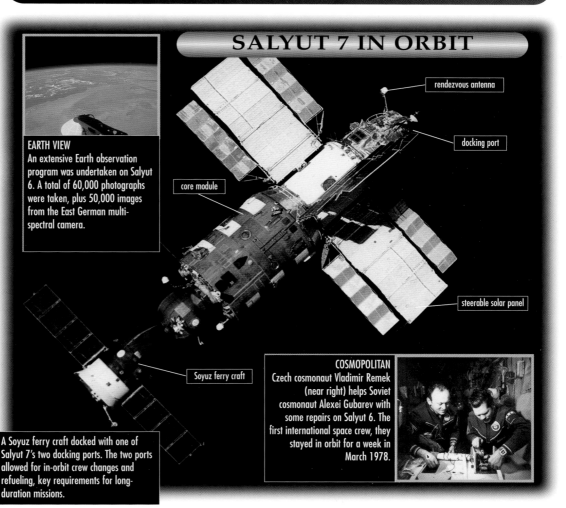

EARTH VIEW
An extensive Earth observation program was undertaken on Salyut 6. A total of 60,000 photographs were taken, plus 50,000 images from the East German multi-spectral camera.

rendezvous antenna

docking port

core module

steerable solar panel

Soyuz ferry craft

A Soyuz ferry craft docked with one of Salyut 7's two docking ports. The two ports allowed for in-orbit crew changes and refueling, key requirements for long-duration missions.

COSMOPOLITAN
Czech cosmonaut Vladimir Remek (near right) helps Soviet cosmonaut Alexei Gubarev with some repairs on Salyut 6. The first international space crew, they stayed in orbit for a week in March 1978.

SOYUZ 11 DISASTER

In the early hours of June 30, 1971, recovery crews were gathered near the Soviet space complex at Baikonur, on the prairie-like steppes of Kazakhstan, to await the landing of the Soyuz 11 spacecraft. Its crew of three—cosmonauts Dobrovolsky, Patsayev and Volkov—had completed a record-breaking 23 days in orbit in the world's first space station, Salyut 1. A heroes' welcome had been prepared, and the ground crew was overjoyed as the craft landed perfectly—but the world soon discovered all was not as it seemed.

THE SOYUZ 11 CREW

VLADISLAV NIKOLAYEVICH VOLKOV	GEORGY TIMAFEYEVICH DOBROVOLSKY	VIKTOR PATSAYEV
BORN: NOVEMBER 23, 1935, IN MOSCOW, SOVIET UNION (NOW IN RUSSIA)	BORN: JUNE 1, 1928, IN ODESSA, SOVIET UNION (NOW IN UKRAINE)	BORN: JUNE 19, 1933, IN AKTYUBINSK, SOVIET UNION (NOW IN KAZAKHSTAN)
PREVIOUS SPACEFLIGHT: SOYUZ 7, 1969	PREVIOUS SPACEFLIGHTS: NONE	PREVIOUS SPACEFLIGHTS: NONE

DESCENT TO DEATH

The modern era of crewed space exploration, which focuses on orbiting space stations, began on June 7, 1971. On that day, Georgy Dobrovolsky, Viktor Patsayev and Vladislav Volkov squeezed through the docking port of their Soyuz 11 spacecraft—callsign Yantar ("Amber")—into Salyut 1, the world's first space station. Soviet space scientists, and many others, saw space stations with replaceable crews as the main highway into space. On these orbiting platforms, the craft that would take humanity to explore the solar system and beyond would be built and launched.

The crew's first task was to check all of the systems in the united craft—especially those of Salyut, which had already been in orbit for almost two months. They then settled into a routine of Earth-science observations and medical and biological experiments. They were to have made solar observations, but the large solar telescope was inoperable because its cover had failed to jettison.

They also had exercise equipment—a treadmill and a bungee-string—to help prevent their muscles from wasting away through lack of use. But what looked good on the ground turned out to be unusable in space. Just one 180-lb (82-kg) man throwing himself around proved more than the combined vehicles could take, and the exercises were abandoned.

Then, about three weeks into the mission, the station itself was abandoned. A series of difficulties, and a small electrical fire a week earlier, had persuaded the Soviets of the need to cut the mission short. The crew gathered up their data, transferred back into Soyuz 11 and returned to Earth.

FINAL JOURNEY

At 9:28 p.m. on the evening of June 29, Georgy Dobrovolsky undocked the Soyuz craft from Salyut 1. After three orbits of the Earth, Dobrovolsky called Mission Control to tell them that they were beginning their descent. Mission Control radioed back, "Goodbye, Yantar, till we see you soon on Mother Earth." At 1:35 a.m., the craft's retrorockets fired and it began its descent through the atmosphere. Then its parachutes deployed and it floated gently down to the ground.

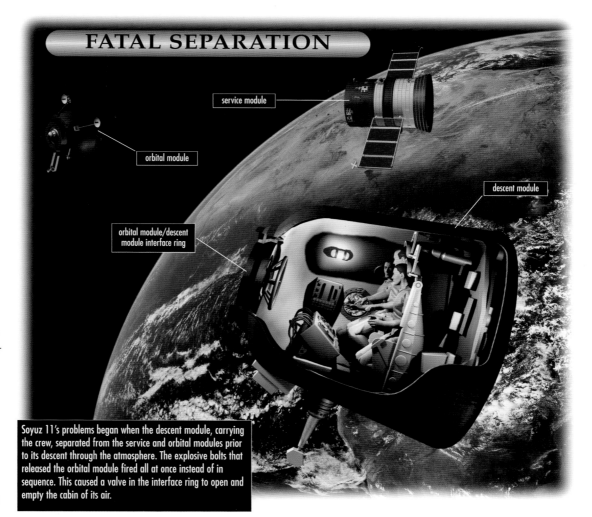

FATAL SEPARATION

service module

orbital module

descent module

orbital module/descent module interface ring

Soyuz 11's problems began when the descent module, carrying the crew, separated from the service and orbital modules prior to its descent through the atmosphere. The explosive bolts that released the orbital module fired all at once instead of in sequence. This caused a valve in the interface ring to open and empty the cabin of its air.

Although the craft made a near-perfect landing, the cosmonauts never reached the ground alive. Some 723 seconds after the retrorockets had fired, the 12 explosive bolts that released the descent module from the orbital module fired at once instead of in a controlled sequence. This shook open an air pressure equalization valve, at an altitude of 104 miles (167 km). With appalling speed, the capsule's air hissed into space.

Patsayev unbuckled his safety harness and tried desperately to close or block the valve, but failed.

Within about nine or 10 seconds, decompression emptied the crew's lungs—none of them was wearing space suits—and they died within about 30 seconds. A mission that should have been a triumph of breakthroughs in Soviet technology had turned into a tragedy.

MISSION DIARY: SOYUZ 11

JUNE 6, 1971, 04:55 A.M. SOYUZ 11 LIFTS OFF FROM THE BAIKONUR SPACE COMPLEX IN KAZAKHSTAN.
JUNE 7 SOYUZ 11 DOCKS WITH THE SALYUT 1 SPACE STATION. THE CREW ENTER SALYUT AND CARRY OUT SYSTEMS CHECK.
JUNE 7 TO JUNE 28 CREW SETTLES INTO ROUTINE OF EXPERIMENTS AND EARTH OBSERVATIONS.
JUNE 17 A SMALL FIRE BREAKS OUT IN SOME ELECTRICAL CABLES. THE CREW PREPARE TO ABANDON THE STATION, BUT THE FIRE IS EXTINGUISHED. THE RETURN TO EARTH IS POSTPONED, BUT MISSION CONTROL LATER DECIDES TO END THE 30-DAY MISSION EARLY.
JUNE 29, 1971, 9:28 P.M. SOYUZ 11 DISENGAGES FROM SPACE STATION.
JUNE 30, 1971, 1:35 A.M. RETROROCKETS FIRE, SOYUZ 11 BEGINS ITS DESCENT AND A

PARACHUTE SYSTEM DEPLOYS TO BRING IT GENTLY TO THE GROUND. DURING DESCENT, GROUND CONTROL TRIES TO CONTACT COSMONAUTS BUT IS NOT ALARMED WHEN THEY FAIL TO RESPOND.
JUNE 30, 1971 DISBELIEVING RECOVERY TEAM MEMBERS DISCOVER THAT THE COSMONAUTS OF SOYUZ 11 ARE DEAD, AND TRY FRANTICALLY TO RESUSCITATE THEM.
JULY 1, 1971 THOUSANDS OF RUSSIAN MOURNERS FILE PAST THE COFFINS OF THE THREE COSMONAUTS IN RED SQUARE, MOSCOW. SOVIET PRESIDENT NIKOLAI

PODGORNY, PRIME MINISTER KOSYGIN AND COMMUNIST PARTY GENERAL SECRETARY LEONID BREZHNEV TAKE TURNS STANDING WATCH AS PART OF THE HONOR GUARD (ABOVE). PRESIDENT NIXON SENDS THE SYMPATHY OF THE AMERICAN PEOPLE TO THE SOVIET UNION, AND AMERICAN ASTRONAUT TOM STAFFORD ATTENDS THE CEREMONY.

SKYLAB

The Apollo Applications Program was started in 1966 to conduct extended lunar operations and long-duration crewed missions in orbit around the Earth. Using the vast power of the Saturn 5 rocket, the program planned an ambitious series of space stations in orbit. When budget cuts forced mission planners to scale down their ideas, just one project survived: The Skylab Orbital Workshop. Launched in 1973, Skylab was America's first space station, paving the way for the International Space Station (ISS)—and still holds the record as the world's largest orbiting spacecraft.

SKYLAB SPECS

OVERALL LENGTH (INCLUDING CSM)	118.5 FT (36 M)	ORBITAL WORKSHOP	
OVERALL WORKING VOLUME	11,700 CU FT (481 M³)	LENGTH	48.1 FT (14.6 M)
POWER OUTPUT	4,000 WATTS AT	DIAMETER	21.6 FT (6.6 M)
	28 VOLTS DC	WEIGHT (WITH SOLAR PANEL)	167,850 LB (76,135 KG)
		WORKING VOLUME	9,550 CU FT (270 M³)
		AMBIENT TEMPERATURE	70°F (21°C)

BASE IN SPACE

The great advantage of Skylab was that it was already half-built even before it was formally approved as a new project in 1969. The idea had occurred to master rocket designer Wernher von Braun four years earlier. During lunch one day, he casually doodled on a paper napkin how his invention, the Saturn 5 rocket, could be recycled as an Earth-orbiting space station.

Normally, the third stage of the Saturn 5 carried fuel for the Apollo spacecraft's trip out of Earth orbit to the Moon. But if this stage remained in Earth orbit, the propellants and rocket engines for the Moon journey would not be needed, and neither would the fuel to power them. The huge tanks could be filled with air instead, divided into compartments and made into a giant facility for astronauts to live and work in.

CONVERTED ROCKET

In 1970, when two Apollo Moon landing missions were canceled, the available Saturn 5 was converted into Skylab. Inside, what was once the hydrogen tank was converted into a two-story space where three astronauts could live and work together. They would breathe a mixture of nitrogen and oxygen, while a thermal and ventilation system provided an ambient temperature of 70°F (21°C). The first story was divided into living areas, with a ward room, sleeping compartments and a bathroom. Above was the work space, where the crew could "swim" in weightless conditions and carry out experiments. Enough food, water and clothing was stowed on board for all three missions scheduled to visit Skylab.

Outside, Skylab carried what were then the largest solar panels ever used on a spaceship. On top was the Apollo Telescope Mount (ATM), a solar observatory with an array of instruments including X-ray, infrared and visible light cameras. ATM allowed the Sun's structure and chemistry to be observed in great detail for the first time. Skylab was launched unmanned on May 14, 1973, on the last-ever Saturn 5 booster to fly. In all, three crews visited it over two years, and the space station provided NASA and these nine astronauts with their first valuable experiences of living and working in orbit for long periods.

After six years and 34,981 orbits, Skylab met its end. Increased sunspot activity had expanded the Earth's atmosphere, and this, together with difficulties in maintaining a low-drag attitude, meant that the space station was drawn inexorably Earthward. On July 11, 1979, Skylab crashed home. Though some large pieces of the space station landed in Western Australia, most of the debris—mainly the craft's "skin"—fell harmlessly into the Indian Ocean.

CLEAN CREW

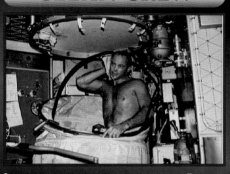

SKYLAB ASTRONAUTS COULD HAVE A WARM SHOWER: THE WATER WAS CONTAINED BY A CURTAIN AND SUCKED AWAY BY A VACUUM SYSTEM. BUT THE CREW COULD NOT WASH THEIR CLOTHES. INSTEAD, THEY WORE DISPOSABLE GARMENTS. THE STATION'S LOCKERS CONTAINED 39 JACKETS AND 69 PANTS, 30 PAIRS OF BOOTS AND 197 SETS OF UNDERWEAR.

FOOTHOLD
Triangular weights fitted to the undersides of the astronauts' shoes gripped the wire grid floor to prevent the crew from floating away in zero gravity.

FINGERTIP
Skylab 3's crew worked hard at their physical exercises, which were part of the experiments in living in weightlessness and guarded against muscle wastage. Here, Commander Carr jokingly "balances" Pilot Pogue on his head with just one finger.

DOCKED
The Apollo command and service module that carried the three-man crew to Skylab remained attached to Skylab. Sometimes, astronauts would retreat into it for a moment of peace and privacy.

SKYLAB

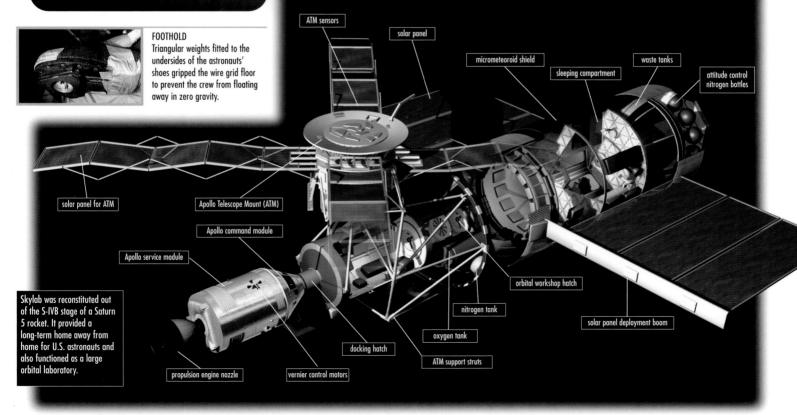

Skylab was reconstituted out of the S-IVB stage of a Saturn 5 rocket. It provided a long-term home away from home for U.S. astronauts and also functioned as a large orbital laboratory.

ATM sensors

solar panel

micrometeoroid shield

sleeping compartment

waste tanks

attitude control nitrogen bottles

solar panel for ATM

Apollo Telescope Mount (ATM)

Apollo command module

Apollo service module

orbital workshop hatch

nitrogen tank

solar panel deployment boom

docking hatch

oxygen tank

propulsion engine nozzle

vernier control motors

ATM support struts

COLUMBIA'S FIRST FLIGHT

Until the launch of the Space Shuttle Columbia in 1981, almost all rockets were used only once—an immensely wasteful practice. Columbia was designed to take off vertically as a rocket and land horizontally as an airplane. Only the main tank was disposable. The new Space Shuttle's orbiter section, with crew cabin, payload bay, wings and engines, was built to survive up to 100 missions over 20 years. Even the solid fuel boosters were reusable. But Columbia's debut flight had some alarming moments.

STS-1 STATISTICS

CRAFT	COLUMBIA		TOTAL LIFTOFF WEIGHT	4,457,111 LB (2,021,711 KG)
MISSION	STS-1 (SPACE TRANSPORTATION SYSTEM 01)		LANDING WEIGHT	195,472 LB (88,664 KG)
MISSION DURATION	2 DAYS, 6 HOURS, 20 MINUTES		CREW	COMMANDER: JOHN YOUNG
ORBITS	36			PILOT: ROBERT CRIPPEN

FIRST FLIGHT

Six years had passed since the last U.S. astronauts were launched into space. NASA's vaunted Shuttle was two years late in its development, and had been much more difficult and expensive to prepare than managers had expected. So when commander John Young and pilot Robert Crippen strapped themselves into Columbia's cabin for launch on April 10, 1981, tensions were high for everyone watching.

Inside the crew cabin, five computers cross-checked results to guarantee accuracy. For safety reasons, at least four of them had to match before Columbia could fly. But 20 minutes before the scheduled liftoff time, the onboard computers could not agree. Young and Crippen had to turn their spacecraft over to the engineers.

Two days later, pilot and commander once again climbed into their bulky, uncomfortable ejection seats. These seats would be replaced with seven crew couches once the Shuttle had proved itself to be reliable. On the first test flight, though, everyone was glad that the seats were there.

RETURN TO SPACE

At last, just after 7 a.m. on April 12, Columbia got off the launchpad and ascended flawlessly to orbit. America was back in space, and public reaction to the flight was tremendous. More than a million spectators thronged the beaches and fields beyond the Kennedy Space Center to watch the liftoff as it happened.

Once in orbit, Young and Crippen benefited from Columbia's large cabin, which was much roomier than previous space capsules. There was even a second deck beneath the cockpit, with food storage, spacesuit racks, an airlock, and a private washroom cubicle.

GROUNDED

COLUMBIA WAS NOT THE FIRST SHUTTLE. IN 1977, THE ENTERPRISE WAS CARRIED ALOFT BY A SPECIAL BOEING 747 AND THEN DROPPED FOR GLIDE AND LANDING TESTS. BUT ENTERPRISE NEVER FLEW IN SPACE.

MISSION DIARY: SHUTTLE MISSION STS-1

APRIL 12, 1981, 07:00:03 A.M. EST COLUMBIA'S THREE MAIN ENGINES ARE IGNITED, FUELED BY LIQUID HYDROGEN AND LIQUID OXYGEN (RIGHT).
7:00:09 A.M. THE TWIN SOLID ROCKET BOOSTERS FIRE. THE SPACE SHUTTLE LIFTS OFF THE LAUNCH PAD.
7:02:10 A.M. THE SOLID BOOSTERS COMPLETE THEIR BURN. COLUMBIA IS NOW AT A 31-MILE (50-KM) ALTITUDE. THE BOOSTERS FALL AWAY. LATER, THEY ARE RECOVERED FROM THE SEA AND REUSED.
7:08:38 A.M. COLUMBIA'S MAIN ENGINES SHUT DOWN AT AN ALTITUDE OF 72 MILES (116 KM). THE EXTERNAL FUEL TANK IS DISCARDED AND FALLS INTO THE SEA.
7:10:37 A.M. COLUMBIA FIRES TWO SMALL ORBITAL MANEUVERING SYSTEM (OMS) ENGINES TO COMPLETE THE ASCENT TO ORBIT. THE SPACECRAFT NOW HAS AN ALTITUDE OF

152 MILES (245 KM), AND A VELOCITY OF 17,322 MPH (27,877 KM/H).
7:52 A.M. THE CARGO BAY DOORS ARE OPENED (BELOW LEFT) TO EXPOSE SOLAR PANELS THAT HELP POWER THE SHUTTLE'S EQUIPMENT. YOUNG AND CRIPPEN BEGIN TWO DAYS OF SYSTEMS TESTING.
1:20:49 P.M. ANOTHER OMS BURN CHANGES COLUMBIA'S ORBIT TO AN ALTITUDE OF 170 MILES (273 KM).
APRIL 14, 12:21:34 P.M. THE OMS ENGINES SLOW COLUMBIA, AND IT BEGINS FALLING TOWARD EARTH. AFTER 17 MINUTES, THE SHUTTLE BEGINS TO HEAT UP FROM REENTRY FRICTION.
1:20:56 P.M. COLUMBIA TOUCHES DOWN ON THE RUNWAY (BELOW) AT EDWARDS AIR FORCE BASE IN CALIFORNIA.

Two days later, Columbia plunged back into the Earth's atmosphere and glided toward Edwards Air Force Base. It was a critical moment. With no engine power available, the pilots had to land first time around. To NASA—and America's—huge relief, they made a perfect touchdown.

Finally NASA had a vehicle that could deliver humans and cargo into space, and then be refurbished.

Behind the crew cabin was a payload bay 60 ft (18 m) long and 15 ft (4.5 m) wide. One day soon it would carry pressurized space laboratories, or large probes and satellites for release into space.

FLOATING
As Columbia orbits the Earth, Robert Crippen takes a break from the Shuttle's controls to enjoy some zero-g acrobatics.

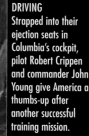

DRIVING
Strapped into their ejection seats in Columbia's cockpit, pilot Robert Crippen and commander John Young give America a thumbs-up after another successful training mission.

SHAVING
John Young gets the hang of shaving in zero gravity conditions. Attached to the locker on his right are various food items, including a sandwich.

SPACELAB

Spacelab was born in the early 1970s of a collaboration between two of the world's leading space agencies. NASA had the go-ahead for the Space Shuttle but was denied funding for a space station to go with it. The European Space Agency (ESA) wanted to send scientists into space but had no means of getting them there. The answer was to build a laboratory module that could be fitted inside the Shuttle's payload bay. First launched in 1983, Spacelab was a great success and heralded the age of space science.

SPACELAB STATS

MAX. WEIGHT 32,000 LB (14,500 KG)	CORE MODULE/EXPERIMENT SEGMENT (PRESSURIZED)	DIAMETER 3.3 FT (1 M)
PARTICIPATING ESA NATIONS		INSTRUMENT POINTING SYSTEM
BELGIUM, DENMARK, FRANCE, GERMANY	LENGTH 9 FT (2.7 M)	WEIGHT 2,600 LB (1,180 KG)
IRELAND, ITALY, NETHERLANDS, SPAIN,	DIAMETER 13.5 FT (4 M)	PAYLOAD 6,600 LB (2,993 LB)
SWITZERLAND, U.K.		
BUILDERS	PALLET (EXPERIMENTS ONLY)	IGLOO (INSTRUMENTS ONLY)
ERNO-VFW FOKKER CONSORTIUM	LENGTH 10 FT (3 M)	HEIGHT 7.9 FT (2.4 M)
(PRESSURIZED MODULES), BRITISH	DIAMETER 13.1 FT (4 M)	DIAMETER 3.6 FT (1.1 M)
AEROSPACE (PALLETS), SABCA (IGLOO),	WEIGHT 1,600 LB (725 KG)	WEIGHT 1,400 LB (635 KG)
DORNIER (IPS), McDONNELL-DOUGLAS	PAYLOAD 3 TONS MAXIMUM	
(TUNNEL) MISSIONS 15 (CREWED	TUNNEL LENGTH 8.7/18.9 FT	
MODULE), 6 (IGLOO/PALLETS)	(2.65/5.7 FT)	

SCIENCE LAB IN ORBIT

NASA's primary objectives after the Apollo Moon landings were to develop a reusable launch vehicle and to have human beings living and working in space for long periods of time. The government agreed to the first objective and gave a green light to the Space Shuttle program. But after Skylab, there was to be no money for the second aim. If NASA wanted a space station, it would have to go somewhere else to find it.

NASA went to Europe. In 1973, it signed an agreement with the European Space Agency (ESA) to develop a scientific research lab that could be carried into space in the Shuttle's payload bay. The result was Spacelab, the first major U.S.-European collaboration in space and Europe's first chance to put humans in orbit.

The Spacelab system is a set of modules that can be used in different combinations, depending on the kind of work to be done. The core segment is a pressurized laboratory, linked to the Orbiter's crew compartment by a 3-ft (1-m) -wide tunnel. The lab is fitted with a workbench and equipment racks, each loaded with up to 645 lb (292 kg) of experiments. Usually, an almost identical experiment segment is bolted on to the core segment to extend the lab space. Each segment has a hole in the roof that can be fitted with either a window for photography or an airlock for exposing experiments to open space. Oxygen, power, heat and communications with Earth are all provided by the Shuttle.

ON THE OUTSIDE

The other components of the Spacelab system are designed to operate by remote control in open space. They consist of a set of 10 U-shaped structures called pallets that mount scientific equipment in the Orbiter's payload bay. Some Spacelab missions are designated "pallets-only" and do without the pressurized lab segments. On such missions, up to five pallets can be carried, and the experiments are controlled by mission specialists from a console at the back of the Orbiter's flight deck. The control systems and utilities that normally reside in the core segment are housed in the cargo bay inside a pressurized, temperature-controlled enclosure called the igloo.

Spacelab was not an independent space station like Skylab or Mir, and while in orbit it remained firmly clamped in the Shuttle's cargo bay. Yet its low-key missions were important all the same. Along with its partner Shuttles, Spacelab proved that space technology can be reusable—each module was designed to last 50 missions. Spacelab's greatest legacy, though, is likely to be the experience gained by visiting humans, not with hardware. Each flight took one to four civilian scientists into orbit, where only career astronauts had gone before. It was a significant step toward the large-scale habitation of space.

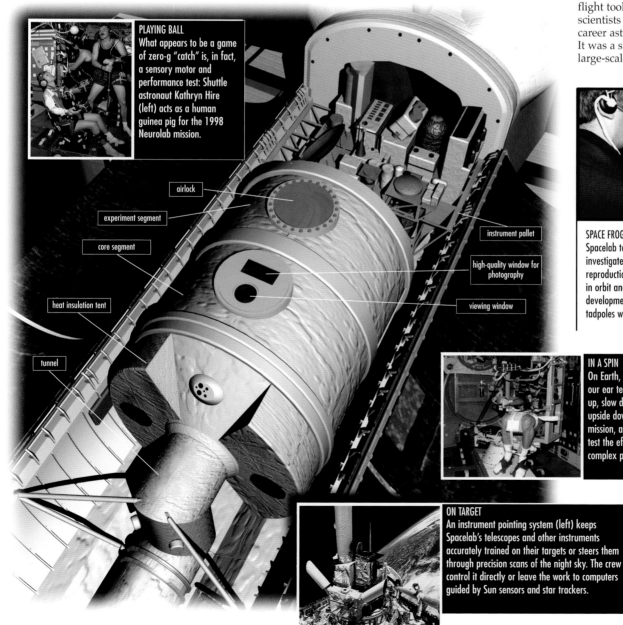

PLAYING BALL
What appears to be a game of zero-g "catch" is, in fact, a sensory motor and performance test: Shuttle astronaut Kathryn Hire (left) acts as a human guinea pig for the 1998 Neurolab mission.

airlock
experiment segment
core segment
heat insulation tent
tunnel
instrument pallet
high-quality window for photography
viewing window

SPACE FROGS
Spacelab took frogs into space in 1992 to investigate the effects of microgravity on reproduction and growth. The frogs laid eggs in orbit and scientists studied the development of the resulting embryos and tadpoles with interest.

IN A SPIN
On Earth, the movement of fluids in our ear tells the brain when we speed up, slow down, change direction or turn upside down. As part of the Neurolab mission, an astronaut is spun (left) to test the effects of microgravity on this complex process.

ON TARGET
An instrument pointing system (left) keeps Spacelab's telescopes and other instruments accurately trained on their targets or steers them through precision scans of the night sky. The crew control it directly or leave the work to computers guided by Sun sensors and star trackers.

FLYING THE SHUTTLE

apturing a faulty satellite... Docking with a space station to bring new crews and equipment... Operating a space laboratory... Servicing a space telescope... Such activities were routine for the astronauts involved in the Space Shuttle program. Classed as a partially reusable manned spaceplane, the Shuttle was the most versatile spacecraft ever built. Even though it completed scores of missions since its maiden flight in 1981, Shuttle launches received live TV coverage and regularly attracted thousands of spectators to the Kennedy Space Center until its retirement in 2011.

SHUTTLE MISSIONS

ENTERPRISE (OV-101) WAS A TEST VEHICLE AND WAS NOT INTENDED FOR SPACE MISSIONS.

CHALLENGER (OV-99) FLEW 10 MISSIONS FROM 1983 TO 1986. SHE WAS LOST APPROXIMATELY 73 SECONDS AFTER TAKEOFF ON MISSION STS-51-L IN 1986.

ATLANTIS (OV-104) HAS FLOWN 26 MISSIONS FROM 1985 TO 2002, AND REMAINED IN SERVICE UNTIL 2011.

ENDEAVOUR (OV-105) HAS FLOWN 19 MISSIONS FROM 1992 TO 2002. ENDEAVOUR REMAINED IN SERVICE UNTIL 2011.

COLUMBIA (OV-102) FLEW 28 MISSIONS FROM 1981-2003, INCLUDING STS-1, THE VERY FIRST SHUTTLE MISSION. SHE WAS LOST SHORTLY BEFORE TOUCHDOWN ON MISSION STS-107.

DISCOVERY (OV-103) HAS FLOWN 31 MISSIONS FROM 1984 TO THE PRESENT. DISCOVERY MADE THE FIRST RETURN-TO-FLIGHT MISSION AFTER THE LOSS OF COLOMBIA IN AUGUST 2005.

SPACE WAGON

The Space Shuttle was a general-purpose space truck, whose job was to ferry people and cargo to and from orbit above the Earth. Given its limitations, it performed its task with remarkable efficiency.

The Shuttle was launched like a conventional rocket, which jettisoned its twin reusable solid-fuel boosters two minutes after liftoff. The Orbiter spaceplane then climbed under the power of its own rocket engines, which were fed with liquid propellant from a giant external fuel tank. Six minutes later the Shuttle reached orbit and shed its tank, which then burned up in the Earth's atmosphere. Shortly after this, astronauts and payload specialists were able to begin their work.

WORKING IN SPACE

The Orbiter's payload bay contained satellites, repair equipment or pressurized modules for conducting space experiments. Some payloads are deployed by remote control; others are operated directly by the crew who are able to access the payload bay via a tunnel.

Shuttle missions usually lasted an average of nine days, though some extended to three weeks. The crew then had to live and work in the cramped flight deck or lower mid-deck—which also serves as a galley, sleeping quarters, and bathroom. Some missions were divided into shifts to allow for 24-hour work days.

On completion of a mission, the Shuttle's engines redirected it back to Earth. After a bumpy ride through the atmosphere, protected by its heat-shield tiles, it came in to land like an airplane. Always a popular craft, the Shuttle was only retired after 30 years' service.

MISSION DIARY: SHUTTLE MISSION STS-87

NOVEMBER 19, 1997 THE CREW OF MISSION STS-87 MAKES ITS WAY TO THE LAUNCH PAD WHERE THEY BOARD THE SPACE SHUTTLE COLUMBIA FOR A 16-DAY FLIGHT. THE SIX MEMBERS OF THE CREW ARE KALPANA CHAWLA, KEVIN KREGEL (MISSION COMMANDER), TAKAO DOI, WINSTON SCOTT, LEONID KADENYUK AND STEVEN LINDSEY.

NOVEMBER 22, 1997 SHUTTLE PILOT STEVEN LINDSEY AND MISSION SPECIALIST KALPANA CHAWLA CHECK ON THE PROGRESS OF AN EXPERIMENT CARRIED IN COLUMBIA'S MID-DECK AREA. EXPERIMENTS SCHEDULED TO BE PERFORMED DURING THIS MISSION INCLUDE THE POLLINATION OF PLANTS AND THE PROCESSING OF MATERIALS UNDER WEIGHTLESS CONDITIONS.

DECEMBER 3, 1997 DURING A SPACEWALK IN COLUMBIA'S PAYLOAD BAY, MISSION SPECIALIST WINSTON SCOTT RELEASES A PROTOTYPE OF THE FREE-FLYING AUTONOMOUS EXTRAVEHICULAR ACTIVITY ROBOTIC CAMERA SPRINT (AERCAM SPRINT). THIS SPHERICAL, BASKETBALL-SIZED DEVICE HOUSES A TV CAMERA AND IS INTENDED TO BE USED FOR REMOTE-CONTROLLED INSPECTIONS OF THE EXTERIOR OF THE INTERNATIONAL SPACE STATION.

DECEMBER 5, 1997 WITH ITS DRAG 'CHUTE DEPLOYED TO HELP SLOW IT DOWN, COLUMBIA LANDS AT 7:20:04 A.M. EST ON RUNWAY 33 AT THE KENNEDY SPACE CENTER. ITS MISSION, THE 87TH IN THE SHUTTLE PROGRAM, HAS TAKEN IT A TOTAL DISTANCE OF 6.5 MILLION MILES (10.5M KM) AND HAS LASTED FOR EXACTLY 15 DAYS, 16 HR AND 34 MIN.

WHAT THE SHUTTLE DID

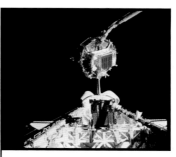

ROCKET ENGINES
The Shuttle's rocket engines were fuelled by liquid oxygen and hydrogen. Most of this bulky mixture was carried in the throwaway external fuel tank. A small amount was retained on board for orbital maneuvering and reentry.

DOCKING SYSTEM
The Shuttle had a specially designed pressurized module and docking mechanism that allowed it to ferry supplies and equipment to and from the Russian space station Mir. This proved to be of enormous value when Mir experienced technical difficulties in the mid 1990s.

PAYLOAD BAY
Stretching over half the length of the Orbiter, external access was via a pair of outward swinging doors.

FLIGHT DECK
Divided into operational and living quarters. A tunnel gave access to the payload bay.

GALILEO
The Galileo space probe, destined for Jupiter, was launched from the Shuttle's payload bay on October 18, 1989. Consisting of an orbiter and an entry probe, Galileo reached Jupiter in late 1995 and sent back many astounding pictures of the planet's surface.

HEAT SHIELD
The Shuttle's famous ceramic tile outer skin offered protection during reentry. The dark underside takes the full force of the heat, caused by friction with the Earth's atmosphere.

RETRIEVAL
A Japanese satellite is retrieved (above) from orbit by the robot arm of the Shuttle Endeavour on January 13, 1996. The square object in the foreground, another satellite, was launched during the same mission on January 15 and was retrieved two days later.

SPACELAB
This was the name given to the Shuttle's original pressurized laboratory module. Spacelab is primarily used by U.S. and European engineers, scientists and astronauts to study the long-term effects of weightlessness on living things.

SHUTTLE REENTRY

Few rides can be as hair-raising as the final stage of a Shuttle mission: reentry into Earth's atmosphere from space. As the orbiter headed home, it had to transform itself from spacecraft to glider—and lose most of its 17,500-mph (28,000 km/h) orbital velocity.

The Shuttle had to turn in space, fire braking rockets, and then plunge into the atmosphere for a fiery 3,000°F (1,650°C) ride until friction slowed it to orthodox flying speeds. Then, with engines silenced, it glided toward the landing strip and touchdown.

REENTRY SPECS

Altitude	Operation	Speed	Miles (km) from Touchdown
557,000 ft (170,000 m)	Deorbit	17,000 mph (27,500 km/h)	5,000 (8,000)
400,000 ft (122,000 m)	Entry Interface	17,000 mph (27,500 km/h)	3,500 (5,600)
83,000 ft (25,000 m)	Terminal Area	1,700 mph (2,750 km/h)	60 (100)
49,000 ft (15,000 m)	Subsonic	760 mph (1,220 km/h)	25 (40)
10,000 ft (3,000 m)	Glide slope	330 mph (530 km/h)	8 (12)

HELLO EARTH

Reentry preparation started about four hours before the Shuttle reentered the atmosphere. Crews complete their work, life support systems are rechecked, and the star-guidance system is shut down. With an hour to go, crewmembers strapped themselves into their seats. The pilot nudged the craft around so that it faced backward, ready for the engines to fire and start the descent from orbit. The crew enters the correct coordinates into the computer system: height, speed, distance from touchdown. When it had received this information, the computer fired the engines for about 2.5 minutes, cutting the speed by about 500 mph (800 km/h) to some 17,000 mph (27,400 km/h), to start the long, slow fall into the upper atmosphere.

Another piloted maneuver swung the orbiter around again to fly nose-first, descending at precisely the right angle. Accuracy was critical—2° shallower and the orbiter would skip back into space; 2° steeper and it would burn up in the air like a meteor.

From now on, the orbiter could approach touchdown entirely under the control of its computer, although the autopilot could be overridden. Another 25 minutes of downhill coasting brings the orbiter to an altitude of 100 miles (160 km), with some 5,000 miles (8,000 km) to go to touchdown.

Five minutes later, at an altitude of 75 miles (120 km), with some 3,500 miles (5,600 km) to go, sensors pick up atmospheric traces. The orbiter plows into the air belly-first, its six maneuvering jets ensuring that the right amount of surface area is presented to the air.

HOT BELLY

This first contact with atmosphere—Entry Interface (EI)—creates great friction, and the temperature of the spacecraft's skin soars. The heat is dissipated by heat shields, but it is mostly the 23,000 ceramic tiles that protected the underside and leading edges of the main body. Damage to these tiles is what caused the loss of Columbia in 2003, when super-heated gas penetrated the wing.

There is virtually no chance of survival for a Shuttle whose heat shield fails, so techniques for discovering, locating, and repairing damage—and for preventing it in the first place—were a critical part of the Return to Flight mission planning. During their August 2005 mission, the Discovery crew were able to demonstrate these techniques and repair their craft.

About 50 miles (80 km) up, the temperature reaches almost 3,000°F (1,650°C)—enough to ionize the surrounding air and cloak the orbiter in a sheath of glowing atomic fragments that blocks radio waves. For about 16 minutes, as the craft falls another 20 miles (32 km), it is in a communications limbo.

Once out of the cocoon of silence, the computer receives signals from navigation beacons on the ground that helped it to balance angle and speed of descent with skin temperature. Speed is varied by changing the angle of attack and turning to left or right. Often, the orbiter rolls back and forth in a series of S-turns, to lose speed yet stay on course. From now on, the orbiter could be steered to a new course, if necessary, landing anywhere up to 1,250 miles (2,000 km) from its original destination.

At 15 miles (24 km) up and 60 miles (100 km) from home the jets that control roll were no longer needed. Instead, the Shuttle is an airplane again. Ailerons on the wings steady the craft and, as the air thickens, other flaps controlling pitch and yaw begin to kick in.

By the time the craft is some eight miles up, having slowed to 1,700 mph (2,700 km/h), all jets are off and the orbiter has become a supersonic glider. Eight miles from touchdown, at 10,000 ft (3,000 m), its speed dropped to some 330 mph (530 km/h) and the orbiter entered its final approach. The Shuttle eased back to a shallower angle for its final approach, and there was a double sonic boom as it passed through Mach 1.

After circling the landing area, it approached the runway at a 22° angle. The main landing gear touched down at 215 mph (350 km/h), followed seconds later by the nosewheel. Finally, the combination of the drag chute and some deftly applied braking brought the orbiter safely to a halt.

SHUTTLE REENTRY

Mission accomplished, the Shuttle heads for home—tail first. Performing intricate maneuvers, it cuts through the atmosphere in a fiery passage of deceleration and swooped to land like a glider without any engine power.

1 TURN AND...
Before the deorbit burn, the Shuttle is turned around to tail-first attitude. The OMS (Orbital Maneuvering System) engines are then fired to slow down the spacecraft.

SEEING LIGHTS
Shuttle crew experience the dazzle of the plasma sheath that is created by electromagnetic forces generated by the searing heat of reentry.

2 ...TURN AGAIN UNTIL...
Soon after the Shuttle has slowed down, the RCS (Reaction Control System) rockets turn it back into a nose-first attitude.

WELCOME BACK
A chase plane escorts the Shuttle to its landing site. At this stage, the orbiter is on a glide, with only aerodynamic control surfaces—rudder, ailerons, elevators and flaps—to maneuver it.

3 ...WHITE HEAT SLOWS...
Thirty minutes before landing and at an altitude of about 400,000 ft (120,000 m), the orbiter is enveloped in a sheath of plasma caused by the fierce heat of reentry through the atmosphere.

4 ...TO A GLIDE
At 45,000 ft (13,000 m), the powerless Shuttle begins "area energy management maneuvers" to adjust its course and speed to fit the planned landing approach.

CHALLENGER DISASTER

There was an almost carnival atmosphere at the Kennedy Space Center, Florida, on January 28, 1986, as crowds gathered for the 25th flight of the Space Shuttle. On board the Shuttle Orbiter Challenger was the first "ordinary American citizen," a teacher named Christa McAuliffe, whose cheerful personality had already endeared her to the public. After a long series of delays, at 11:38 EST the Shuttle lifted off the launchpad into a clear, blue sky. Tragically, only seventy-three seconds later, Challenger was gone.

THE CHALLENGER CREW

BACK ROW, LEFT TO RIGHT
ELLISON SHOJI ONIZUKA (MISSION SPECIALIST), BORN JUNE 14, 1946
SHARON CHRISTA CORRIGAN McAULIFFE (PAYLOAD SPECIALIST),
BORN SEPTEMBER 2, 1948
GREGORY BRUCE JARVIS (PAYLOAD SPECIALIST), BORN AUGUST 24, 1944
JUDITH ARLENE RESNIK (MISSION SPECIALIST), BORN APRIL 5, 1949

FRONT ROW, LEFT TO RIGHT
MICHAEL JOHN SMITH (PILOT), COMMANDER U.S. NAVY,
BORN APRIL 30, 1945
FRANCIS RICHARD SCOBEE (COMMANDER), BORN MAY 19, 1939
RONALD ERWIN McNAIR (MISSION SPECIALIST), BORN OCTOBER 21, 1950

FATAL FLAW

NASA intended 1986 to be a landmark year for the space program. The Space Shuttle was to make 15 flights, and President Reagan was confidently expected to give the go-ahead for the project that would see a U.S. space station in orbit by 1994. It needed to be a good year. Mission 61-C Columbia had been progressively delayed from the year before, public interest in space was on the wane, and rumors were circulating in the media of repeated NASA incompetence. Its reputation as the foremost space agency in the world was beginning to slip.

It seemed that if anything could restore government and public confidence, it would be Shuttle launch 51-L Challenger. NASA saw to it that the inclusion of the first woman civilian astronaut, schoolteacher Christa McAuliffe, received maximum media coverage. The nation warmed to her—and to the idea that ordinary people might be going into space.

WAITING TO HAPPEN

Behind the scenes, there was growing concern among NASA technicians about the safety of the Shuttle. The focus of this concern was the flexible sealing system of putty and synthetic-rubber O-rings used on the "field joints" between sections of the reusable solid rocket boosters (SRBs). In-flight damage to the seals had been noticed on previous missions, implying a design fault, but no action was taken to solve the problem.

With Challenger already behind schedule after delays in the

Columbia mission, the pressure mounted for a swift launch. The crew finally boarded on January 27, only to be told, just 30 minutes from liftoff, that the mission was postponed due to a hatch fault. Meanwhile, engineers at Morton Thiokol, makers of the SRBs, voiced serious concerns about the effects of cold weather on the O-

ring seals, which might weaken them more. A severe cold front was forecast to hit Florida the following day that would see temperatures plummet to 23°F (-5°C). The engineers suggested postponing the launch until the cold snap passed, but their suggestion was overruled by NASA officials and the launch went ahead.

One week later, as the nation mourned its dead, President Reagan assigned a commission to investigate the cause of the accident. Their report, published on June 6, 1986, stated that the cause "was the failure of the pressure seal in the aft field joint of the right-hand solid rocket booster...due to a faulty design..."

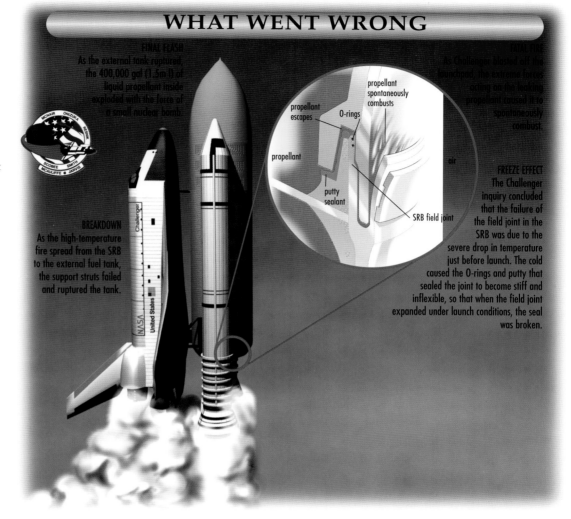

WHAT WENT WRONG

FINAL FLASH
As the external tank ruptured, the 400,000 gal (1.5m l) of liquid propellant inside exploded with the force of a small nuclear bomb.

BREAKDOWN
As the high-temperature fire spread from the SRB to the external fuel tank, the support struts failed and ruptured the tank.

propellant escapes
propellant spontaneously combusts
propellant
O-rings
putty sealant
air
SRB field joint

FATAL FIRE
As Challenger blasted off the launchpad, the extreme forces acting on the leaking propellant caused it to spontaneously combust.

FREEZE EFFECT
The Challenger inquiry concluded that the failure of the field joint in the SRB was due to the severe drop in temperature just before launch. The cold caused the O-rings and putty that sealed the joint to become stiff and inflexible, so that when the field joint expanded under launch conditions, the seal was broken.

MISSION DIARY: COUNTDOWN TO DISASTER

T+0.6 SEC A LAUNCH CAMERA PHOTOGRAPHS PUFFS OF SMOKE LOW-DOWN ON THE RIGHT-HAND SOLID ROCKET BOOSTER. THE SMOKE IS THE FIRST SIGN OF THE PROPELLANT THAT HAS BEGUN TO LEAK FROM A FAULTY O-RING SEAL IN THE AFT FIELD JOINT.
T+35 SEC AFTER A SEEMINGLY PERFECT LAUNCH, THE CHALLENGER'S MAIN ENGINES ARE THROTTLED DOWN TO 65 PERCENT AS THE CRAFT ENTERS THE PERIOD OF MAXIMUM DYNAMIC PRESSURE.
T+37 SEC SEVERE FLUCTUATIONS IN THE FLIGHT PATH BEGIN; THESE CONTINUE FOR ANOTHER 26 SECONDS AND ARE LATER ATTRIBUTED TO "WIND SHEAR" — AN

EXPLANATION QUESTIONED BY MANY ANALYSTS.
T+51 SEC ENGINES ARE SET TO FULL THROTTLE.
T+58 SEC FLAMES APPEAR AROUND THE FAULTY FIELD JOINT (CIRCLED, ABOVE). BY THIS TIME THE O-RING SEAL HAS FAILED COMPLETELY.
T+60 SEC THE FLAMES SPREAD RAPIDLY OVER THE STRUTS THAT SECURE THE SRBS AND THE EXTERNAL FUEL TANK (ET).

T+64 SEC THE ET IS BREACHED, BRINGING THE FLAMES INTO CONTACT WITH THE LIQUID HYDROGEN THAT IS LEAKING FROM THE TANK.
T+72 SEC IN A RAPID SEQUENCE OF EVENTS: THE STRUT LINKING THE RIGHT-HAND SRB TO THE ET FRACTURES; THE AFT DOME FALLS AWAY, RIPPING PARTS OF THE TANK APART; THEN THE SEVERED SRB HITS THE ET, CAUSING LIQUID OXYGEN TO MIX WITH LIQUID HYDROGEN IN A LETHAL COCKTAIL.
T+73 SEC THE MIXTURE OF LEAKING LIQUID FUELS ERUPTS IN AN EXPLOSION (RIGHT). THE ET DISINTEGRATES AND BOTH SRBS FLY OFF OUT OF CONTROL, LATER TO BE REMOTE-DETONATED BY THE RANGE SAFETY OFFICER.

THE ORBITER IS BLOWN CLEAR BUT INSTANTLY BREAKS UP DUE TO AERODYNAMIC FORCES. THE ONBOARD FUEL EXPLODES, THROWING THE CABIN CLEAR OF THE FIREBALL AND LEAVING THE WRECKAGE TO PLUNGE INTO THE ATLANTIC OCEAN. IT IS BELIEVED THAT SOME OF THE CREW INITIALLY SURVIVED THE EXPLOSION.

MIR

Mir was the first permanent space station, a unique complex specifically designed for expansion. Originally of Soviet origin, visiting spacecraft from a variety of nations could attach as many as nine modules to it. With many docking compartments to choose from, no one could predict what would be added, or when, or where. In the end, the space station looked like the product of a bizarre engineering experiment in zero gravity. Despite the many problems and near disasters Mir suffered, its relay of crews made it work astonishingly well—and for far longer than was originally expected.

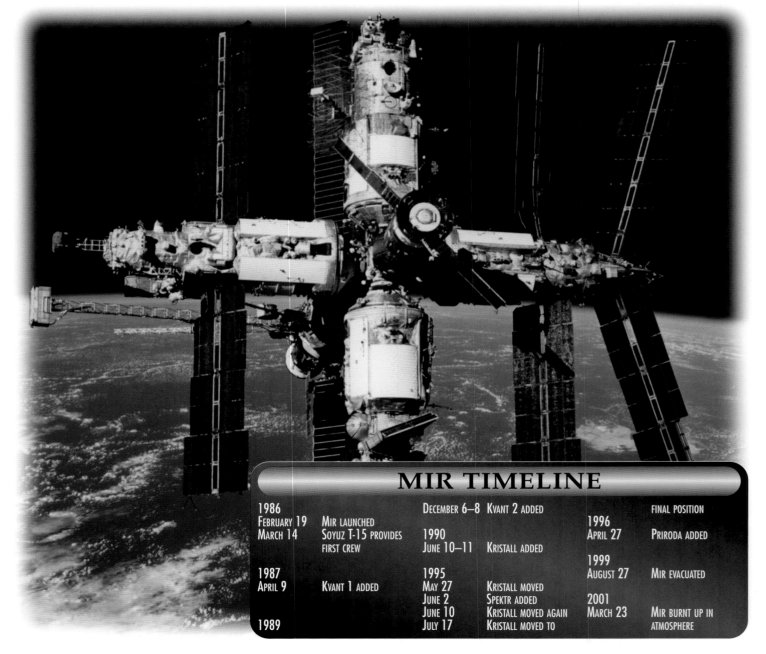

MIR TIMELINE

1986		DECEMBER 6–8	KVANT 2 ADDED		FINAL POSITION
FEBRUARY 19	MIR LAUNCHED			1996	
MARCH 14	SOYUZ T-15 PROVIDES	1990		APRIL 27	PRIRODA ADDED
	FIRST CREW	JUNE 10–11	KRISTALL ADDED		
				1999	
1987		1995		AUGUST 27	MIR EVACUATED
APRIL 9	KVANT 1 ADDED	MAY 27	KRISTALL MOVED		
		JUNE 2	SPEKTR ADDED	2001	
		JUNE 10	KRISTALL MOVED AGAIN	MARCH 23	MIR BURNT UP IN
1989		JULY 17	KRISTALL MOVED TO		ATMOSPHERE

COSMIC JALOPY

During its 14-year existence, Mir grew from a single core unit to a complex of six. At its heart was the central module, with a work room, an intermediate room and an adapter: a spherical 7-ft (2.1-m) unit with five docking ports. Cosmonauts lived and worked in the main room, 43 ft (13 m) long and 13.6 ft (4 m) across. It contained the control station, physical fitness machinery, cabins and two tables with special compartments for working in zero gravity.

In April 1987, after two crewed missions ensured that Mir was in good running order, it acquired its first addition—Kvant, an astrophysics research module. Without engines of its own, Kvant had a little "tug" that maneuvered it in orbit to its docking port. Instruments on the 19-ft (5.7-m), 22-ton (20-tonne) module included an X-ray observatory and powerful gyroscopes that would keep the station stable, so that the telescopes could remain fixed on faint objects.

Over the next two years and eight months, Mir-Kvant received 20 visits, several of them from international-crewed space missions. Progress craft—uncrewed space ferries—arrived every month or two, to bring new supplies and carry away trash.

The next add-on unit, Kvant 2, arrived in December 1989, turning Mir from a straight-line station into an L-shape. It brought extra power to make Mir more self sufficient: The station could now remove carbon dioxide and recycle water vapor and urine to make oxygen.

HOME IMPROVEMENTS

In June 1990, the third module, Kristall, was attached. It was a specialist unit for research into the manufacture of materials for semiconductors. Its retractable and detachable solar panels upgraded the power supply.

But now Mir was reaching the limits of its capacity. Originally, it was to have been replaced around 1992 by Mir 2, but the Soviet Union's successor, Russia, had no cash for a replacement.

Only when the U.S. agreed to make use of Mir in 1995 could Russia plan on the final units, Spektr and Priroda. The half-dozen Shuttle-Mir missions of 1995–7 gave the aging station a new injection of cash, as well as a new lease on life. In June 1995, Spektr was bolted on. Finally, in April 1996, Priroda, laden with a mass of environmental sensors, became Mir's final addition. Together, the two modules gave the station a formidable ability to gather and correlate information about the Earth's environment.

But there were problems. In 1997, crews had to cope with a fire, a crash that had knocked out one of Spektr's panels, and the near-collapse of power systems. The crises made it clear that it would take all the crews' time simply to keep Mir alive. Scientific work ceased and the last team abandoned ship on August 27, 1999. Despite occasional suggestions that Mir might somehow be rescued, it became obvious that the station's time was over. In 2001 the engines of the Progress supply rocket docket to the station were fired for the last time, braking the station so that it fell into Earth's atmosphere.

Much of the station burned up in the Earth's atmosphere, putting on a final spectacular show. Parts of the station—possibly as much as 25 tons (22.5 tonnes)—fell into the Pacific Ocean in a target zone specifically chosen to eliminate any risk to people on the ground.

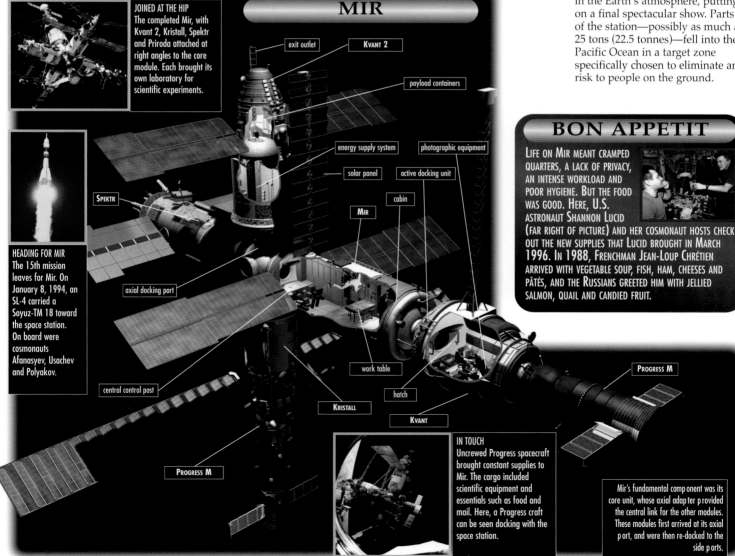

JOINED AT THE HIP The completed Mir, with Kvant 2, Kristall, Spektr and Priroda attached at right angles to the core module. Each brought its own laboratory for scientific experiments.

HEADING FOR MIR The 15th mission leaves for Mir. On January 8, 1994, an SL-4 carried a Soyuz-TM 18 toward the space station. On board were cosmonauts Afanasyev, Usachev and Polyakov.

BON APPETIT LIFE ON MIR MEANT CRAMPED QUARTERS, A LACK OF PRIVACY, AN INTENSE WORKLOAD AND POOR HYGIENE. BUT THE FOOD WAS GOOD. HERE, U.S. ASTRONAUT SHANNON LUCID (FAR RIGHT OF PICTURE) AND HER COSMONAUT HOSTS CHECK OUT THE NEW SUPPLIES THAT LUCID BROUGHT IN MARCH 1996. IN 1988, FRENCHMAN JEAN-LOUP CHRÉTIEN ARRIVED WITH VEGETABLE SOUP, FISH, HAM, CHEESES AND PÂTÉS, AND THE RUSSIANS GREETED HIM WITH JELLIED SALMON, QUAIL AND CANDIED FRUIT.

IN TOUCH Uncrewed Progress spacecraft brought constant supplies to Mir. The cargo included scientific equipment and essentials such as food and mail. Here, a Progress craft can be seen docking with the space station.

Mir's fundamental component was its core unit, whose axial adapter provided the central link for the other modules. These modules first arrived at its axial port, and were then re-docked to the side ports.

Labels on diagram: exit outlet · KVANT 2 · payload containers · energy supply system · photographic equipment · solar panel · active docking unit · MIR · cabin · SPEKTR · axial docking port · work table · PROGRESS M · central control post · hatch · KRISTALL · KVANT · PROGRESS M

MIR

SHUTTLE AND MIR LINKUP

Looking through the overhead windows, astronaut Robert Gibson could see the Mir space station above him. The docking assembly was 10 ft (3 m) away in the payload bay and out of his line of sight. Using observations from the crew of both craft, along with TV cameras positioned around the Shuttle Atlantis, Gibson closed in and gently nudged the thrusters to make contact. After some anxious moments, history was made. For the first time in 20 years, an American and a Russian spacecraft were linked in Earth orbit.

STS-71 MISSION STATS

MISSION	STS-71, 69TH SHUTTLE MISSION; 100TH U.S. HUMAN SPACEFLIGHT LAUNCHED FROM FLORIDA; FIRST SHUTTLE-MIR DOCKING MISSION	CREW COMMANDER	ROBERT L. "HOOT" GIBSON (CAPT. USN), 48, 5TH FLIGHT
		PILOT	CHARLES J. PRECOURT (LT. COLONEL, USAF), 39, 2ND FLIGHT
LAUNCH VEHICLE	SPACE SHUTTLE ATLANTIS OV104 (14TH FLIGHT)/SRB BI-072 /20 ET-70/SSME 2028 (#1), 2034 (#2), 2032 (#3)	MISSION SPECIALIST 1	ELLEN S. BAKER (MD), 42, PAYLOAD COMMANDER, 3RD FLIGHT
		MISSION SPECIALIST 2	GREGORY J. HARBAUGH (CIVILIAN), 34, FLIGHT ENGINEER, 3RD FLIGHT
LAUNCH SITE	LC39A, KENNEDY SPACE CENTER, FLORIDA	MISSION SPECIALIST 3	BONNIE J. DUNBAR (PHD), 46, 4TH FLIGHT

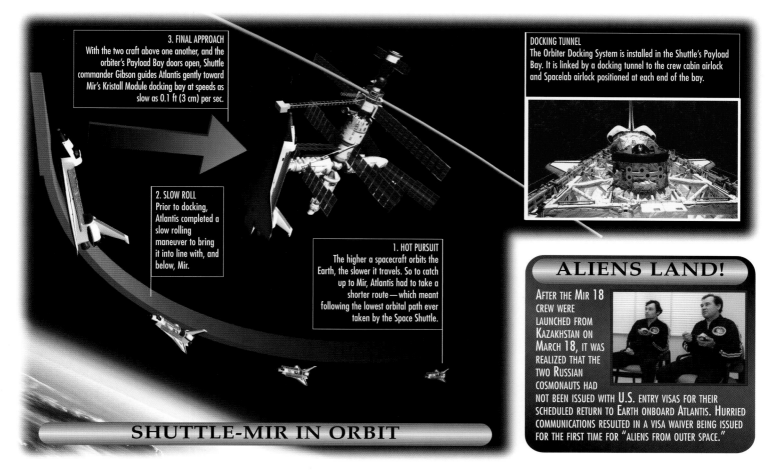

3. FINAL APPROACH
With the two craft above one another, and the orbiter's Payload Bay doors open, Shuttle commander Gibson guides Atlantis gently toward Mir's Kristall Module docking bay at speeds as slow as 0.1 ft (3 cm) per sec.

DOCKING TUNNEL
The Orbiter Docking System is installed in the Shuttle's Payload Bay. It is linked by a docking tunnel to the crew cabin airlock and Spacelab airlock positioned at each end of the bay.

2. SLOW ROLL
Prior to docking, Atlantis completed a slow rolling maneuver to bring it into line with, and below, Mir.

1. HOT PURSUIT
The higher a spacecraft orbits the Earth, the slower it travels. So to catch up to Mir, Atlantis had to take a shorter route—which meant following the lowest orbital path ever taken by the Space Shuttle.

SHUTTLE-MIR IN ORBIT

ALIENS LAND!
AFTER THE MIR 18 CREW WERE LAUNCHED FROM KAZAKHSTAN ON MARCH 18, IT WAS REALIZED THAT THE TWO RUSSIAN COSMONAUTS HAD NOT BEEN ISSUED WITH U.S. ENTRY VISAS FOR THEIR SCHEDULED RETURN TO EARTH ONBOARD ATLANTIS. HURRIED COMMUNICATIONS RESULTED IN A VISA WAIVER BEING ISSUED FOR THE FIRST TIME FOR "ALIENS FROM OUTER SPACE."

SPACE DOCK

The STS-71 mission launched from the Kennedy Space Center on June 27, 1995, with five astronauts and two cosmonauts—the Mir 19 relief crew—aboard. The flight was to be the first in a planned three-year series of Shuttle-Mir dockings, in preparation for the day when the presence of the International Space Station (ISS) will make such maneuvers routine. Just as in the historic docking of Apollo and Soyuz in 1975, the Shuttle Atlantis carried a docking mechanism that had been specially constructed for the task. Located in the orbiter's Payload Bay, and linked by a tunnel to the crew cabin, the crew had high hopes that it would prove its space worthiness.

Two days after launch, Atlantis approached Mir. As the two craft closed in, Shuttle commander Gibson carefully guided the orbiter upward from its position below the space station and brought it to a flawless docking with Mir's Kristall Module docking port. Together, the U.S. and the Russians had created the largest spacecraft ever.

RUSSIAN WELCOME

About 90 minutes after the successful linkup, the hatches were opened and Robert Gibson and his Mir 18 counterpart, Vladimir Dezhurov, warmly greeted each other in the docking tunnel. It was the start of five days of celebrations and joint activities for the 10 astronauts and cosmonauts aboard. But ceremonial toasts and gift exchanges aside, there was much hard work to be done. In the Shuttle's Spacelab module, an extensive program of medical examinations on the Mir 18 crew was undertaken. This was the first time that the Americans had had the chance to study the effects of extended weightlessness on the human body since Skylab in the 1970s.

At the end of the 10-day mission, Gibson brought Atlantis to a safe landing at Kennedy Space Center on July 7. It was good to be back on Earth. But for the crew of Mir 18, their return marked the beginning of yet another round of medical tests.

MISSION DIARY: STS-71

APRIL 26 ATLANTIS SITS ON PAD 39A. PLANNED FOR MAY, THE LAUNCH SLIPS BACK TO THE THIRD WEEK OF JUNE.
JUNE 23 LAUNCH IS SCRUBBED; RESCHEDULED FOR NEXT DAY, THEN SCRUBBED AGAIN. THE SHUTTLE CREW, BACKUP CREW, AND MIR 19 RELIEF CREW, WAIT ANXIOUSLY.
3:32 P.M. EST JUNE 27 STS-71 FINALLY LAUNCHES FROM PAD 39A IN PURSUIT OF THE ORBITING MIR.
8:00 A.M. JUNE 29 ATLANTIS DOCKS WITH THE KRISTALL MODULE ON MIR WHILE SUSPENDED 216 NAUTICAL MILES (400 KM) ABOVE THE LAKE BAIKAL REGION OF THE RUSSIAN FEDERATION. THE DOCKING SYSTEM WORKS PERFECTLY. ONCE PRESSURE CHECKS HAVE BEEN MADE, THE DOCKING HATCHES ARE OPENED AND THE U.S. AND RUSSIAN CREWS BEGIN THEIR JOINT MISSION.

JUNE 30 THE CREWS EXCHANGE GIFTS, AND THEN SET TO WORK. HALF A TON OF WATER, 53 LB (24 KG) OF OXYGEN AND 80 LB (36 KG) OF NITROGEN IS TRANSFERRED TO MIR. OTHER WORK INVOLVES SUBJECTING THE MIR 18 CREW TO SEVEN DIFFERENT KINDS OF MEDICAL INVESTIGATION — CARDIOVASCULAR FUNCTIONS, HUMAN METABOLISM, NEUROSCIENCE, HYGIENE, SANITATION AND RADIATION, AND BEHAVIORAL PERFORMANCE AND BIOLOGY.
3:32 P.M. JULY 3 THE FAREWELL CEREMONY OVER, MIR CLOSES ITS HATCH.
3:48 P.M. JULY 3 ATLANTIS BOLTS ITS HATCH AND BEGINS TO DEPRESSURIZE THE TUNNEL IN PREPARATION FOR UNDOCKING.
7:10 A.M. JULY 4 ATLANTIS UNDOCKS FROM MIR. THE RUSSIAN SPACECRAFT IS LEFT TEMPORARILY UNOCCUPIED AS THE

RECENTLY ARRIVED MIR 19 COSMONAUTS (RIGHT, PICTURED WHILE STILL ON ATLANTIS) UNDOCK THEIR SOYUZ TM TO RECORD THE SHUTTLE'S DEPARTURE.
10:54 A.M. JULY 7 ATLANTIS MAKES A SAFE LANDING AT THE KENNEDY SPACE CENTER, WITH MIR 18 VISITOR NORMAN E. THAGARD ABOARD.

BUILDING THE ISS

The International Space Station, successor to Mir, is the single most expensive item ever built, but given the enormity of the task this is not too surprising. ISS is made up of several modules connected together (and designed to be swapped out and replaced if the need arises). It was projected that over 80 Shuttle and rocket flights would be necessary to construct the complete station, but with the retirement of Shuttle flights and other difficulties it is proving difficult to keep work on the ISS going at all.

The station is currently operating with a reduced crew and is being very slowly expanded. Many more modules were planned and may some day be launched, but at the moment just keeping the station going day to day is proving to be a big job.

ISS COMPONENTS

Name	Purpose	Launch Date
Zarya	Early orbit control & power	November 1998
Unity	Connector Module	December 1998
Zvezda	Service Module (Living quarters, orbit control)	July 2000
Photovoltaic Module	Solar panels for power	October 2000
Pressurised Mating Adapter	Docking Port Support Truss	
Destiny Laboratory Module	Research laboratory	February 2001
Harmony Module	Utility hub	October 2007
Tranquility module	Storage and exercise	February 2010

PLUG AND PLAY

Like a giant model kit, the International Space Station (ISS) is to be assembled piece by piece in Earth orbit. Back in 1973, the U.S. lofted the Skylab station—and everything it needed for its two-year life—on one Saturn 5 rocket. But with today's smaller, cheaper boosters, ISS must be launched in sections over several years.

In its original designed form, the ISS was to comprise more than 100 major components ranging from complete research laboratories to radio antennas. The parts, hauled into orbit by U.S. Space Shuttles and Russian boosters, are put together by spacewalking astronauts, aided by robot arms controlled from the ISS and the Space Shuttle.

It is likely that the design of the ISS will be revised as new launch vehicles become available, though many of the modules were under construction or at least into late design work when shuttle flights were suspended. These modules will likely form part of the final station, whatever its form. The Canadian-built Space Vision System provides computer graphics views of what the robot arms are doing, even when they are out of sight. The robot arms are fitted with grapple devices at both ends so that they lock on to any part of the ISS. The biggest arm, the Space Station Remote Manipulator System (SSRMS), will eventually be attached to a mobile platform that will be able to travel the whole length of the station's structure.

Dressed in either the Russian Orlan-M spacesuit or an upgraded Shuttle spacesuit, astronauts and cosmonauts are scheduled to make about 160 spacewalks during the construction period—more than have been performed in the entire history of spaceflight. And ISS spacewalks could be tough duty: The space station cannot be turned from shade into sunlight as easily as the Shuttle's cargo bay, and conditions may be much colder or darker than on a Shuttle mission.

The astronauts will move around ISS with the help of extending poles similar to those used on Mir, robot arms and open trolleys that run along the main ISS girderwork structure. As the world's first space construction gang, they will use

a host of manual and power tools to connect components and their numerous cables and pipes. A rocket called SAFER is attached to each astronaut's backpack as the space equivalent of a lifejacket in water. Astronauts will wear safety tethers, but should a tether break, SAFER has enough fuel to bring them back to the ISS. The astronauts will have robotic assistants for their spacewalks— the NASA AERCam and German Inspector. These devices float nearby and provide TV views for spacewalk controllers.

The work crew will need all the help they can get. Every piece has to fit as planned and the whole ISS has to work the first time: The station cannot be tested before it is launched into space and then built.

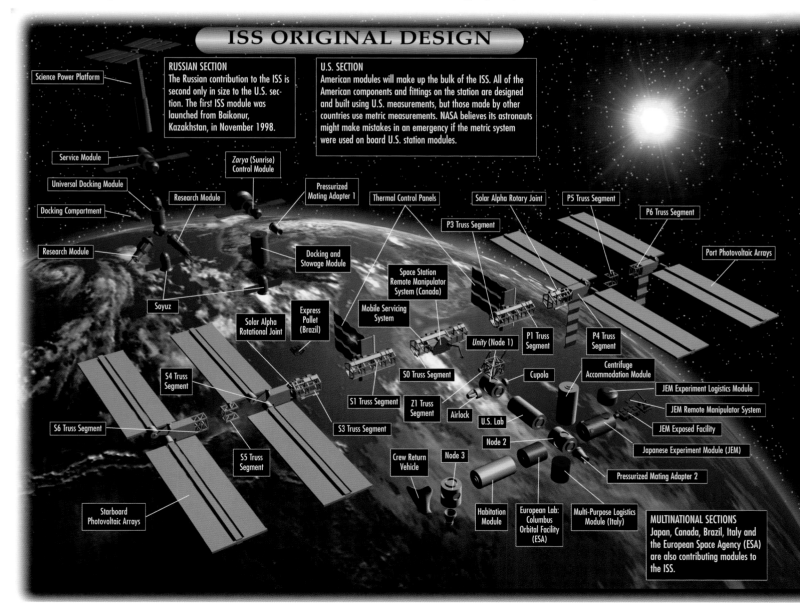

ISS ORIGINAL DESIGN

RUSSIAN SECTION
The Russian contribution to the ISS is second only in size to the U.S. section. The first ISS module was launched from Baikonur, Kazakhstan, in November 1998.

U.S. SECTION
American modules will make up the bulk of the ISS. All of the American components and fittings on the station are designed and built using U.S. measurements, but those made by other countries use metric measurements. NASA believes its astronauts might make mistakes in an emergency if the metric system were used on board U.S. station modules.

Science Power Platform
Service Module
Universal Docking Module
Docking Compartment
Research Module
Research Module
Soyuz
Zarya (Sunrise) Control Module
Pressurized Mating Adapter 1
Thermal Control Panels
Solar Alpha Rotary Joint
P5 Truss Segment
P6 Truss Segment
Port Photovoltaic Arrays
P3 Truss Segment
Docking and Stowage Module
Space Station Remote Manipulator System (Canada)
Mobile Servicing System
Solar Alpha Rotational Joint
Express Pallet (Brazil)
S4 Truss Segment
S6 Truss Segment
S1 Truss Segment
S3 Truss Segment
S5 Truss Segment
Starboard Photovoltaic Arrays
S0 Truss Segment
Z1 Truss Segment
Airlock
U.S. Lab
Node 2
Node 3
Crew Return Vehicle
Habitation Module
European Lab: Columbus Orbital Facility (ESA)
Multi-Purpose Logistics Module (Italy)
Unity (Node 1)
P1 Truss Segment
Cupola
P4 Truss Segment
Centrifuge Accommodation Module
JEM Experiment Logistics Module
JEM Remote Manipulator System
JEM Exposed Facility
Japanese Experiment Module (JEM)
Pressurized Mating Adapter 2

MULTINATIONAL SECTIONS
Japan, Canada, Brazil, Italy and the European Space Agency (ESA) are also contributing modules to the ISS.

INTERNATIONAL SPACE STATION

The International Space Station (ISS) will be the biggest space structure ever built, with assembly due for completion in 2014. In its low Earth orbit (LEO), 220 miles (355 km) up, it should be easy to see in the night sky. The ISS as designed was to be assembled in orbit from components flown up on Space Shuttle flights and Russian Proton and Soyuz missions. The station will provide living quarters, workshops and laboratories for astronauts from the U.S. and nations around the world throughout its working life, and may be upgraded and adapted with the replacement or addition of modules.

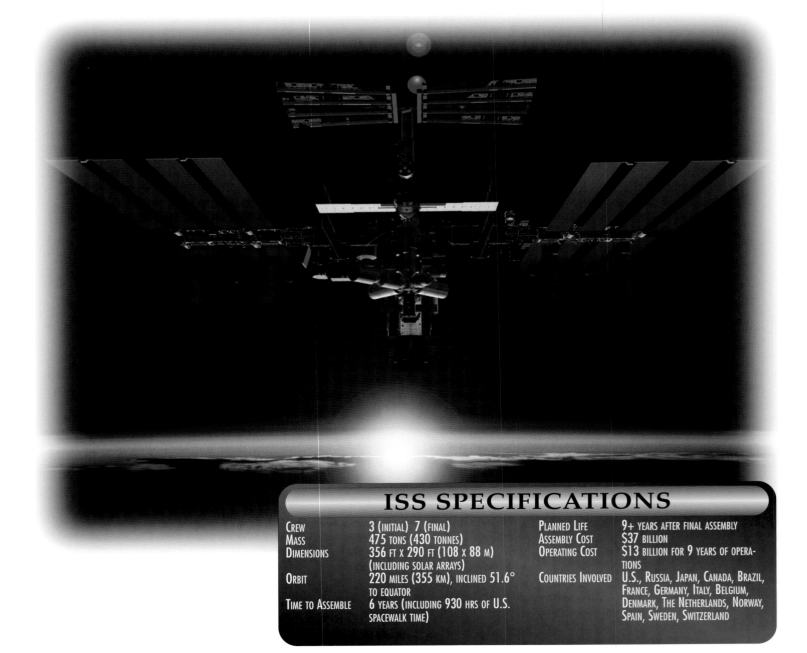

ISS SPECIFICATIONS

CREW	3 (INITIAL) 7 (FINAL)	PLANNED LIFE	9+ YEARS AFTER FINAL ASSEMBLY
MASS	475 TONS (430 TONNES)	ASSEMBLY COST	$37 BILLION
DIMENSIONS	356 FT X 290 FT (108 X 88 M) (INCLUDING SOLAR ARRAYS)	OPERATING COST	$13 BILLION FOR 9 YEARS OF OPERATIONS
ORBIT	220 MILES (355 KM), INCLINED 51.6° TO EQUATOR	COUNTRIES INVOLVED	U.S., RUSSIA, JAPAN, CANADA, BRAZIL, FRANCE, GERMANY, ITALY, BELGIUM, DENMARK, THE NETHERLANDS, NORWAY, SPAIN, SWEDEN, SWITZERLAND
TIME TO ASSEMBLE	6 YEARS (INCLUDING 930 HRS OF U.S. SPACEWALK TIME)		

SCIENCE IN ORBIT

The crew of a Space Shuttle arriving at the newly completed International Space Station (ISS) would be greeted by a massive structure 356 ft (108 m) long and 290 ft (88 m) wide, nearly the size of two football fields. The station is currently behind schedule and the Shuttle may or not continue flying, but the dream is still alive—the ISS has a crew aboard and is carrying out its mission as well as possible under the circumstances.

Clustered at the center of this sprawling space complex are the modules containing laboratories, workshops and the living quarters for up to seven crew members. The work of the crew involves scientific, medical and technological research that can only be carried out in the near-weightless conditions of orbit in space. It includes studies of the human body to search for new ways of preventing and treating diseases, and the development of new types of materials, including semiconductor crystals, plastics and drugs.

The station is also an excellent platform for observing the Earth, because its orbit takes it over 85 percent of the planet's surface. From their high vantage point, scientists study weather patterns, land usage, the spread of deserts and the destruction of rain forests.

Crews are taken to and from the ISS by U.S. Space Shuttles and Russian Soyuz ferry craft. Supplies and propellants are delivered by Shuttle flights and by unmanned ferries including Russian Progress vehicles, the European ATV and the Japanese HTV.

LIFE-SUPPORT SYSTEMS

On board the station, the life-support systems maintain comfortable "shirt-sleeve" conditions for the comfort of the crew. Water is used for drinking and washing and is also electrolyzed to produce oxygen for breathing. This oxygen is mixed with nitrogen to create a fair approximation of the air on Earth.

The temperature and humidity of the air are regulated by air conditioners, and the air is circulated around the ISS by fans. Molecular sieves remove carbon dioxide from it, and activated charcoal filters and catalytic oxidizers scrub away contaminants. Waste water from the air conditioners, sinks, showers and toilets is recycled for drinking.

The main hazards of life in low Earth orbit are radiation, space debris and micrometeorites. During periods of maximum solar activity, when solar flares create high levels of radiation, the crews "hide" in the best-shielded parts of the station.

The modules are built to withstand impacts of space debris and meteorite particles up to half an inch (12 mm) in size. The U.S. modules, for instance, are made from 1.25-in (30-mm) aluminum with layers of Nextel impact protection material and thermal insulation—making the walls about three in (75 mm) thick in total. Particles larger than four in (100 mm) across can be tracked from Earth, and, given enough warning, the ISS can maneuver to avoid a collision. But any impacts from particles between half an inch (12 mm) and four in (100 mm) in size are potentially dangerous.

BEYOND FRONTIERS
Floating 220 miles (355 km) above the Earth's surface, the International Space Station will be home to astronauts and scientists from at least 15 nations.

INTERNATIONAL SPACE STATION

science power platform solar panel array

science power platform

Progress-M ferry craft

service module (life-support systems and Russian crew quarters)

Zarya control module

thermal control system (radiators dump waste heat into space)

life-support module

solar panel array

radiator

U.S. centrifuge module

European Space Agency module

pressurized mating adapter for Space Shuttle docking

Japanese experiment module

radiator

Soyuz crew rescue vehicle

U.S. laboratory module

integrated truss structure (the 310-ft (95-m) main girderwork structure of ISS)

U.S. habitation module (living quarters for four crew)

RECYCLED SOLDIER

THE FIRST COMPONENT OF ISS TO BE LAUNCHED, THE ZARYA CONTROL MODULE, WAS BUILT BY THE KHRUNICHEV COMPANY IN MOSCOW. BUT IT WAS PAID FOR BY NASA AND ITS CONSTRUCTION WAS MANAGED BY BOEING. IT WAS DEVELOPED FROM A SOVIET MILITARY CREW/SUPPLY FERRY, TKS, WHICH WAS DESIGNED IN THE 1960s AND TEST-FLOWN IN THE 1970s.

COLUMBIA DISASTER

The launch of the Shuttle Columbia on its 28th mission on January 16, 2003, appeared to be entirely routine and successful as the crew of seven astronauts began a two-week long scientific mission designated STS-107, the 113th flight of a Space Shuttle orbiter. Less than two minutes after launch, a piece of insulating foam from the huge external fuel tank, barely noticed at the time, fell off and struck the Shuttle's left wing, setting in motion a sequence of events leading to the break-up of Columbia on reentry.

THE CREW OF STS-107

THE CREW OF COLUMBIA CONSISTED OF SEVEN ASTRONAUTS FROM THREE NATIONS.

RICK HUSBAND, MISSION COMMANDER
U.S. AIR FORCE COLONEL RICK HUSBAND, BORN 1957, HAD MADE ONE PREVIOUS FLIGHT, PILOTING STS-96 IN 1999. HE WAS CHIEF OF SAFETY IN NASA'S ASTRONAUT OFFICE.

WILLIAM McCOOL, PILOT
US NAVY COMMANDER WILLIAM McCOOL, BORN 1961, WAS MAKING HIS FIRST SHUTTLE FLIGHT.

MICHAEL ANDERSON, PAYLOAD COMMANDER
A USAF LIEUTENANT COLONEL BORN IN 1959, MIKE ANDERSON HAD FLOWN ON ENDEAVOUR IN 1998

ILLAN RAMON, PAYLOAD SPECIALIST
BORN 1954, ILLAN RAMON WAS THE FIRST ISRAELI TO FLY IN SPACE. HE WAS A COLONEL IN THE ISRAELI AIR FORCE AND TOOK PART IN THE 1981 ATTACK ON IRAQ'S OSIRAK NUCLEAR REACTOR.

KALPANA CHAWLA, MISSION SPECIALIST
BORN IN INDIA IN 1961, KALPANA CHALWA WAS AN AEROSPACE ENGINEER WHO FLEW ON COLUMBIA IN 1996. SHE WAS THE SECOND INDIAN TO FLY IN SPACE.

DAVID BROWN, MISSION SPECIALIST
NAVY CAPTAIN, AVIATOR AND FLIGHT SURGEON DAVID BROWN, BORN 1954, WAS ON HIS FIRST SHUTTLE MISSION.

LAUREL CLARK, MISSION SPECIALIST
BORN IN 1961, LAUREL CLARK WAS A NAVY COMMANDER AND FLIGHT SURGEON, ALSO MAKING HER FIRST SPACE FLIGHT.

DOOMED BY DEBRIS

The impact of the foam caused a breach in the shuttle's Thermal Protection System, allowing superheated air to penetrate the leading edge insulation and progressively melt the aluminium structure of the left wing, followed by destruction of the orbiter. The piece of foam weighed only 1.67 lb (750 g) but was travelling at approximately 750 ft per second (228 m/s), or 511 mph (822 km/h) when it struck the orbiter at an estimated impact angle of less than 20 degrees.

From the moment the foam debris struck the wing, Columbia was doomed, but there remained a slim possibility the crew could have been saved by a rescue mission if the extent of damage was understood. A review of launch film on the day of launch did not pick up the debris strike and when it was spotted the following day it was found that no camera position covered the underside of the Shuttle. Various "Debris Assessment Team" meetings and requests for imagery from military sensors achieved little and the crew were not informed of the ground engineers' concerns, the assumption being that the (unseen) damage couldn't be too bad.

The initially successful mission lasted 15 days, 22 hours, 20 minutes and 32 seconds during which the crew performed over 80 experiments testing applications of microgravity. The shuttle was travelling at approximately 12,500mph (20,000 km/h or Mach 18) when it broke up over Texas at an altitude of 207,000 ft (63,000 m), spreading debris over a wide area of Texas and into Louisiana.

In August 2003 the accident investigation board delivered a 248-page report, which criticised NASA's safety culture and the report warned that "the scene is set for another accident" without sweeping changes. Recommendations included a redesigned external tank, better imagery of launches, using an extended robot arm with a camera to examine the underside of the Shuttle in orbit and carrying a kit to repair broken thermal tiles with a spacewalk. Shuttle launches were suspended until July 2005.

MISSION DIARY: STS-107 COLUMBIA

JANUARY 16, 2003, 9:39 A.M. CST LAUNCH FROM KENNEDY SPACE CENTER.
9:40 A.M. EIGHTY-ONE SECONDS AFTER LAUNCH A PIECE OF INSULATING FOAM PUNCTURES THE UNDERSIDE OF THE LEFT WING LEADING EDGE
FEBRUARY 1, 2003, 7:15 A.M DEORBIT BURN PROCEDURE BEGUN TO BRING COLUMBIA OUT OF ORBIT FOR LANDING

7:23 A.M. SHUTTLE REORIENTED TO FORWARD-FACING NOSE-UP REENTRY ATTITUDE
7:53 A.M. GROUND CONTROLLERS LOSE DATA FROM FOUR TEMPERATURE INDICATORS ON THE LEFT SIDE OF THE SHUTTLE
7:56 A.M. SENSORS DETECT RISE IN TEMPERATURE TYRE PRESSURE ON THE LEFT-SIDE LANDING GEAR
7:58 A.M. DATA LOST FROM THREE TEMPERATURE SENSORS IN THE SHUTTLE'S LEFT WING

7:59 A.M. LAST RADIO TRANSMISSION
8:04 A.M. DEBRIS IN SKY OVER TEXAS
8:14 A.M. CONTINGENCY PLANS ORDERED INTO ACTION
8:16 A.M. SCHEDULED LANDING TIME AT KENNEDY SPACE CENTER
3:05 P.M. PRESIDENT BUSH SPEAKS TO THE NATION: "THE COLUMBIA IS LOST. THERE ARE NO SURVIVORS."

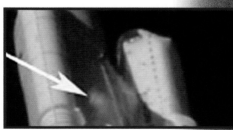

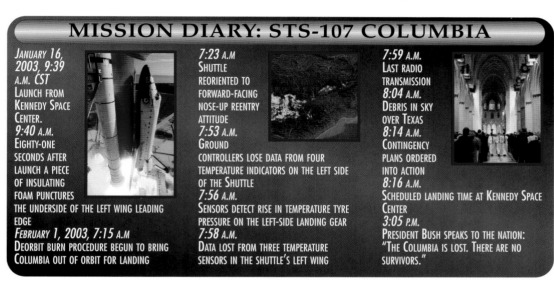

UNFOLDING TRAGEDY
Visible in the two images at left are (top) the pieces of foam falling from the fuel tank and (bottom) the shower of particles caused by the debris hitting the left hand wing of the orbiter. The chilling images of the shuttle breaking up at high altitude and speeds (main image) were broadcast live around the world.

MEMORIALS

SEVEN ASTEROIDS ORBITING THE SUN BETWEEN MARS AND JUPITER WERE NAMED AFTER THE COLUMBIA CREW. THE ASTEROIDS WERE DISCOVERED AT THE PALOMAR OBSERVATORY NEAR SAN DIEGO IN JULY 2001 BY ASTRONOMER ELEANOR F. HELIN, WHO RETIRED IN JULY 2002.

THE SEVEN ASTEROIDS RANGE IN DIAMETER FROM 3.1 TO 4.3 MILES (5 TO 7 KM). THE NAMES, PROPOSED BY NASA'S JET PROPULSION LABORATORY (JPL), WERE APPROVED BY THE INTERNATIONAL ASTRONOMICAL UNION IN AUGUST 2003.

TIANGONG-1

China's first space station module was launched on September 29, 2011 and is the first part of the Tiangong program. This program will use Tiangong-1 as a test run for its technologies, with the intention of launching a larger station by 2020. The temporary Tiangong-1 is due to be replaced some time in 2013 by more sophisticated modules (Tiangong-2 and 3). The name means "heavenly palace" in Chinese. On its completion China intend to permanently man their finalized space station just as the International Space Station (ISS) is manned, keeping an uninterrupted presence in space. Tiangong-1 is also known for being visited by China's first female astronauts.

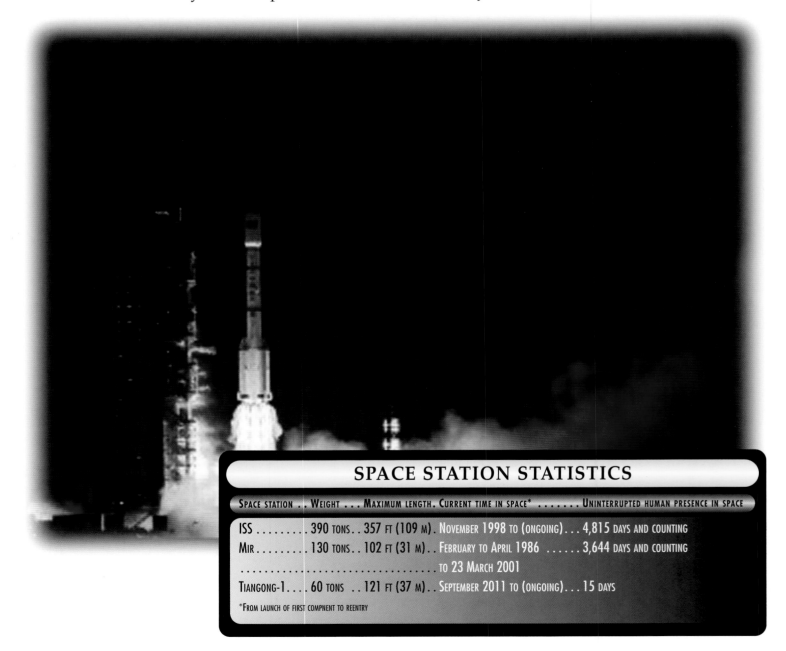

SPACE STATION STATISTICS

SPACE STATION	WEIGHT	MAXIMUM LENGTH	CURRENT TIME IN SPACE*	UNINTERRUPTED HUMAN PRESENCE IN SPACE
ISS	390 TONS	357 FT (109 M)	NOVEMBER 1998 TO (ONGOING)	4,815 DAYS AND COUNTING
MIR	130 TONS	102 FT (31 M)	FEBRUARY TO APRIL 1986 TO 23 MARCH 2001	3,644 DAYS AND COUNTING
TIANGONG-1	60 TONS	121 FT (37 M)	SEPTEMBER 2011 TO (ONGOING)	15 DAYS

*FROM LAUNCH OF FIRST COMPNENT TO REENTRY

CHINA'S "HEAVENLY PALACE"

The initial launch of China's first space station module was first planned for August 2011, but was delayed after failure of the planned Long March carrier rocket occurred on August 18, 2011. The rescheduled September launch was successful, with Tiangong-1 being placed into low Earth orbit (LEO) from the south launch site at the Jiuquan Satellite Launch Center, situated in the province of Gansu. Tiangong-1 is a cylindrical craft that is based on solar power, with silver-zinc batteries used to provide power during orbital nights.

Tiangong-1 will enable China to develop and build new components of a Space Station that will be permanently manned just like the ISS. This initial module enables astronauts to undergo tests in preparation for living in space, as well as scientific experiments and practice runs of the rendezvous and docking technology.

Initially designed by the China National Space Administration (CNSA), this module will remain active until late 2013, when it will be deorbited. Some time in 2015, it will be replaced by the larger and updated Tiangong-2 module, with plans for Tiangong-3 to follow by 2016.

The current module measures 34 feet (10.4 m) long, with a diameter of 11 feet (3.35 m). As well as the habitable zone, it consists of a service module and transition section. With space at a premium, the habitable zone consists of two sleep stations—meaning the astronauts sleep in shifts—and exercise equipment. The walls are painted in two colors to represent the sky and ground. This color scheme helps astronauts orient themselves while working in zero gravity. When docked, the three-person Shenzhou crew also used sleep quarters on that craft.

The first spacecraft to dock with Tiangong-1 was Shenzhou 8. This unmanned spacecraft made China's first orbital docking on November 2, 2011. The craft then undocked on November 14, before retesting the docking procedure with a second rendezvous and docking. Shenzhou 8 later returned to Earth, landing in Inner Mongolia. As the number of automated drills carried out were all successful, the next mission to Tiangong-1 was manned. Shenzhou 9 successfully carried three astronauts—including China's first female astronaut—to Tiangong-1, where they spent almost two weeks testing docking and other procedures. Shenzhou 9 was followed in June 2013 by Shenzhou 10, which docked successfully and remained for 15 days, marking China's longest manned mission in space to date.

SPACE POLITICS

There has been some controversy regarding Tiangong-1 and the American spaceplane X-37B, which was alleged to be carrying out surveillance on China's space station in January 2012, perhaps to do with American fears that there may be a military element to China's interest in a permanently manned space station. These claims were later completely refuted when it was pointed out that X-37B was in a different orbit to Tiangong-1 and did not have the capabilities for surveillance at such a range. The closest the U.S. spaceplane ever got to Tiangong-1 is when the orbit of both crafts occasionally intersect. The X-37B project began in 1999, with its first flight in April 2006. It is able to return to Earth through the atmosphere like a spacecraft, before landing on a runway as a plane does. No information about X-37B's mission have been released.

TIANGONG-1

IN ORBIT
Tiangong-1 has been testing its capabilities for orbital transfer maneuvers and, to date, has been in orbit for 853 days. Both these maneuvers and the docking tests were carried out from the Beijing Aerospace Command and Control Center. The Chinese Space Program command center is also responsible for several interplanetary missions.

Service module

Orbital module

Service module

Tiangong-1

Shenzhou spacecraft

Solar panels

CHINA'S SPACE STATION
Shown in the main image docked with a Shenzhou spacecraft, Tiangong-1 has no toilet or kitchen facilities. Instead, the visiting astronauts need to use these facilities on the Shenzhou craft.

SHENZHOU 9

China's first manned spaceflight took place in June 2012, when Shenzhou 9 was launched by a Chinese Long March 2F rocket from the Jiuquan Satellite Launch Center in Gansu Province. The spacecraft successfully docked with Tiangong-1, China's first space station module, on June 18, 2012, where it stayed for twelve days, carrying out various procedural experiments and testing the manual docking capabilities. The first Shenzhou craft—Shenzhou 8—was unmanned to trial these procedures. Shenzhou 10, which followed Shenzhou 9, also carried a manned crew of three to further prepare the astronauts for prolonged periods in space, as well as to carry out continued tests in the initial Space Station module.

SHENZHOU HISTORY

Space Craft	Time in Space	Mission Aim
1	21 hours	Unmanned test flight
2	7 days 10 hours	Test flight with animals
3	6 days 18 hours	Test dummy flight and observation
4	6 days 18 hours	Test dummy and scientific experiments carried
5	21 hours	Manned flight in LEO with one crew member
6	4 days 19 hours	Manned flight with two crew members
7	2 days 20 hours	Manned flight with three crew members, spacewalk performed
8	16 days 13 hours	Unmanned mission, docked with Tiangong-1
9	12 days 15 hours	Manned mission with three crew members, docked with Tiangong-1
10	15 days	Manned mission with three crew members, docked with Tiangong-1

BREAKING NEW BOUNDARIES

Featuring China's first female astronaut and launching 49 years to the day after Valentina Tereshkova—the first ever female cosmonaut—went to space, Shenzhou 9 was the first manned spacecraft to dock with the Tiangong-1 space station on June 18, 2012. Shenzhou 9 followed Shenzhou 8, an unmanned craft that had been the first to dock with Tiangong-1 in November 2012, thereby testing its automatic docking capabilities. On June 15, the crew were introduced to the world press, as well as an eager China. While there had been two prospective female astronauts for the mission, Liu Yang alone was eventually chosen as the first Chinese female to enter space. Joining her were crew members Jing Haipeng, the first repeat Chinese astronaut, who commanded the mission, and

the pilot, Liu Yang. Liu Yang was a member of the People's Liberation Army Air Force, where she clocked over 1,600 hours of flight experience. She trained for two years as an astronaut before being selected for the Shenzhou 9 mission. During the mission, Yang was responsible for carrying out experiments in space medicine. As yet, Yang has not returned to space.

Shenzhou 9 was the ninth flight of the Shenzhou program—which was conceived in 1992 and put China's first citizen into space on October 15, 2003—and its fourth manned spaceflight. Shenzhou spacecraft follow the basic design of the Russian Soyuz series. There are three modules, comprised of an orbital module, a reentry capsule and a service module. The crafts are bigger than the Soyuz series, and might in the future be even larger to accomodate four astronauts instead of three.

Shenzhou 9 and its three astronauts landed safely back to Earth on June 29, 2012. The craft's modules separated on the 28th, allowing only the reentry capsule to enter a trajectory on course for the landing site in Inner Mongolia. After the reentry, the craft's parachute deployed to slow the fall, which was combined with ignition of the rockets to further reduce touchdown speed. Although Shenzhou 9 flipped once on landing, all crew members landed safely and in good health. With the Shenzhou 10 mission being equally successful, the future looks bright for China's presence in space over the next ten years.

PRESENT AND FUTURE

Shenzhou 10 followed 9 by also docking with Tiangong-1. It was launched on June 11, 2013 and docked with the space station after two days in orbit. Shenzhou 10's crew featured Wang Yaping, China's second female astronaut, as well as two male astronauts. The crew performed a series of experiments in the space station's laboratory and followed on from Shenzhou 9's experiments by testing space medicines—as well as practicing successful docking tests, spending a total of fifteen days aboard the space station. Wang Yaping also gave a science lecture from Tiangong-1 that was broadcast to approximately 60 million Chinese students. Her lecture included five experiments that she carried out for everyone to see, including showing how water droplets form a ball when in space. There are currently no more Shenzhou missions underway.

WANG YAPING
China's second female astronaut, Wang Yaping, is shown here in one of the many promotional images returned from Shenzhou 10. She is also a captain in the People's Liberation Army Air Force.

DOCKING
Shown here docking with Tiangong-1, Shenzhou 9 managed the first manned docking with the space station module.

TIANGONG AND SHENZHOU

Shenzhou-9 spacecraft

Tiangong-1 space module

FALLING FROM SPACE
The Shenzhou 9 spacecraft is shown (right) on its safe return to Earth. All its crew members survived the return journey from Tiangong-1 in good health.

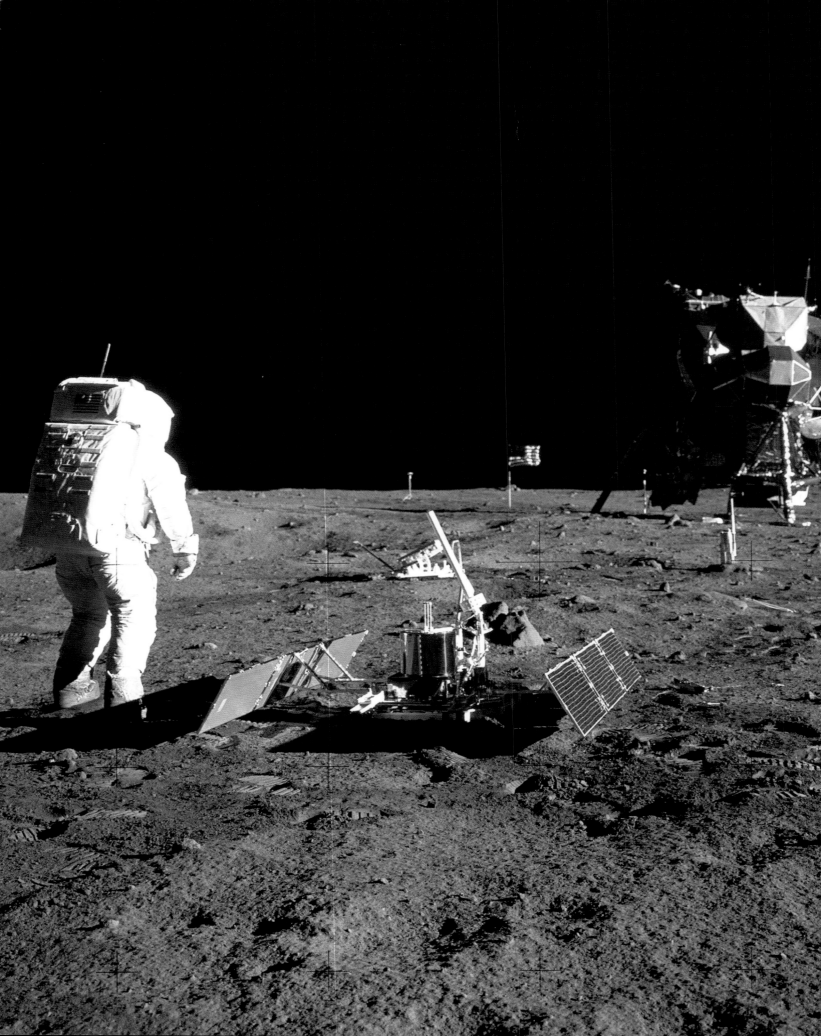

TO THE MOON

Jules Verne imagined the first Moon voyagers would arrive by cannon shell, but is sketchy on how they might have returned. Getting to the Moon may have seemed easy, but the first attempts by the U.S.A. and U.S.S.R. to send probes to impact the moon in the late 1950s ended ignominiously when the launchers failed. A manned orbiter—Apollo 8—was not to come until a decade later. At the same time the Russians were restricting themselves to unmanned orbiters, landers, and rovers. Their unmanned missions achieved just one sample return to Earth, while the Apollo program delivered a dozen men to the Moon, returning them and many lunar rock and soil samples to Earth.

Getting two men and some equipment to the Moon required one of the most complicated machines ever built, the Saturn V launcher and associated Command Module, Lunar Module, and Service Module, built by a variety of contractors. Over 90 percent of these expensive components were burned up, sent into eternal orbit, or abandoned on the moon, with only a cramped capsule returning to splash down on Earth. Any future Moon mission, if not as efficient as Verne's one-way projectile, will have to be less wasteful, but no less an adventure.

Astronaut "Buzz" Aldrin Jr. is photographed on the moon during the Apollo 11 mission: in the center background is the United States flag; in the left background is the black and white lunar surface television camera; in the far right background is the Lunar Module "Eagle."

SOVIET LUNAR PROGRAMME

When President John F. Kennedy declared in 1961 that the United States was going to put a man on the Moon by the end of the decade, NASA burst into activity—ready to meet the challenge. But NASA was not alone in their efforts. The Soviet Union had decided that it was going to beat America to the Moon. Thus began a frantic race between the two superpowers to develop the necessary technology and expertise to be the first to put a man on the Moon. It was a race the Soviets did not plan to lose.

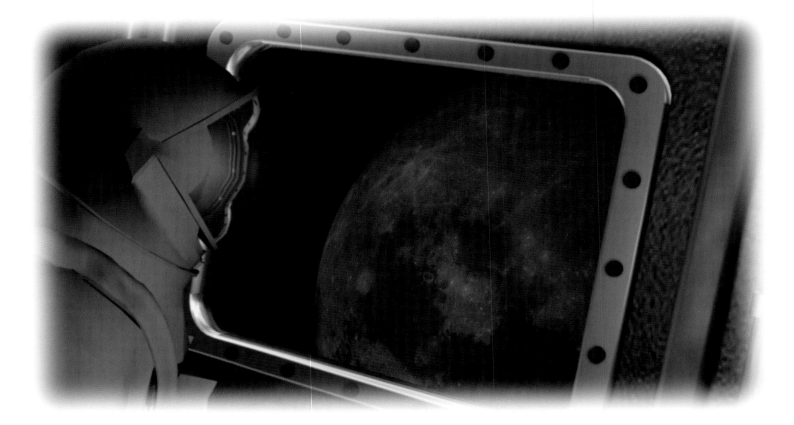

SOVIET STEPS TO THE MOON

January 30, 1956	Politburo hears plans for landing a cosmonaut on the Moon	February 21, 1969	First N-1 launch attempt fails
May 1962	N-1 vehicle design complete	July 3, 1969	Second N-1 launch attempt ends in failure
September 24, 1962	Politburo authorizes construction of N-1	June 27, 1971	Third N-1 launch attempt ends in failure
August 3, 1964	Central Committee issues decree to beat the U.S. to the Moon	November 23, 1972	Fourth N-1 launch attempt ends in failure
September 1965	Zond 5 orbits Moon	May 1974	Mishin replaced by Valentin Glushko, who ends lunar program
January 14, 1966	Sergei Korolev dies, replaced by Vasili Mishin		

NEVER THE MOON

Though most people think the Moon race began with President Kennedy's famous 1961 speech, the Soviet Union had already been planning a crewed lunar landing for quite some time. The government's cabinet or Politburo had heard plans for such a mission on January 30, 1956. But the Soviets wasted valuable time. It was not until 1964—when they realized that the U.S. was serious about its lunar ambitions—that the Central Committee issued a decree that would place a Soviet cosmonaut on the Moon before the Americans got there.

Unlike the United States, the Soviet Union did not have a single organization for space exploration. Premier Nikita Khrushchev believed that competition between rival bodies would create better designs. Three design bureaus had been working on plans to land on the Moon: OKB 1, run by Sergei Korolev, the man behind the triumphs of Sputnik and Yuri Gagarin; OKB 586, run by Michael Yangel; and OKB 52 run by Vladimir Chelomei. Each proposed, designed and began building different vehicles for lunar missions. In the end, Korolev's Nositel ("carrier") 1 rocket, or N-1, was selected as the booster and his LOK as the orbiter, with Yangel's LK lander chosen for the descent to the surface. The first landing was planned for 1968.

The plans did not go smoothly. The original flight profile was to have several rockets lift different modules to rendezvous in low Earth orbit. The units would dock, transfer fuel and crew, then boost for the Moon. But this plan soon had to be modified.

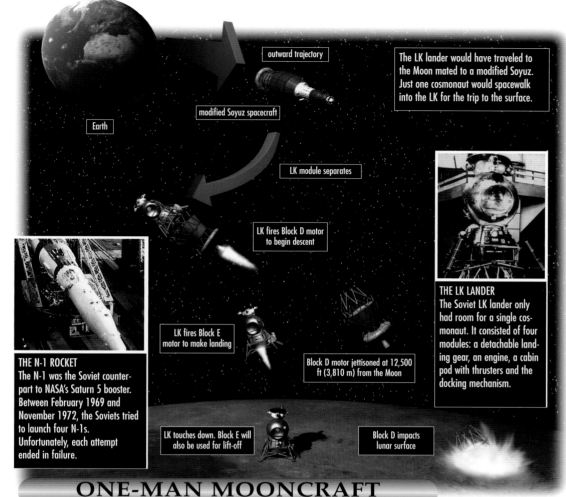

outward trajectory

modified Soyuz spacecraft

Earth

The LK lander would have traveled to the Moon mated to a modified Soyuz. Just one cosmonaut would spacewalk into the LK for the trip to the surface.

LK module separates

LK fires Block D motor to begin descent

LK fires Block E motor to make landing

Block D motor jettisoned at 12,500 ft (3,810 m) from the Moon

THE N-1 ROCKET
The N-1 was the Soviet counterpart to NASA's Saturn 5 booster. Between February 1969 and November 1972, the Soviets tried to launch four N-1s. Unfortunately, each attempt ended in failure.

LK touches down. Block E will also be used for lift-off.

Block D impacts lunar surface

THE LK LANDER
The Soviet LK lander only had room for a single cosmonaut. It consisted of four modules: a detachable landing gear, an engine, a cabin pod with thrusters and the docking mechanism.

ONE-MAN MOONCRAFT

DEATH AND DOOM

Korolev, who became the project leader in late 1965, was convinced that the multiple-module approach was too difficult, and did not favor Chelomei's designs. Instead, the design for the N-1 was changed, upgrading its payload capacity. The flight profile was changed to two launches, one for the lunar craft and another for the crew.

Korolev was confident that this plan would beat the Americans—but disaster struck.

On January 14, 1966, Korolev died unexpectedly while undergoing surgery. Without his genius behind the program, Soviet hopes were lost. Development of the N-1 booster was quickly bogged down in technical problems and redesigns, taking time the Soviets could ill afford to lose.

The N-1 finally lifted off from Baikonur on February 21, 1969—and exploded 66 seconds later. Soviet engineers modified a second N-1 and quickly prepared it for launch. The lander was not ready, but OKB 1 scientists hoped to get a lunar flyaround under their belt. On July 3 the rocket exploded at launch. The blast obliterated the launch pad. Thirteen days later NASA launched Apollo 11. The race was over.

MISSION DIARY: THE STORY OF THE N-1

APRIL 12, 1961 YURI GAGARIN BECOMES THE FIRST PERSON IN SPACE IN A VOSTOK CAPSULE (VOSTOK REPLICA, RIGHT).
1966 START OF LUNAR COSMONAUT TRAINING.
NOVEMBER 1966 THE FIRST N-1 MOON-ROCKET PARTS ARRIVE FOR ASSEMBLY AT BAIKONUR COSMODROME IN SOVIET KAZAKHSTAN. THE FIRST N-1 LAUNCH IS SET FOR THE THIRD QUARTER OF 1968.
MAY 7, 1968 THE FIRST N-1 MOON ROCKET (4L) IS ERECTED ON THE LAUNCH PAD AT BAIKONUR.
JUNE 6, 1968 THE MAIDEN FLIGHT OF THE N-1 IS POSTPONED AFTER CRACKS ARE FOUND IN ITS FIRST STAGE.

SEPTEMBER 1968 ZOND 5 (RIGHT), A TEST FOR THE CREWED MISSION, COMPLETES CIRCUMLUNAR NAVIGATION.
FEBRUARY 21, 1969 SECOND N-1 ROCKET (3L) LAUNCHED. IT CRASHES TO THE GROUND 66 SECONDS AFTER LAUNCH.
JULY 3, 1969 N-1-5L IS LAUNCHED. THE WHOLE ROCKET FALLS BACK ONTO THE LAUNCH PAD, EXPLODES AND DESTROYS THE PAD (RIGHT, PAD AFTER CRASH).
JULY 20, 1969 APOLLO 11 LANDS ON MOON.
1970 LUNAR COSMONAUT TEAMS ARE DISBANDED.

JUNE 27, 1971 THE NEXT ATTEMPT AT AN N-1 LAUNCH ROLLS OUT OF CONTROL AND FALLS APART 48 SECONDS AFTER LAUNCH.
NOVEMBER 23, 1972 FINAL LAUNCH OF THE N-1 ROCKET (7L). IT REACHES AN ALTITUDE OF 25 MILES (40 KM), BUT AN ENGINE PIPELINE FIRE CAUSES ENGINE SHUTDOWN 107 SECONDS AFTER LAUNCH.
1974 SOVIETS END LUNAR PROGRAM.

LUNA 1, 2 AND 3

At the beginning of 1959, the space race was less than two years old—with the Soviet Union, thanks to Sputnik 1, firmly in the lead. Now the Soviets were about to surge even further ahead. In the course of the year, they sent three spacecraft to the Moon.

The Soviet Luna probes were relatively crude, but Luna 2 became the first human-made object to reach another celestial body. And Luna 3 sent back the first photographs of the Moon's far side ever seen on Earth, making Soviet technology the envy of the world.

LUNA PROBE FACTS

	Luna 1	Luna 2	Luna 3
Mission	Lunar impact attempt	First lunar impact of lunar far side	photographed 70%
Launch Date	January 2, 1959	September 12, 1959	October 4, 1959
Weight	797 lb (361 kg)	860 lb (390 kg)	614 lb (278 kg)
Summary	Passes within 3,100 miles (5,000 km) of the Moon 34 hours after launch. Achieves solar orbit.	Impacts with Moon after 33.5 hours of flight	After 11 orbits and 177 days in space, Luna 3's controllers switch the probe off

THE FAR SIDE

Just 15 months after the successful Sputnik 1 mission, the Soviet Union began its Luna program—an ambitious project to send the first spacecraft to the Moon. The Luna probes would provide new information on the Earth's closest celestial neighbor—and Soviet space science would demonstrate to an enthralled world that the Soviet Union was well ahead of its American rivals.

All three Luna missions went astonishingly well. Luna 1, launched on January 2, 1959, became the first artificial object to exceed escape velocity and leave the Earth forever. Designed to impact on the Moon, the probe missed by a mere 3,100 miles (5,000 km)—but sent back data on the Moon's gravity and magnetic field all the same.

Luna 2, launched on September 12, was dead on target. The probe took just 33.5 hours to reach the Moon. En route, Luna 2 released a cloud of light-reflecting sodium vapor that allowed astronomers to track it visually all the way until—at a speed of two miles per second—the spacecraft

MISSION DIARY: LUNA 1, 2 AND 3

JANUARY 2, 1959 LUNA 1 (REPLICA, RIGHT) WAS THE FIRST SPACECRAFT TO EXCEED ESCAPE VELOCITY. *JANUARY 3, 1959* PROBE RELEASES SODIUM VAPOR FOR TRACKING. A BRIGHT ORANGE TRAIL IS VISIBLE OVER INDIAN OCEAN. *JANUARY 4, 1959* LUNA 1 MAKES ITS CLOSEST LUNAR FLYBY BEFORE DISAPPEARING INTO SOLAR ORBIT. *SEPTEMBER 12, 1959* LUNA 2 (REPLICA,

RIGHT) IS LAUNCHED. *SEPTEMBER 13, 1959* PROBE RELEASES SODIUM VAPOR. *SEPTEMBER 14, 1959* HITS THE MOON NEAR THE CRATER ARCHIMEDES. *OCTOBER 4, 1959* LUNA 3 (REPLICA, RIGHT) LIFTS OFF FROM BAIKONUR. *OCTOBER 6, 1959* LUNA 3 ORBITS AND PHOTOGRAPHS THE DARK SIDE OF THE MOON. *APRIL 28, 1960* LUNA 3 IS SHUT DOWN.

plowed into the lunar surface. The abrupt silence from its transmitters was cheered by Soviet controllers. Before impact, data from the module had confirmed the absence of any strong magnetic fields or radiation belts around the Moon.

Luna 3, launched on October 4, gave the Soviet Union even more reason to cheer. The probe's ambitious figure-eight trajectory took it right around the Moon. As it hurtled past, just 41,500 miles

(66,787 km) from the surface, onboard cameras took the first pictures of a landscape previously unseen: the far side of the Moon. A course correction nudged Luna 3 into a barycentric orbit—that is, an orbit around the gravitational center of the Earth and Moon system. As the probe approached Earth, its transmitters began to send back the images. This was Luna 3's last duty. Its film exhausted but its mission accomplished, the probe made 11

orbits and spent 177 days in space before its controllers finally switched it off.

Luna 3's fuzzy pictures of the Moon's far side were a major event in space exploration, and at that time Luna 3 was the most impressive achievement of either the U.S. or Soviet space programs. But the success of the Luna program was measured not only in scientific discoveries—it was also a political coup, and the Soviet Union was jubilant.

HARD EVIDENCE

THE HIDDEN HEMISPHERE
Just as the Earth rotates on its axis, so does the Moon. But the Moon rotates at exactly the same rate as it orbits the Earth—a phenomenon caused by the Earth's gravity and known as synchronous rotation. As a result, only one lunar hemisphere can be seen from the Earth. The far side always remains hidden out of sight.

LUNA 2
The second Soviet moonshot (red trajectory) is on target. Luna 2 then hits the Moon (the impact shown here is exaggerated for clarity) after a 33.5-hour flight.

LUNA 1
The first of the three Soviet probes (yellow trajectory) skims past the Moon at a distance of 3,100 miles (5,000 km). Luna 1 continues into an orbit around the Sun.

LUNA 3
Heavier than its two predecessors, Luna 3 (blue trajectory) carries camera equipment that photographs the far side of the Moon. The probe then takes up an orbit around both the Earth and Moon.

SPACE FAX

LUNA 3 TOOK 40 MINUTES TO PHOTOGRAPH 70 PERCENT OF THE MOON'S HIDDEN HEMISPHERE AND USED TWO LENSES. THE HEAT-RESISTANT FILM WAS DEVELOPED WITHIN THE MODULE: AN EARLY VERSION OF A FAX MACHINE SCANNED THE IMAGES AND THE PROBE'S RADIO THEN BEAMED THEM  BACK TO EARTH. THE PICTURES RECEIVED WERE HAZY, BUT THE MOUNTAINOUS NATURE OF THE MOON'S FAR SIDE WAS CLEARLY VISIBLE. ALTHOUGH FEW FEATURES WERE RECOGNIZABLE, THE SOVIET UNION BEGAN ASSIGNING NAMES TO THEM. LATER PICTURES SHOWED THAT SOME—THE "SOVIETSKY MOUNTAINS," FOR EXAMPLE—DID NOT EXIST.

LUNA
10–12

In 1966, the race for the Moon was still an open contest between superpowers America and Russia. Both had successfully placed soft landers on the lunar surface, proving that machinery—and therefore humans—could stand there. The next hurdle was to place a satellite in lunar orbit. As well as commanding considerable prestige, such a mission could gather more information about the Moon's alien environment and collect pictures of potential landing sites. The Russians led the way with Lunas 10, 11 and 12.

LUNA 10–12 STATS

	Luna 10	Luna 11	Luna 12
MASS AT LAUNCH	3,480 LB (1,578 KG)	3,608 LB (1,636 KG)	3,564 LB (1,616 KG)
MASS IN LUNAR ORBIT	539 LB (244 LB)	2,420 LB (1,097 KG)	2,500 LB (1,133 KG)
ORBIT TIME (APPROX.)	3 HOURS	3 HOURS	3 HOURS
LUNAR ORBIT INCLINATION	71.9°	27.0°	10.0°
NUMBER OF LUNAR ORBITS	460	277	602
NUMBER OF TRANSMISSIONS	219	137	302

LUNAR LONERS

By the mid-1960s, both America and the Soviet Union had soft-landed craft on the lunar surface and were now rehearsing—in Earth orbit—the maneuvers needed to land a crewed spacecraft on the Moon. The next step was to place a satellite in lunar orbit, in order to provide more information about the lunar environment and to search for potential landing sites.

The Soviets were in the lead. In 1959, Luna 2 became the first human-made object to hit the Moon, and in the same year Luna 3 transmitted the first images of the Moon's far side. The U.S.S.R. was also the first to achieve a soft landing with Luna 9.

April 3, 1966, marked yet another Soviet triumph, as Luna 10 became the first spacecraft to orbit the Moon. Where Luna 9 was aimed directly at the landing site, using springs and airbags to cushion the impact, Luna 10 made the journey attached to a larger parent craft, and on approaching the Moon, fired a retro-rocket that slowed it enough to be grasped by the Moon's gravity. Twenty minutes later, the orbiter was

detached from the parent craft and was released into orbit.

At 5 ft (1.5 m) long and around 18 inches (50 cm) in diameter, Lunar 10 spun at two revolutions per minute and completed one orbit every 178 minutes. Its limited payload implied that science took second place to national pride: There were devices for measuring electrical, magnetic and radiation fields, but no camera. After 56 days in orbit, Luna 10's batteries died and the craft fell silent.

PRESERVING THE IMAGE

By the time of the launch of Luna 11, five months later, the U.S. had streaked ahead in the Moon race with Lunar Orbiter 1, which snapped 211 high-quality images of the Moon's surface. Despite Soviet scientists' best efforts, Luna 11 did not match the U.S. probe's success. After entering lunar orbit on August 28, the spacecraft

appeared to vanish. The Soviets' official story was that although Luna 11 carried an imaging camera, its mission was simply to test spacecraft systems in lunar orbit, not to take any actual photographs. Russian sources have since revealed that in fact, Luna 11 suffered attitude control problems: It did return images, but they were merely of empty space.

In October 1966, the Soviet news agency Tass announced that Luna 12 would be launched to photograph the Moon's surface from lunar orbit. While it was externally similar to Luna 11, it carried a much larger payload than earlier Luna craft, including a camera system with a built-in "dark room" that developed, fixed and dried the film. The developed pictures were then scanned electronically and transmitted back to Earth in a process similar to that used by fax machines.

Luna 12 achieved lunar orbit as planned on October 25, 1966. To make the most of its limited battery power, it began collecting images of the Moon's equatorial regions almost immediately.

To the delight of Soviet space scientists and Communist Party officials, Luna 12's faxing system worked perfectly and images of the lunar surface were promptly beamed across the nation on Soviet television. But the tide of events had already turned in favor of the U.S. space program. The images provided by Luna 12 were inferior to those of Lunar Orbiter 1, and on January 19, 1967, the spacecraft ceased transmission. American technology was finally beginning to outpace that of its superpower rival. After Luna 12, the Soviet race to the Moon began to run out of steam.

MISSION DIARY

MARCH 31, 1966 LUNA 10 LAUNCHED FROM BAIKONUR COSMODROME; WITHIN ONE HOUR, THE PARENT CRAFT IS ON COURSE FOR THE MOON.
APRIL 1, 1966 LUNA 10's ENGINE FIRES TO MAKE A MID-COURSE CORRECTION EN ROUTE TO THE MOON.
APRIL 3, 1966 LUNA 10 ENTERS LUNAR ORBIT AND BEGINS COLLECTING DATA.
MAY 30, 1966 THE BATTERIES ABOARD THE LUNA 10 ORBITER (RIGHT) FAIL; ITS TRANSMITTERS ARE SWITCHED OFF.
AUGUST 24, 1966 LUNA 11 LAUNCHED FROM BAIKONUR COSMODROME.
AUGUST 28, 1966 LUNA 11 ENTERS LUNAR ORBIT AND RETURNS FURTHER INFORMATION ON FIELD FLUXES.
OCTOBER 1, 1966 GROUND CONTACT IS LOST WITH LUNA 11 AFTER ITS BATTERIES FAIL.

OCTOBER 22, 1966 LUNA 12 LAUNCHED FROM BAIKONUR COSMODROME.
OCTOBER 23, 1966 LUNA 12 MAKES SIMILAR MID-COURSE CORRECTION TO THOSE MADE BY LUNAS 10 AND 11.
OCTOBER 25, 1966 LUNA 12 ENTERS ORBIT AROUND THE MOON.
OCTOBER 27, 1966 LUNA 12 SENDS BACK FIRST IMAGES OF LUNAR SURFACE.
JANUARY 19, 1967 LAST SIGNAL FROM LUNA 12 IS RECEIVED AS ITS BATTERIES FAIL.

RINGS AROUND THE MOON

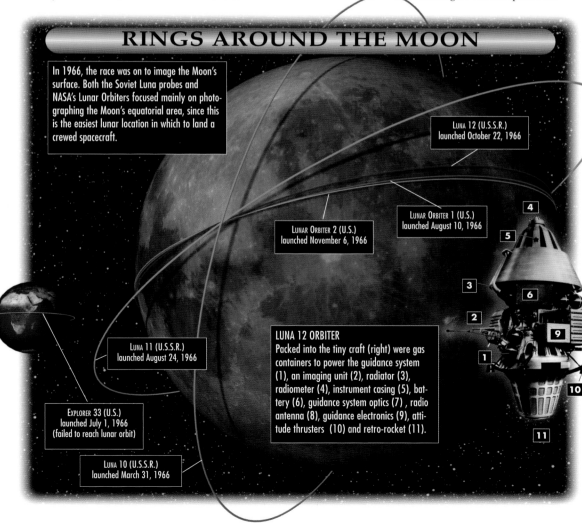

In 1966, the race was on to image the Moon's surface. Both the Soviet Luna probes and NASA's Lunar Orbiters focused mainly on photographing the Moon's equatorial area, since this is the easiest lunar location in which to land a crewed spacecraft.

LUNA 12 (U.S.S.R.)
launched October 22, 1966

LUNAR ORBITER 1 (U.S.)
launched August 10, 1966

LUNAR ORBITER 2 (U.S.)
launched November 6, 1966

LUNA 11 (U.S.S.R.)
launched August 24, 1966

EXPLORER 33 (U.S.)
launched July 1, 1966
(failed to reach lunar orbit)

LUNA 10 (U.S.S.R.)
launched March 31, 1966

LUNA 12 ORBITER
Packed into the tiny craft (right) were gas containers to power the guidance system (1), an imaging unit (2), radiator (3), radiometer (4), instrument casing (5), battery (6), guidance system optics (7), radio antenna (8), guidance electronics (9), attitude thrusters (10) and retro-rocket (11).

RANGER AND SURVEYOR

Back in May 1961, when President John F. Kennedy gave the go-ahead to land a man on the Moon, no one knew much about the lunar surface. Was it solid rock or was it covered in treacherous moondust, a quicksand that could swallow an entire spacecraft and its crew? NASA had to know. From 1961 through 1968, the robot Ranger and Surveyor missions were launched to find the answers to the questions that perplexed Apollo planners. These little spacecraft blazed the trail for the first humans on the Moon.

LUNA LANDING SITES

Mission	Latitude	Longitude	Mission	Latitude	Longitude
Ranger 4	15.5° S	130.5° W	Surveyor 1	2.4° S	43.3° W
Ranger 6	9.39° N	21.51° E	Surveyor 2	5.5° N	12.0° W
Ranger 7	10.35° S	20.58° W	Surveyor 3	3.0° N	23.3° W
Ranger 8	2.6° N	24.7° E	Surveyor 4	0.4° N	1.33° W
Ranger 9	13.3° S	3.0° W	Surveyor 5	1.5° N	23.2° E
			Surveyor 6	0.53° N	1.4° W
			Surveyor 7	40.9° S	11.5° W

MOON PROBED

During the Mercury flights of the early 1960s, when U.S. astronauts first ventured into space, NASA was already aiming for the Moon. Its Ranger spacecraft were designed to crash headlong into our nearest neighbor, beaming back progressively better pictures as they hurtled toward the surface. But the early lunar missions were far less successful than Project Mercury. The first two Rangers, launched in 1961, failed to leave Earth orbit. The following year, Rangers 3, 4 and 5 also ended in failure. Rangers 3 and 5 missed the Moon completely and Ranger 4 tumbled uselessly onto its surface. Ranger 6 reached the Moon successfully in 1964, but was unable to send back any images because its cameras were faulty.

Success finally came later that year with Ranger 7, which collected pictures of the northern basin of the Sea of Clouds during the last 20 minutes before impact. It returned 4,316 images, and the last of them,

taken just before the craft struck the Moon at around 5,800 mph (9,344 km/h), were 1,000 times better than any that had been taken from Earth. The views showed the maria (seas) of the Moon are relatively smooth and similar to lava flows on Earth.

Two further missions, Rangers 8 and 9 in 1965, also made precision flights and sent back thousands more close-up images. Ranger 8 aimed for the Sea of Tranquillity, later the site of the first human steps on the Moon, while Ranger 9 headed for the hills. It relayed images of the Alphonsus crater in the southern highlands, an area thought to have once been volcanically active. Ranger 9's impact on the lunar surface brought the series to a successful close.

CLOSE-UP VIEW

The next objective was to soft-land on the Moon and take close-up images of the lunar surface. The first craft sent to do this, Surveyor 1, landed only 8.7 miles (14 km) off-target in June 1966 and sent back

panoramic views of the landscape. Over the next two years, it was followed by six more Surveyors, not all of which were as successful.

Mission control lost contact with Surveyor 2, when a thruster failure caused it to tumble out of control onto the Moon, and with Surveyor 4, just minutes before touchdown. But Surveyors 3, 5, 6 and 7 all made it safely to the lunar surface.

They provided a mass of information, both from their cameras and from on-board instruments that sampled and analyzed the lunar surface. Among their detailed findings was the reassuring confirmation that the surface of the Moon was similar to that of fine-grained soil on Earth and would pose no problem to crewed Moon landings.

NASA RANGERS

AUGUST 23, 1961 RANGER 1 FAILS TO LEAVE EARTH ORBIT.

NOVEMBER 18, 1961 RANGER 2 FAILS TO LEAVE EARTH ORBIT.

JANUARY 26, 1962 RANGER 3 IS LAUNCHED BUT MISSES THE MOON BY MORE THAN 22,800 MILES (36,700 KM).

APRIL 23, 1962 RANGER 4 IS LAUNCHED BUT FAILS TO RETURN ANY DATA.

OCTOBER 18, 1962 RANGER 5 IS LAUNCHED BUT MISSES THE MOON BY 450 MILES (720 KM).

JANUARY 30, 1964 RANGER 6 IS LAUNCHED BUT FAILS TO TRANSMIT ANY IMAGES.

JULY 28, 1964 RANGER 7 IS LAUNCHED. IT IS THE FIRST U.S. PROBE TO PHOTOGRAPH THE MOON (RIGHT).

FEBRUARY 17, 1965 RANGER 8 LAUNCHED; 3 DAYS LATER, IT SENDS ITS LAST PICTURE FROM A HEIGHT OF 2,100 FT (640 M).

MARCH 21, 1965 RANGER 9 SETS OFF FOR THE CRATER ALPHONSUS, WHERE IT IMPACTS SUCCESSFULLY.

MAY 30, 1966 SURVEYOR 1 IS LAUNCHED ON A SUCCESSFUL SOFT-LANDING MISSION. ON JUNE 2, THE PROBE SETTLES GENTLY ON THE FLOOR OF THE CRATER FLAMSTEED.

SEPTEMBER 20, 1966 SURVEYOR 2 IS LAUNCHED BUT CRASHES INTO THE MOON INSTEAD OF MAKING A SOFT LANDING.

APRIL 20, 1967 SURVEYOR 3 LANDS SUCCESSFULLY IN THE MOON'S OCEAN OF STORMS.

JULY 14, 1967 SURVEYOR 4 IS LAUNCHED BUT RADIO CONTACT IS LOST EN ROUTE TO THE MOON.

SEPTEMBER 11, 1967 SURVEYOR 5 LANDS IN THE SEA OF TRANQUILITY.

NOVEMBER 10, 1967 SURVEYOR 6 LANDS SAFELY — THEN "HOPS" 25 YARDS (23 M) ON ITS THRUSTERS.

JANUARY 10, 1968 SURVEYOR 7 LANDS IN THE CRATER TYCHO, FAR FROM THE POTENTIAL APOLLO SITES.

HARD PUNCHER
Ranger 7 carried six TV cameras, two with 25-mm wide-angle lenses and the other four with 75-mm lenses. It weighed nearly 800 lb (363 kg), the span of its solar panels was about 15 ft (4.6 m) and it was nearly 12 ft (3.7 m) high.

SOFT LANDER
Surveyor 3 (shown here) weighed about 665 lb (302 kg) and its equipment included a TV camera and soil sampler. The Surveyor craft were all of the same basic design, but the scientific instruments they carried varied from one mission to another.

MOON BUGS

DURING THE APOLLO 12 MISSION IN NOVEMBER 1969, ASTRONAUTS PETE CONRAD AND ALAN BEAN VISITED SURVEYOR 3 AND REMOVED SOME PIECES OF IT FOR ANALYSIS. BACK ON EARTH, RESEARCHERS FOUND EARTH BACTERIA IN A PIECE OF PLASTIC FOAM FROM INSIDE SURVEYOR'S TV CAMERA. THESE WERE THOUGHT TO HAVE BEEN IN THE FOAM SINCE BEFORE SURVEYOR WAS LAUNCHED; THEY SURVIVED FOR ALMOST THREE YEARS ON THE LUNAR SURFACE.

THE FINAL COUNTDOWN
Ranger 8 beamed back these pictures (right) in the last 9 sec before it hit the surface of the Moon at almost 6,000 mph (10,000 km/h).

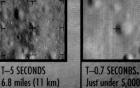

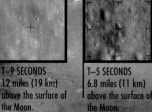

T–9 SECONDS
12 miles (19 km) above the surface of the Moon.

T–5 SECONDS
6.8 miles (11 km) above the surface of the Moon.

T–0.7 SECONDS. Just under 5,000 ft (1,524 m) to final lunar impact.

APOLLO TEST FLIGHTS

The mandate of the Apollo program—to put a man on the Moon by the end of the 1960s—demanded a huge leap forward in spacecraft technology. To meet the goal, NASA devised the Saturn rocket family. Uncrewed missions were carried out to test Apollo before the U.S. made a final commitment to sending astronauts toward the lunar target. On the whole, the missions were successful: Mission Control was able to finesse some useful data out of the technical glitches that occurred. But on the fourth test mission—the first to involve a crew of three, these glitches were to turn deadly.

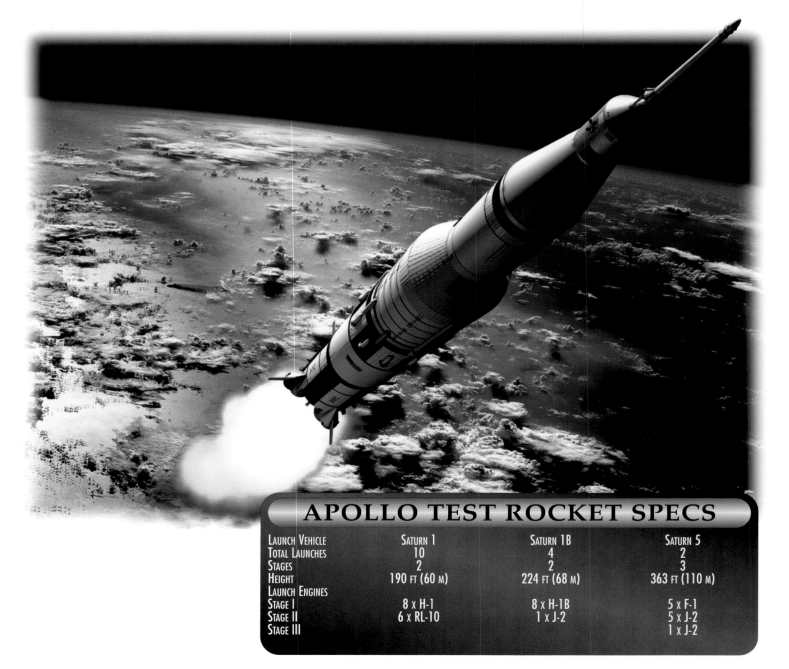

APOLLO TEST ROCKET SPECS

Launch Vehicle	Saturn 1	Saturn 1B	Saturn 5
Total Launches	10	4	2
Stages	2	2	3
Height	190 ft (60 m)	224 ft (68 m)	363 ft (110 m)
Launch Engines			
Stage I	8 x H-1	8 x H-1B	5 x F-1
Stage II	6 x RL-10	1 x J-2	5 x J-2
Stage III			1 x J-2

AS 201–3
These three flights on Saturn 1B rockets (AS-201, left) tested the Apollo module. The rocket's second stage became the third stage of the Saturn 5 rocket that would take the Apollo craft from Earth up to lunar orbit.

APOLLO 1
During a test atop an empty Saturn 1B rocket, a spark from faulty wiring ignited a fire that burned out of control in the oxygen-rich capsule (left). NASA astronauts Gus Grissom, Ed White and Roger Chaffee died in the accident.

APOLLO 4
The first launch of the new Saturn V launcher was an unqualified success. Its command module endured temperatures of 5,000°F (2,800°C) before splashing down, scalded, in the Pacific ocean (left).

The fully equipped Saturn 5 launch vehicle (left) towered 140 ft (43 m) over its predecessor, the Saturn 1B rocket (below). Four Apollo test flights flew in a Saturn 1B; two used the Moon-bound Saturn 5.

APOLLO 5
The last Saturn 1B rocket used in an Apollo mission had an oddly shaped cargo (shown above). This mission tested only the ascent and descent stages of the Lunar Module without a Command/Service Module.

TRIED & TESTED

The six test flights for the Apollo mission examined the hardware for the main stages of the Apollo lunar mission, from launch to stage separation to space maneuvers. The first three missions—AS-201, 202 and 203—launched in 1966 on a Saturn 1B rocket. These missions also checked the separation of the stages of the launcher, their electrical systems and parts of the spacecraft, including the Command Module (CM) for launch and reentry, the Service Module (SM) for orbiting around the Moon, and the Lunar Module (LM).

Planned as the first of a series of crewed test flights in Earth orbit, Apollo 1 ended in tragedy on the launchpad in January, 1967. A flash fire in the Apollo 1 capsule killed the three astronauts and grounded the Apollo crewed missions for 21 months.

The rest of the test flights were uncrewed. Ten months after Apollo 1, the Apollo 4 Command and Service Module (CSM) was sent into Earth orbit on the new, huge Saturn 5 rocket. Apollo 4 reached a height of 11,000 miles (17,700 km) and reentered the atmosphere at 24,900 mph (40,000 km/h).

Apollo's final Saturn 1B mission in late January 1968 was the first—and only—test launch of the Lunar Module. Once in orbit, the Apollo 5 Lunar Module separated from the second stage of the Saturn launcher. After checking the onboard systems, the descent engine was fired up for a mock lunar landing. Four seconds later, onboard systems cut the engine off. A built-in safety system had detected that the engine was not firing powerfully enough, aborted the descent and decoupled the ascent stage of the Lunar Module.

ON TO PLAN B

Although NASA engineers did not obtain data on the Lunar Module's descent engine, they did learn that their backup safety systems worked flawlessly.

The last Apollo test flight, in April, 1968, did not go so smoothly. The first stage was wrenched back and forth by sloshing rocket fuel. Then two of the second-stage engines shut down, forcing the Service Module to ignite to accelerate the spacecraft to escape velocity. Although the spacecraft did not have enough fuel to reach the planned 7-mile-per-second (11 km/s) reentry speed, it did allow NASA to test its contingency procedures. Now the ground was cleared for crewed tests.

MISSION DIARY: APOLLO TEST FLIGHTS

MAY 25, 1961 PRESIDENT KENNEDY COMMITS TO A MANNED LUNAR LANDING WITHIN THE DECADE.
NOVEMBER 7, 1963 FIRST OF SIX FLIGHT TESTS OF APOLLO LAUNCH ESCAPE SYSTEM ON TEST ROCKET.
JANUARY 29, 1964 FIRST ORBITAL FLIGHT OF SATURN 1.
MAY 28, 1964 FIRST FLIGHT OF CM TO PROVE COMPATIBILITY WITH SATURN 1.
SEPTEMBER 18 1964 THIRD ORBITAL FLIGHT OF SATURN 1 ROCKET, PREDECESSOR OF SATURN 1B.
JANUARY 20, 1966 FIRST FLIGHT-RATED APOLLO CAPSULE ON SIXTH AND FINAL LITTLE JOE ABORT TEST.

FEBRUARY 26, 1966 FIRST SUB-ORBITAL FLIGHT OF SATURN 1B WITH CSM INSTALLED.
JULY 5, 1966 FIRST ORBITAL FLIGHT OF SATURN 1B.
JANUARY 27, 1967 APOLLO 1 FIRE KILLS CREW OF FIRST MANNED ORBITAL TEST OF APOLLO ON SATURN 1B.
NOVEMBER 9, 1967 FIRST UNMANNED LAUNCH OF SATURN 5—APOLLO 4 MISSION—WITH MOCK LUNAR MODULE; PHOTOGRAPHS THE EARTH FROM 11,000 MILES (17,000 KM).
JANUARY 22, 1968 FIRST UNMANNED LAUNCH OF LM ON SATURN 1B ROCKET.
APRIL 4, 1968 SECOND UNMANNED LAUNCH OF SATURN 5:

APOLLO 6 SPLASHES DOWN SAFELY (ABOVE).
OCTOBER 1968 FIRST MANNED APOLLO CSM FLIGHT: THE APOLLO 7 MISSION.
DECEMBER 1968 FIRST MANNED SATURN 5 FLIGHT: APOLLO 8.
MARCH 1969 FIRST APOLLO LAUNCH OF SATURN 5 COMPLETE WITH LM (APOLLO 9).
JULY 1969 LUNAR LANDING: APOLLO 11.

APOLLO 1 DISASTER

Fire, I smell fire." Delivered almost casually over the radio at 6:31 p.m. on January 27, 1967, Roger Chaffee's words heralded the end of Apollo 1's crewed flight simulation. Sixteen seconds later, the crew capsule was split by the intense heat. Fueled by the capsule's pure oxygen atmosphere, fire and smoke had quickly overwhelmed the three men on board and then beat back rescue workers. The three crew members all died and, as America mourned, the Apollo program all but ground to a halt.

APOLLO 1 CREW

COMMAND PILOT	SENIOR PILOT	PILOT
VIRGIL IVAN "GUS" GRISSOM; LIEUTENANT COLONEL, U.S. AIR FORCE	EDWARD HIGGINS WHITE, II; LIEUTENANT COLONEL, U.S. AIR FORCE	ROGER BRUCE CHAFFEE; LIEUTENANT COMMANDER, U.S. NAVY
DATE & PLACE OF BIRTH	DATE & PLACE OF BIRTH	DATE & PLACE OF BIRTH
APRIL 3, 1926; MITCHELL, INDIANA	NOVEMBER 14, 1930; SAN ANTONIO, TEXAS	FEBRUARY 15, 1935; GRAND RAPIDS, MICHIGAN
PREVIOUS MISSIONS	PREVIOUS MISSIONS	PREVIOUS MISSIONS
MERCURY 4, JULY 21, 1961; GEMINI 3, MARCH 23, 1965	GEMINI 4, JUNE 3, 1965	NONE

FATAL FURNACE

Shortly before 1:00 p.m. on January 27, 1967, three white-suited astronauts walked to launch complex 34 at Cape Canaveral. They were Virgil "Gus" Grissom and Ed White—both old hands from the Gemini program—and rookie Roger Chaffee. Their job was to put Apollo through what should have been a routine ground test.

The simulation was to resemble spaceflight as closely as possible. But the capsule in which the men sat contained pure oxygen at a higher-than-normal pressure of 17 pounds per square inch (1.1 bar), in order to protect the spacecraft's electronics from inflows of humid Florida air. The hatches were sealed and locked. Communication would be by radio only. The only deviation from a real launch setup was that the Saturn 1B rocket beneath the capsule had empty fuel tanks. Nothing unusual was expected, and fire crews were ordered on standby rather than full alert.

The three astronauts took their places awkwardly and without much enthusiasm. Chaffee occupied the center couch, with Grissom, the commander, on his left and White, on his right. It was a frustrating period, dogged by constant holdups. By 6:30 p.m. the men had been aboard the capsule for five-and-a-half hours and were looking forward to the end of the test. The countdown stood at T minus 10 minutes.

Then, at 6:31 p.m., a brief power surge was picked up in the capsule's 12 miles (19 km) of electrical wiring. It went unnoticed at the time. Ten seconds later, Chaffee reported a fire. White began to wrestle with the hatch's six retaining bolts.

APOLLO 1 COMMAND MODULE

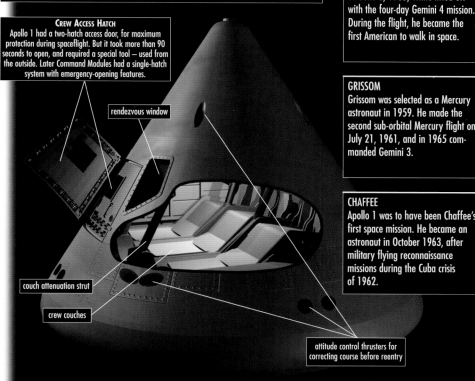

The Command Module—code-named "spacecraft 012"—sat atop the Saturn 1B rocket on the launchpad. Once the two-piece hatch was sealed, the cabin was pressurized with pure oxygen at 17 psi (1.1 bar).

CREW ACCESS HATCH
Apollo 1 had a two-hatch access door, for maximum protection during spaceflight. But it took more than 90 seconds to open, and required a special tool — used from the outside. Later Command Modules had a single-hatch system with emergency-opening features.

rendezvous window

couch attenuation strut

crew couches

attitude control thrusters for correcting course before reentry

WHITE
Selected as an astronaut in 1962, on June 3, 1965, White lifted off with the four-day Gemini 4 mission. During the flight, he became the first American to walk in space.

GRISSOM
Grissom was selected as a Mercury astronaut in 1959. He made the second sub-orbital Mercury flight on July 21, 1961, and in 1965 commanded Gemini 3.

CHAFFEE
Apollo 1 was to have been Chaffee's first space mission. He became an astronaut in October 1963, after military flying reconnaissance missions during the Cuba crisis of 1962.

OUT OF CONTROL

The flames spread rapidly in the oxygen-rich environment. Soon the capsule was filled with smoke. Chaffee's final message was, "We've got a bad fire... We're burning up here!" Then came only unintelligible shouts and the noise of frantic pounding. Finally, silence. From start to tragic conclusion, the disaster had taken just 16 seconds.

Technicians struggled to open the hatch, unable to see more than six inches ahead through the blinding smoke, their white coats already peppered with burn holes from flying debris. When the first firefighter arrived four-and-a-half minutes later, it was too late. The three astronauts were dead. Grissom lay with his ft on the left-hand couch and his head below the center one, as if he had been trying to find shelter.

Chaffee was still strapped in at his post. White had died struggling to undo the hatch.

An autopsy concluded that the men had died of asphyxiation: Once the fire had burned through their spacesuits' supply hoses, they were left breathing the choking fumes in the cabin. Gruesomely, intense heat had melted the suits to their seats. It was seven hours before the bodies could be recovered.

MISSION DIARY: APOLLO 1

MARCH 21, 1966 GRISSOM, WHITE AND CHAFFEE (RIGHT) ARE NAMED AS THE APOLLO 1 CREW.
OCTOBER 18, 1966 APOLLO'S FIRST CREWED TEST IS TERMINATED BY TRANSISTOR FAILURE.
OCTOBER 21, 1966 A SECOND TEST IS HALTED DUE TO A BROKEN OXYGEN REGULATOR.
OCTOBER 27, 1966 ENTIRE ENVIRONMENTAL UNIT IS REMOVED AFTER FURTHER PROBLEMS EMERGE.
NOVEMBER, 1966 WALTER SCHIRRA, DONN EISELE AND WALTER CUNNINGHAM ARE APPOINTED AS BACKUP TEAM.

DECEMBER 5, 1966 REPLACEMENT ENVIRONMENTAL UNIT BREAKS AND IS SENT BACK FOR REPAIRS.
JANUARY 6, 1967 APOLLO IS FINALLY MATED TO ITS LAUNCH VEHICLE.
1:00 P.M. JANUARY 27, 1967 GRISSOM, WHITE AND CHAFFEE BEGIN THE FINAL CREWED SIMULATION.
1:20 P.M. TEST IS HALTED BECAUSE OF STRANGE SMELL IN THE OXYGEN SUPPLY. COUNTDOWN RESTARTS AT 2:42 P.M.
5:40 P.M. ANOTHER HALT IS CALLED TO CHECK OUT THE FAULTY RADIO COMMUNICATION SYSTEM.

6:20 P.M. COUNTDOWN IS HALTED DUE TO FAULTY AUDIO CIRCUITS.
6:31 P.M. CAPSULE IGNITES, KILLING THE CREW.
12:30 A.M. JANUARY 28, 1967 RESCUERS BEGIN REMOVING THE ASTRONAUTS' BODIES.
JANUARY 30, 1967 MEMORIAL SERVICE IN HOUSTON. PRESIDENT JOHNSON LATER ATTENDS GRISSOM'S FUNERAL AT ARLINGTON NATIONAL CEMETERY (LEFT).
FEBRUARY 1967 APOLLO ACCIDENT REVIEWS BEGIN (ABOVE).

APOLLO COMMAND MODULE

Apollo's Command Module took men to the Moon—and brought them back again. Built to house the crew during launch, provide them with air, food and water for the journey, and serve as a base of operations during lunar landings, the tiny craft also had to survive the rigors of reentry into the Earth's atmosphere with little more than a heat shield for brakes. The demands on it to return its crew members safely were extraordinary. Yet over nine lunar voyages and two Earth orbital missions, the Command Module never failed its passengers, even when it was feared the worst might happen.

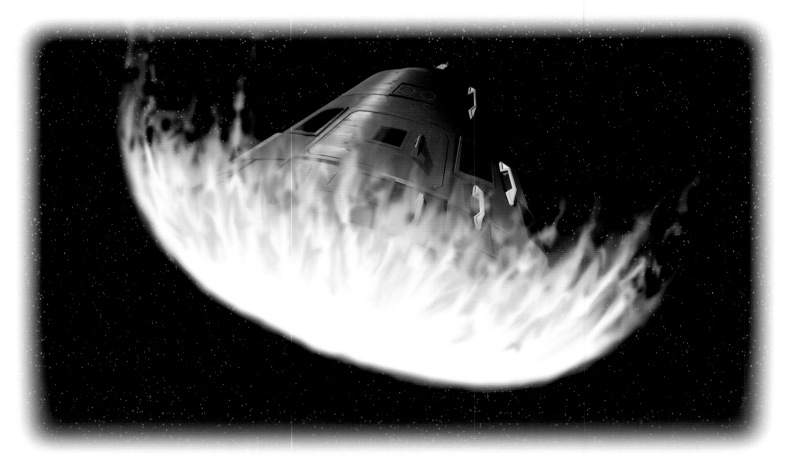

APOLLO CM SPECS

PRIME CONTRACTOR	NORTH AMERICAN AVIATION	PROPELLANTS	175 LB (79 KG)
CREW	THREE	ELECTRICAL EQUIPMENT	1,550 LB (703 KG)
HABITABLE VOLUME	210 CU FT (5.9 M³)	COMMUNICATIONS SYSTEMS	225 LB (102 KG)
LENGTH	10 FT 6 IN (3.2 M)	NAVIGATION EQUIPMENT	1,100 LB (499 KG)
DIAMETER	12 FT 10 INCHES (3.9 M)	ENVIRONMENTAL CONTROLS	450 LB (204 KG)
OVERALL MASS	12,800 LB (5,800 KG)	CREW SEATS AND PROVISIONS	550 LB (249 KG)
HEAT SHIELD	1,900 LB (861 KG)	RECOVERY EQUIPMENT	550 LB (249 KG)
THRUSTER SYSTEM	900 LB (408 KG)	MISCELLANEOUS CONTINGENCY	450 LB (204 KG)

SPACE WOMB

Constructed from two million separate components, the three-person Apollo Command Module (CM) was an incredibly complex machine by any standards—let alone those of the 1960s. Its task was to act as mother ship during the Moon landing missions. Out of the crew of three, one astronaut stayed in the CM during lunar orbit; the other two traveled to the surface in a separate landing craft.

The CM's cramped interior included instruments, navigation computers and life-support equipment designed with the experience gained from the earlier Mercury and Gemini programs.

However, the outer shape of the craft required a totally radical approach.

For safety's sake, NASA planners insisted that a CM returning from the Moon had to be capable of surviving reentry without using a rocket engine to slow it down beforehand. This was in case something went wrong with Apollo's propulsion systems during the mission. Because of its return trajectory across a quarter of a million miles of space, the CM would hit the Earth's atmosphere at a colossal 25,000 mph (40,000 km/h). This was 7,000 mph (11,000 km/h) faster than previous Mercury or Gemini craft returning from missions in Earth orbit.

Apollo CM designers Maxime Faget and Caldwell Johnson created a cone-shaped craft with a blunt heat shield, similar in some ways to earlier capsules, but with a smoother exterior. Then a lucky accident helped them improve the shape. The diameter of the upper stage of the Saturn 5 rocket under the CM was cut by two inches (five cm).

SMOOTH SHAPE

Faget and Johnson decided to round off the edge of the blunt heat shield at the base, so the CM would fit on top of the rocket stage. The result was more aerodynamic than expected, and this new shape turned out to be a crucial benefit.

The CM had to be controllable in air as well as in space. As the module plunged back into the atmosphere, air resistance pushed up against the heat shield. If the angle of entry was incorrect by a fraction of a degree, the craft would bounce off the atmosphere and back into space, like a flat stone skimming across the surface of a pond. But if the entry was too steep, the CM would burn to a crisp. The rounded edge allowed the CM to behave like a fat aircraft wing. The astronauts could control the exact angle of approach with 12 tiny thrusters.

In 1970, the CM's engineering saved the day, as well as the lives of the crew. When Apollo 13's oxygen tank exploded, the craft lost almost all its power. In the chill of interstellar space, sweat from the astronauts soon condensed on interior surfaces such as the instrument panel. But when the astronauts turned on the power for crucial last maneuvers, there were no electrical shorts that could have stranded them. The CM brought the astronauts back to Earth.

INSIDE THE CM

COCKPIT
CM Pilot Vance Brand (left) at the controls during the 1975 Apollo-Soyuz Test Project, during which the CM docked with the Soviet craft via a special docking adapter.

The Apollo CM consisted of an outer shell and heat shield, and an interior capsule with room for three crewmembers, plus instruments, instrument panels, batteries and a small amount of storage space.

docking probe

crew compartment heat shield

honeycomb-construction aluminum wall

control panel instruments

batteries, computers and flight equipment

CO₂ absorbers

storage

parachute ejector

parachute

pitch thruster

rendezvous window

Apollo hatch (removed)

yaw thrusters

drinking water tank

heat shield lip

liquid waste pipe

roll thrusters

waste water pipe

support strut

pitch thrusters

environmental control systems

UP TOP
Above the CM is a solid-fuel rocket that pulls the CM free of the Saturn 5 rocket if the launch goes wrong.

HARD EVIDENCE

THE CENTRAL SHIP
On the Apollo lunar missions, the combined Command Module and lunar-booster Service Module (CSM) orbited the Moon, while the Lunar Module (LM) detached and descended to the surface. After their moonwalk, the landing crew blasted back into lunar orbit in the upper stage of the LM, docked with the CSM and reentered the through the CM's docking port (shown above). The Service Module's engine was then fired for the return journey home, leaving the module itself to be jettisoned shortly before reentry.

TRIAL BY FIRE
The CM was enveloped in an asbestos/epoxy resin heat shield. The mixture was squeezed into a honeycomb layer on the CM's skin, where it hardened like glue and was covered with foil. The shield slowly burned away during reentry, staining the skin (above left).

APOLLO LUNAR MODULE

The Apollo Lunar Module was the first vehicle designed to operate purely in the vacuum of space. It was never intended to survive reentry into the earth's atmosphere. Unlike the main Apollo crew capsule, it had no need for an aerodynamic shape or heat shielding. Instead, its priority was to be light and easily maneuverable. Most of its outer skin was nothing more than lightweight metallic foil, and even the small two-person crew compartment could have been punctured easily. This fragile, bug-like machine was created for a very specialized task—landing astronauts on the Moon.

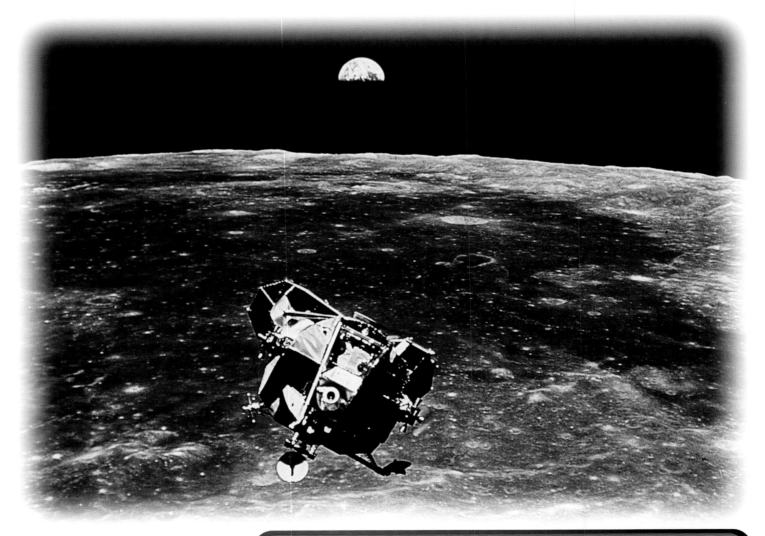

LUNAR LANDER

WEIGHT	9,180 LB (4,163 KG) DRY; 32,331 LB (14,665 KG) FUELED	WIDTH	31 FT 2 IN (9.5 M) (LEGS EXTENDED)
HEIGHT	22 FT 11 IN (7 M)	DESCENT STAGE ENGINE	1,050–9,870 LB (5-43 KN)
WIDTH	14 FT 1 IN (4.2 M) (LEGS STOWED POSITION)	BURN TIME	15 MIN 10 SEC
		ASCENT STAGE ENGINE	3,500 LB (15 KN)
		BURN TIME	7 MIN 40 SEC

LUNAR DELIVERY

President John F. Kennedy pledged to the nation in 1961 that a lunar landing would be undertaken within the next 10 years. NASA mission planners, influenced by the ideas of the German-born rocket engineer Wernher von Braun, conceived a spacecraft called "Apollo" to touch down tail-first on the Moon and then blast off back to Earth at the end of its mission.

Other designers, led by NASA engineer John Houbolt, thought this was the wrong approach. If Apollo had to carry fuel for its return to Earth, plus reentry heat shielding and parachutes for splashdown, why must it take all this bulky equipment to the lunar surface? It would just have to be lifted off again, imposing a serious weight penalty on the design.

NASA agreed, and in 1962 the emerging Apollo concept was split into two distinct components: a Command-Service Module (CSM) and a detachable Lunar Module (LM) that would land the astronauts on the Moon. The LM had to be light enough to be launched from Earth aboard the same Saturn V rocket that carried the CSM. Saving weight would prove to be a very difficult challenge for the LM's designers.

Once the spacecraft was successfully in orbit around the Moon, two astronauts clambered aboard the LM for the landing. The third remained aboard the CSM to monitor systems and rendezvous with the LM when it returned from the lunar surface.

The LM consisted of two sections. On completion of its lunar surface operations, the landing legs, rocket engine and empty fuel tanks in the lower descent stage were abandoned to save weight. Only the compact crew module, the ascent stage, lifted off for the return trip, using the main fuel tank and engine. After making a rendezvous with the CSM in lunar orbit, the entire ascent stage was thrown away altogether, saving yet more weight, and leaving just the CSM for the voyage back to earth.

The greatest danger was that the two astronauts in the ascent stage might not be able to locate the CSM in the vastness of space after their ascent from the Moon. Scientists at the Massachusetts Institute of Technology (MIT) designed a computerized navigation system with a radar altimeter. This sophisticated system solved the problem with pinpoint accuracy.

Between 1969 and 1972, the LM performed flawlessly. It flew nine crewed missions to the Moon and back, carried out an Earth orbital test, a lunar practice descent, six touchdowns and one incredible rescue—that of Apollo 13.

FULL HOUSE

THE LM CABIN'S INTERIOR WAS SO CRAMPED THAT THE ASTRONAUTS HAD TO STAND UP DURING FLIGHT. EVEN DURING REST PERIODS ON THE MOON, THEY FOUND IT IMPOSSIBLE TO LIE DOWN COMFORTABLY, BECAUSE THE ASCENT ENGINE COVER OCCUPIED MOST OF THE FLOOR.

FLYING LLRV

APOLLO ASTRONAUTS TRAINED ON A JET-POWERED LUNAR LANDING RESEARCH VEHICLE (LLRV) NICKNAMED THE "FLYING BEDSTEAD." THE LLRV WAS VERY DIFFICULT TO CONTROL: NEIL ARMSTRONG CRASHED ONE WHILE TRAINING FOR HIS MOON-LANDING MISSION AND HAD TO USE HIS EJECTION SEAT TO ESCAPE UNHARMED.

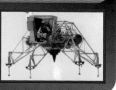

APOLLO LUNAR MODULE

- S-band steerable antenna
- rendezvous radar
- entrance to pressurized cabin
- LM pilot's console
- cabin air recirculation fan
- exhaust deflectors
- entrance/exit platform and rails
- ladder
- LM/CM docking hatch
- VHF antenna
- relay box
- attitude-control oxidizer
- attitude-control fuel
- attitude-control pressurant (helium)
- attitude-control thrusters
- ascent fuel tank
- ascent engine
- descent structure
- descent oxidizer tank
- descent engine
- descent fuel tank
- secondary shock absorber strut
- primary shock absorber strut
- foot pad

LM LANDING PROFILE

1 At the end of the braking phase: altitude 10,000 ft (3,028 m), thrust 6,000 lb (26.6 kN).

2 Coming into view of the landing site: altitude 9,860 ft (3,005 m), thrust 5,600 lb (24.8 kN).

3 Commencing landing: altitude 3,000 ft (915 m).

4 Main descent: altitude 500 ft (150 m), thrust 2,800 lb (12.4 kN), vertical velocity 27 ft (8 m) per second.

5 Dropping in: vertical velocity 3 ft (1 m) per second.

6 Landing: 6 miles (9.5 km) from stage 2.

Next to the Lunar Roving Vehicle (LRV), the Lunar Module (LM) sits on its spindly legs—deployed for landing by powerful springs—and an astronaut sets off to collect lunar samples. On departure, the astronauts would board the LM before hoisting the samples up with a line and pulley.

APOLLO 8

The crew of Apollo 8 were the first three humans to break the bonds of Earth's gravity and travel to another world. Their six-day journey included 20 hours in orbit around the Moon. For NASA, the successful mission represented another step toward a lunar landing before 1970. But as the astronauts circled the Moon on Christmas Eve 1968, transmitting their descriptions of the lunar surface to a fascinated television and radio audience around the world, the Apollo 8 mission made history in its own right.

APOLLO 8 FACTS

CREW	FRANK BORMAN, COMMANDER JAMES A. LOVELL, LUNAR MODULE PILOT (NAVIGATOR) WILLIAM A. ANDERS, COMMAND MODULE PILOT (FLIGHT ENGINEER)	TRANSLUNAR INJECTION BURN	DECEMBER 21, 10:42 A.M. EST
		LUNAR ORBIT INSERTION	DECEMBER 24, 4:59 A.M. EST
LAUNCH	7:51 A.M. EST, DECEMBER 21, 1968, KENNEDY SPACE CENTER	MAXIMUM ALTITUDE ABOVE EARTH	235,000 MILES (378,000 KM)
		CLOSEST APPROACH TO THE MOON	69 MILES (111 KM)
VEHICLE	SATURN 5 ROCKET; FIRST CREWED LAUNCH OF A SATURN 5	DURATION OF FLIGHT	6 DAYS, 3 HOURS, 1 MINUTE
EARTH ORBITAL ALTITUDE	115 MILES		

LUNARWATCHER

Astronaut Frank Borman and his crew, Jim Lovell and Bill Anders, were training for an Apollo flight test in Earth orbit in August 1968. But then CIA intelligence revealed that the Soviets were preparing to send a Soyuz spacecraft on a trip around the Moon.

NASA was determined not to be beaten to the Moon. They knew the lunar module (LM) remained in production. But the Saturn vehicle and the command module would be tested in orbit in October, and if all went well, Apollo 8 could orbit the Moon in December, without the LM. Borman told his crewmates they had new orders: They were going to the Moon for Christmas.

The watching world was captivated as the first flight to the Moon lifted off on December 22. After two Earth orbits, Capcom Michael Collins gave the historic order: "Apollo 8, you are Go for TLI." Translunar injection, or TLI, was the engine burn that sent Apollo to the Moon.

CHRISTMAS PRESENT

In the early hours of Christmas Eve, after nearly three days in space, Apollo 8 fired its engine to decelerate, and the Moon's gravity pulled the spacecraft into its orbit. As soon as they could, the crew radioed their impressions of the surface. "Essentially gray, no color…Looks like plaster of Paris," said Lovell. Anders chipped in, "Or sort of a grayish beach sand." The crew described and photographed the features of the far side of the Moon, which had never before been seen by human eyes.

On the fourth revolution, the astronauts were startled by the beautiful sight of Earth rising above the lunar horizon. And on the ninth orbit, Apollo 8 made its famous Christmas Eve television broadcast to the people of Earth, the planet Lovell called "a grand oasis in the big vastness of space." Twenty hours after reaching lunar orbit, Apollo 8 headed back to Earth and straight into the history books.

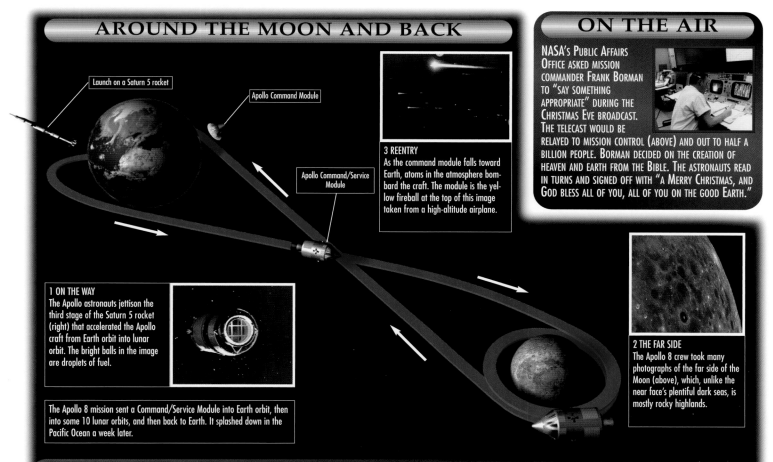

AROUND THE MOON AND BACK

Launch on a Saturn 5 rocket

Apollo Command Module

Apollo Command/Service Module

3 REENTRY
As the command module falls toward Earth, atoms in the atmosphere bombard the craft. The module is the yellow fireball at the top of this image taken from a high-altitude airplane.

1 ON THE WAY
The Apollo astronauts jettison the third stage of the Saturn 5 rocket (right) that accelerated the Apollo craft from Earth orbit into lunar orbit. The bright balls in the image are droplets of fuel.

The Apollo 8 mission sent a Command/Service Module into Earth orbit, then into some 10 lunar orbits, and then back to Earth. It splashed down in the Pacific Ocean a week later.

2 THE FAR SIDE
The Apollo 8 crew took many photographs of the far side of the Moon (above), which, unlike the near face's plentiful dark seas, is mostly rocky highlands.

ON THE AIR

NASA's PUBLIC AFFAIRS OFFICE ASKED MISSION COMMANDER FRANK BORMAN TO "SAY SOMETHING APPROPRIATE" DURING THE CHRISTMAS EVE BROADCAST. THE TELECAST WOULD BE RELAYED TO MISSION CONTROL (ABOVE) AND OUT TO HALF A BILLION PEOPLE. BORMAN DECIDED ON THE CREATION OF HEAVEN AND EARTH FROM THE BIBLE. THE ASTRONAUTS READ IN TURNS AND SIGNED OFF WITH "A MERRY CHRISTMAS, AND GOD BLESS ALL OF YOU, ALL OF YOU ON THE GOOD EARTH."

MISSION DIARY: APOLLO 8

DECEMBER 21, 1968, 2:36 A.M. EST
ASTRONAUTS BORMAN, LOVELL AND ANDERS (RIGHT) ARE AWAKENED TO BEGIN FINAL PREPARATIONS FOR THE FIRST FLIGHT FROM THE EARTH TO THE MOON.
7:51 A.M. APOLLO 8 LAUNCHES. THE SATURN 5 ROCKET AND ITS FIRST CREW CLEARS THE LAUNCH TOWER BURNING 15 TONS OF FUEL PER SECOND.
10:42 A.M. LOVELL PUSHES THE TRANSLUNAR INJECTION BUTTON, WHICH IGNITES THE SATURN 5'S THIRD STAGE ENGINE AND SENDS APOLLO 8 ON ITS WAY TO THE MOON.
11:12 A.M. THE SPENT THIRD STAGE SEPARATES.

DECEMBER 22, 3:06 P.M. APPROXIMATELY HALFWAY BETWEEN THE EARTH AND THE MOON, THE CREW OF APOLLO 8 MAKES ITS FIRST TELEVISION BROADCAST, BUT HAS DIFFICULTY TRANSMITTING A CLEAR PICTURE OF THE EARTH. THEY STILL MANAGE TO TAKE PHOTOGRAPHS.
DECEMBER 23, 3:00 P.M. WITH PICTURE PROBLEMS CORRECTED, APOLLO 8 GIVES THE PEOPLE OF EARTH THEIR FIRST LOOK AT THEIR WHOLE PLANET.
3:29 P.M. AS APOLLO 8 CROSSES THE POINT WHERE THE MOON'S GRAVITY EXERTS MORE PULL THAN THE EARTH'S, THE SPACECRAFT BEGINS TO PICK UP SPEED.
DECEMBER 24, 4:59 A.M. LOVELL STARTS THE LUNAR ORBIT INSERTION BURN. THE SERVICE PROPULSION ENGINE BURNS FOR 4 MINUTES TO SLOW APOLLO 8 AND SEND IT IN AN ELLIPTICAL ORBIT AROUND THE MOON.

9:34 P.M. THE CREW BROADCAST THEIR PERSONAL IMPRESSIONS OF THE FLYBY TO HALF A BILLION LISTENERS.
CHRISTMAS DAY, 1:08 A.M.
APOLLO 8 LEAVES LUNAR ORBIT ON A TRAJECTORY FOR EARTH.
DECEMBER 27, 10:52 A.M. SPLASHDOWN IN THE PACIFIC OCEAN (RIGHT).

APOLLO 11

On July 20, 1969, as the whole world held its breath, Apollo 11's lunar lander, the Eagle, touched down on the Moon. Later, after a few hours rest, the mission commander Neil Armstrong descended the exit ladder followed by Edwin "Buzz" Aldrin and planted the Stars and Stripes in the dust of the Sea of Tranquillity. It was the culmination of a $25 billion program started by President John F. Kennedy in 1961. Neil Armstrong and Buzz Aldrin became the first human beings ever to set ft on another world.

APOLLO 11 STATS

CREWED SPACEFLIGHT	NUMBER 33	MASS OF LUNAR SAMPLES	48.5 LB (22 KG) RETURNED
AMERICAN CREWED SPACEFLIGHT	NUMBER 21		
CREWED FLIGHT TO THE MOON	NUMBER 3	PRIOR FLIGHTS OF CREW	ARMSTRONG: GEMINI 8
PREVIOUS CREWED FLIGHTS	APOLLO 8 AND 10 TEST MISSIONS TO THE MOON		COLLINS: GEMINI 10
			ALDRIN: GEMINI 12
FLIGHT OF SATURN 5 ROCKET	NUMBER 5	TRANQUILLITY BASE LOCATION	MOON COORDINATES 0.68°N
FLIGHT TIME	8 DAYS, 3 HR, 18 MIN, 35 SEC		23.43°E
TIME ON MOON	21 HR, 36 MIN		

ONE GIANT LEAP

Apollo 11 carried three astronauts, two of whom—Neil Armstrong and Buzz Aldrin—would be the first to set ft on the Moon. The third, Michael Collins, was assigned to remain in the command module, Columbia, taking care of business while it orbited the Moon. The mission began on July 16, 1969, with Armstrong, Aldrin and Collins perched on top of a 363-ft (110-m) Saturn 5 rocket as 7.5 million lb (33,350 kN) of thrust blasted them into space. Once in Earth orbit, the third and final stage of the Saturn 5 shut down. Apollo 11 then swung around the Earth and the third stage reignited to propel the craft on its 3-day journey to the Moon.

On arrival in lunar orbit, Armstrong and Aldrin crawled into the landing craft, Eagle, which had been tucked into the top of the third stage to protect it during launch. The two spacecraft separated. Then the Eagle's descent engine fired to propel it toward the landing site in the Sea of Tranquillity. As the Eagle made its final approach, Armstrong spotted that it was overshooting the landing site and prepared to abort. Mission Control in Houston ordered him to continue.

GOOD JUDGMENT

As the Eagle prepared to land, Armstrong found that the onboard computer was steering it into a rocky crater, with potentially disastrous results. He immediately seized control and flew over the crater with less than 30 seconds of fuel left, leaving Mission Control powerless to do anything other than watch and trust in his judgment.

With about 20 seconds of fuel left, the craft touched down. "Houston, Tranquillity Base here," said Armstrong. "The Eagle has landed."

Later, Armstrong emerged from the Eagle's hatch and climbed down the exit ladder, watched by a huge worldwide TV audience. As he set foot on the Moon's surface, he uttered the famous words: "That's one small step for man, one giant leap for mankind" (actually a mistake: he meant to say "...one small step for a man...").

Aldrin then joined Armstrong on the surface, where they spent about two hours gathering rocks and deploying experiments. Then they returned to the Eagle and lifted off. Finally, after a delicate docking maneuver with the Columbia command module, Collins fired the rocket engine that would fly the crew home—and into history.

TRACKS

THE APOLLO 11 ASTRONAUTS LEFT $800,000 WORTH OF DISCARDED EQUIPMENT ON THE MOON: TWO STILLS CAMERAS, LUNAR BOOTS, PORTABLE LIFE-SUPPORT SYSTEM BACKPACKS, MOON TOOLS — AND THE AMERICAN FLAG ON ITS POLE, WHICH WAS KNOCKED OVER BY THE BLAST OF THE EAGLE'S ENGINE. AS THERE IS NO WIND OR RAIN ON THE MOON, THE FTPRINTS LEFT BY THE ASTRONAUTS WILL REMAIN THERE FOR CENTURIES.

5 DOCKING
Collins took this remarkable photo of the Eagle ascent stage and Earthrise as the lunar module approached the Columbia command module in lunar orbit.

THE APOLLO 11 MISSION

6 SPLASHDOWN
Columbia splashed down beneath 3 parachutes 825 miles (1,327 km) southwest of Honolulu. The crew was on the deck of the recovery ship, *USS Hornet*, one hour later to be greeted by President Nixon.

3 LUNAR LANDING
"Picking up some dust," said Aldrin. "30 ft, 2½ down...faint shadow...4 forward... 4 forward...drifting to the right a little...contact light...OK engine stop."

4 TAKEOFF
Lifting off at a speed of 80 ft (24 m) per second, the Eagle used its spent descent stage as a launchpad as it cleared the dusty, airless surface of Tranquillity Base.

1 SATURN 5
The rocket that powered the Apollo mission is the most powerful ever built in the U.S. At launch, its five F-1 first-stage engines gulped 5,000 gal (19,000 l) of liquid oxygen and kerosene a second.

2 ESCAPE FROM EARTH
The Saturn 5's S4B third stage was fired to accelerate Apollo 11 to over 25,000 mph (40,000 km/h) — the escape velocity required to enable the craft to break free of the Earth's gravitational field.

MISSION DIARY: APOLLO 11

MAY 1961 PRESIDENT JOHN F. KENNEDY COMMITS THE U.S. TO PUTTING A MAN ON THE MOON "BEFORE THE DECADE IS OUT." THE PROGRAM IS NAMED APOLLO.
JULY 16, 1969, 9:32 A.M. EDT APOLLO 11 IS LAUNCHED (RIGHT).
9:44 A.M. APOLLO 11 ENTERS EARTH ORBIT.
12:22 P.M. THE THIRD STAGE OF THE SATURN 5 ROCKET REIGNITES, BLASTING APOLLO 11 OUT OF EARTH ORBIT AND TOWARD THE MOON.

12:49 P.M. THE APOLLO 11 COMMAND AND SERVICE MODULE SEPARATE, TURN AROUND AND DOCK WITH THE LUNAR MODULE.
JULY 19, 1:28 P.M. APOLLO 11 GOES INTO ORBIT AROUND THE MOON.
JULY 20, 1:46 P.M. THE LUNAR MODULE EAGLE SEPARATES FROM THE ORBITING COMMAND MODULE COLUMBIA.
3:08 P.M. EAGLE BEGINS ITS POWERED DESCENT.
JULY 20, 4:18 P.M. "THE EAGLE HAS LANDED."
10:56 P.M. ARMSTRONG BECOMES THE FIRST PERSON ON THE MOON.

JULY 21, 1:54 P.M. THE EAGLE LEAVES THE SURFACE OF THE MOON.
5:35 P.M. EAGLE DOCKS WITH COLUMBIA; THE CREW TRANSFER TO THE COMMAND MODULE.
JULY 22, 12:56 A.M. COLUMBIA BLASTS OUT OF LUNAR ORBIT BACK TOWARD EARTH.
JULY 24, 12:51 P.M. COLUMBIA AND ITS JUBILANT CREW MEMBERS SPLASH DOWN SAFELY IN THE PACIFIC OCEAN (ABOVE).

APOLLO 13

Launched on April 11, 1970, Apollo 13 was NASA's third attempt at a manned landing on the Moon. The launch itself was a low-key occasion, the press and public having already grown used to the idea of lunar exploration. But then, just over two days into the mission, the world was shocked to attention by the crew's famous radio message: "Houston...we've had a problem here." An onboard explosion had put the lives of the astronauts in serious jeopardy—along with the future of the U.S. space program.

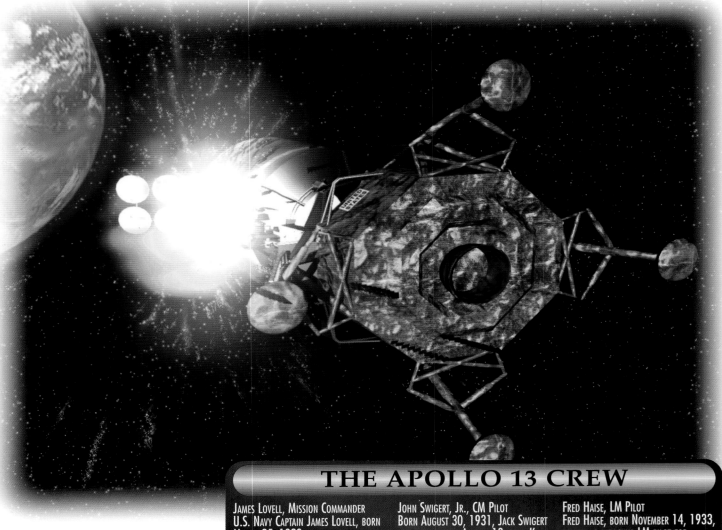

THE APOLLO 13 CREW

JAMES LOVELL, MISSION COMMANDER
U.S. NAVY CAPTAIN JAMES LOVELL, BORN MARCH 25, 1928, WAS A VETERAN OF THREE SPACEFLIGHTS AND ON APOLLO 13 BECAME THE FIRST PERSON TO MAKE FOUR. HE TOLD OFFICIALS BEFORE THE LAUNCH THAT APOLLO 13 WOULD BE HIS LAST MISSION. LOVELL WROTE THE BOOK APOLLO 13, ON WHICH THE MOVIE WAS BASED.

JOHN SWIGERT, JR., CM PILOT
BORN AUGUST 30, 1931, JACK SWIGERT WAS ASSIGNED TO APOLLO 13 WHEN KEN MATTINGLY WAS DROPPED FOR MEDICAL REASONS. IN 1982, HE WAS ELECTED A REPUBLICAN CONGRESSMAN BUT DIED OF CANCER BEFORE HE ENTERED OFFICE.

FRED HAISE, LM PILOT
FRED HAISE, BORN NOVEMBER 14, 1933, SERVED AS A BACKUP LM PILOT FOR APOLLOS 8 AND 11. AFTER APOLLO 13, HAISE WAS BACKUP COMMANDER OF APOLLO 16 AND DUE TO COMMAND THE CANCELED APOLLO 19.

"HOUSTON...WE'VE HAD A PROBLEM HERE"

As their mighty Saturn 5 launch vehicle thundered into the afternoon skies above the Kennedy Space Center, Apollo 13 astronauts James Lovell, Fred Haise and Jack Swigert began to look forward to their long journey to the Moon. But inside bay 4 of the Service Module, a fault in the number 2 oxygen tank had already turned their spacecraft into a bomb, primed and ready to blow apart.

The tank was part of the Apollo craft's fuel cell system, which produced electricity and water from hydrogen and oxygen. It contained a stirring fan, a heating element and two thermostatic control switches. These switches were designed to operate at 28 volts, but the spacecraft's power supply had been upgraded to 65 volts. As a result, during tests in the weeks before the launch, the higher voltage caused arcing that welded the switches shut. This somehow went unnoticed. During later testing, the faulty switches allowed the temperature of the tank assembly to reach over 1,000°F (540°C), which damaged the insulation of the fan wiring.

The tank finally exploded just under 56 hours into the mission, when Apollo 13 was 205,000 miles (330,000 km) from Earth and the crew was increasing the hydrogen and oxygen pressures to keep the fuel cells functioning properly.

THE JOURNEY HOME

When the accident happened, there was a loud bang and the crew felt the craft shudder.

The damaged fan wiring had shorted out, leading to a violent tank explosion that ripped a 13-ft-by-6-ft (4-m-by-1.8-m) panel out of the Service Module. Soon, the Command Module was effectively without power, oxygen and water. Additionally, the main engine, part of the Service Module, was completely immobilized and unresponsive.

The crew transferred from the Command Module to the Lunar Module, Aquarius. This tiny two-man craft became a "lifeboat," providing essential life-support systems. It also provided propulsion from its descent engine, which was fired several times to send the crew around the Moon and back to Earth. For much of the journey home, Lovell, Swigert and Haise huddled in the cold Lunar Module, desperately conserving oxygen, water and power. As Apollo 13 rapidly plunged back to Earth, Aquarius was discarded and the crew transferred back to the Command Module. This splashed down safely in the Pacific Ocean, just 4 miles (6.5 km) from the recovery ship *Iwo Jima*. The crew were not harmed by their terrifying ordeal.

MISSION DIARY: APOLLO 13

APRIL 11, 1970, 2:13 P.M. LAUNCH FROM KENNEDY SPACE CENTER.
4:48 P.M. THE SATURN 5 ROCKET CARRIES THE CRAFT TOWARD THE MOON.
6:14 P.M. THE COMMAND MODULE DOCKS WITH THE LUNAR MODULE. APRIL 12, 8:53 P.M. A MID-COURSE MANEUVER PUTS THE CRAFT ON COURSE FOR THE MOON.
APRIL 13, 10:07 P.M. OXYGEN TANK EXPLODES.
APRIL 14, 3:43 A.M. FIRST LM ENGINE BURN TO SEND CRAFT AROUND THE MOON AND BACK TO EARTH.
9:40 P.M. SECOND LM ENGINE BURN TO CUT JOURNEY TIME.

APRIL 17, 8:14 A.M. SERVICE MODULE IS JETTISONED.
11:43 A.M. LM IS JETTISONED.
1:07 P.M. SPLASHDOWN (LEFT).

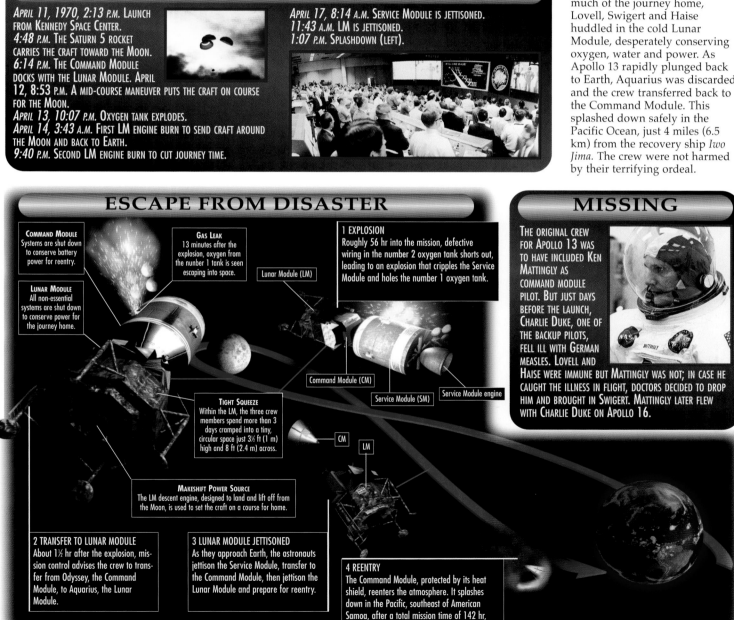

ESCAPE FROM DISASTER

COMMAND MODULE
Systems are shut down to conserve battery power for reentry.

LUNAR MODULE
All non-essential systems are shut down to conserve power for the journey home.

GAS LEAK
13 minutes after the explosion, oxygen from the number 1 tank is seen escaping into space.

Lunar Module (LM)

1 EXPLOSION
Roughly 56 hr into the mission, defective wiring in the number 2 oxygen tank shorts out, leading to an explosion that cripples the Service Module and holes the number 1 oxygen tank.

Command Module (CM)

Service Module (SM)

Service Module engine

TIGHT SQUEEZE
Within the LM, the three crew members spend more than 3 days cramped into a tiny, circular space just 3½ ft (1 m) high and 8 ft (2.4 m) across.

CM

LM

MAKESHIFT POWER SOURCE
The LM descent engine, designed to land and lift off from the Moon, is used to set the craft on a course for home.

2 TRANSFER TO LUNAR MODULE
About 1½ hr after the explosion, mission control advises the crew to transfer from Odyssey, the Command Module, to Aquarius, the Lunar Module.

3 LUNAR MODULE JETTISONED
As they approach Earth, the astronauts jettison the Service Module, transfer to the Command Module, then jettison the Lunar Module and prepare for reentry.

4 REENTRY
The Command Module, protected by its heat shield, reenters the atmosphere. It splashes down in the Pacific, southeast of American Samoa, after a total mission time of 142 hr, 54 min and 41 sec.

MISSING

THE ORIGINAL CREW FOR APOLLO 13 WAS TO HAVE INCLUDED KEN MATTINGLY AS COMMAND MODULE PILOT. BUT JUST DAYS BEFORE THE LAUNCH, CHARLIE DUKE, ONE OF THE BACKUP PILOTS, FELL ILL WITH GERMAN MEASLES. LOVELL AND HAISE WERE IMMUNE BUT MATTINGLY WAS NOT; IN CASE HE CAUGHT THE ILLNESS IN FLIGHT, DOCTORS DECIDED TO DROP HIM AND BROUGHT IN SWIGERT. MATTINGLY LATER FLEW WITH CHARLIE DUKE ON APOLLO 16.

APOLLO 14

pollo 14 began the heavy-duty exploration of the Moon. Edgar Mitchell and Alan Shepard, America's first man in space, spent two days on the lunar surface, pushing the limits of what could safely be done. By the launch of the mission, on January 31, 1971, the Apollo program was a smoothly running machine. The Apollo 14 spacecraft had been modified to correct the failures of Apollo 13 and to extend their capabilities. But, as all engineers know, anything that can go wrong, will go wrong.

MISSION DATA

LAUNCH	JANUARY 31, 1971, 5:03 P.M. EST	LUNAR TOUCHDOWN	FEBRUARY 5, 1971, 4:18 A.M. EST
CREW	MISSION COMMANDER ALAN SHEPARD	LUNAR LIFTOFF	FEBRUARY 6, 1:48 P.M EST
	COMMAND MODULE PILOT STUART ROOSA	SPLASHDOWN	FEBRUARY 9, 1971, 4:05 P.M. EST
	LUNAR MODULE PILOT EDGAR MITCHELL	FRA MAURO BASE	3° 40' 24" SOUTH,
TIME IN LUNAR ORBIT	67 HOURS (34 ORBITS)		17° 27' 55" WEST.
MISSION DURATION	9 DAYS 2 MIN		
TIME ON MOON	33.5 HOURS		

LUCKY FOURTEEN

Apollo 14 blasted off from Cape Canaveral into a cloudy and rainy afternoon sky on January 31, 1971, to become a textbook example of how to cope with minor problems. Commander and former Mercury astronaut Alan Shepard, Command Module Pilot Stuart Roosa and Lunar Module Pilot Ed Mitchell had inherited the mission and target base of the failed Apollo 13, with extra objectives and new space techniques to try out.

They were bound for Fra Mauro, a cratered highland area that geologists hoped would provide samples of the earliest bedrock of the Moon and give clues to the early history of the Earth. They would stay longer, conduct more tests, and test the endurance of their spacesuits and themselves more than anyone had done before.

The problems that they were to face would be ironed out by the astronauts and by the well-oiled organization behind them at Mission Control. They had already modified their orbit to make up for the 40-minute launch delay caused by the bad weather.

After the spacecraft had moved into lunar orbit, Roosa maneuvered the Command Module Kitty Hawk to dock with the Lunar Module Antares, still attached to the third stage of the booster. The tiny teeth on the Lunar Module failed to engage. Two more tries were unsuccessful. By this time, engineers at Mission Control had dragged in an identical mechanism to try to find the problem. The fault remains a mystery, but on his sixth try, Roosa locked on. The mission continued, and Apollo 14 entered lunar orbit on February 4.

MOON TRACKS

Sunlight glints on tracks leading across the Moon's Fra Mauro highlands from the Lunar Module Antares. The tracks were made by Apollo 14's Modularized Equipment Transporter during Shepard and Mitchell's first trip away from Antares.

LOST
The rolling highlands of Fra Mauro made navigation difficult. Shepard and Mitchell (above, consulting a map) often lost sight of each other and had difficulty keeping a fix on landmarks.

THE FLYING RICKSHAW
An artist's impression (left) shows Shepard and Mitchell setting out on their first EVA. Shepard, on the right, is pulling the Modularized Equipment Transporter (MET), otherwise known as the "Flying Rickshaw." This 2-wheeled buggy held up to 360 lb (163 kg) of equipment, but the two astronauts sometimes found it easier to carry it than to pull it through the lunar dust.

LUNAR GOLF

As Antares prepared to land, Shepard and Mitchell had to reprogram its control computer while they went through their descent preparations, because the module's "Abort" button was malfunctioning. To everyone's relief, their reprogramming was successful and the module touched down safely on a 7° slope only 175 ft (53 m) from its target. Shepard and Mitchell now began setting up an automated scientific laboratory. This included an instrument to measure lunar seismic activity; a series of experiments to measure charged particles near the surface; a small nuclear generator; and a station to transmit all their data to earth. On their return to the Lunar Module, they collected some Moon rocks, but they picked up most of their geological samples during their second extravehicular activity (EVA).

Back at the Lunar Module, Shepard produced a golf ball and an improvised club. On his second swing, he claimed that the ball had gone for "miles and miles and miles." It wasn't true, but he had become the first lunar golfer. Shepard later confessed that he had tears in his eyes as he first stood on the Moon.

MISSION DIARY: APOLLO 14

JANUARY 31, 1971 APOLLO 14 CREW SUITS UP (RIGHT) FOR LAUNCH. EIGHT MINUTES BEFORE THE LAUNCH, IT IS DELAYED FOR 40 MINUTES 2 SECONDS DUE TO HEAVY CLOUDS.
JANUARY 31, 4:03 P.M. EST APOLLO 14 LIFTS OFF, CARRIED BY A SATURN 5 LAUNCHER.
FEBRUARY 5, 11:50 P.M. LUNAR MODULE ANTARES, CARRYING ALAN SHEPARD AND ED MITCHELL, SEPARATES FROM COMMAND MODULE KITTY HAWK, PILOTED BY STUART ROOSA.
FEBRUARY 5, 4:18 A.M. ANTARES (RIGHT) TOUCHES DOWN ON

A GENTLE SLOPE IN THE HIGHLANDS NEAR THE MOON'S FRA MAURO CRATER. THE LANDING SITE, AT LATITUDE 3° 40' 24" SOUTH AND LONGITUDE 17° 27' 55" WEST, IS ONLY 175 FT FROM THE PLANNED TOUCHDOWN POSITION.
FEBRUARY 5, 9:42 A.M. ALAN SHEPARD AND ED MITCHELL BEGIN THEIR FIRST MOONWALK, OR EXTRAVEHICULAR ACTIVITY (EVA), LASTING 4 HOURS 49 MINUTES.
FEBRUARY 6, 5:11 A.M. SHEPARD AND MITCHELL SET OFF ON THEIR SECOND AND FINAL EVA, LASTING 4 HOURS 35 MINUTES.
FEBRUARY 6, 1:48 P.M. AFTER 33.5 HOURS ON THE MOON,

ANTARES LIFTS OFF FOR A RENDEZVOUS WITH KITTY HAWK.
FEBRUARY 9, 4:05 P.M. SPLASHDOWN AFTER 9 DAYS 2 MINUTES IN SPACE. SHEPARD, MITCHELL AND ROOSA GO INTO QUARANTINE (ABOVE) ON *USS NEW ORLEANS*.

YUTU (JADE RABBIT)

Yutu, or Jade Rabbit, is China's first lunar rover. Capable of taking radar readings of the lunar crust, as well as travelling over uneven terrain, Yutu's main purpose is to gather scientific data, but the rover will also search for mineral deposits that could potentially be mined in the future. Since landing on the Moon on December 14, 2013,

Yutu has been able to begin exploring the Moon as well as photograph its companion lander, Chang'e 3. Yutu was then due to enter sleep mode to pass the frigid two-week lunar night without damage. However, the rover recently experienced some technical difficulties than the Beijing Aerospace crew are working to resolve.

COMPARING ROVERS

Lunar rovers	Mass (rover only)	Power/Height	Length	Active dates*	Wheels
Yutu	310 lb (140 kg)	solar	4 ft 9 in (1.5 m)	Dec 14 2013–present	6
Lunokhod 1	1,670 lb (756 kg)	180 watts	7 ft 7 in (2.3 m)	Nov 17, 1970–Sept 14 1971	8
Lunokhod 2	1,850 lb (850 kg)	4ft 5in (1.35 m)	5 ft 7 in (1.7 m)	Jan 15 1973– May 11 1973	8
Apollo lunar roving vehicles	463 lb (210 kg)	battery	10 ft (3 m)	Jul 31, 1971–Dec 19, 1972	4

*From landing to final contact

EXPLORING THE MOON

Landing in Mare Imbrium, very close to its planned landing site of the Sinus Iridium lava plain, Yutu is able to explore this largely flat plain at a top rate of around 656 feet (200 m) per hour. At a relatively small size, especially when compared to the latest NASA Mars rover, Curiosity, Yutu is around 310 lb (140 kg) in mass, with a payload of 44lb (20 kg). However, it runs on a comparable six-wheel axis and is similarly equipped with cameras as well as infrared and X-ray spectrometers. Its solar panels supply the energy needed for daylight hours, and the mission is initially planned to run for three months.

China launched Yutu as part of its ambitious space programme.

This also includes the Chang'e 3 lander that was launched with Yutu, which landed on December 14, 2013. Its soft landing—the first since Lunar 24 in 1976 and one of only three countries to successfully manage this—was followed by an ongoing survey of the surface and geology of the Moon surface, which will extend down by up to 98 ft (30 m). The mission was launched by a Long March rocket on behalf of the China National Space Administration (CNSA), as part of the Chinese Lunar Exploration Program. China plan to send another lander and rover to the Moon in 2015 (Chang'e 4), followed by their first return mission in 2017, which will bring back samples of lunar soil. These missions will build up to a manned landing on the Moon with the projected date of 2025. There is

even speculation that China plan to set up a more permanent base on the Moon—even one that is continuously manned.

Following its successful landing in December, Yutu took a series of pictures of Earth prior to entering sleep mode. However, reported "mechanical control abnormalities" have meant that the rover is not responding to commands. At the time of writing, China have not ruled out being able to restore Yutu, but the rover's delicate equipment is in danger of becoming unusable if the rover cannot defend itself against the harsh conditions it will experience on the Moon. Chang'e 3 is still working and should be able to fulfil the mission's key aim of testing future technologies to ensure continued progress in China's space exploration.

JADE RABBIT

Yutu got its nickname from an ancient Asian folk tale about a rabbit that lived on the Moon. This rabbit is often known as Jade Rabbit and is a companion of Chang'e, the beautiful and kind Chinese moon goddess, who gave her name to the lander that traveled with Jade Rabbit. It is said that the rabbit gave its own life to feed a starving beggar, later revealed to be ?akra, a Buddist deity, who saved the rabbit from death and drew his likeness on to the surface of the Moon for all to see. The rabbit is often depicted in a pose using a pestle and mortar, thought to be pounding the herbs needed to make the elixir of immortality for his lovely mistress. The name was selected from an online poll, which over 3.4 million voters took part in.

PANORAMIC VIEW
This lunar panorama was the first to be taken by the Chang'e 3 lander. It clearly shows Yutu exploring the Moon's rocky surface.

LAUNCH
Yutu was launched by a Long March 3B rocket on December 1, 2013, from the Xichang Satellite Launch Centre in Sichuan province, China.

TAKEN TO HEART
Chang'e 3 and Yutu are hugely popular in China, with both the lander and beloved rover gracing these postage stamps (left). China's lunar orbiter program was first established in 2004, with Chang'e 1 launching in 2007 followed by Chang'e 2 in 2010. Both missions were successful, with Chang'e 2 staying in orbit for over six times its original estimated mission length.

YUTU ROVER ON THE MOON

MARS AND VENUS

Earth's nearest neighbors have exerted a fascination on mankind since ancient times. The possibility of intelligent life on either had been ruled out by the time the first probes were sent in the early 1960s. The harsh environment on Venus, with its crushing pressures, howling winds, and extreme temperatures rules out a manned mission, and even unmanned probes last only a short time in the Venusian atmosphere before destruction. Mars is slightly more accommodating, but its constant sub-zero temperatures and frequent dust storms will make human exploration very challenging. The U.S.A.'s Mariner 2 was the first spacecraft to encounter another planet when it flew by Venus in August 1962. A series of attempted and successful flybys and probes flew to Venus before the Soviet Venera 7 probe landed in December 1970. Magellan, launched from the Space Shuttle in 1989, mapped 98 percent of Venus using radar.

Mars has seen many successful probes, landers, and rovers, most recently Spirit, Opportunity and Curiosity, which have exceeded all expectations for longevity. The feasibility of a manned Mars mission has been long studied, but with current technology it will be a lengthy mission due to the narrow launch and return windows caused by the relative orbits of Earth and Mars.

The boulder-strewn field of red rocks reaches to the horizon nearly 2 miles (3 km) from the Viking 2 probe on Mars' Planitia Utopia. Viking 2 landed on Mars on September 3, 1976, some 4,600 miles (7,400 km) from its twin, Viking 1, which touched down on July 20 of the same year.

VENERA 1–3

In 1960, Venus was an enigma, its face veiled by clouds. And it was not only astronomers who were fascinated by this mysterious planet. The Soviet Union and the U.S. were locked into Cold War rivalries and fears. Three years previous, the Soviets had shocked the Americans by placing the first satellite in orbit. Briefly, the U.S. floundered, while the Soviets thrust ahead, seeking any project that would demonstrate their supremacy: More satellites, a man in orbit, and probes to the Moon and Mars—even to Venus.

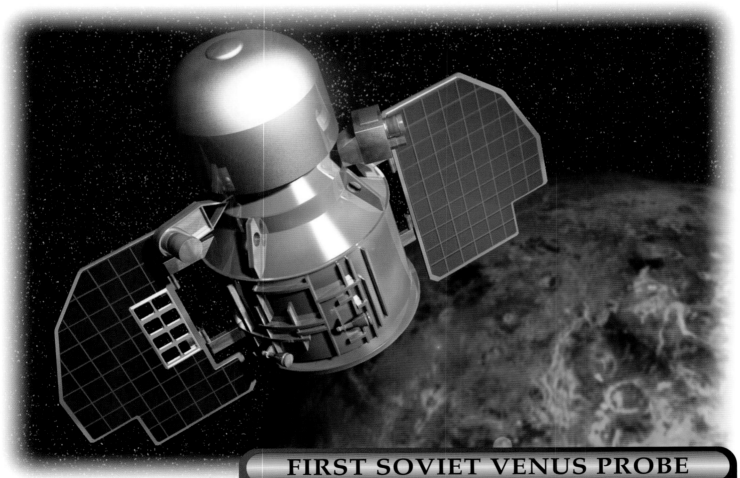

FIRST SOVIET VENUS PROBE

FEBRUARY 4, 1961	SPUTNIK 7	FAILED IN EARTH ORBIT	FEBRUARY 19, 1964	VENERA 1964B	FAILED TO REACH EARTH ORBIT
FEBRUARY 12, 1961	SPUTNIK 8/ VENERA 1	VENUS FLYBY; COMMUNICATIONS FAILURE	MARCH 27, 1964	COSMOS 27	FAILED IN EARTH ORBIT
AUGUST 25, 1962	SPUTNIK 23	FAILED TO LEAVE EARTH ORBIT	APRIL 2, 1964	ZOND 1	VENUS FLYBY; COMMUNICATIONS FAILURE
SEPTEMBER 1, 1962	SPUTNIK 24	FAILED TO LEAVE EARTH ORBIT	NOVEMBER 12, 1965	VENERA 2	VENUS FLYBY; COMMUNICATIONS FAILURE
SEPTEMBER 12, 1962	SPUTNIK 25	FAILED TO LEAVE EARTH ORBIT	NOVEMBER 16, 1965	VENERA 3	HIT VENUS; COMMUNICATIONS FAILURE
FEBRUARY 19, 1964	VENERA 1964A	FAILED TO REACH EARTH ORBIT	NOVEMBER 23, 1965	COSMOS 96	FAILED IN EARTH ORBIT

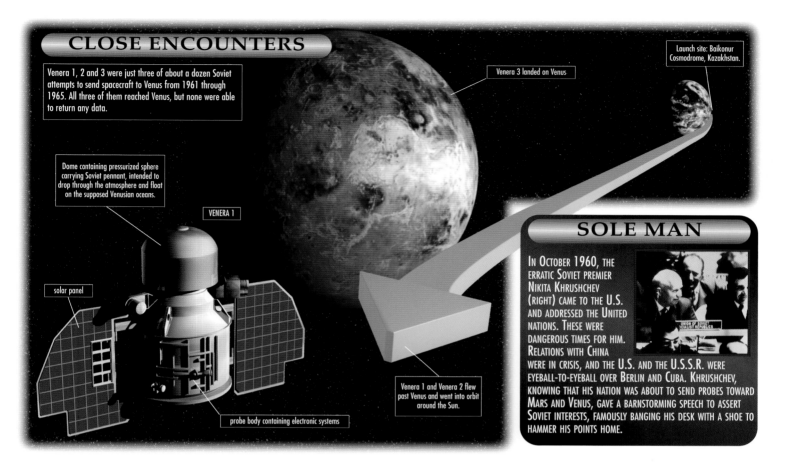

CLOSE ENCOUNTERS

Venera 1, 2 and 3 were just three of about a dozen Soviet attempts to send spacecraft to Venus from 1961 through 1965. All three of them reached Venus, but none were able to return any data.

Venera 3 landed on Venus

Launch site: Baikonur Cosmodrome, Kazakhstan.

Dome containing pressurized sphere carrying Soviet pennant, intended to drop through the atmosphere and float on the supposed Venusian oceans.

VENERA 1

solar panel

probe body containing electronic systems

Venera 1 and Venera 2 flew past Venus and went into orbit around the Sun.

SOLE MAN

In October 1960, the erratic Soviet premier Nikita Khrushchev (right) came to the U.S. and addressed the United Nations. These were dangerous times for him. Relations with China were in crisis, and the U.S. and the U.S.S.R. were eyeball-to-eyeball over Berlin and Cuba. Khrushchev, knowing that his nation was about to send probes toward Mars and Venus, gave a barnstorming speech to assert Soviet interests, famously banging his desk with a shoe to hammer his points home.

VOYAGES TO VENUS

In January 1961, when new U.S. president John F. Kennedy announced that "the torch had been passed to a new generation," he took over a nation with no clear sense of mission in space. Later that year, he would dictate an agenda that would take the U.S. to the Moon. But currently the Soviets were reveling in firsts, including the first satellite in orbit and the first probe to photograph the Moon's dark side.

They were also aiming for the planets. Two attempts to launch

Mars probes failed, but then Venus swung closer to the Earth, offering a four-month journey time—which was only half of that to Mars. On February 4, 1961, a three-stage rocket made it into orbit with a Venus probe in its fourth stage. But when the moment came to ignite the fourth stage and blast it toward Venus, nothing happened. The Soviets canceled the mission, which they called Sputnik 7, after one orbit, and explained the failure as a successful test of an Earth-orbiting platform from which a planetary probe could be launched.

A week later, Sputnik 8 carried a second probe into orbit and sent it on its way to Venus. This time, all went well, and the Soviets code-named the probe Venera 1. Weighing half a ton, it had two solar panels and instruments to study cosmic radiation, micrometeorites and charged particles. But seven days after launch, at a distance of 1.2 million miles (1.9m km), Venera 1's communications failed and the course could not be altered. The mute probe eventually passed within 62,000 miles (100,000 km) of Venus, and on into solar orbit.

MINOR TRIUMPH

Three more failures in 1962 and four in 1964—which the Soviets tried to conceal—were crowned by modified success in November 1965. Venera 2 was launched on November 12 and followed by Venera 3 four days later. Venera 2 was to make a close-up approach of Venus and take photographs. Venera 3 was to enter the atmosphere, transmit data on temperature and pressure, and then release a descent capsule which would parachute down to the planet's surface.

On February 27, 1966, after more than three months of travel, Venera 2 passed the planet at a distance of 15,000 miles (24,000 km), but again, just as the first pictures should have been sent, the communications system failed. Venera 3, after many mid-course corrections, was perfectly on target. On March 1, it hit Venus as planned but it, too, failed to transmit any information. The Soviets had to be content with a more minor triumph than they had originally hoped for: Theirs was the first probe to reach another planet. But Venus would hold on to her secrets for a few more years.

MISSION DIARY: VENERA 1–3

FEBRUARY 4, 1961 FAILURE OF SPUTNIK 7, THE FIRST SOVIET ATTEMPT TO SEND A PROBE TO VENUS.
FEBRUARY 12, 1961 SPUTNIK 8, PUT INTO ORBIT BY A MOLNIYA 8K78 ROCKET, SUCCEEDS IN LAUNCHING VENERA 1 TOWARD VENUS FROM EARTH ORBIT.
FEBRUARY 19, 1961 CONTACT WITH VENERA 1 IS LOST.
NOVEMBER 12, 1965 VENERA 2 IS LAUNCHED FROM BAIKONUR BY A MOLNIYA 8K78M (R-7) ROCKET (ABOVE).
NOVEMBER 16 VENERA 3 LAUNCHED. NOVEMBER–DECEMBER SOME

13,000 MEASUREMENTS TAKEN TO ASSESS COURSES OF VENERAS 2 AND 3. A TOTAL OF 26 COMMUNICATIONS SESSIONS INDICATE ALL IS WELL.
DECEMBER 26 COURSE CORRECTION PLACES VENERA 3 ON TARGET TO IMPACT VENUS (RIGHT) THREE MONTHS LATER.
FEBRUARY 27, 1966 VENERA 2 FLIES PAST VENUS AT 15,000 MILES (24,000 KM), BUT RETURNS NO DATA.
MARCH 1 VENERA 3 IMPACTS VENUS 250 MILES (400 KM) FROM CENTER OF VISIBLE FACE, BUT IT ALSO RETURNS NO DATA.

MARINER TO MARS

The first close-up images of Mars, sent back by Mariner 4 in 1965, shattered many illusions about the Red Planet. Until then, many people—including scientists—had supposed that Mars was an Earthlike planet, with water and perhaps a breathable atmosphere. There had even been speculation that lines on the surface, visible through telescopes, were canals built by the planet's inhabitants. But the information sent back by Mariner 4 and its sister craft revealed that Mars is a dry, barren, uninhabited world.

MARINER MARS PROBES

MARINER 4		DIMENSIONS	10 FT 10 IN (3.2 M) TALL, 19 FT ⅜ IN (5.8 M) LONG (WITH SOLAR PANELS EXTENDED)
WEIGHT AT LAUNCH	575 LB (261 KG)		
DIMENSIONS	6 FT (1.8 M) TALL, 22 FT (6.7 M) LONG (SOLAR PANELS EXTENDED)	POWER	450–500 WATTS FROM 4 PANELS OF SOLAR CELLS
POWER	195 WATTS FROM 4 PANELS OF SOLAR CELLS	DATA STORAGE.	195 MBITS NON-REUSABLE TAPE (MARINERS 6 & 7); 51.22 KBITS REUSABLE MAGNETIC TAPE (MARINER 9)
DATA STORAGE	MAGNETIC TAPE		
CAMERA	VIDICON TV CAMERA		
TELESCOPE	30.5-MILLIMETER FOCAL LENGTH REFLECTOR	CAMERAS	NARROW- AND WIDE-FIELD VIDICON TV CAMERAS (508- AND 52-MM FOCAL LENGTH FOR MARINERS 6 & 7; 50-MM FOR MARINER 9)
MARINER 6, 7 AND 9			
WEIGHT AT LAUNCH	910 LB (412 KG) (MARINERS 6 &7); 300 LB (136 KG) (MARINER 9)		

MARINER 4
In 1965 Mariner 4 sent back 21 complete images of the Martian surface. This view of a group of craters, of which the two largest are about 20 miles (32 km) across, was at the time dubbed "Picture of the Century."

MARINER 7
Mariner 7 took this photograph of Mars as it approached the planet on August 8, 1969. The picture was snapped from a distance of 293,200 miles (470,000 km).

The launches of Mariners 3 and 8 were unsuccessful.

Mariners 4, 6 and 7 flew past Mars and went into orbit around the Sun.

MARINER 9
One of the most famous images from Mariner 9 is this view of Olympus Mons. The extinct volcano rises to a height of more than 78,000 ft (24,000 m), and its base is more than 300 miles (480 km) across.

Mariner 9 went into orbit around Mars.

DEEP SCAR

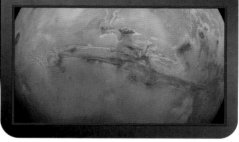

VALLES MARINERIS, THE ENORMOUS RIFT VALLEY 2,450 MILES (4,000 KM) LONG AND UP TO FOUR MILES (6.5 KM) DEEP THAT SCARS THE SURFACE OF MARS, WAS NAMED FOR ITS DISCOVERER, MARINER 9.

FIRST TO THE RED PLANET

NASA's Mariner missions to Mars contributed enormously to our knowledge of the planet, and the program was undeniably a great success despite the loss of two of the six probes shortly after they were launched. The first of these failures came on November 5, 1964, when Mariner 3 was lost after the nose fairing of its Atlas Agena D launch vehicle failed to jettison and free the craft for its journey to the Red Planet. But three weeks later, its sister craft, Mariner 4, was launched successfully. When it swung past Mars at a distance of just 6,116 miles (9,842 km) on July 14, 1965, it sent back the first-ever TV images of the Martian surface.

When scientists received Mariner 4's images and other data from Mars, they were stunned by what they saw. The TV images showed Mars to be a barren, cratered world, very different from the Earthlike planet that many had expected. As Mariner 4 dipped behind the far side of Mars, the planet's atmosphere distorted its radio signals slightly. From this distortion, the atmospheric pressure was calculated to be between five to 10 millibars—far too low to allow liquid water to exist on the surface. Furthermore, surface temperatures were estimated to be –148°F (-100°C). The findings made depressing reading for those who had hoped that Mars harbored life.

The images from Mariner 4 were limited and of poor quality, but Mars came into sharper focus when the more sophisticated Mariners 6 and 7 flew by in 1969, a memorable year for NASA. Hot on the heels of the historic Apollo 11 Moon mission, Mariners 6 and 7 swooped by Mars at a "grazing" distance of about 2,100 miles (3,370 km). Cameras attached to scanning platforms enabled each craft to collect sharp images of the Martian surface, and filters placed in front of the cameras meant that color photographs could be created. These showed the now-familiar rusty orange-red color of the planet's surface. But by chance, the cameras missed some of the most spectacular features of Mars' ancient terrain— its huge volcanoes, including the largest in the solar system, Olympus Mons.

MARINERS 8 AND 9

To achieve a global survey of Mars and find landing sites for future Viking craft, NASA needed a spacecraft in Martian orbit. Mariners 8 and 9 were built to achieve this, but the initiative got off to a disastrous start when Mariner 8 plunged into the Atlantic Ocean shortly after its launch in May 1971. Mariner 9 was launched successfully, and on November 13, 1971, it became the first artificial satellite of Mars. But the first images showed absolutely nothing—for a planet-wide dust storm was at its height. When the storm finally subsided, Mariner 9 made many important discoveries, including the Olympus Mons volcano and the 2,450-mile (4,000-km) -long Valles Marineris valley. The probe sent back a total of 7,329 images and was a fitting end to the Mariner missions.

STAR TRACK

CANOPUS

MARINER 4 WAS THE FIRST U.S. SPACECRAFT TO USE THE BRIGHT STAR CANOPUS AS AN AID TO NAVIGATION. CANOPUS SIGHTINGS WERE USED EXTENSIVELY FOR ATTITUDE CONTROL AND NAVIGATION BY SUBSEQUENT INTERPLANETARY PROBES AND MANNED APOLLO MISSIONS.

MISSION DIARY: EXPLORING MARS

NOVEMBER 5, 1964 MARINER 3 IS LOST IN AN ACCIDENT SHORTLY AFTER LAUNCH.
NOVEMBER 28, 1964 MARINER 4 IS LAUNCHED SUCCESSFULLY FROM CAPE CANAVERAL, FLORIDA, ON AN ATLAS AGENA ROCKET.
JULY 14, 1965 MARINER 4 PASSES WITHIN 6,100 MILES (9,800 KM) OF MARS AND SENDS BACK THE FIRST CLOSE-UP IMAGE OF THE PLANET.
OCTOBER 1, 1965 THE LAST TELEMETRY FROM MARINER 4 IS

RECEIVED WHEN THE SPACECRAFT IS 192 MILLION MILES (308M KM) FROM EARTH.
FEBRUARY 24, 1969 MARINER 6 IS LAUNCHED SUCCESSFULLY.
MARCH 27, 1969 MARINER 7 IS LAUNCHED SUCCESSFULLY.
JULY 28, 1969 THE FIRST MARINER 6 IMAGES ARE TRANSMITTED: 33 PICTURES OF THE FULL MARS GLOBE.
JULY 31, 1969 THE CLOSEST APPROACH OF MARINER 6 ALSO MARKS THE END OF ITS MISSION.
AUGUST 5, 1969 MARINER 7'S CLOSEST APPROACH OCCURS

WHEN THE CRAFT FLIES OVER THE MARTIAN SOUTH POLE AT A MINIMUM ALTITUDE OF 2,177 MILES (3,500 KM).
MAY 8, 1971 MARINER 8 IS LOST AFTER LAUNCH.
MAY 30, 1971 MARINER 9 IS LAUNCHED SUCCESSFULLY.
NOVEMBER 13, 1971 MARINER 9 BECOMES THE FIRST ARTIFICIAL SATELLITE OF MARS WHEN IT ENTERS AN ELLIPTICAL ORBIT OF 1,050 MILES (1,689 KM) OF THE SURFACE.
OCTOBER 27, 1972 CONTACT WITH MARINER 9 IS CUT, SIGNIFYING THE END OF THE MARINER MISSIONS.

VENERA 9 AND 10

efore the advent of space flight, Venus was an intriguing mystery to scientists. The Moon and Mars had been extensively studied by telescope for centuries, but the surface of Venus was hidden from view by impenetrable cloud cover, meaning that very little was known about it. In 1961, the Soviets began the Venera program—a long-term attempt to land a probe on the surface of Venus. After many attempts, some of which ended in success and some in failure, Venera 9 and 10 sent back to Earth the first—long anticipated—black and white pictures of the surface of Venus in October 1975.

VENERA 9 AND 10

	VENERA 9	VENERA 10
LAUNCH DATE	JUNE 8, 1975	JUNE 14, 1975
DATE OF SEPARATION	OCTOBER 20, 1975	OCTOBER 23, 1975
DATE OF LANDING	OCTOBER 22, 1975	OCTOBER 25, 1975
LANDING TIME	5:13 A.M. GMT	5:17 A.M. GMT
LANDING SITE	32° S, 291° E	16° N, 291° E
DURATION OF SURFACE OPERATION	53 MINUTES	65 MINUTES

VENUS BOUND

By 1975, eight Venera spacecraft had left Earth orbit en route to Venus. The Venera series had proved highly successful, exposing many of the planet's mysteries for the first time. Two of the eight craft had descended into the atmosphere, sending back data describing a hostile environment with an atmospheric pressure 90 times that of Earth, surface temperatures over 900°F (480°C) and an atmosphere composed of 97 percent carbon dioxide.

For the next series of Venera, the Soviet Union developed more advanced craft, capable of returning pictures from the surface for the first time. The Soviets launched two new missions to Venus during the 1975 launch window. Venera 9 lifted off on June 8, 1975, followed six days later by Venera 10. Once placed in orbit by a Proton booster, mission controllers gave them a final check before igniting the rocket stage to propel the spacecraft on their three-and-a-half month journey to explore Venus.

Two days before arriving at Venus, the lander and the orbiter separated to follow different trajectories. The lander was encased in an 8-ft (2.4-m) diameter spherical capsule which would provide protection during entry. The hermetically sealed sphere distributed the heat load and prevented the craft from imploding due to the immense atmospheric pressure. This protective heat shield was designed to survive temperatures up to 21,630°F (12,000°C). To give it even more protection from the fiery atmosphere, the lander was cooled with refrigerant before it began its descent.

1 Venera orbital station before research station separation.

2 After entering the atmosphere, the hemispherical covers of the research station separate.

3 Three main parachutes deploy at 40 miles (65 km) above the surface.

4 On landing, a shock-absorbing landing ring cushions the impact.

DESCENT INTO A HOT WORLD

VENERA 9
The craft consisted of a cylinder with two solar panels and a parabolic antenna. A bell-shape unit holding the propulsion system was attached to the cylinder's base and the 8-ft (2.4-m) diameter sphere held the lander.

SURFACE PHOTO
The Venera 9 lander operated for 53 minutes, long enough to return this one image of the surface of Venus. Angular and weathered rocks, 11–15 in (25–40 cm) across, dominate the landscape.

SUCCESSFUL LANDING

Forty miles from the surface, the heat shield was discarded and parachutes were deployed to stabilize the lander and slow descent. At 31 miles (50 km) from the surface, the dense atmosphere allowed aerodynamic braking. A circular collar around the top of the craft generated enough drag to slow the rate of descent. Final touchdown, 75 minutes after entering the atmosphere, was cushioned by a metallic shock-absorbing ring.

The Venera 9 operated for 53 minutes before failure. Three days later, Venera 10 touched down 1,364 miles (2,195 km) away and survived for 65 minutes. Surface data and video images collected by the probes were transmitted to the orbiter for later relay back to Earth.

The probes had also taken measurements of the composition of the atmosphere and structure of the clouds during descent.

The Venera orbiters relayed the data from the landers back to Earth and studied the planet's atmosphere. But the first photographs of Venus were the mission highlight. The images of the rocky landscape provided the first clues to our understanding of planetary evolution.

MISSION DIARY: VENERA 9 AND 10

June 8, 1975 Venera 9 is launched into orbit by Proton rocket (right) from Baikonur Cosmodrome in Kazakhstan. After one Earth orbit Venera 9 rocket stage ignites.
June 14 Venera 10 is launched into orbit from Baikonur Cosmodrome. After one Earth orbit Venera 10 rocket stage ignites.
October 20 Venera 9 descent craft separates from its orbiter.
October 22 Venera 9 instrument compartment cooled to 14°F (-10°C).

Descent to 78 miles (125 km) above surface Venera 9 capsule enters the Venusian atmosphere (right) at 6.6 miles (10 km) per second. The temperature is 21,630°F (12,000°C). The covers protecting the lander separate. At a velocity of 820 ft (250 m) per second, the drogue parachute deploys.
40 miles (65 km) from the surface Three main parachutes deploy.
31 miles (50 km) from the surface Parachutes jettison; drag slows craft further.
October 22, 5:13 a.m. GMT Venera 9 lands on the surface with an impact velocity of 20–26 ft (6–8 m) per second. The TV camera covers eject and camera and instruments switch on.
October 22, 6:06 a.m. Venera 9 ceases to function

after 53 minutes.
October 23 Venera 10 descent craft separates from its orbiter.
October 25, 5:17 a.m. Venera 10 lands on surface of Venus. The first photos of the surface (above) are relayed to the orbiter.
6:22 a.m. Venera 10 ceases to function after 65 minutes.

VIKING TO MARS

After a 10-month journey through interplanetary space, two U.S. spacecraft reached orbit around Mars in the summer of 1976. Vikings 1 and 2 were the most sophisticated robot probes yet built, and they had a mission to match their capabilities. While the orbiters mapped the Red Planet from high above its atmosphere, each one sent a Viking lander to make a soft touchdown on the surface. The probes beamed back the first images of the rock-strewn landscape, sniffed the Martian air and soil, took measurements of its chemical composition—and, most tantalizingly, searched for signs of life.

VIKING PROBE STATISTICS

VIKING 1		VIKING 2	
LAUNCH	AUGUST 20, 1975, KENNEDY SPACE CENTER	LAUNCH	SEPTEMBER 9, 1975, KENNEDY SPACE CENTER
LAUNCH VEHICLE	TITAN 3E-CENTAUR	LAUNCH VEHICLE	TITAN 3E-CENTAUR
TOTAL MASS (UNFUELED)	3,247 POUNDS	TOTAL MASS (UNFUELED)	3,247 LB (1,473 KG)
MARS ORBIT INSERTION	JUNE 19, 1976	MARS ORBIT INSERTION	AUGUST 7, 1976
LANDING	JULY 20, 1976, CHRYSE PLANITIA	LANDING	SEPTEMBER 3, 1976, UTOPIA PLANITIA
ORBITER SHUTDOWN	AUGUST 17, 1980	ORBITER SHUTDOWN	JULY 25, 1978
LOSS OF CONTACT WITH LANDER	NOVEMBER 13, 1982	LOSS OF CONTACT WITH LANDER	APRIL 11, 1980

VIKING EXPLORERS

The Red Planet's first Earth visitor was a Soviet probe that landed in 1971. The probe transmitted TV pictures for 20 seconds and then went silent, possibly because of a radio relay failure—or perhaps as an unlucky result of the planet's most violent dust storm in decades. As that storm raged, the U.S. Jet Propulsion Laboratory was steering Mars' first artificial satellite, Mariner 9, into orbit. When the skies cleared, Mariner shot detailed TV pictures of the planet's volcanoes and valleys.

The data transmitted by Mariner 9 proved vital in preparations for Viking's journey to Mars four years later. But Viking was a far more ambitious project than Mariner. The Viking team managed to launch two lander-orbiter combination craft within weeks of each other, bringing both Vikings into Martian orbit after a 10-month cruise halfway around the Sun. The mission was one of the most complex ever attempted, as well as one of the most expensive uncrewed space projects to date, costing about a billion dollars. But Viking was worth every penny.

Both landers successfully separated from their orbiters and touched down on the planet's surface to begin examinations of Martian biology and sample the chemistry of this distant world.

Neither lander found the hoped-for signs of life. Nevertheless, Viking was a great success. The orbiters sent back tens of thousands of images of Mars and its moons, Phobos and Deimos. They measured the structure and composition of the atmosphere, and detected water vapor. And the landers kept working for several years, providing valuable data on climate and seismology, as well as vivid panoramas of the dusty reddish landscape.

MISSION DIARY

NOVEMBER 15, 1968 PROJECT VIKING INITIATED (RIGHT) AS A JOINT VENTURE OF THE JET PROPULSION LABORATORY AND NASA'S LANGLEY RESEARCH CENTER. WORK SOON BEGINS ON THE LANDER'S PROTECTIVE AEROSHELL.
AUGUST 20, 1975 AT CAPE CANAVERAL, A TITAN ROCKET LAUNCHES VIKING 1 ON ITS 62-MILLION-MILE (100M KM) VOYAGE TO MARS.
SEPTEMBER 9, 1975 VIKING 2 LAUNCHED.

JUNE 14, 1976 APPROACHING THE RED PLANET, VIKING 1 CAMERAS COME TO LIFE, TAKING IMAGES OF THE GLOBE OF MARS (ABOVE).
JUNE 19 VIKING 1 BRAKING MANEUVER PUTS THE SPACECRAFT INTO MARTIAN ORBIT.
JUNE 21 AFTER AN ADJUSTMENT TO ITS ORBIT, VIKING 1 SCANS THE PLANET FOR A SUITABLE LANDING SITE.
JULY 20, 3:32 A.M. VIKING 1 LANDER SEPARATES FROM THE ORBITER AND BEGINS ITS DESCENT.

JULY 20, 6:53 A.M. VIKING 1 LANDER TOUCHES DOWN IN CHRYSE PLANITIA; 25 SECONDS LATER IT TRANSMITS A PICTURE OF ONE OF ITS OWN FOOTPADS ON FIRM, ROCKY GROUND (RIGHT).
AUGUST 7 VIKING 2 ARRIVES IN MARTIAN ORBIT.
AUGUST 9 WITH THE HELP OF DATA FROM ITS TWIN, VIKING 2 BEGINS THE SEARCH FOR A LANDING SITE.
SEPTEMBER 3, 5:37 P.M. VIKING 2 LANDER SETTLES ON THE SURFACE THOUSANDS OF MILES FROM VIKING 1, AT UTOPIA PLANITIA.
JULY 25, 1978 VIKING 2 ORBITER IS POWERED DOWN AFTER A SERIES OF ATTITUDE CONTROL THRUSTER GAS LEAKS.

APRIL 11, 1980 VIKING 2 LANDER TERMINATED AFTER BATTERY FAILURE.
AUGUST 17, 1980 CONTACT LOST WITH VIKING 1 ORBITER.
NOVEMBER 13, 1982 PROJECT VIKING ENDS WITH LOSS OF SIGNAL FROM THE VIKING 1 LANDER.

1 LOOKING FOR A LANDING SITE
On arrival in orbit, the Viking 1 orbiter scans the planet for a suitable landing site. This painstaking investigation lasts for a month, until the region of Chryse Planitia (the "Plains of Gold") is finally chosen.

2 SEPARATION
On July 20, the Viking 1 lander and its aeroshell receive the command to separate from the orbiter. The aeroshell slows the craft as it begins its descent and protects it from friction heating as it passes through the Martian atmosphere.

MARTIAN PANORAMA
Six minutes after touchdown, Viking 1 transmits a panoramic view of the Martian surface. Suspended dust particles make the sky appear brighter than had been expected.

SOIL SAMPLES
Using a robotic arm, Viking takes samples of soil for use in four onboard chemical experiments that attempt to find signs of bacterial life. Results from both landers were inconclusive.

3 TOUCHDOWN
Four miles above the surface, the lander's 52-ft (16-m) diameter parachute opens. Seven seconds later the aeroshell is jettisoned; eight seconds after that the three lander legs are extended. At 1 mile (1.6 km), retrorockets fire and Viking makes a gentle touchdown on the surface of Mars.

MARS GLOBAL SURVEYOR

Mars Global Surveyor (MGS) is a surveyor satellite, weather satellite and communications satellite all rolled into one. In circular polar orbit around Mars from March 1999 to the end of its extended career in 2006, its onboard cameras have taken thousands of high-resolution surface photos. It also returned daily temperature and atmospheric moisture data, lasting far longer than its planned two-year mission. Surveyor played a crucial role in Martian exploration and told scientists much about the Red Planet.

MARS GLOBAL SURVEYOR

MISSION PHASES		BEGIN MAPPING	APRIL 4, 1999
LAUNCH	NOVEMBER 7 1996	PAYLOAD	MARS ORBITER CAMERA (MOC)
MARS ARRIVAL	SEPTEMBER 12, 1997		MARS ORBITER LASER ALTIMETER (MOLA)
AEROBRAKING 1	NOVEMBER 7, 1997		THERMAL EMISSION SPECTROMETER PROJECT (TES)
SCIENCE	MARCH 27, 1998		MAGNETOMETER AND ELECTRON REFLECTOMETER
AEROBRAKING 2	SEPTEMBER 23, 1998		(MAG/ER)

MAPPING MISSION

Mars Global Surveyor (MGS) began its 466-million mile (750 million km) journey from Cape Canaveral Air Station on November 7, 1996. Once out of Earth orbit, the craft unfurled its twin solar panels, only for mission controllers to find that the latch on one of the panels had cracked, leaving the panel itself stuck at an angle. The panels were designed to provide power as well as to help the craft assume the proper orbit. Normally, this is accomplished by using the rocket engine to slow the craft. But the rocket used to launch MGS lacked the propellant to both lift the craft from Earth and slow it down once in Mars orbit. Instead, the plan was for Surveyor to initially assume a highly elliptical orbit. At the low point of this orbit, the craft would just skim the Martian atmosphere. Friction would slow the craft on each pass, until it finally assumed the correct orbit.

But engineers now worried that the stress of aerobraking could cause the damaged panel to break off entirely, causing further problems. Mission operators rescheduled the aerobraking procedure to place less stress on the damaged panel, revising the original four-month schedule to a longer, 12-month schedule.

During the longer hiatuses from aerobraking, MGS was able to conduct scientific studies. During one such study, Surveyor's Magnetometer and Electron Reflectometer (MER) detected local "fossil" magnetic fields from Mars' oldest rocks.

On April 4, 1999, Surveyor finally attained mapping orbit and its original 687-day mapping mission finally began.

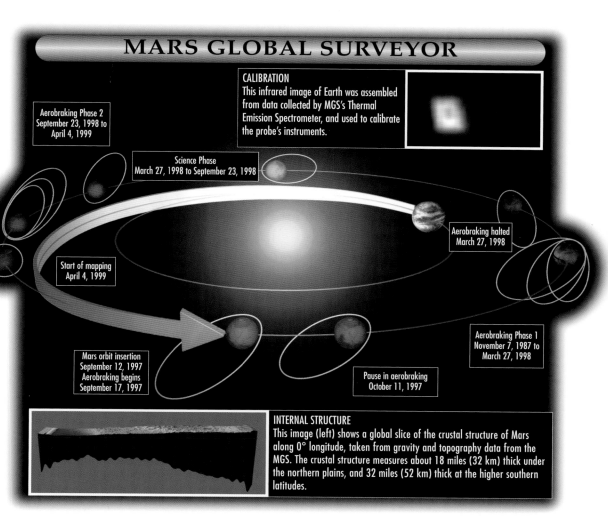

MARS GLOBAL SURVEYOR

CALIBRATION
This infrared image of Earth was assembled from data collected by MGS's Thermal Emission Spectrometer, and used to calibrate the probe's instruments.

Aerobraking Phase 2
September 23, 1998 to April 4, 1999

Science Phase
March 27, 1998 to September 23, 1998

Start of mapping
April 4, 1999

Aerobraking halted
March 27, 1998

Mars orbit insertion
September 12, 1997
Aerobraking begins
September 17, 1997

Pause in aerobraking
October 11, 1997

Aerobraking Phase 1
November 7, 1987 to
March 27, 1998

INTERNAL STRUCTURE
This image (left) shows a global slice of the crustal structure of Mars along 0° longitude, taken from gravity and topography data from the MGS. The crustal structure measures about 18 miles (32 km) thick under the northern plains, and 32 miles (52 km) thick at the higher southern latitudes.

MAJOR DISCOVERIES

MGS's Mars Orbiter Laser Altimeter (MOLA) uses reflected laser beams to gather topographical details of the Martian surface. MOLA has turned up vast plains in the northern hemisphere of Mars, flatter than any of those yet found on Earth. These plains could be sheets of sediment left by evaporating oceans as the planet cooled over time, or possibly vast frozen lakes left covered in layers of dust.

The MGS's onboard Thermal Emission Spectrometer (TES) charts the temperature and chemical composition of both the Martian surface and atmosphere to provide a detailed mineral map of the entire planet. The most spectacular data are the 25,000 photographs taken by MGS. These reveal a dynamic world of winds and dust dunes. It is also a mysterious world, with numerous landforms scientists cannot explain. The two Martian poles appear completely different—the north is flat and pitted while the south has a series of holes and mesas. More mysterious still are numerous gullies that seem to have been caused by recent liquid water flows—which should be impossible according to conventional views of Martian geology.

MISSION DIARY: MARS GLOBAL SURVEYOR

November 7, 1996
Mars Global Surveyor (right, in assembly) is launched from Cape Canaveral Air Station by Delta 7925 rocket (second right).

September 12, 1997 MGS arrives at Mars. A 22-minute firing of main rocket engines places the spacecraft in an elliptical orbit.

September 17, 1997 Start of aerobraking. MGS performs a series of orbit changes to skim the Martian atmosphere, using air resistance to slow down a tiny amount with every orbit.

October 11, 1997 Pause in aerobraking. Two of Surveyor's solar panels had bent slightly under pressure — aerobraking was halted to allow them to resume position.

November 7, 1997 Resumption of aerobraking, at a slower pace.

March 27, 1998 Aerobraking is halted to allow Surveyor to drift into the proper position with respect to the Sun. The hiatus is used to collect scientific data.

September 23, 1998 Resumption of aerobraking to shrink the high point of Surveyor's orbit down to 205 miles

(330 km) from the Martian surface (view of Mars taken March 1999, right).

April 4, 1999 Surveyor's orbit reaches a distance of 205 miles (330 km) and science operations begin. MGS begins mapping Mars and investigating sites of interest.

2005 MGS mission continues relaying data to Earth.

November 2, 2006 Earth receives its final communication from MGS. Further attempts to communicate with the satellite are unsuccessful.

PATHFINDER TO MARS

On July 4, 1997, an object that looked like a cluster of beachballs hit Mars' rusty surface, bounced and came to rest in an ancient flood channel. The Mars Pathfinder mission had landed. The first spacecraft to visit Mars in 21 years, Pathfinder and its companion rover Sojourner spent almost three months probing the Red Planet. As planned, they beamed back reams of valuable new information about Martian geology and climate. Perhaps more importantly, as the pioneers of NASA's Discovery program, the two little probes inaugurated an exciting new era in space exploration.

PATHFINDER FACTS

LAUNCH VEHICLE	DELTA 2 7925 WITH PAM-D UPPER STAGE	CAMERA	STEREO; 140° FIELD OF VIEW
	PATHFINDER LANDER	**SOJOURNER ROVER**	
DIMENSIONS	TETRAHEDRON, 3 FT (0.9 M) TALL; WITH CAMERA, 5 FT (1.5 M) TALL	DIMENSIONS	2 FT (0.6 M) LONG, 1.5 FT (0.45 M) WIDE, 10 IN (0.25 M) HIGH
WEIGHT	2,062 LB (935 KG) AT LAUNCH; 793 LB (340 KG) ON MARS; 300 LB (136 KG) IN MARS GRAVITY	WEIGHT	22 LB (10 KG) ON MARS; 8.36 LB (3.79 KG) IN MARS GRAVITY
POWER	178 WATTS (DURING CRUISE); UP TO 850 WATTS (ON MARS)	MAXIMUM SPEED	2 FT (0.6 M) PER MINUTE

LOW BUDGET

The Pathfinder mission was the first in a new era of cost-conscious space exploration, a demonstration that NASA had opted for a "faster, better, cheaper" policy. Each spacecraft in the new Discovery program had to be designed, built and launched within three years. It had to stay within a tight budget of around $150 million. Above all, it had to do the job.

Pathfinder's launch was routine, but its arrival on Mars was not. The probe slammed into the atmosphere at more than 16,500 mph (26,554 km/h). Its heat shield glowed as

friction with Mars' thin air robbed it of its speed. At 1,000 mph (1,600 km/h), a parachute opened. The probe still fell rapidly until, only eight seconds before impact, it fired braking rockets and inflated a cocoon of airbags. At 40 mph (64 km/h), Pathfinder hit the rocky plain of Ares Vallis and bounced to a halt.

The airbag technique had never been tried before, but it worked flawlessly. Pathfinder emerged from its protective cocoon and, four hours later, released the Discovery program's next novelty: Sojourner, a tiny, six-wheeled autonomous rover. The first of its kind to see

active interplanetary service, Sojourner was only 10 in (25 cm) high; yet the rover contained an alpha proton X-ray spectrometer and a miniature processing lab that could analyze specimens of Martian rock and soil. As Sojourner toiled over its samples—each analysis required the rover to be stationary for 10 hours—Pathfinder sent home streams of valuable data on surface weather conditions.

The mission blinked out on September 27, 1997, when the last successful transmission passed between Mars and Earth. NASA's new small-scale, elegant approach had been a triumph.

NAMESAKE

APPROPRIATELY, SOJOURNER MEANS "ONE WHO STAYS A WHILE." BUT THE MARS ROVER WAS NAMED FOR SOJOURNER TRUTH (RIGHT), AN AFRICAN-AMERICAN LEADER WHO WAS ACTIVE DURING THE CIVIL WAR. SHE WAS THE SUBJECT OF A WINNING ESSAY IN A NASA SCHOOLS' COMPETITION.

MISSION DIARY: MARS PATHFINDER

1994 PROJECT PLANNING BEGINS.
JUNE 1995 DESCENT SYSTEMS — ROCKETS PLUS AIR BAGS — ARE TESTED. SOJOURNER IS DEVELOPED ON A SIMULATED MARTIAN LANDSCAPE (RIGHT).
JANUARY 31, 1996 PATHFINDER LANDER IS TEAMED WITH SOJOURNER AND TEST-FITTED IN THE CASING (SECOND RIGHT)

THAT WILL CARRY THEM TO MARS.
AUGUST 14, 1996 COMPLETE MARS PATHFINDER PROBE ARRIVES AT CAPE CANAVERAL TO PREPARE FOR SUBSEQUENT LAUNCH.
DECEMBER 5, 1996 MARS PATHFINDER IS

LAUNCHED ON A DELTA 2 (LEFT) FROM CAPE CANAVERAL PAD 17B.
JULY 4, 1997 THE PROBE LANDS ONLY 13 MILES (21 KM) OFF TARGET IN THE ARES VALLIS REGION OF MARS (RIGHT).
JULY 6, 1997 THE SOJOURNER ROVER MAKES ITS FIRST TRIP.

TOUCHDOWN ON MARS

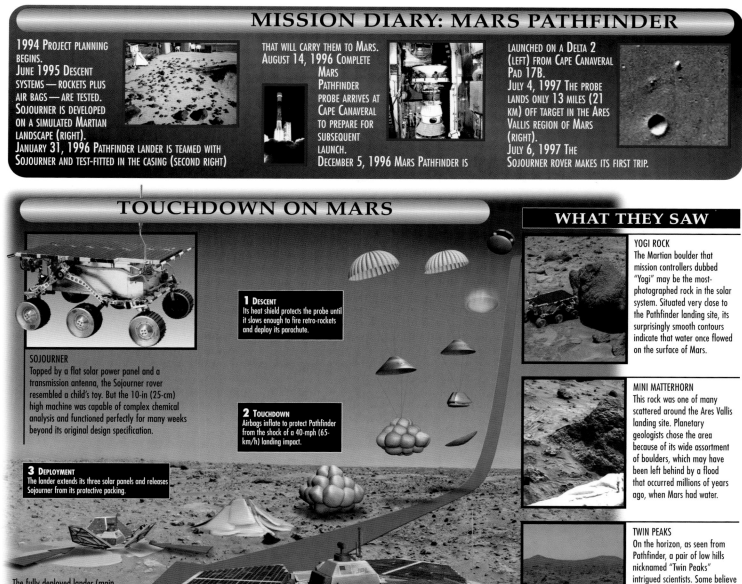

SOJOURNER
Topped by a flat solar power panel and a transmission antenna, the Sojourner rover resembled a child's toy. But the 10-in (25-cm) high machine was capable of complex chemical analysis and functioned perfectly for many weeks beyond its original design specification.

1 DESCENT
Its heat shield protects the probe until it slows enough to fire retro-rockets and deploy its parachute.

2 TOUCHDOWN
Airbags inflate to protect Pathfinder from the shock of a 40-mph (65-km/h) landing impact.

3 DEPLOYMENT
The lander extends its three solar panels and releases Sojourner from its protective packing.

The fully deployed lander (main image) was renamed the Sagan Memorial Station in honor of American space scientist Carl Sagan, who died in December 1996 while Pathfinder was in interplanetary space.

WHAT THEY SAW

YOGI ROCK
The Martian boulder that mission controllers dubbed "Yogi" may be the most-photographed rock in the solar system. Situated very close to the Pathfinder landing site, its surprisingly smooth contours indicate that water once flowed on the surface of Mars.

MINI MATTERHORN
This rock was one of many scattered around the Ares Vallis landing site. Planetary geologists chose the area because of its wide assortment of boulders, which may have been left behind by a flood that occurred millions of years ago, when Mars had water.

TWIN PEAKS
On the horizon, as seen from Pathfinder, a pair of low hills nicknamed "Twin Peaks" intrigued scientists. Some believe that traces of stratification on the hills is another sign that water once played an important part in the shaping of the surface of Mars.

MARS ROVERS: OPPORTUNITY AND SPIRIT

In a quest to discover once and for all whether water ever existed on Mars, two identical six-wheeled rover vehicles have followed the success of the much smaller Mars Sojourner by exploring further and for longer than any other mission to the Red Planet. Their data and successes have led to further exploration of the Red Planet.

MARS ROVER SPECS

MASS AT LAUNCH

ROVER	408 LB (185 KG)
LANDER	767 LB (348 KG)
BACKSHELL / PARACHUTE	742 LB (209 KG)
HEAT SHIELD	172 LB (78 KG)
CRUISE STAGE	425 LB (193 KG)
PROPELLANT	110 LB (50 KG)
TOTAL MASS	2,343 LB (1,063 KG)

REMOTE CONTROL

Launched on Delta II rockets, the Mars landers and rovers entered the Martian atmosphere inside protective "aeroshells". Each was slowed in the thin air by a parachute and Rocket Assisted Descent (RAD) motors that fire 30–50 ft (10–15 m) above the surface, bringing the vehicle to a dead stop. At the same time, a six-lobed airbag inflated and cushioned the impact of the craft striking the surface and subsequent bounces.

The two Rovers landed on opposite sides of Mars, with Spirit landing in the large shallow Gusev Crater near the south rim of the deeper Bonneville Crater. Its heat shield fell on the north rim and was spotted when Spirit drove up to the crater's edge. Opportunity landed on the Meridiani Planum, an area known to be rich in hematite, a material associated with hot springs or standing pools of water.

After several Martian days (sols), two-way communication was established and tested and the rovers were ready to explore Mars in more detail than had ever been possible before. To communicate with Earth, the rovers relay information by way of orbiting craft; 70 percent of the mission data is transmitted via the Mars Odyssey Orbiter and 30 percent by way of the Mars Global Surveyor.

Driving a vehicle by remote control 50 million miles (80 million km) from Earth requires caution. Several cameras are used to select a path, steer the rovers and avoid close obstacles. The rovers are not designed for speed. On a hard, flat surface they could reach up to 2 in (5 cm) per second, but were strictly limited by hazard avoidance software to 10-second runs, followed by 20-second pauses to assess the terrain, giving an average speed of ⅓ in (1 cm) per second. Records for distance driving in one day reached 722 ft (220 m) in March 2005. Driving over a surface and then reversing back allows the cameras to study the tracks and get an idea of the softness or otherwise of the terrain.

Each future move is discussed and planned in great detail before being commanded. A duplicate rover is tested on Earth on various simulated Martian surfaces, which are often tilted to angle equal to slopes faced by the actual rovers. Occasionally, softer than expected sand caused the rovers to become stuck for long periods. Scientists simulated this with various building and gardening materials and developed techniques for driving out of these "sand traps".

After exploring its immediate environment, Spirit then set off towards a feature dubbed the Columbia Hills. Each of the seven peaks is named for one of the astronauts lost in the 2003 Columbia disaster. The hills, rising to 300 ft (90 m) above the plain were estimated as 1 mile (1.6 km) distant, a drive that would take up to 160 sols if the rover lasted that long.

A photograph of the floor of Gusev Crater, taken by the first rover to land, Spirit. This is one of the first images beamed back to Earth from the rover shortly after it touched down, captured by the rover's panoramic camera.

DELTA LAUNCH

BOTH ROVERS WERE LAUNCHED ON DELTA II ROCKETS, ALTHOUGH THE ROVER B MISSION NEEDED A HEAVY VERSION OF THE ROCKET WITH MORE FUEL BECAUSE MARS AND EARTH HAD MOVED FURTHER APART IN THE MONTH SINCE THE FIRST LAUNCH.

EXTENDED WARRANTY

Opportunity drove up to the stadium-sized Endurance Crater. After much debate it was decided to enter the crater as the possible science benefits outweighed the risk of not being able to drive out again. As it happened, Opportunity later became stuck in a sand trap for nearly five weeks but was successfully extracted.

Near its own heat shield, Spirit discovered an iron meteorite—the first meteorite discovered on another world.

Many other discoveries pointed to evidence of the former presence of water on Mars, the main scientific target of the mission. These included: spherules; smile-shaped marks in rocks and ripple patterns on rock surfaces. Evidence of magnesium sulphates pointed to the evaporation of water in the distant past.

The rovers were able to observe the sky as well as the Earth, and photographed the Earth and stars from an unusual viewpoint. They also witnessed lunar eclipses where Mars's moons—Phobos and Deimos—passed in front of the Sun. A streak in the sky in one photo perplexed scientists for some time, but is now thought to have been the Viking 2 orbiter, which is still circling Mars.

The rovers pleased NASA and the Jet Propulsion Laboratory by remaining in functional condition well past the "warranty" of their 90-sol primary missions, which were completed in April 2004. From then on the crews could take greater risks than before. A software update allowed two hours "autonomous" driving each day after an hour of "blind" driving following a route pre-planned on Earth. Autonomous driving, which in fact meant driving for 6 ft 6 in (2 m) then pausing to look for obstacles, allowed the rovers to cover as much ground in just three sols as they had in 70 during early parts of the mission.

Dust accretion on the solar panels caused a reduction in available power from time to time and a partial loss of vision from the cameras, but strong winds later blew the dust clear, giving improved performance. While Spirit finally stopped communicating in 2010, to date Opportunity is still sending data back to Earth, over 10 years since it landed on the surface of Mars.

MISSION DIARY

JUNE 10, 2003 ROVER A MISSION (SPIRIT) LAUNCHED.
JULY 7, 2003 ROVER B MISSION (OPPORTUNITY) LAUNCHED.
JANUARY 3, 2004 SPIRIT LANDS IN GUSEV CRATER.
JANUARY 24, 2004 OPPORTUNITY LANDS ON MERIDIANI PLANUM.
JUNE 8, 2004 OPPORTUNITY ENTERS ENDURANCE CRATER AND SPENDS FOLLOWING SIX MONTHS EXPLORING IT.
JUNE 11, 2004 SPIRIT REACHES COLUMBIA HILLS.
2010 SPIRIT CEASES TO FUNCTION.
2014 OPPORTUNITY CONTINUES ITS JOURNEY.

CURIOSITY

Launched on November 26, 2011 from Cape Canaveral as part of the Mars Science Laboratory mission, Curiosity began its initial two-year mission when it lands on August 6, 2012. Curiosity will continue the work of Sojourner—from NASA's earlier Pathfinder mission—Opportunity and Spirit, by assessing the surface of the moon and analysing its geology and climate. The rover will take these investigations further by evaluating the possibility of Mars ever having microbial life forms. The suspected presence of water on Mars has long made this an intriguing possibility. NASA intend to follow up the Curiosity rover with a further rover mission by 2020, with plans for human exploration in the future.

LUNAR ROVERS

Rover	Launch date	Landing date	Planned duration	Actual current duration*
Curiosity	26 November 2011	6 August 2012	668 sols (686 days)	Ongoing
Opportunity	7 July 2003	25 January 2004	90 sols (92.5 days)	Ongoing
Spirit	10 June 2003	4 January 2004	90 sols (92.5 days)	2623 sols (2695 days)
Sojourner	4 December 1996	4 July 1997	7–30 sols (7.2–30.8 days)	83 sols (85.3 days)

* As of... up to final contact ** Sols = Martian sols; days = Earth days

GETTING TO KNOW THE RED PLANET

The planned landing site for Curiosity was the Gale crater. With a diameter of 96 miles (154 km) and depth of approximately 3 miles (5 km), the crater has a dome in its center called Aeolis Mons, where Curiosity would start its investigations. The landing was successful, with the rover ending its journey only 1.5 miles (2.4 km) from its target, now known as the Bradbury Landing site (named after science fiction author Ray Bradbury). The crater was caused by an impact caused over 3 billion years ago. It was chosen for the landing site as the area is thought to have once contained water. With wind erosion exposing layers of sediment, Curiosity will analyze Martian geology going back billions of years—including the planet's evolution.

The site might also have once held water, a factor that could be key to any signs of life found on the Red Planet.

Curiosity was the first NASA Mars rover to land in an active state. On touchdown, it triggered explosives to free itself from the cables used for the 66 feet (20 m) descent stage. The spacecraft then crash landed at a pre-arranged site. The rover is also the first to collect samples of rock drilled from the surface of Mars.

Approximately twice the size and five times the weight of its predecessors Opportunity and Spirit, Curiosity shares the same basic design of six wheels, a suspension system designed to cope with the uneven surfaces of Mars, and mounted cameras to aid movement and record data and images, of which a huge amount has already been sent back to NASA's

astronomers. The first NASA Mars rover, Sojourner, also shared this structure, although it was much smaller than the approximately 10 feet (3 m) length of Curiosity. The rover also differs in that it can take also drill and gather samples of soil and rocks and even process these samples in its onboard test chambers, to identify and measure mineral levels and compositions. Its power generator means it can run for around two Earth years and cover more inaccessible terrain, while its camera is capable of taking extreme close-up images. Radiation measurements are also taken, which are vital for the future planning of any human exploration trips to Mars and their safe duration for the astronauts.

LIFE ON MARS?

Public support has been overwhelming, with the NASA website crashing when live streams of the first footage was aired on their website. One of the most enduringly popular topics searched for is whether or not Curiosity has been able to find any evidence of life on the Red Planet. So far, Curiosity has found evidence to support the theory that the environment on Mars was capable of supporting life in the past (with Mars now at a later stage in its possibly faster evolution than Earth). Whether Curiosity will be able to find anything that proves there was any actual life forms on Mars is as yet unknown, as well as what happened on the Red Planet to cause the end of any existing life. It may still be a long time before our curiosity is satisfied on this intriguing point, although a follow up NASA Mars rover mission is in the pipeline for 2020.

ROVING AROUND MARS

THE GALE CRATER
The trenches of the Gale Crater hold a mountain known as Aeolis Mons, known as Mount Sharp.

GETTING BIGGER
These tyres give a representation of the difference in size of each lunar rover, ranging from Sojourner to Curiosity.

CURIOSITY
The main objectives of Curiosity are to determine whether Mars once held life and what its climate once looked like.

OPPORTUNITY AND SPIRIT
TThe main objectives of the combined Mars Exploration Rover mission are to analyze the geology and climate of Mars.

SOJOURNER
The main objectives of the Mars Pathfinder mission were to test run the equipment at lower costs than NASA's Viking missions.

WATER ON MARS
This image, taken by Curiosity, shows areas where the rover has found evidence of water existence on the Moon, usually found as ice or vapor. These areas are shown in color, with the brightest and reddest areas highlighting the presence of the greatest remains of water.

YINGHUO-1 AND FOBOS-GRUNT ORBITERS

Fobos-Grunt and Yinghuo-1 were launched together on November 8, 2011, in an interplanetary mission between Russian and China with the aim of finding out more about Mars and its largest moon, Phobos. The Russian Fobos-Grunt probe (also known as Phobos-Grunt, like the moon it was intended to study) carried a lander that would have landed on the moon of Phobos, as well as a return vehicle that was to carry soil samples back to Earth. Launched by China as their first probe to explore Mars, Yinghuo-1 was due to orbit Mars, studying the surface, atmosphere and magnetic field. Unfortunately, neither spacecraft fulfilled their mission.

ORBITER SUCCESSES AND FAILURES

Orbiter	Launch	Destruction	Successes	Failures
Yinghuo-1	November 8, 2011	January 15, 2012	None	Declared lost before undergoing destructive reentry
Fobos-Grunt	November 8, 2011	January 15, 2012	None	Declared lost before undergoing destructive reentry
Columbia	April 12, 1981	February 1, 2003	Columbia completed 27 missions successfully	Columbia disintegrated on reentry, killing its seven crew members
Challenger	April 4, 1983	January 28, 1986	Challenger completed 9 missions successfully	Challenger broke apart just over a minute after launch of its tenth mission

FAILURE TO ORBIT

After the initially successful launch into Earth's orbit from Kazakhstan's Baikonur Cosmodrome, Fobos-Grunt did not perform the burns necessary to launch the crafts out of low Earth orbit (LEO) and onto their course for Mars. Both crafts fell from their 91 mile (147 km) orbit and underwent destructive reentry into Earth's atmosphere on January 15, 2012. They disintegrated over the Pacific Ocean that same day.

The Fobos-Grunt spacecraft was the initiative of the Russian Space Research Institute (Roscosmos) and was based on the design of the failed Phobos program of the 1980s. Originally planned for launch in October 2009, Fobos-Grunt was delayed because of delays in the development of the craft—specifically its computers. This meant the much later launch window of 2011. The initial launch into Earth's orbit went as planned, but it was quickly discovered that Fobos-Grunt and Yinghuo-1 had not left the parking orbit as two vital rocket burns had not taken place. With scientists unable to make contact with or control the craft, it began to lose altitude and fall. While some communications with Fobos-Grunt were successful, they were not enough to discover the source of the problem and reset the craft on its projected trajectory out of LEO and on towards Mars. With Roscosmos trying to control the craft despite opportunities fast running out, Fobos-Grunt continued to fall out of elliptical orbit before it finally reentered Earth's atmosphere and disintegrated.

Fears abounded regarding the payload of Fobos-Grunt, which included quantities of hydrazine and nitrogen tetroxide fuels. These highly toxic fuels could freeze on reentry, meaning they would not burn out as planned. However, the craft was reported to have fallen into the Pacific ocean, causing no injury or ill effects. Controversy on a foreign institution causing the mission to fail on purpose was never proved.

Yinghuo-1 also never made it out of LEO and was destroyed with Fobos-Grunt on reentry. The planned mission was to spend a year orbiting Mars, analysing the environment, magnetic field, sand storms and surface dust. The orbiter would also have photographed the surface of the Red Planet. The mission was part of a landmark international and interplanetary agreement between China and Russia. The combined data from Fobos-Grunt and Yinghuo-1 would be shared, as would some of the experimental data. Following successful launch on to the trajectory for Mars, Yinghuo-1 would have separated from Fobos-Grunt to enter orbit around Mars.

SECRETS OF MARS AND PHOBOS

The launch also carried the Living Interplanetary Life Experiment from the Planetary Society. This mission was to carry living microorganisms on the three-year journey to Mars and back to earth, testing whether the organisms could withstand this time in deep space. The Life Experiment was destroyed with the rest of the crafts. Although similar experiments are in the pipeline, this experiment was criticized for the potential of contaminating Mars or Phobos with live bacteria, which remains a threat to any similar mission despite the strict procedures in place to prevent such a potential catastrophe. An earlier test run of the LIFE experiment had been undertaken on flight STS-134 of the Endeavour, the final Space Shuttle flight prior to its retirement in May 2011.

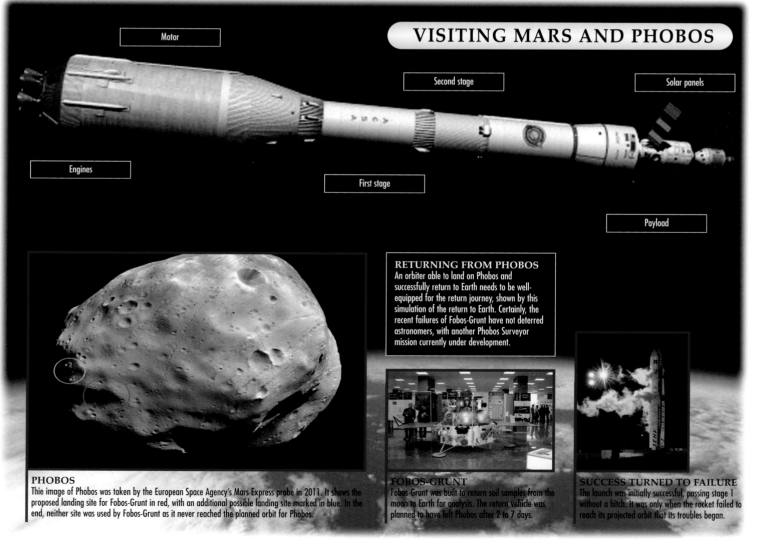

VISITING MARS AND PHOBOS

Motor

Second stage

Solar panels

Engines

First stage

Payload

PHOBOS
Thie image of Phobos was taken by the European Space Agency's Mars Express probe in 2011. It shows the proposed landing site for Fobos-Grunt in red, with an additional possible landing site marked in blue. In the end, neither site was used by Fobos-Grunt as it never reached the planned orbit for Phobos.

RETURNING FROM PHOBOS
An orbiter able to land on Phobos and successfully return to Earth needs to be well-equipped for the return journey, shown by this simulation of the return to Earth. Certainly, the recent failures of Fobos-Grunt have not deterred astronomers, with another Phobos Surveyor mission currently under development.

FOBOS-GRUNT
Fobos-Grunt was built to return soil samples from the moon to Earth for analysis. The return vehicle was planned to have left Phobos after 2 to 7 days.

SUCCESS TURNED TO FAILURE
The launch was initially successful, passing stage 1 without a hitch. It was only when the rocket failed to reach its projected orbit that its troubles began.

MAVEN

The Mars Atmosphere and Volatile Evolution (MAVEN) was launched by NASA on November 18, 2013 from Cape Canaveral, Florida. MAVEN is planned to enter orbit around Mars on September 22, 2014, following an areocentric elliptical orbit around the planet. MAVEN's aim is to discover more about the Martian upper atmosphere and climate, including how it was lost to space over time. The mission will last at least one year and data gleaned from MAVEN will be combined with surface data and measurements from the Curiosity Mars Rover and aims to send back new data on the many mysteries still shrouding Mars.

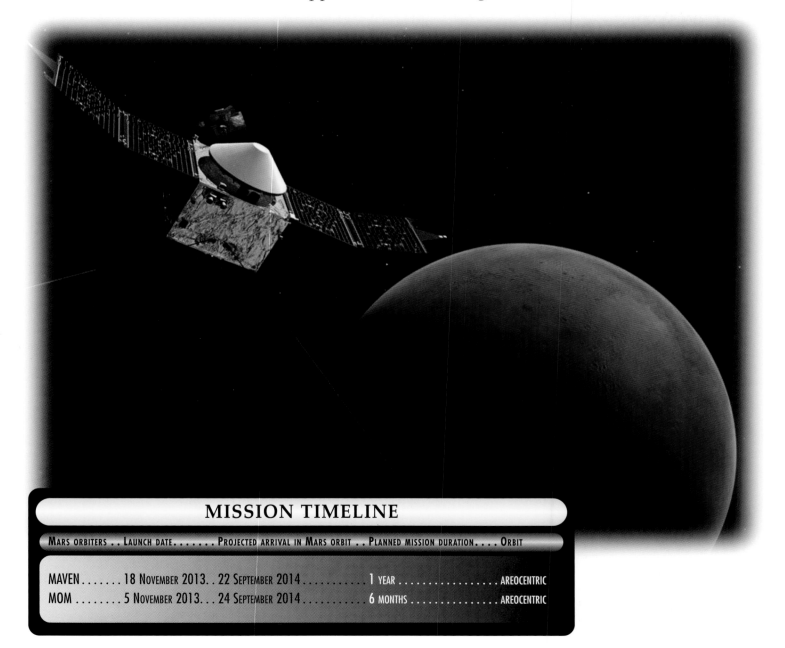

MISSION TIMELINE

Mars orbiters	Launch date	Projected arrival in Mars orbit	Planned mission duration	Orbit
MAVEN	18 November 2013	22 September 2014	1 year	AREOCENTRIC
MOM	5 November 2013	24 September 2014	6 months	AREOCENTRIC

THE RACE IS ON

If its schedule goes to plan, MAVEN will beat MOM into orbit around Mars by a mere two days. The Mars Orbiter Mission is another orbiter, which was launched by the Indian Space Research Organisation on November 5, 2013. MOM marks the first ISRO interplanetary mission and will make it the fourth space agency to reach Mars. The purpose of the mission is to both explore the surface and atmosphere of Mars, and develop India's launch systems and spacecraft technology.

Both MAVEN and MOM will be key to discovering more about Mars' climate and how it changed so much. MAVEN will be focusing on Mars' upper atmosphere to find out why any water that might once have existed on Mars has now disappeared, perhaps escaping as gas through the diminishing atmosphere. MAVEN will be able to plot an orbit of 93 to 3,728 miles (150 to 6,000 km) above the planet's surface, including taking five "deep dips" down to just 93 miles (150 km) minimum altitude in order to take samples of the remaining upper atmosphere. The surface temperature of Mars is now too cold to support water as liquid, due to the planet's core cooling over millions of years. However, certain features of the surface of Mars suggest that water was present in large quantities, perhaps as rivers or lakes. There is also evidence of mineral deposits that require the existence of water, plus layers of sediment.

Additionally, the magnetic field around Mars has decayed over time, which has possibly resulted in the planet's low atmospheric pressure. This means that for the last few billion years, electrically charged solar winds of up to 1,000,000 mph (1,609,000 km/ph) would have begun to sweep away much of the atmosphere that helped keep the water on the planet's surface. MAVEN will be able to measure the rate by which atmospheric gases are lost, discovering more about Mars' history and atmospheric changes. In addition, data from Curiosity on the chemical composition of the surface of Mars will be used to measure current rates of atmosphere loss.

Built by Lockheed Martin Space Systems, MAVEN weighed 5,400 lb (2,454 kg) at launch and stretches 37 feet (11 m) from wingtip to wingtip, with its core cubical module being 7.5 feet (2.3 m) high. It was rigorously tested to ensure it can survive the extreme temperatures and winds around Mars. The orbiter is equipped with a Particles and Field package, which measures solar wind and energy particles, as well as magnetic fields and ions. MAVEN's mission is currently estimated to last one Earth year.

STAYING ON SCHEDULE

After ten years of preparation and a budget of $650 million, government personnel strikes almost cost MAVEN its launch date, which would have meant missing the narrow launch window of 20 days. If missed, it would be 26 months until Mars moved back into the correct alignment with Earth, meaning that MOM would have beaten MAVEN into orbit by quite some time. The 17-day strikes—which took place only seven weeks before the launch date—were only resolved when emergency funding was released to allow the launch to go ahead as scheduled. It was also partly due to the effective team members being slightly ahead of schedule and being so eager to return to work and ensure the launch went ahead.

DISCOVERING MARS

THE RED PLANET
Mars has intrigued astronmers ever since it was discovered that its atmosphere could have once held life.

LAUNCH
This picturesque image shows MAVEN being successfully launched from Cape Canaveral. MAVEN remains on course for many future successes.

MARS NOW
This artist's interpretation shows the surface of Mars as it is today; dry, dusty and waterless.

MARS THEN
Here Mars is shown awash with mountains and lakes, with a blue cloudy sky much like Earth's.

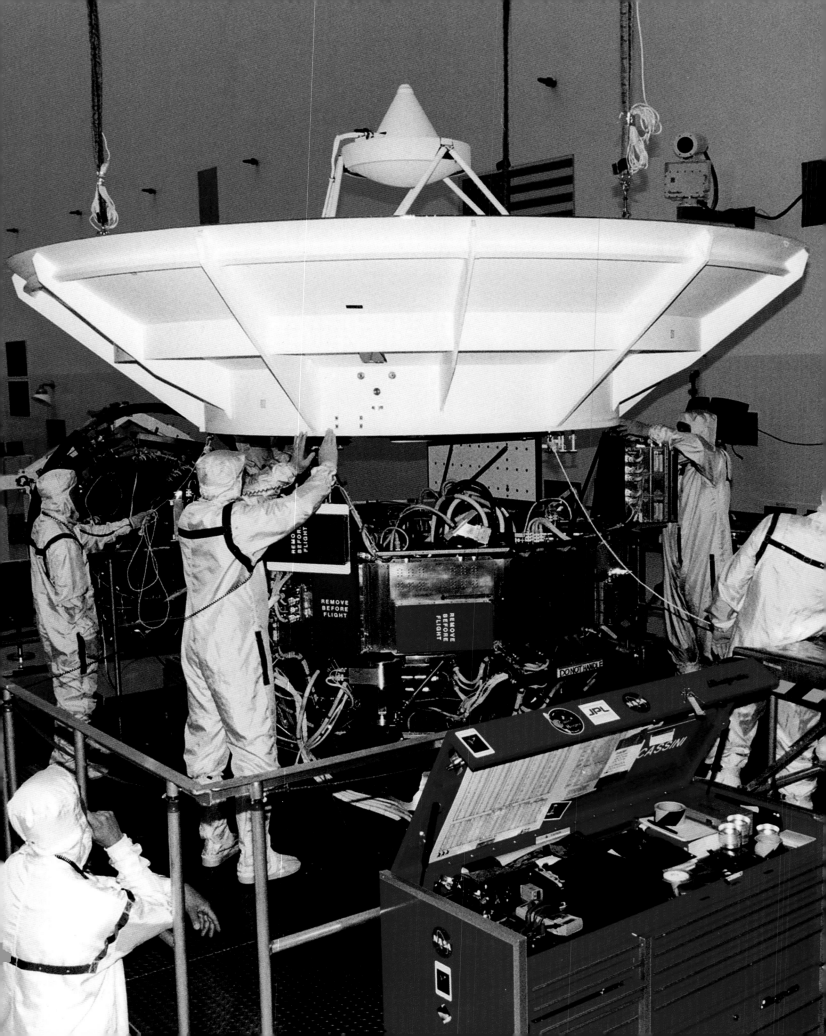

EXPLORING FURTHER

Exploration of the outer planets is a time-consuming business due to the great distances involved. The length of some missions has exceeded the careers of the scientists who devised and nurtured them. Pioneer 10 passed Jupiter in December 1973, and in 1990 it became the first man-made object to leave the solar system. It was last heard from in 2003 when over 10.6 billion miles (17 billion km) from Earth. The Huygens probe touched down on Saturn's moon Titan in January 2005, making the furthest landing from Earth. The Cassini mothership continues to study Saturn, Titan and Saturn's 32 other moons. Experiments are underway to use solar wind to power future spacecraft, with photons from the sun pushing against a sail made of Mylar or a similar thin, lightweight fabric. Such a craft would accelerate very slowly, but would eventually reach enormous velocities. For example, a future probe to the outer solar system could reach 60,000 mph (100,000 km/h) in three years, enough to reach the dwarf planet Pluto in about half the time of a conventionally-powered spacecraft.

Cassini-Huygens is a joint NASA/ESA/ASI unmanned space mission to study Saturn and its moons. This photograph shows scientists performing final checks on the Cassini spacecraft's antennae prior to its launch on October 15, 1997.

PIONEER SOLAR MISSIONS

Although the earliest U.S. interplanetary probes lost the race to the Moon, they discovered something more interesting along the way: a torrent of charged particles emanating from the Sun. Instead of jockeying for a piece of lunar territory, the later Pioneer probes were sent into orbit around our nearest star. Weighing in at about 140 lb (64 kg), these little explorers proved that interplanetary space—previously thought to be empty—is filled with powerful magnetic fields and a strong wind that blows from the Sun.

PIONEER SOLAR MISSIONS

Name	Launch Date	Mission Length	Operational Life	Weight	Instruments	Experiments
Pioneer 5	Nov 11, 1960	10 months	29 years	95 lb (43 kg)	4	4
Pioneer 6	Dec 12, 1965	6 months	30 yr 8 mo	141 lb (64 kg)	6	10
Pioneer 7	Aug 17, 1966	6 months	29 yr 6 mo	141 lb (64 kg)	6	8
Pioneer 8	Dec 13, 1967	6 months	29 yr 8 mo	141 lb (64 kg)	6	8
Pioneer 9	Aug 11, 1968	6 months	24 years	141 lb (64 kg)	6	8

SOLAR SUCCESS

The Pioneer program got off to a rocky start. Originally planned to be a series of lunar probes, only one of the first five Pioneer probes, Pioneer 4, made it anywhere near the Moon. Another of the early probes, Pioneer 3, discovered a second belt of trapped radiation around Earth—the first belt was discovered by the first U.S. satellite, Explorer 1, in 1958. But these early Pioneers were largely regarded as failures. With the Moon proving difficult to reach, the next five Pioneer probes were designed to study the space between the Earth and the Sun, and they would do so with spectacular success.

On March 3, 1960, Pioneer 5 was launched from Cape Canaveral. Once out in interplanetary space, the probe—which operated for 106 days—detected complex magnetic patterns. Like the earlier Pioneers, Pioneer 5 carried an instrument to detect the levels of radiation trapped in the Earth's magnetic fields. The probe also carried two other high-energy particle detectors and a magnetic-field detector. It correlated changes in magnetic fields with the eruption of solar flares and proved that the Sun made space an extremely dangerous place for an unprotected astronaut.

The next Pioneer design, which lasted for four missions, was designed to investigate these intriguing electrical and magnetic phenomena in greater detail. After the early failures, the Pioneer program was finally ready to make some important contributions to the emerging field of space science.

EXTRA LONG LIFE

In addition to Pioneer 5's instrumentation, Pioneers 6 to 9 also had two instruments designed to measure the density of electrons in the solar wind. NASA's ingenious scientists even monitored changes in the probe's tracking signal to glean information about the wind the transmission passed through. All this information allowed a better understanding of the structure and flow of the solar wind.

Among the new technology tested on the Pioneer probes was a gyroscope-type stabilization system. Like a spinning top or a rotating bicycle wheel, a space

probe is less likely to wander off course if it is spinning. First used with the Pioneer 6 probe, the technique proved so stable—the probe spun successfully at about 60 rpm—that it became standard on all NASA's subsequent deep-space probes.

Each of the next three Pioneers—Pioneer 7 was launched in August 1966, 8 in December 1967 and 9 in November 1968—had a slightly different orbit so that a network of solar outposts began to form.

The probes allowed scientists to forecast solar storms accurately up to two weeks in advance—plenty of time to prepare to study the event. The solar network continued to operate until the early 1970s, providing a wealth of information about the complex electrical and magnetic lines that swirl around the Sun.

The satellites themselves operated far longer than the network. The youngest satellite, Pioneer 9, was the first to go—it stopped transmitting in 1983.

The other three probes held on for another decade. NASA's Deep Space Network last made contact with Pioneer 7 in 1995, when only one of its instruments was still working. The story was the same for Pioneer 8, contacted a year later. Most surprising of all was the oldest sibling, Pioneer 6, which was still sending back data in 2000. Launched in 1977, Voyager 2 has made it into the record books as NASA's oldest operational probe, still transmitting data in March 2014.

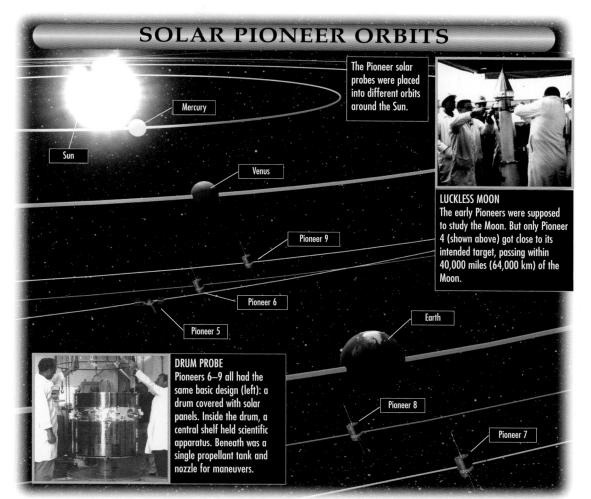

SOLAR PIONEER ORBITS

Mercury

Sun

Venus

Pioneer 9

Pioneer 6

Pioneer 5

Earth

Pioneer 8

Pioneer 7

The Pioneer solar probes were placed into different orbits around the Sun.

LUCKLESS MOON
The early Pioneers were supposed to study the Moon. But only Pioneer 4 (shown above) got close to its intended target, passing within 40,000 miles (64,000 km) of the Moon.

DRUM PROBE
Pioneers 6–9 all had the same basic design (left): a drum covered with solar panels. Inside the drum, a central shelf held scientific apparatus. Beneath was a single propellant tank and nozzle for maneuvers.

MISSION DIARY: PIONEER 6

DECEMBER 16, 1965 PIONEER 6 (RIGHT) IS LAUNCHED FROM LAUNCH COMPLEX 17A, CAPE CANAVERAL.
NOVEMBER 1968 PIONEER 6 GOES BEHIND THE SUN. BY MONITORING HOW ITS TRACKING SIGNAL CHANGES, SCIENTISTS LEARN ABOUT THE COMPOSITION OF THE SUN'S CORONA.
NOVEMBER 8, 1968 WITH THE LAUNCH OF PIONEER 9, THE PIONEER SOLAR STORM OBSERVATION NETWORK NOW NUMBERS FIVE MEMBERS — FOUR SATELLITES AND THE EARTH.

DECEMBER 15, 1995 PIONEER 6'S PRIMARY TRANSMITTER FAILS.
JULY 11, 1996 NASA'S RADIO TELESCOPE COMMUNICATION SYSTEM — THE DEEP SPACE NETWORK (RIGHT) — TRACKS PIONEER 6 AND SUCCESSFULLY COMMANDS THE PROBE TO SWITCH TO ITS BACK-UP TRANSMITTER. AFTER 30 YEARS AND 8 MONTHS, PIONEER 6 IS STILL WORKING.
OCTOBER 6, 1997 PIONEER 6 IS TRACKED FOR THE LAST TIME BY DEEP SPACE STATION 43 NEAR CANBERRA, AUSTRALIA.
NOVEMBER 1997 NASA FORMALLY ABANDONS PIONEER 6.

PIONEER 10 AND 11

Pioneer 10 and 11 are humanity's first emissaries to the galaxy at large. Launched in the early 1970s to investigate Jupiter and Saturn, they were the first spacecraft designed to leave the solar system behind. Now, they are more than 7 billion miles from home and still traveling outwards through space. Pioneer 11's power ran down in 1995, but Pioneer 10—officially retired—made contact with NASA in 2003, and may still be transmitting although communications are now down. Should either one encounter an alien race in the vastness of interstellar space, each carries a message from humanity.

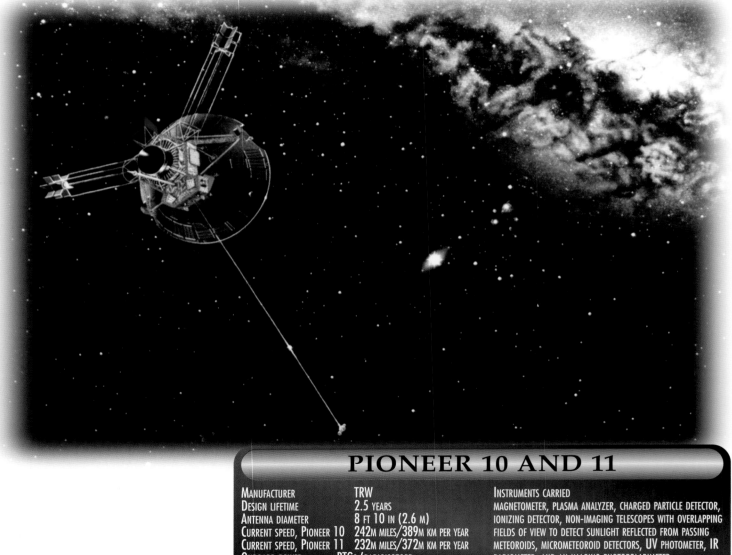

PIONEER 10 AND 11

MANUFACTURER	TRW	**INSTRUMENTS CARRIED**
DESIGN LIFETIME	2.5 YEARS	MAGNETOMETER, PLASMA ANALYZER, CHARGED PARTICLE DETECTOR,
ANTENNA DIAMETER	8 FT 10 IN (2.6 M)	IONIZING DETECTOR, NON-IMAGING TELESCOPES WITH OVERLAPPING
CURRENT SPEED, PIONEER 10	242M MILES/389M KM PER YEAR	FIELDS OF VIEW TO DETECT SUNLIGHT REFLECTED FROM PASSING
CURRENT SPEED, PIONEER 11	232M MILES/372M KM PER YEAR	METEOROIDS, MICROMETEOROID DETECTORS, UV PHOTOMETER, IR
ONBOARD POWER	RTGs (RADIOISOTOPE THERMONUCLEAR GENERATORS) PROVIDING 155 W	RADIOMETER, AND AN IMAGING PHOTOPOLARIMETER. PIONEER 11 ALSO CARRIED A LOW-SENSITIVITY FLUXGATE MAGNETOMETER.
COMMUNICATIONS RATE	16–2,048 BPS THROUGH NASA DSN STATIONS	

DISTANT TRAVELERS

Pioneer 10 left for Jupiter on March 3, 1972. It was the latest in a long line of Pioneer probes designed to explore interplanetary space. At Jupiter's distance from the Sun, Pioneer 10 and its sibling Pioneer 11 could not rely on solar cells for energy. Instead, they carried a nuclear generator that drew power from the heat produced by radioactive plutonium. The most visible feature of both craft was an umbrella-like antenna 9 ft (2.75 m) across, needed to transmit data to Earth and to receive instructions from Mission Control. These instructions were vital—1970s computers were too heavy for the probes to carry, so there were no onboard brains. Instead, controllers had to put up with the fact that the probes would be so far distant that radio signals would take an hour and a half to reach them.

Pioneer 10, spinning five times a minute to stabilize its antenna, plunged into the asteroid belt beyond Mars in mid-July 1972, and emerged unharmed in February 1973. The project scientists had worried that it would be crippled or destroyed by a 30,000-mph (50,000 km/h) collision with an interplanetary pebble, but Pioneer 10's survival gave them the confidence to launch Pioneer 11 in its wake.

Pioneer 10 began its encounter with Jupiter on November 26, 1973, when its instruments registered the presence of the giant planet's stormy magnetosphere. In the 26 days of its flypast, the little probe was battered by the intense radiation belts that surround Jupiter. As Pioneer skimmed past the planet, 81,000 miles (130,000 km) above the cloud tops, its instruments turned on Jupiter's most striking feature—the Great Red Spot. Pioneer's pictures

confirmed that the Spot was in fact a giant storm. Its encounter over, Pioneer 10 headed out of the solar system at 25,000 mph (40,000 km/h) and passed the orbit of Pluto in 1990.

After Pioneer 10's success, there seemed no need to repeat the same program. Pioneer 11 was given a course correction that pointed it toward Jupiter's south pole rather than its equator, and took the spacecraft much closer to the planet than its predecessor—only 21,000 miles (33,796 km/h) above the clouds. As Pioneer 11 whipped past, Jupiter's gravity accelerated the probe to a speed of 107,373 mph (172,800 km/h) and flung it onward to a second planetary encounter—with Saturn. At Saturn, Pioneer 11 swung past only 1,200 miles (1,931 km) from the ring system, and 13,000 miles (20,920 km) above the clouds. It discovered that Saturn had radiation belts and a strong magnetic field, found two

new rings and a moon, and helped scientists understand much more about the structure and composition of the gas giant. Its mission completed, Pioneer 11 also headed out of the solar system, heading in the opposite direction to its predecessor.

SNAPSHOTS

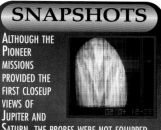

ALTHOUGH THE PIONEER MISSIONS PROVIDED THE FIRST CLOSEUP VIEWS OF JUPITER AND SATURN, THE PROBES WERE NOT EQUIPPED WITH CAMERAS. INSTEAD, THEY SCANNED THEIR TARGETS WITH A DEVICE CALLED A PHOTOPOLARIMETER. BY COMBINING SEVERAL SETS OF RAW DATA (SHOWN ABOVE), MISSION SCIENTISTS WERE ABLE TO CREATE PERFECT FULL-COLOR IMAGES OF THE PLANETS.

MISSION DIARY: PIONEER 10 AND 11

MARCH 3, 1972 PIONEER 10 LAUNCHED FROM CAPE CANAVERAL ON ATLAS-CENTAUR BOOSTER.
JULY 1972–FEBRUARY 1973 PIONEER 10 SUCCESSFULLY TRAVERSES THE ASTEROID BELT BETWEEN MARS AND JUPITER.
APRIL 6, 1973 PIONEER 11 LAUNCHED.
NOVEMBER 26, 1973 PIONEER 10 PASSES WITHIN SINOPE'S ORBIT, JUPITER'S OUTERMOST KNOWN MOON.
DECEMBER 4, 1973, 6:26 P.M. PIONEER 10'S CLOSEST APPROACH TO JUPITER, 81,000 MILES (130,000 KM) ABOVE THE PLANET'S CLOUDS.
DECEMBER 3, 1974 PIONEER 11'S CLOSEST APPROACH TO JUPITER 26,725 MILES (43,000 KM).

SEPTEMBER 1, 1979 PIONEER 11'S CLOSEST APPROACH TO SATURN, AT 13,000 MILES (20,920 KM).
JUNE 13, 1983 PIONEER 10 CROSSES THE ORBIT OF NEPTUNE (THEN THE OUTERMOST PLANET DUE TO THE ECCENTRICITY OF PLUTO'S ORBIT) AND BECOMES THE FIRST CRAFT TO LEAVE THE SOLAR SYSTEM.
FEBRUARY 23, 1990 PIONEER 11 LEAVES THE SOLAR SYSTEM.
SEPTEMBER 22, 1990 PIONEER 10 REACHES 50 TIMES THE EARTH'S DISTANCE FROM THE SUN.
NOVEMBER 1995 LAST COMMUNICATIONS RECEIVED FROM

PIONEER 11.
MARCH 31, 1997 FORMAL END OF PIONEER MISSIONS.
FEBRUARY 17, 1998 VOYAGER 1 SPACECRAFT OVERTAKES PIONEER 10 TO BECOME MOST DISTANT HUMAN OBJECT.
2 MILLION A.D. PIONEER 10 REACHES THE NEIGHBORHOOD OF THE RED STAR ALDEBARAN.
4 MILLION A.D. PIONEER 11 MAKES A CLOSE APPROACH TO A SMALL STAR IN THE CONSTELLATION AQUILA (ABOVE).

ONWARD AND OUTWARD

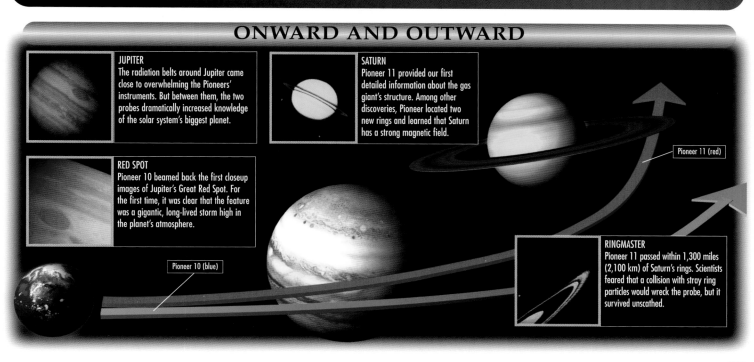

JUPITER
The radiation belts around Jupiter came close to overwhelming the Pioneers' instruments. But between them, the two probes dramatically increased knowledge of the solar system's biggest planet.

RED SPOT
Pioneer 10 beamed back the first closeup images of Jupiter's Great Red Spot. For the first time, it was clear that the feature was a gigantic, long-lived storm high in the planet's atmosphere.

SATURN
Pioneer 11 provided our first detailed information about the gas giant's structure. Among other discoveries, Pioneer located two new rings and learned that Saturn has a strong magnetic field.

Pioneer 11 (red)

Pioneer 10 (blue)

RINGMASTER
Pioneer 11 passed within 1,300 miles (2,100 km) of Saturn's rings. Scientists feared that a collision with stray ring particles would wreck the probe, but it survived unscathed.

VOYAGER MISSIONS

The twin spacecraft Voyagers 1 and 2 have transformed our understanding of the outer solar system. Originally designed to study only Jupiter and Saturn, these two intrepid probes have visited all the gas giants—Jupiter, Saturn, Uranus and Neptune. They have sent back many startling images of churning atmospheres, complex ring systems and exotic moons, some of which are large enough to be worlds in their own right. Now, as the Voyagers head for the stars, they continue to report from the very edge of the solar system, with Voyager 1 the first manmade object to enter interstellar space.

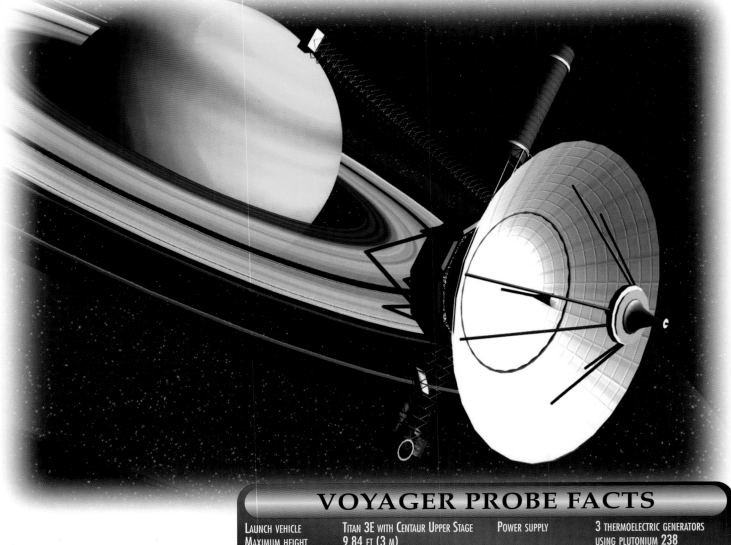

VOYAGER PROBE FACTS

LAUNCH VEHICLE	TITAN 3E WITH CENTAUR UPPER STAGE	POWER SUPPLY	3 THERMOELECTRIC GENERATORS
MAXIMUM HEIGHT	9.84 FT (3 M)		USING PLUTONIUM 238
BOOM LENGTH	EXTENDABLE TO 42.5 FT (13 M)	HIGH GAIN ANTENNA	12 FT IN DIAMETER (3.6 M)
SPACECRAFT WEIGHT	1,820 LB (825 KG)	TRANSMITTER POWER	23 WATTS
SCIENCE INSTRUMENT WEIGHT	234 LB (106 KG)	CAMERAS	TELEPHOTO 0.4°, WIDE ANGLE 3°
DATA STORAGE CAPABILITY	538 MILLION BITS		

THE GRAND TOUR

Voyagers 1 and 2 set off on their epic journeys of discovery in 1977. Their launches were timed to take advantage of a rare planetary alignment. Every 176 years, the giant planets of the outer solar system are aligned in such a way that a well-aimed spacecraft can use their gravitational fields to slingshot its way from one to the other. After each encounter, the spacecraft picks up speed—enough to have reached Neptune by 1989 in the case of Voyager 2. Without such boosts, the trip would have taken at least 30 years.

First port of call on the "Grand Tour" was Jupiter. Voyager 1 got there first, in the spring of 1979, followed by its sister ship in July of the same year. The two probes investigated Jupiter's Great Red Spot, found a previously undiscovered ring system and even detected powerful lightning bolts on the planet.

Hurled onward to Saturn by Jupiter's gravity, the Voyagers reached the planet in 1981 and beamed back our first detailed pictures of its intricate system of rings and moons. Voyager 1 made a close fly-by of the moon Titan, where it found an atmosphere denser than the Earth's. But the Titan mission was the spacecraft's last: The moon's gravity swung Voyager 1 high above the ecliptic (the orbital plane of the solar system) and onward into interstellar space.

Voyager 2 continued to Uranus and sent back images of a planet that up until then had been little more than a blank disk to earthbound astronomers. At Neptune, the spacecraft passed within 3,000 miles (4,800 km) of the surface, its closest approach to any planet since it had left Earth. Its last encounter was with Neptune's largest moon, Triton. There, almost 3 billion miles (4.8 billion km) from the Sun, Voyager 2 made the totally unexpected discovery of ice volcanoes. The probes were still in contact up to September 2013, when Voyager 1 entered interstellar space.

MISSION DIARY: VOYAGER

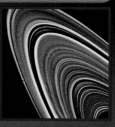

AUGUST 20, 1977 VOYAGER 2 IS LAUNCHED FROM CAPE CANAVERAL.

SEPTEMBER 5, 1977 VOYAGER 1 IS LAUNCHED FROM THE CAPE 16 DAYS LATER (ABOVE RIGHT).

MARCH 5, 1979 VOYAGER 1 REACHES JUPITER. EN ROUTE, IT OVERTOOK VOYAGER 2 AND JUSTIFIED ITS DESIGNATION.

JULY 9, 1979 VOYAGER 2 MAKES A FLYBY OF JUPITER ON A COMPLEMENTARY COURSE TO VOYAGER 1. IT MAKES A CLOSE APPROACH TO THE MOON EUROPA AND INVESTIGATES JUPITER'S SOUTHERN LATITUDES.

NOVEMBER 12, 1980 VOYAGER 1 PASSES SATURN. AFTER A CLOSE ENCOUNTER WITH TITAN, IT IS HURLED OFF-COURSE BY TITAN'S GRAVITY.

AUGUST 26, 1981 VOYAGER 2 PLUNGES THROUGH SATURN'S RINGS

(RIGHT) AND PICKS UP ENOUGH SPEED FROM ITS GRAVITY TO CARRY ON TO URANUS.

JANUARY 24, 1986 VOYAGER 2 SURVEYS URANUS AND ITS MANY SATELLITES.

AUGUST 25, 1989 VOYAGER 2 PHOTOGRAPHS THE COLDEST PLACE TO BE FOUND SO FAR FOUND IN THE SOLAR SYSTEM — THE SURFACE OF NEPTUNE'S LARGEST MOON TRITON (BELOW).

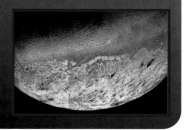

TRAVEL SNAPSHOTS

Night looms over the top right of Uranus. Its far side always appears to be dark.

Uranus is unusual for lying on its side. Its polar region is shown here in red.

Saturn's flattened sphere is obvious as Voyager 2 makes its approach to the planet.

These streaks on Dione were caused by the fracturing of the moon's surface.

Voyager 2 discovers six new Neptune satellites, including lumpy Proteus.

The shadow of the moon Ganymede falls on Jupiter. Fiery Io is to the right.

The stormy Great Red Spot churns on Jupiter. It is 15,000 miles (24,000 km) from top to bottom.

A high-altitude cloud soars far above the blue haze of Neptune's surface.

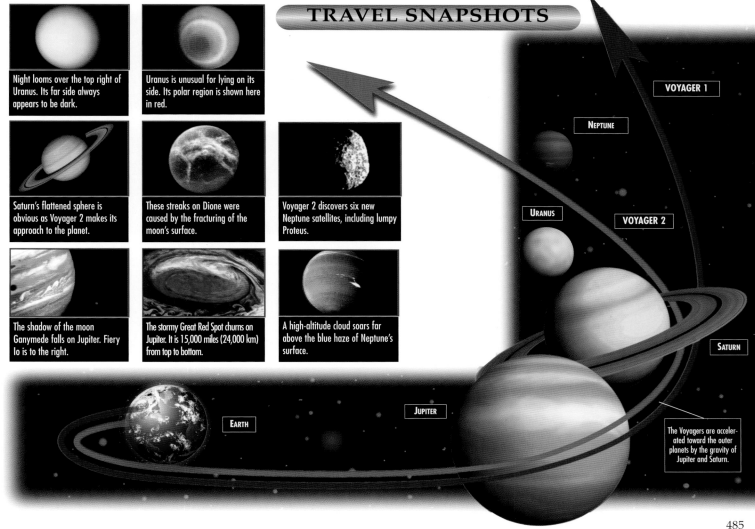

VOYAGER 1

NEPTUNE

URANUS

VOYAGER 2

SATURN

EARTH

JUPITER

The Voyagers are accelerated toward the outer planets by the gravity of Jupiter and Saturn.

485

VEGA 1 AND 2

Halley's comet headed sunward in 1986, as it does every 76 years—but this time it had company. Twin Soviet probes, Vega 1 and 2, were part of an international flotilla of spacecraft on an intercept course. Vega 1's camera returned the first close-up image of Halley's nucleus. The twins had already proved their worth, though: Their mission explored two alien bodies for the price of one. To reach Halley, the probes swung by Venus, where they deployed landers and balloons into the planet's corrosive atmosphere.

VEGA SPECS

COUNTRY	SOVIET UNION	HEIGHT	15 FT 10 IN (4.8 M)
MISSION	VENUS LANDER AND BALLOON,	CLOSEST APPROACH TO HALLEY NUCLEUS	
	COMET HALLEY FLYBY		5,544 MILES/8,922 KM (VEGA 1),
LAUNCH VEHICLE	PROTON, FROM BAIKONUR		5,018 MILES/8,075 KM (VEGA 2)
SPACECRAFT MASS	10,824 LB (4,900 KG)	FLYBY SPEED	49 MILES/79 KM PER SECOND (VEGA 1),
"WINGSPAN" (SOLAR PANELS)	33 FT 2 IN (10 M)		48 MILES/77 KM PER SECOND (VEGA 2)

DOUBLE DEAL

Together, Vega 1 and 2 made up the last successful Soviet interplanetary mission—and by far the most triumphant. Originally, the twin probes had been intended to be simply the latest in the long-running Venera series of Venus probes. The Soviets had been sending Venera spacecraft into the Venusian atmosphere ever since 1967. Their designs had improved enough for successive landers to penetrate clouds of sulfuric acid and survive, at least briefly, the planet's hellish surface. There, temperatures reach almost 900°F (480°C)—hot enough to melt lead—and pressures are 90 times that of those found on Earth.

SCIENTIFIC COCKTAIL

Vega 1 and 2 were originally planned as orbiter-lander combinations in the same sequence of probes, designated Venera 17 and 18. These probes were the first major Soviet mission to invite contributions from foreigners. French scientist Jacques Blamont suggested that

the probes could deploy balloon "aerostats" to explore the Venusian atmosphere. And Blamont was also ultimately responsible for the redirection of the mission towards Halley's comet. At a 1980 cocktail party, U.S. space scientist Louis Friedman joked that Venus would be a great place to see Halley's comet when it came around again in 1986, because it would get closer to Venus than it did to the Earth. Blamont considered the feasibility of sending the probes on to Halley by swinging past Venus. The Russians immediately liked the idea, particularly after NASA announced that it would not be sending a Halley probe of its own. An exploratory Soviet comet mission to Venus would not only be a scientific bonanza, it would be a fantastic propaganda coup.

INTERNATIONAL SCIENCE

So the probes were renamed Vega 1 and 2, for "Venera-Galley" (there is no "H" in the Russian alphabet). The lander design was left unchanged, but the orbiter

needed adaptation. The spacecraft was protected against dust impacts by aluminum sheeting. A movable instrument platform carried narrow- and wide-angle cameras, a spectrometer and an infrared sounder to measure the nucleus' surface temperature. The spacecraft's computers made sure that the panel pointed constantly at the nucleus. Other instruments on board included magnetometers and cometary dust collectors that would measure particle size. While classed as a Soviet mission, the Vega mission was also a fine example of international cooperation. Once the aerostats

were released into the Venusian atmosphere, their passage across the planet was tracked by 12 radio observatories in 10 separate countries. And data from Vega's Halley flybys was used to pinpoint the course of another space probe zeroing in on the comet. Thanks to Vega's initial observations, the European Space Agency's Giotto spacecraft came within 372 miles (600 km) of the Halley nucleus.

EURO PARTNER
The European Space Agency's Giotto probe (shown right) made the closest approach—within 400 miles (640 km)—to Comet Halley. But its close pass was only possible thanks to data discovered by from Vega 1 and Vega 2.

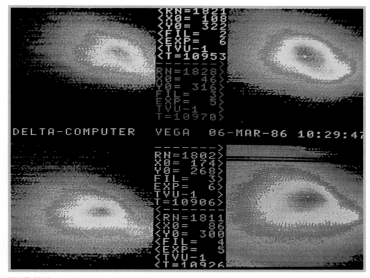

DELTA-COMPUTER   VEGA   06-MAR-86 10:29:47

COMET CORE
These false-color images of Comet Halley's nucleus were beamed back by Vega 1 near its closest approach on March 6, 1986. From blue to red, the pictures show the increasing gas density around Halley's core.

BACK-DOOR FRIEND

VEGA WAS THE FIRST SOVIET MISSION OPENED UP TO SUBSTANTIAL PARTICIPATION BY THE INTERNATIONAL SPACE SCIENCE COMMUNITY (RIGHT). BUT POLITICAL TENSIONS WERE A PROBLEM. RESEARCHER JOHN SIMPSON FROM THE UNIVERSITY OF CHICAGO CONTRIBUTED COMET-DUST DETECTORS TO THE PROBES, BUT IN ORDER TO AVOID ANY CONTROVERSY HE HAD THE INSTRUMENTS MANUFACTURED IN WEST GERMANY AND PUBLICIZED AS A WEST GERMAN CONTRIBUTION.

MISSION DIARY: VEGA 1 AND 2

1981 SHORT OF FUNDS, NASA CANCELS ITS PROPOSED COMET HALLEY PROBE.
1981 SOVIET UNION UPGRADES TWO PLANNED VENUS PROBES FOR A HALLEY ENCOUNTER.
OCTOBER 16, 1982 MOUNT PALOMAR'S HALE TELESCOPE TRACKS COMET HALLEY FOR THE FIRST TIME EVER.
DECEMBER 15, 1984 VEGA 1 IS LAUNCHED FROM BAIKONUR IN THE SOVIET REPUBLIC OF KAZAKHSTAN.
DECEMBER 21 VEGA 2 (ABOVE) UNDERGOES FINAL CHECKS AND

IS LAUNCHED FROM BAIKONUR ON THE SAME TRAJECTORY AS VEGA 1.
JUNE 11, 1985 VEGA 1 REACHES VENUS. IT DEPLOYS ITS LANDER AND RECEIVES A SPEED-BOOSTING GRAVITY ASSIST FROM VENUS.
JUNE 15 VEGA 2 VENUS ENCOUNTER AND LANDER DEPLOYMENT. BOTH PROBES DEPLOY BALLOONS IN THE VENUSIAN ATMOSPHERE (ABOVE).
SEPTEMBER 11, 1985 NASA SPACECRAFT INTERNATIONAL COMETARY EXPLORER TRAVERSES THE PLASMA TAIL OF COMET

GIACOBINI-ZINNER, A DRY RUN FOR THE COMING HALLEY FLYBYS.
FEBRUARY 9, 1986 HALLEY PASSES PERIHELION, ITS CLOSEST APPROACH TO THE SUN. BOTH VEGAS NEAR THEIR TARGET.
MARCH 6 VEGA 1 MAKES ITS CLOSEST HALLEY FLYBY (5,544 MILES/8,922 KM).
MARCH 9 VEGA 2 MAKES ITS CLOSEST HALLEY FLYBY (5,018 MILES/8,075 KM). SOVIET SCIENTISTS (ABOVE) SOON SHARE DATA FROM THE VEGA MISSIONS WITH THE REST OF THE WORLD.
MARCH 14 ESA'S GIOTTO USES VEGA DATA TO MAKE THE CLOSEST HALLEY FLYBY, AT JUST 372 MILES (600 KM).

GALILEO ORBITER

Galileo is one of the most complex spacecraft ever built, and it orbited Jupiter for eight years making detailed measurements of the planet and its moons. While Galileo's orbiter photographed the moons and analyzed Jupiter's strong magnetic field, the probe it had carried descended into the atmosphere on a one-way journey to destruction. Galileo's operations were scheduled to end in January 2000, but the spacecraft was functioning so well that NASA extended its mission until 2003.

GALILEO ORBITER

ORBITER		ATMOSPHERIC PROBE	
LAUNCH MASS	4,691 LB (2,128 KG)	TOTAL MASS	747 LB (339 KG)
DIMENSIONS	20 FT 8 IN (6.3 M) HIGH, MAX.	DIMENSIONS	5 FT (1.5 M) IN DIAMETER
	16 FT (4.9 M) IN DIAMETER	DESCENT MODULE MASS	266 LB (121 KG)
SCIENCE PAYLOAD MASS	260 LB (117 KG)	SCIENCE PAYLOAD MASS	66 LB (30 KG)
PROPELLANT MASS	2,035 LB (923 KG)		

The Galileo spacecraft consisted of the orbiter section plus the probe that was dropped into Jupiter's atmosphere. To protect the spacecraft's sensitive equipment from extremes of temperature, the vehicle had insulating blankets 60 times more effective than ordinary fiberglass insulation.

THUNDERSTORM

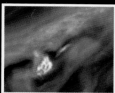

On June 26, 1996, Galileo photographed this massive thunderstorm (left) on Jupiter. The white thunder-cloud is 620 miles (1,000 km) across and extends for 15 miles (24 km) above the surrounding cloudbase.

magnetometer (magnetic field detector)

plasma wave detector

magnetometer boom

low-gain radio antenna

sunshields

high-gain radio antenna

particle detector

magnetometers (magnetic field detectors)

dust detector

spun section

retropropulsion module

RTG

thrusters

despun section

RTG

scan platform carrying camera, spectrometers, radiometer

probe relay antenna

atmospheric probe

HARD EVIDENCE

COMET STRIKE

In July 1994, when Comet Shoemaker-Levy plunged into Jupiter, the planet's immense gravitational pull broke it into 20 large pieces. On impact, these fragments together released more energy into the planet's atmosphere than would result from setting off the Earth's entire nuclear arsenal. Images from the Hubble Space Telescope showed some of the collisions, but only Galileo, 148 million miles (238m km) from the planet, was able to witness the full six-day onslaught and destructive power of the impacts. The bright point in this Galileo image (above) is an impact on the dark side of Jupiter.

TESTING

Before it was launched, the Galileo spacecraft was tested in an environmental chamber (left) that simulated the conditions it would encounter in space. The chamber is at NASA's Jet Propulsion Laboratory (JPL) in Pasadena, California.

LAUNCH

Galileo was launched from the Space Shuttle Atlantis on October 18, 1989 (above). When it was safely clear of the Shuttle, its Inertial Upper Stage booster fired to fling it out of Earth orbit, then separated from it.

CLOSE-UP

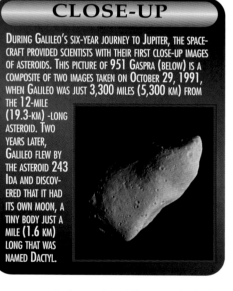

DURING GALILEO'S SIX-YEAR JOURNEY TO JUPITER, THE SPACECRAFT PROVIDED SCIENTISTS WITH THEIR FIRST CLOSE-UP IMAGES OF ASTEROIDS. THIS PICTURE OF 951 GASPRA (BELOW) IS A COMPOSITE OF TWO IMAGES TAKEN ON OCTOBER 29, 1991, WHEN GALILEO WAS JUST 3,300 MILES (5,300 KM) FROM THE 12-MILE (19.3-KM) -LONG ASTEROID. TWO YEARS LATER, GALILEO FLEW BY THE ASTEROID 243 IDA AND DISCOVERED THAT IT HAD ITS OWN MOON, A TINY BODY JUST A MILE (1.6 KM) LONG THAT WAS NAMED DACTYL.

JUPITER OBSERVER

Galileo was built to give scientists a better understanding of Jupiter, the largest planet in the solar system. The 2.5-ton (2.3-tonne) vehicle was one of the most complex spacecraft ever built and consisted of three sections—a spinning section to provide stability, a non-spinning section that carried the cameras, and a probe that undocked from the main spacecraft to plunge down through the Jovian atmosphere.

The first objective of the Galileo mission was to deliver the probe, which slammed into Jupiter's atmosphere at 106,000 mph (170,500 km/h) on December 7, 1995. After entry, the probe switched on its instruments and measured the composition of Jupiter's atmosphere for 58 minutes before it was destroyed by the building pressure and heat. The information it had gathered was relayed to Earth via the orbiter, traveling high above the planet and well away from its dangerous atmosphere. The orbiter itself went on to complete a long tour of duty studying Jupiter's moons.

Sending the spacecraft 500 million miles across space had presented its designers with a number of problems. For instance, it had to carry a lot of fuel for course corrections and orbital maneuvers, and this fuel amounted to about 40 percent of its takeoff weight. And at Jupiter the sunlight is only four percent the strength it is at Earth, so it could not use solar panels to generate its electricity. Instead, Galileo had to use small nuclear power sources— radioisotope thermoelectric generators (RTGs).

SPINNING SCIENCE

During its long operational life, the Galileo orbiter generated a massive amount of data that will keep scientists busy for many years to come. Its science instruments were divided between the rotating upper section of the craft and the "despun" lower section.

The upper section turned at about three rpm and housed instruments that needed to sweep around to gather information. These included sensors to detect and measure charged particles, cosmic and planetary dust and the magnetic fields of Jupiter and its moons. It also carried the spacecraft's power supply, propulsion system and most of its electronics. The lower section carried instruments that needed to point directly at specific targets, such as the camera system and spectrometers for the purposes of analyzing gases and surface chemistry.

GIOTTO

Every 76 years, Halley's Comet swings back into the inner solar system and passes close enough to the Earth to be seen with the naked eye. Halley's last return, in 1986, was different from all its previous visits because a tiny European spacecraft called

Giotto flew out to study it at close range. Giotto met up with Halley in March 1986. Despite taking a battering from cometary debris, it shot some remarkable close-up photographs of the comet, and its instruments recorded a wealth of valuable data.

GIOTTO MISSION FACTS

LAUNCH	JULY 2, 1985, 11.35 GMT ABOARD AN ARIANE 1 ROCKET	NUMBER OF SCIENTIFIC INSTRUMENTS	10
LAUNCH SITE	KOUROU, FRENCH GUIANA (ELA 1)	TARGETS	COMETS HALLEY AND GRIGG-SKJELLERUP
SPACECRAFT MASS	2,117 LB (960 KG)	CLOSEST APPROACH TO HALLEY	370 MILES (595 KM)
SPACECRAFT DIMENSIONS	6 FT (1.8 M) IN DIAMETER, 9 FT (2.7 M) HIGH	CLOSEST APPROACH TO GRIGG-SKJELLERUP	125 MILES (201 KM)
		ORIGINAL MISSION (HALLEY)	END DATE APRIL 2, 1986
		EXTENDED MISSION (GRIGG-SKJELLERUP)	END DATE JULY 23, 1992

HALLEY HUNTER

Giotto was blasted into space aboard an Ariane 1 rocket launched from Kourou, French Guiana, on July 2, 1985. It arrived at Halley's Comet on the night of March 13–14, 1986, and during the early evening it crossed the "shock front" that formed the boundary between the solar wind and the outer regions of the comet's dusty atmosphere. The spacecraft's camera was switched on and immediately began to transmit the first fuzzy, close-up images of Halley back to the mission controllers on Earth. The pictures showed the comet to be a dark, peanut-shape body, blacker than coal, with bright jets of material spouting from its surface.

To protect Giotto and its payload of instruments from the hazardous dust around the comet, the spacecraft was fitted with a tough, two-layer aluminum and Kevlar dust shield. The payload, tucked away safely behind the shield, included a camera, instruments to measure the composition of the comet's gas and dust, a dust impact detector, experiments to study the solar wind and charged particles, and an instrument to study changes in the magnetic field. There was also an optical probe that could study the brightness of the comet's atmosphere and a radio science experiment to detect electrons. Giotto's electrical power was supplied by a solar array wrapped around the outside of its cylindrical body, and at the opposite end from the dust shield was the main communication dish that beamed images and data back to Earth.

EXTENDED MISSION

Giotto's dust shield began to prove its worth about two hours before the spacecraft's closest approach to Halley, when the first of 12,000 impacts of cometary dust were recorded. The impact rate increased as Giotto closed in on Halley and passed through the jets of material, heated by the Sun, that were being blasted from the comet's surface. Then, only 14 seconds before its closest approach, Giotto was sent into a spin when it was hit by a tiny particle thought to

GIOTTO MEETS HALLEY

Giotto launched, July 2, 1985

Giotto makes its fly-by of Halley at a distance of 370 miles (595 km) on March 13–14, 1986

Giotto's encounter with Halley in 1986 was the first time a spacecraft had flown close to a comet. Its mission was extended so that it could make another cometary close encounter with Grigg-Skjellerup in 1992.

Giotto flies on for a rendezvous with Comet Grigg-Skjellerup on July 10, 1992

Halley's orbit

Comet Halley

COMET HALLEY NUCLEUS
The image above shows Halley's nucleus as seen by the camera aboard Giotto. The nucleus (to the right) is a dark, peanut-shape body partially hidden by jets of gas and dust.

ESOC CONTROL

GIOTTO, EUROPE'S VERY FIRST INTERPLANETARY SPACE MISSION, WAS MONITORED AND CONTROLLED FROM THE EUROPEAN SPACE OPERATIONS CENTER (ESOC). LOCATED IN THE CITY OF DARMSTADT, GERMANY, ESOC IS THE EUROPEAN SPACE AGENCY'S PRIMARY SPACE MISSION CONTROL CENTER. IT MONITORS THE LAUNCH AND OPERATION OF EUROPEAN SATELLITES AND SPACE PROBES USING ESTRACK, ITS GLOBAL NETWORK OF TRACKING STATIONS.

be about the size of a grain of rice and weighing less than 1/30th of an ounce.

At Giotto's mission control—the European Space Operations Center in Darmstadt, Germany—computer screens went blank and contact with the spacecraft was lost. But to everyone's amazement and relief, the tough little spacecraft soon began to send bursts of data back to Earth, and after half an hour it settled down to normal transmissions. Giotto continued its up-close survey of Halley's Comet for nearly a day. Its instruments were turned off in the early hours of March 15 as the spacecraft and the comet went their separate ways.

No one had expected Giotto to survive its bruising encounter with Halley, but although several instruments were damaged, the

spacecraft was still operational and still had fuel on board. Sending Giotto to study a second comet was now a real possibility. So Giotto was put into a "hibernation" mode, and four years later its course was altered: It skimmed past Earth on its way to its second target—Comet Grigg-Skjellerup.

Giotto met up with the much smaller and less active Grigg-Skjellerup on July 10, 1992, passing

only 125 miles (201 km) from the comet's surface—the closest any spacecraft had been to a comet. Giotto's camera was out of action, but eight of its science instruments returned useful information. Giotto's science instruments were turned off for the last time on July 11, 1992, and on July 23, the spacecraft was returned to its deep-sleep mode, from which it would never be reawakened.

MISSION DIARY: GIOTTO

1979 STUDIES BEGIN ON THE DESIGN OF A JOINT U.S.-EUROPEAN SPACECRAFT TO RENDEZVOUS WITH HALLEY'S COMET. **1980** THE U.S. WITHDRAWS FROM THE PROJECT DUE TO THE HIGH COSTS. THE EUROPEAN SPACE AGENCY (ESA) PROCEEDS ALONE. **1982** CONSTRUCTION OF GIOTTO BEGINS (SHOWN ABOVE). **JULY 2, 1985** GIOTTO IS LAUNCHED BY AN ARIANE 1 ROCKET FROM THE ESA LAUNCH SITE AT KOUROU, FRENCH GUIANA.

MARCH 13–14, 1986 GIOTTO HAS ITS CLOSE ENCOUNTER WITH HALLEY'S COMET, PASSING IT AT A DISTANCE OF ABOUT 370 MILES (595 KM). **APRIL 2, 1986** "HIBERNATION." **FEBRUARY 1990** GIOTTO IS "AWAKENED" BY GROUND CONTROLLERS. **JULY 2, 1990** SWINGS PAST EARTH TO GET ON COURSE FOR A SECOND ENCOUNTER. **JULY 23, 1990** BEGINS A SECOND PERIOD OF HIBERNATION. **MAY 4, 1992** AWAKENED AGAIN. **JULY 10, 1992** PASSES WITHIN 125 MILES (201 KM) OF COMET GRIGG-SKJELLERUP. **JULY 23, 1992** OPERATIONS END.

DEEP SPACE 1

Deep Space 1 is a revolutionary new spacecraft. It is powered by a new, super-efficient engine and carries an intelligent computer that pilots the craft with minimal instructions from ground control. The mission of this little probe is to test out these and other new—and potentially high-risk—technologies in space. It is the first spaceflight NASA has launched purely to test innovations. It is part of NASA's New Millennium Program, which will help shape the spacecraft of the future.

DS1 SPECIFICATIONS

TOTAL COST	$152.3M (FY95-99)	HIGH GAIN ANTENNA DIAMETER	11 IN (28 CM)
LAUNCH DATE	OCTOBER 24, 1998	COMMUNICATIONS FREQUENCIES	X, KA
LAUNCH SITE	CAPE CANAVERAL, FLORIDA	MAXIMUM DATA RATE	20 KILOBITS PER SECOND
END OF MISSION DATE	DECEMBER 2001	MAXIMUM POWER	2,500W (2,100W USED TO POWER ION ENGINE)
LAUNCH MASS (SPACECRAFT AND PROPELLANTS)	1072.13 LB (486.3 KG)		

SPACE GUINEA PIG

When it blasted into orbit aboard a Delta rocket on October 28, 1998, Deep Space 1 (DS1) carried on board no fewer than 12 new technologies for testing. Some will make the spacecraft of the future smaller and cheaper; others aim to increase the precision of space astronomy. But the key innovations aboard DS1 are its engine and its control system.

DS1 is propelled by an ion engine. In a chemical rocket like the Space Shuttle, a continuous controlled explosion hurls burning gas out of the rocket nozzle, driving the vehicle onward and upward. An ion engine is somewhat more sedate. Instead of a chemical reaction, it uses electric power to accelerate charged particles of gas out of the engine nozzle. Instead of thundering sheets of flame, the ion engine produces an eerie blue glow. And instead of hundreds of tons of thrust, the ion engine produces a thrust of just one-third of an ounce (0.275 N)—or about one-tenth of the weight of an apple.

But appearances can be misleading. Ion engines are deceptively powerful and extremely efficient. They can go on producing thrust continuously for months on end. Deep Space 1's supply of 180 lb (82 kg) of xenon gas is enough to provide thrust continuously for 20 months, during which time the engine will have gradually accelerated the spacecraft up to speeds of 10,000 mph (16,000 km/h).

SOLAR-POWERED IONS

The ion engine is powered by an array of solar cells. At full throttle, the engine consumes 2.5 kilowatts of power—about the same as a large electric heater. This is a great deal of power to generate using solar cells, so Deep Space 1 is testing a new type of high-powered solar array. The spacecraft has two "wings," each one measuring 14 ft 9 in (4.5 m) by 5 ft 3 in (1.6 m) in size and composed of 360 silicon lenses that focus sunlight onto 1,800 solar cells. These "solar concentrator arrays" yield up to 20 percent more power than the best existing solar cell designs.

Deep Space 1's sophisticated automatic pilot system is just as ground-breaking as its revolutionary engine. It makes DS1 virtually independent of NASA's tracking network and ground controllers. The system has two main components. The first, AutoNav, can determine exactly where DS1 is in the solar system so that the probe can fine-tune its own flight path. To do this, it carries a database of the orbits of 250 asteroids and the positions of 250,000 background stars. By regularly taking pictures of asteroids and comparing the images to its stored data, DS1 can calculate its own position and adjust the thrust of its ion engine as required. The second component of the control system is a piece of software called "Remote Agent." NASA ground controllers feed only very general instructions into Remote Agent. The software then calculates not only how it should carry out the orders, but also the best sequence in which to execute them.

While there were some issues with the major new technologies aboard DS1, most outperformed expectations. The craft's failures have been educational and its successes have set the stage for future ion-propelled missions.

CLEAN FUEL

THE ION DRIVE POWERING DS1 IS THE MOST EFFICIENT ENGINE EVER FLOWN IN SPACE—HUNDREDS OF TIMES MORE SO THAN THE SPACE SHUTTLE ENGINES, WHICH REQUIRED HUGE RESERVES OF FUEL. BUT WHERE EACH OF THOSE MONSTERS PRODUCES AROUND 200 TONS (181 TONNES) OF THRUST, THE THRUST FROM DS1'S ION ENGINE IS LITTLE MORE THAN THE WEIGHT OF A SINGLE SHEET OF PAPER.

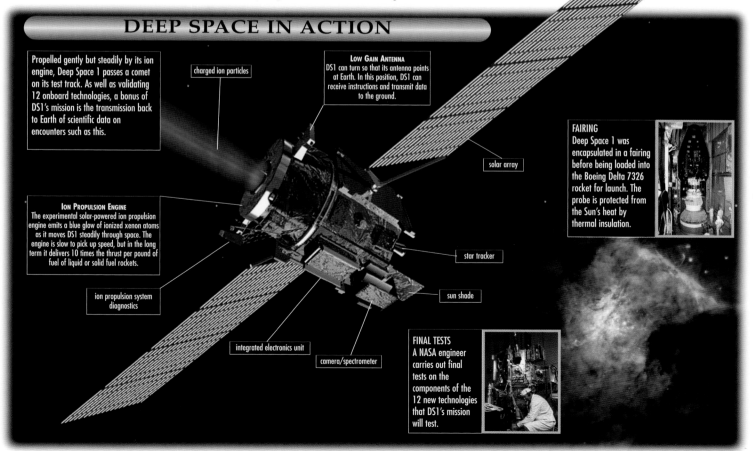

DEEP SPACE IN ACTION

Propelled gently but steadily by its ion engine, Deep Space 1 passes a comet on its test track. As well as validating 12 onboard technologies, a bonus of DS1's mission is the transmission back to Earth of scientific data on encounters such as this.

charged ion particles

LOW GAIN ANTENNA
DS1 can turn so that its antenna points at Earth. In this position, DS1 can receive instructions and transmit data to the ground.

solar array

FAIRING
Deep Space 1 was encapsulated in a fairing before being loaded into the Boeing Delta 7326 rocket for launch. The probe is protected from the Sun's heat by thermal insulation.

ION PROPULSION ENGINE
The experimental solar-powered ion propulsion engine emits a blue glow of ionized xenon atoms as it moves DS1 steadily through space. The engine is slow to pick up speed, but in the long term it delivers 10 times the thrust per pound of fuel of liquid or solid fuel rockets.

ion propulsion system diagnostics

star tracker

sun shade

integrated electronics unit

camera/spectrometer

FINAL TESTS
A NASA engineer carries out final tests on the components of the 12 new technologies that DS1's mission will test.

CASSINI-HUYGENS

A quarter of a century after Pioneer 11 took the first close-up pictures of Saturn, the ringed planet came under the gaze of a new NASA craft. The massive Cassini-Huygens spacecraft reached Jupiter in 2000. In December 2004, the Huygens probe—released from Cassini—plunged into the thick atmosphere of Saturn's moon Titan, sending back enough data to keep scientists busy for decades. The $3.25 billion project is set to be the last big-budget probe mission for some time. And if all goes according to plan, it should also be one of the longest in duration, with extensions currently planned until 2017.

CASSINI-HUYGENS STATS

	CASSINI ORBITER	HUYGENS PROBE
NUMBER OF INSTRUMENTS	18	7
POWER GENERATION	PLUTONIUM THERMOELECTRIC GENERATORS	LITHIUM SULFUR DIOXIDE BATTERIES
UNFUELED NAVIGATION	GRAVITY ASSISTS	GRAVITY, PARACHUTES
FUELED NAVIGATION	TWO 100-LB-FORCE (440 N) THRUSTERS	THREE 112-LB-FORCE (498 N) SPRINGS
PROPELLANT	MONO-METHYL-HYDRAZINE, NITROGEN TETROXIDE	NONE
UNFUELED WEIGHT	4,750 LB (2,154 KG)	770 LB (349 KG)
WEIGHT OF FUEL	6,905 LB (3,132 KG)	NONE
DIMENSIONS	22 FT (6.7 M) HIGH, 13 FT (4 M) WIDE	9 FT (2.7 M) IN DIAMETER
DURATION OF MISSION	43 MONTHS	3 HOURS

SATURN SAILOR

After its long journey from Earth, Cassini made its closest approach to Jupiter on December 30, 2000, and began taking measurements and photographs. In all, 26,000 images of Jupiter were taken, allowing for the creation of the most detailed global portrait ever made of the planet.

One area of new study was the rings of Jupiter, barely visible from Earth. Cassini showed that they were made of irregular, rather than spherical particles, suggesting they were ejected from Jupiter's moons Metis and Adrastea by micrometeorite impacts.

The scientific discoveries of Cassini are almost too numerous to describe. Among them are two new moons of Saturn, spotted in June 2004. These bodies are very small, but have been named Methone and Pallene (after two sisters from Greek mythology).

Direct observation of the planets and moons of the outer solar system was only one area of study. The Cassini science team took the opportunity to put Einstein's theory of general relativity to the test. They experimented with radio signals from Cassini to prove that a massive object like the Sun causes space-time to curve, and a beam of radio waves or light that passes by the Sun has to travel further because of the curvature and the delay in reaching Earth can be used to measure the amount of curve. Results from Cassini have not conclusively proved the theory, but have increased scientific confidence in it greatly.

The most spectacular experiment conducted by Cassini was the despatch of the Huygens probe to the surface of Titan. After a large number of preliminary flybys, Cassini ejected Huygens towards Titan on December 25, 2004, although it didn't arrive for a further three weeks.

As Huygens entered Titan's atmosphere it sent data and images to Earth via Cassini. Betting that the landing site was as likely to be liquid methane as solid rock, the probe was designed to float. With a battery life of only three hours, most of which would be taken up with the descent, only 30 minutes of surface data was expected.

As it fell toward Titan suspended on a parachute, photos were transmitted of what looked like a shoreline and islands. Methane clouds or haze were also seen before the probe plopped into a clay-like material described as "Titanian Mud". The colour of Titan's surface was described as orange or "creme brulée".

An operator mistake in forgetting to turn on Cassini's receiver for one of two Huygens data channels led to the loss of all measurements of descent winds, and of 350 of the 700 images taken before landing. Nonetheless, the probe survived on the surface where it transmitted data for over an hour and 12 minutes. It is regarded as a great success.

CASSINI ORBITER

low-gain antenna (1 of 2)

13-ft (4-m) high-gain antenna

14-yard (12-m) magnetometer boom

remote sensing pallet

radar bay

Huygens probe

main engine (1 of 2)

radioisotopic thermoelectric generator (1 of 3)

descent module with scientific instruments

parachute compartment

back cover

front shield

heat shield

batteries

SPACE CASE
Cassini-Huygens is fitted into its payload fairing at Cape Canaveral. The casing — 66 ft (20 m) high and 17 ft (5 m) wide — also enclosed the Centaur second-stage rocket that would blast the spacecraft toward Saturn.

RINGED THINGS

DUTCH ASTRONOMER CHRISTIAAN HUYGENS (1629–93) DISCOVERED TITAN IN 1655, AND WAS THE FIRST TO SAY THAT SATURN'S SHAPE COULD BE EXPLAINED BY RINGS. TWENTY YEARS LATER, FRENCH ASTRONOMER GIOVANNI DOMENICO CASSINI (1625–1712; ABOVE) DISCOVERED FOUR MORE SATURNIAN MOONS, AS WELL AS THE GAP BETWEEN TWO OF THE RINGS.

HUYGENS PROBE

TITAN RIDE
Weighing in at over 6 tons (5.4 tonnes), Cassini-Huygens is the heaviest U.S. planetary probe ever built. It was launched atop a 210-ft (64 m) two-stage Titan 4-B rocket (shown above).

BEATING HEAT
During its descent into Titan's atmosphere, the Huygens probe faced temperatures in excess of 20,000°F (11,000°C), more than double the surface temperature of the Sun. The probe's front heat shield (above) was made from a silica fiber compound — similar to the tiles used on the Space Shuttle — to protect Huygens' scientific instruments from the searing heat.

LOST PROBES

Exploration has always had its dangers, and exploring space presents many hazards to the robotic spacecraft that have been sent out to investigate the mysteries of the solar system. These probes have to survive the extremely hostile environment of space, often for long periods of time, and despite their usually reliable technology, they occasionally break down and are never heard from again. But each failure teaches spacecraft designers valuable lessons that will help to improve the success rate of future missions.

SPACECRAFT LOSSES

Moon Missions		Surveyor 4	U.S.	Phobos 1	Russia	Venus Missions	
Luna 1	U.S.S.R.	Luna 18	U.S.S.R.	Phobos 2	Russia	Venera 1	U.S.S.R.
Pioneer 4	U.S.			Mars Observer	U.S.	Zond 1	U.S.S.R.
Ranger 3	U.S.	Mars Missions		Climate Orbiter	U.S.	Venera 2	U.S.S.R.
Ranger 4	U.S.	Mars 1	U.S.S.R.	Polar Lander	U.S.	Venera 3	U.S.S.R.
Ranger 5	U.S.	Zond 2	U.S.S.R.	Beagle 2	U.K.		
Luna 4	U.S.S.R.	Mars 2	U.S.S.R.	Yinghuo-1	China		
Ranger 6	U.S.	Mars 3	U.S.S.R.	Fobos-Grunt	Russia		
Luna 6	U.S.S.R.	Mars 6	U.S.S.R.				

LOST IN SPACE

Since the very earliest days of spaceflight, probes have been launched out into the solar system. The Moon was the first target, since the U.S. and the Soviet Union needed to gather data and accumulate technical experience in preparation for crewed lunar missions. And with the Cold War rivalry between the two superpowers increasing, each tried to prove they had the world's best technology: Missions to Mars and Venus soon followed the first Moonshots.

But in the early 1960s, so little was known of conditions in space that many satellites and probes failed within days of launch. To reach Mars or Venus, a spacecraft had to survive a flight lasting nine months or more, so the probes had to be highly reliable. This was achieved by adding backup systems that would take over if a primary system failed. Backups could be supplied for most of the essential functions of the spacecraft, but there were always a small number of components and systems whose failure would end the mission. Such devices had "single-point criticality."

The largest single-point-critical element in any space mission is the launcher. If the booster fails during ascent to orbit, the mission ends before it has even left the Earth. And even when it has safely entered its interplanetary trajectory, a spacecraft still faces dangers meaning it might malfunction. For instance, a computer or thruster failure can leave the spacecraft facing in the wrong direction, so that its communication antenna loses contact with the Earth.

LEARNING FROM FAILURES

Although many missions have been lost, their scientific instruments have usually managed to return a small amount of information before failure. Using this data, scientists have been able to understand the space environment more, which in turn has helped engineers to improve probe design. As designs have improved, so has the success rate, but failures have by no means been eliminated.

In preparation for the human exploration of Mars, NASA has once again turned its attention to that planet. Two spacecraft are sent during each launch window but problems have plagued almost every flight. During the 1990s, Mars Pathfinder was a success but Mars Orbiter, Mars Climate Orbiter and Mars Polar Lander were all lost. Mars Polar Lander disappeared in December 1999. It probably reached the surface of the planet, but no signals were ever received from it. But new interplanetary missions are currently underway.

DATA BLOCK

SOON AFTER THE 1989 LAUNCH OF GALILEO (RIGHT) TO JUPITER, CONTROLLERS FEARED THEY WOULD LOSE THE SPACECRAFT WHEN ITS MAIN ANTENNA FAILED TO DEPLOY PROPERLY. A LATER PROBLEM WITH A TAPE RECORDER ALSO JEOPARDIZED THE MISSION. BY UPLOADING NEW SOFTWARE, NASA RETRIEVED MOST OF THE CRAFT'S SCIENTIFIC DATA, BUT ITS DATA TRANSMISSION RATE WAS LESS THAN A TEN-THOUSANDTH OF ITS PLANNED 134 KILOBITS PER SECOND.

PROBES TO MARS AND VENUS

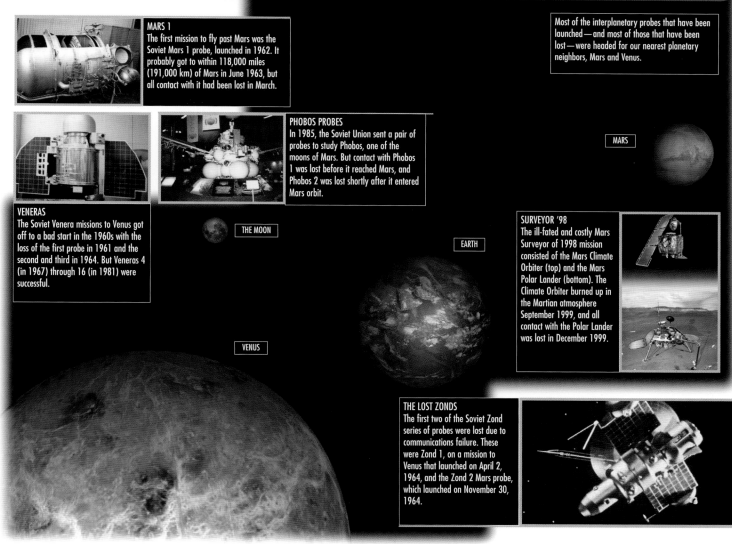

MARS 1
The first mission to fly past Mars was the Soviet Mars 1 probe, launched in 1962. It probably got to within 118,000 miles (191,000 km) of Mars in June 1963, but all contact with it had been lost in March.

PHOBOS PROBES
In 1985, the Soviet Union sent a pair of probes to study Phobos, one of the moons of Mars. But contact with Phobos 1 was lost before it reached Mars, and Phobos 2 was lost shortly after it entered Mars orbit.

VENERAS
The Soviet Venera missions to Venus got off to a bad start in the 1960s with the loss of the first probe in 1961 and the second and third in 1964. But Veneras 4 (in 1967) through 16 (in 1981) were successful.

Most of the interplanetary probes that have been launched—and most of those that have been lost—were headed for our nearest planetary neighbors, Mars and Venus.

MARS

THE MOON

EARTH

SURVEYOR '98
The ill-fated and costly Mars Surveyor of 1998 mission consisted of the Mars Climate Orbiter (top) and the Mars Polar Lander (bottom). The Climate Orbiter burned up in the Martian atmosphere September 1999, and all contact with the Polar Lander was lost in December 1999.

VENUS

THE LOST ZONDS
The first two of the Soviet Zond series of probes were lost due to communications failure. These were Zond 1, on a mission to Venus that launched on April 2, 1964, and the Zond 2 Mars probe, which launched on November 30, 1964.

NEW HORIZONS

On the first ever/NASA mission to reach Pluto and beyond, New Horizons is well on its way to the dwarf planet's system with an estimated arrival of July 14, 2015. This historic mission was ten years in the making before the successful launch on January 19, 2006, meaning that it will take almost another ten years for New Horizons to fulfill its mission objective and reach Pluto. The journey is measured at over 3 billion miles (4.8 billion km), but the probe will not stop there. Flying onwards, it will explore objects within the Kuiper Belt on the very outskirts of our solar system.

NEW HORIZONS TRAJECTORY

Planets New Horizons has passed/is due to pass	Date
Mars	April 7, 2006
Jupiter	February 28, 2007
Saturn	June 8, 2008
Uranus	March 18, 2011
Neptune	ETA August 24, 2014
Pluto	ETA July 14, 2015

PROBING PLUTO AND BEYOND

By studying Pluto and the Kuiper Belt, the NASA space probe New Horizons will live up to its name. The probes launch was delayed twice because of weather and power shortages in the days leading up to its successful launch. Cloud cover around the Cape Canaveral launch site on January 19 almost saw the highly anticipated launch delayed once more. Finally launched without further hitches in January 2006, New Horizons is intended to be the first probe able to fly by, photograph and study Pluto and its moons. The probe is scheduled to enter the Pluto-Charon system in July 2015, where it will study the last unexplored planet in our solar system (Pluto was still classed as a planet when the study was proposed in early 2006). New Horizons will fly within 6,000 miles (9,600 km) of Pluto in 2015. The probe is equipped with technology that will study the geology, surface composition and atmosphere of Pluto in detail, as well as map as much of the dwarf planet and its major moon, Charon, as possible, beginning to document the approach from six months prior to reaching its closest target. At its closest, New Horizons will photograph the ultraviolet emissions from Pluto's atmosphere to map the dwarf planet and Charon. Both bodies will be photographed in detail, allowing images of objects around 200 feet (60 m) to be seen clearly for the first time.

It will then go further still into the Kuiper Belt. Here, the aim is to seek Kuiper Belt objects (KBO) of over 30 miles (50 km) to fly by, photograph and observe. These KBOs need to be within a certain distance from Pluto for the probe to be able to successfully communicate its findings back to Earth. By December 2011, New Horizons has passed closer to Pluto than any other spacecraft, including Voyager 1, the probe that had previously held this record. While it is expected that the New Horizons mission will end in 2026, if the probe lasts until 2038, it will begin to probe the outer heliosphere of the solar system. It is thought unlikely that New Horizons will ever overtake the Voyager probes as the most distant man-made object from Earth.

New Horizons marks the first mission of New Frontiers, a NASA initiative that aims to reach Jupiter and Venus as well as Pluto. New Horizons was the first New Frontiers mission, with Juno launching in August 2011, aiming to reach Jupiter by 2016. The third mission, OSIRIS-REx, will study and return samples of an asteroid. It is due to launch in 2016.

SPIN CYCLE

After careful assembly of the craft, it is rigorously tested before launch. New Horizons and similar spacecrafts have to endure extreme conditions of heat and cold, as well as being flung at high speeds into various trajectories to remain on course. New Horizons is shaped like a triangle, with much of its equipment in a compartment within the outer structure. The radio dish and antenna are external so they can pick up signals with no interference. The titanium body was made big enough so that the equipment could travel safely and be shielded from radiation or electrical charges. As well as withstanding temperature extremes when travelling from the inner to outer solar system, New Horizons is a spinning spacecraft that is constantly in motion. Scientists must ensure that the sensitive equipment inside the probe remains safe so that data can be returned to Earth.

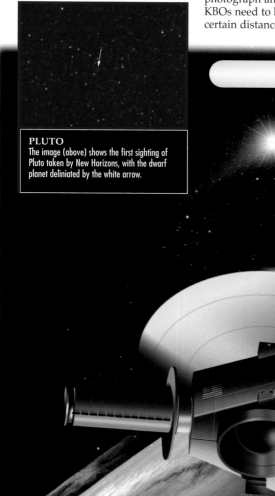

PLUTO
The image (above) shows the first sighting of Pluto taken by New Horizons, with the dwarf planet deliniated by the white arrow.

GETTING TO KNOW PLUTO

KUIPER BELT OBJECTS
The Kuiper Belt consists mainly of debris from the formation of the solar system. These take the form of rocks, metal and icy gaseous masses.

SPIN TESTING
The stringent tests that New Horizons endured during its trials ensure the craft can withstand the intense speeds and temperatures it will encounter on its journey.

HERSCHEL SPACE OBSERVATORY

A space observatory built by the European Space Agency in 2009, Herschel consisted of the largest infrared telescope ever launched into space. Herschel was part of the ESA cornerstone science mission Horizon 2000, along with the Rosetta spacecraft, which was launched in 2004 to study the comet 67P and has just recently been awoken from sleep mode, and the Gaia observatory, recently launched on December 19, 2013 with the aim of creating a three-dimensional map of the Milky Way. Also launched, at the same time as Herschel in May 2009, was the Planck observatory. Herschel's mission was always somewhat limited by time, as the telescope relied on supplies of coolant. Despite its limited life span, Herschel was responsible for making thousands of enlightening observations as well as several exciting new discoveries.

COMPARING TELESCOPES

OBSERVATORY	HERSCHEL	PLANCK	HUBBLE
SIZE OF TELESCOPE	11.5 FEET (3.5 M)	4.9 FEET (1.5 M)	7.9 FEET (2.4 M)
NAMED AFTER	ASTRONOMER WILLIAM HERSCHEL	PHYSICIST MAX PLANCK	ASTRONOMER EDWIN HUBBLE
DATES IN SERVICE	MAY 14, 2009 — APRIL 29, 2013	MAY 14, 2009 — OCTOBER 23, 2013	APRIL 24, 1990 — PRESENT (LIMITED SERVICE)

HERSCHEL TAKES TO THE SKIES

Operational from 2009 to 2013, the Herschel Space Observatory was operated by the ESA until April 29, 2013. Its estimated 3.5 year life was extended since its launch on May 15, 2009, but its coolant supply ran out after almost four years, rendering the Herschel observatory obsolete. Vital for the successful running of its instruments, this liquid helium coolant made it possible for the observatory to observe the formation of galaxies and stars throughout the solar system and Milky Way, as well as objects over billions of light years away. The observatory has the capability to view wavelengths that have never been studied before.

Herschel was also the first observatory able to cover the full spectrum of infrared and sub-millimeter waves. Active since July 21, 2009, Herschel made over 37,000 scientific observations, including the discovery of an unknown stage in the process of star formation and confirmation of the presence of molecular oxygen in space.

Because of its infrared technology, Herschel is able to observe and photograph the "coolest and dustiest" objects in space. It was situated in solar orbit, in the second Langrangian point of the Earth-Sun system at a distance of 930,000 miles (1,500,000 km) from Earth—known as L2. This positioning means that Herschel will not suffer from distortions in temperature from repeatedly passing in and out of Earth's shadow, which also disturbs the view. At its vantage point, Herschel can observe cool areas that may become stars.

The observatory's mission aims included study of the formation and evolution of galaxies, interstellar medium and the process of star formation, and study of the composition of the atmosphere and surfaces of celestial bodies, including planets, comets and asteroids. In addition to its key aims and observations, Herschel will be available for experiments sent by scientists all over the world. Herschel includes the largest mirror ever used in a space telescope, which is made from the durable sintered silicone carbide instead of glass. The telescope was able to work at temperatures down to -456°F (-271°C). The coolant that eventually ran out was liquid helium. The store of over 2,000 liters was the maximum the craft could hold and meant that Herschel could run for at least 3 years. In the end, it was closer to four years, and Herschel was deactivated before being launched safely into solar orbit.

NEW DISCOVERIES

Herschel began operating on July 21, 2009. Since its operational launch, Herschel has discovered a previously unknown galaxy, which has now been designated HFLS3. This starburst galaxy is thought to have come into existence around 880 million years after the Big Bang occured and is much bigger than most other galaxies of its age. It has been able to observe and shed light on a previously undiscovered step in the process of the formation of a star, and how star forming regions discard some of the matter that they are surrounded with. Herschel also detected Cosmic Microwave Background (CMB) radiation caused by light bending as it travels across the universe and meets huge objects. This means scientists are one step closer to finding the earliest gravitational waves produced a millisecond after the universe came into being.

MIRROR, MIRROR
Herschel's mirror measured 11.5 feet (3.5 m) in diameter, making it bigger than Hubble's mirror.

SENSING GAS
Herschel has been able to detect far more molecular gas in the Milky Way than was ever imagined to be present. This discovery has led to increased knowledge of how star-forming clouds containing molecular gases, especially hydrogen, eventually become stars. It also sheds light on how these clouds are formed.

HERSCHEL'S LEGACY

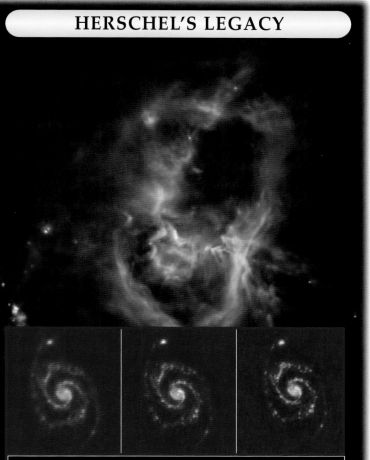

M51
Herschel photographed the whirlpool galaxy M51 as a test run one month following its launch. These three far-infrared images were taken at different wavelengths: left, 160 microns; center, 100 microns; and right, 70 microns, with the darker red areas showing the colder dust.

PLANCK

The Planck observatory was launched to observe remaining radiation caused by the Big Bang, known as Cosmic Microwave Background (CMB) radiation. While there have been similar operations, Planck was the first able to measure the temperature variations of this relic radiation with such sharp accuracy, meaning that theories on the evolution of the Universe could be proven or disproved and that questions on the conditions for evolution could begin to be answered. It might even be impossible ever to better the images and data observed by Planck, as its level of accuracy is at the limit of astrophysics as we know it.

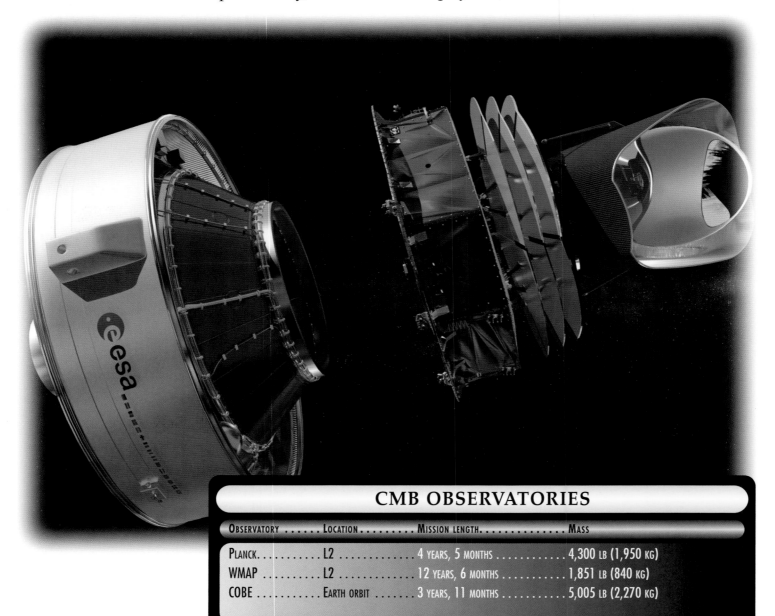

CMB OBSERVATORIES

Observatory	Location	Mission length	Mass
PLANCK	L2	4 YEARS, 5 MONTHS	4,300 LB (1,950 KG)
WMAP	L2	12 YEARS, 6 MONTHS	1,851 LB (840 KG)
COBE	EARTH ORBIT	3 YEARS, 11 MONTHS	5,005 LB (2,270 KG)

MICROWAVE IMAGES

The red and yellow regions show the CMB.

The blue and white regions show interstellar dust.

The white area on the lower left indicates Perseus.

Orion can be seen in the white area directly below.

OBSERVING CREATION
One of the coldest objects in space, Planck was able to return data of the Cosmic Microwave Background (CMB) pictured in exceptional clarity. This all-sky map contains information on the most ancient light in the universe, dating right back to the Big Bang at nearly 14 billion years ago.

| COBE | WMAP | Planck |

SEEING CLEARLY
Many of the existing data on the universe has been confirmed by Planck. It is only because of the additional detail Planck is capable of observing compared to earlier telescopes that we have been able to see minute fluctuations in the early universe, that was previously thought to be uniform.

MAPPING MICROWAVES

Launched in 2009 by the ESA, Planck was initially called COBRAS/SAMBA before being renamed in honour of Max Planck, Nobel Prize winner for physics in 1918 and the originator of quantum theory.

Planck was launched with the Herschel observatory in May 2009 and soon separated from Herschel, beginning its primary mission objective, to map an all-sky survey, in February 2010. Along with the Herschel space observatory, Planck took up position in orbit in the L2 region of the Earth-Sun system, positioning itself here for optimum viewing. This positioning allows Planck to avoid stray light that might block the dim CMB radiation. While all-sky maps have been made before, Planck's CMB technology allows the observatory to view the oldest light in the universe, dating back an incredible 13.7 billion years, with unprecedented accuracy. The telescope can also map areas of cold dust where new stars are on the brink of coming into existence.

The masses of information Planck is able to return to Earth builds upon those made by the NASA Wilkinson Microwave Anisotropy Probe (WMAP), which was launched in 2001 and carried out nine years of observations. WMAP in turn built upon NASA's Cosmic Background Explorer (COBE) satellite in the 1990s. Planck's data was superior in that it could measure anisotropies at higher resolution and sensitivities than WMAP, resulting in the enhanced data and quality of images sent back to earth.

As well as the all-sky survey, Planck's main mission objectives included studying how stars and galaxies form, as well as the process by which the Universe came to life following the Big Bang and the conditions that made evolution possible. Planck is also able to study all constituents of the Universe in greater detail than ever, adding valuable pieces of information to the many questions surrounding the birth and formation of the Universe.

The Planck telescope consists of a primary mirror that is 4.9 feet (1.5 m) in diameter, made of a carbon-fiber-reinforced plastic, which makes it durable enough to withstand much of the stresses and temperature differences of its launch. Planck was decommissioned in January 2012 when supplies of its liquid helium coolant ran out. Some equipment was still able to function, so certain scientific operations continued until October 2013. Planck was finally sent into heliocentric orbit before being deactivated on October 23, 2013.

STAYING COOL

Planck was fitted with a cryogenic coolant system allowing it to maintain an incredible temperature of 0.1 degrees above absolute zero. The optimum temperature has to remain stable for Planck to work efficiently, meaning that an increase of less than one degree could affect the equipment. The cooling system consists of a passive system, which uses thermal shields to pre-cool the coolant. This coolant then goes through a three-stage process in the active cooling system. While the Low Frequency Instrument (LFI) could function at a slightly higher temperature, the High Frequency Instrument (HFI) cannot function without the constant supply of coolant to maintain these temperatures.

NUSTAR TELESCOPE

The NASA Nuclear Spectroscopic Telescope Array (NuSTAR) mission uses X-ray technology combined with the first orbiting telescope. Its primary purpose is to map regions of the sky for analysis of massive black holes, collapsed stars, supernova remnants, and the movement of particles in active galaxies. Launched as part of NASA's Small Explorer satellite program (SMEX-11), NuSTAR is able to study regions of the electromagnetic spectrum by focusing light which allows it to view high energy X-rays. In addition, NuSTAR is able to adapt its gaze in the case of unexpected supernovae and gamma-ray bursts almost as they occur.

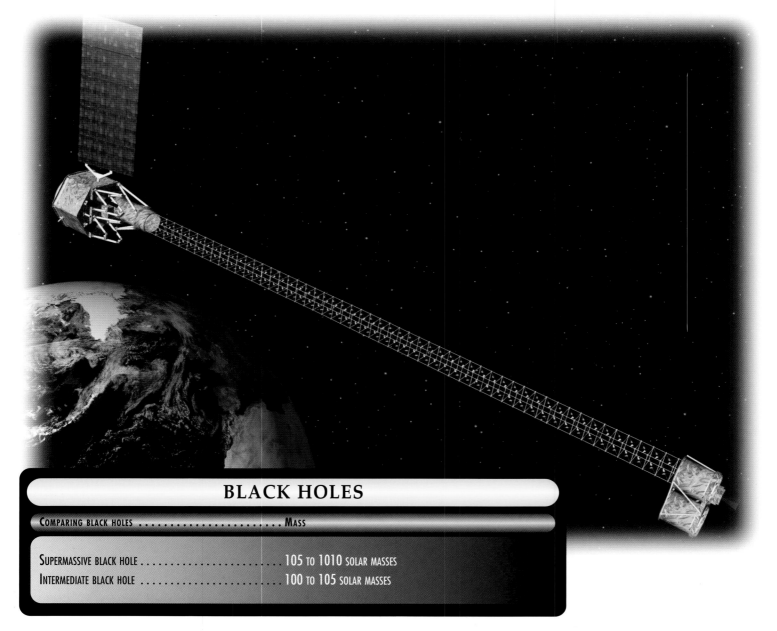

BLACK HOLES

COMPARING BLACK HOLES	MASS
SUPERMASSIVE BLACK HOLE	105 TO 1010 SOLAR MASSES
INTERMEDIATE BLACK HOLE	100 TO 105 SOLAR MASSES

BLACK HOLES OF ALL SIZES

Launched on June 13, 2012 by a Pegasus XL rocket, which itself was dropped from an L-1011 spacecraft—known as "Stargazer"—NuSTAR was soon able to send back data on ten supermassive black holes. One such black hole is thought to be present in the Milky Way galaxy—as well as most spiral and elliptical galaxies—in the area known as Sagittarius A in the center of our galaxy. While black holes can be tiny in size, especially when compared to their mass, supermassive black holes can hold the mass of over one million suns. NuSTAR has not yet discovered any new black holes, but its high resolution telescope means it can see high-energy X-ray light through the masses of dust and gas that surround black holes to a degree that no telescope ever has. Due to this, NuSTAR is able to shed new light on many questions surrounding the black hole, building on previous data sent from NASA's Chandra Observatory, which launched in 1999 and is still ongoing.

One of NuSTAR's capabilities is to respond to sudden occurrences in space, which the telescope can then be quickly aimed at to track. This very thing happened in April 2013 in the Milky Way, when flares near the middle of our galaxy lit up for hours. In another serendipitous example, NuSTAR was already observing Markarian 421 in the Ursa Major ("Great Bear") constellation when it observed a brightening of up to 50 times the normal levels. Markarian 421 is classed as a blazar—a galaxy with a supermassive black hole that actively sucks in matter. This feeding causes the black holes to light up and eject streams of energy and materials, which are sometimes directed at Earth.

Selected as the eleventh Small Explorer mission in January 2005, the NuSTAR mission was cancelled a year later due to cuts in the NASA science budget. It was not until September 2007 that the program was again green-lighted, with a proposed launch date of August 2011. The initial two-year mission is due to be completed in June 2014, unless the decision is made to extend it so that NuSTAR can continue to send back new information on black holes and how they work.

EYES IN THE SKY

NuSTAR is equipped with a Wolter telescope built specifically with optics for viewing X-rays. The telescope was the brainchild of Hans Wolter (1911–78), who proposed three ways of using X-ray mirrors in telescopes in 1952. These mirrors are known as grazing incidence mirrors and they have a low plane

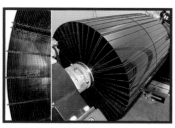

WOLTER'S WORK
The Wolter telescope focuses the high energy X-rays emitted by objects in space, allowing for the accurate observation of collapsed stars and black holes.

of reflection. While these mirrors give a focused view of X-rays, the view of the light is limited. Wolter therefore proposed using two mirrors to widen the field of view and catch more light. The NuSTAR Wolter telescope employs two of these mirrors or optics, which are made up of concentric shells to maximize reflectivity. Wolter telescopes have been used in similar X-ray telescopes, such as the Chandra Observatory and the SWIFT Gamma-Ray Burst Mission launched by NASA in 2004.

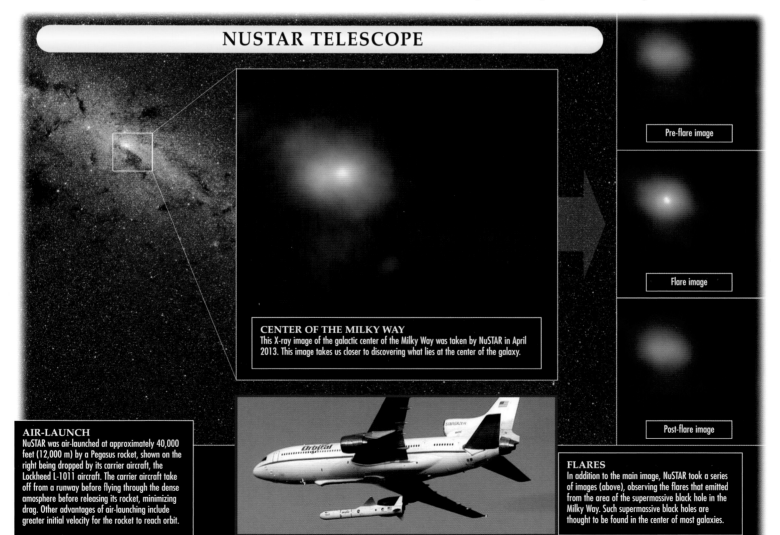

NUSTAR TELESCOPE

CENTER OF THE MILKY WAY
This X-ray image of the galactic center of the Milky Way was taken by NuSTAR in April 2013. This image takes us closer to discovering what lies at the center of the galaxy.

Pre-flare image

Flare image

Post-flare image

AIR-LAUNCH
NuSTAR was air-launched at approximately 40,000 feet (12,000 m) by a Pegasus rocket, shown on the right being dropped by its carrier aircraft, the Lockheed L-1011 aircraft. The carrier aircraft take off from a runway before flying through the dense atmosphere before releasing its rocket, minimizing drag. Other advantages of air-launching include greater initial velocity for the rocket to reach orbit.

FLARES
In addition to the main image, NuSTAR took a series of images (above), observing the flares that emitted from the area of the supermassive black hole in the Milky Way. Such supermassive black holes are thought to be found in the center of most galaxies.

INDEX

Picture Credits

All images are taken from the card set *Secrets of the Universe* (six volumes) published by International Masters Publishers AB, except the following:

Alamy: 454 (Xinhua)
CNSA: 454 all
Corbis: 357 top left (EPA), 363 top left (Tony Hallas/Science Faction), 424 (Peter

Kujundzic/Reuters), 425 top left (Ho/Reuters), 425 main (Liu Chan/Xinhau Press), 426 (He Yuan/EPA), 427 top (Xinhua/Xinhua Press), 427 main (Lu Zhe/Xinhua Press), 427 bottom (Ren Junchuary/Xinhau Press), 475 main (Walter Myers/Stocktrek), 475 bottom right (Oleg Urosov/Reuters)
ESA: 500–503 all

ISRO: 356, 357 top right & main
NASA: 6, 222, 223 both top, 360–362 all, 363 bottom left & main, 472–474 all, 475 bottom left & centre, 476–477 all, 498–499 all, 504–505 all
SpaceX: 358–359 all